W9-AKB-818

How The World Works and Your Place in It

Third Edition

Jane L. Person

J.M. LeBel Enterprises

Dallas / Edmonton

Reviewers and Consultants

Richard A. Person
nuclear science and chemistry consultant, reviewer, and photographer

Steven Courtney, PhD
Vice-president for Research, Sustainable Ecosystems Institute, Portland OR.

Donna Foulk
Agricultural Program Associate, Rutgers University, N.J.

Don Miller
Pocono Mountain School District, PA.

Kathy Dubin
Stroudsburg School District, PA.

Helen Vakkas
East Stroudsburg School District, PA.

Eugene Sheard
District Conservationist, Natural Resources Conservation Service, PA.

Ed White
PA State Soil Scientist, Natural Resources Conservation Service, PA.

William B. Katz
Oakton Community College, IL.

Debbie Berecki
Fillmore USD, Fillmore, CA.

Don Baylor
Aquatic Biologist, Stroudsburg, PA.

Melissa Harrison
Reading Specialist, Richardson ISD, Richardson, TX.

Components

Textbook, 528 pages (four color)	ISBN 0-920008-92-5
Annotated Teacher's Edition	ISBN 0-920008-94-1
Issues and Investigations (64)	ISBN 0-920008-96-8
Study Guide	ISBN 0-920008-98-4
Answers to Study Guide	ISBN 0-920008-93-3
Computer Test Program	ISBN 0-920008-97-6

Photo Credits:
Agricultural Research Service-USDA, 224, 250, 265, 276–9, 281; Albert Motz, 173; Barbara Wagner, 39; Cartesia (maps), 11, 17, 60, 119; Corbis; Corel, 287, 306, 313; Don Baylor, 316; Gary Berger, 134, 198, 433, 451, 456; Jane or Richard Person, all others; Jean Farmer, 428; Jim Rathert, Missouri Dept. of Conservation, 357; Lonnie G. Thompson, 111; Robert Lee, 199; Sterling International, 10; USDA-NRCS, Harrisburg, PA, 215, 216, 220, 221

Reviewer: Lise Le Bel

Copy Editor: Paul W. Conant

Design: FiWired.com

Illustrations: FiWired.com

Environmental Science (Student Edition)
ISBN 0-920008-92-5

J.M. LeBel Enterprises

1-800-882-0667

6420 Meadowcreek Drive, Dallas, Texas 75240

10335-61 Avenue, Edmonton, Alberta T6H 1K9

www.lebel.com info@lebel.com

Contents

Unit 1 Introduction to Ecology – The Basics

Unit 2 The Atmosphere – Is the Sky Falling

Unit 3 Food for the Table – Changes through Science and Technology

Unit 4 WATER AS AN ECOSYSTEM — A STUDY OF AQUATIC LIFE

Unit 5 WATER FOR THE PEOPLE

Unit 6 ENERGY — PAST, PRESENT AND FUTURE

Appendix LAB & FIELD INVESTIGATIONS AND ENVIRONMENTAL ISSUES

UNIT ONE
Introduction to Ecology

1.1 Ecology—a Study of Relationships

OBJECTIVES

- ✔ **Relate** the development of technology to the study of planet Earth.
- ✔ **Compare** and **contrast** the physical conditions that exist in different biomes.
- ✔ **Explain** the relationships between limiting factors and population size.
- ✔ **Contrast** human-made and natural ecosystems.
- ✔ **Relate** human activities to changes in natural ecosystems.

September 1991 marked the deployment by the Space Shuttle of the Upper Atmosphere Research Satellite, or UARS.

To view satellite images of environmental change at various locations around the globe, visit www.usgs.gov/Earthshots.

The term ecology comes from two Greek words meaning "the study of the home." Like biology, ecology is a science. While some biologists study organisms in a laboratory, others study organisms living in their natural environment. Wildlife biologists and conservation biologists study organisms as they interact with other organisms and with their environment. These biologists are sometimes called **ecologists**. **Ecology** is the study of organisms in their natural environment—their home.

Our home, the planet Earth, consists of large masses of air, water and land that support a thin layer of life—the **biosphere**. Everywhere that life exists on planet Earth—from the warm climate of the tropical forests to the cold waters of the Arctic Ocean—scientists are seeking information that will help us better understand our world and how it works. While scientists conducting field studies here on Earth gather information, sensors aboard spacecraft gather additional data.

Viewing planet Earth from Space

In addition to sensors at ground level and aboard airplanes, scientists at the National Aeronautics and Space Administration (NASA) launch spacecraft to study the Earth and other planets. Although they are expensive to launch, satellites are an economical way to gather data. **Sensors** aboard satellites can quickly gather data from a very large region, and they continue to gather data for a very long time.

Spacecraft can gather information from distant planets because all objects absorb, reflect, and give off energy in the form of **electromagnetic radiation** (EMR). Any type of object, whether living or non-living, can be detected by its distinctive pattern of electromagnetic radiation. Extremely sensitive instruments that detect this radiation allow scientists to monitor the health of planet Earth from outer space.

Images from remote-sensing equipment aboard spacecraft give us a global view of the biosphere. Computer enhanced photographs of the infrared radiation allow scientists to monitor the temperature of the planet. Images that capture the visible wavelengths of radiation show the distribution and abundance of plant life on land and in the oceans.

Scientists also study the chemistry of the atmosphere. Using a **total ozone mapping spectrometer** (TOMS) aboard orbiting satellites, scientists monitor ozone levels in the upper atmosphere and predict possible effects of the changing levels. At the same time, other scientists monitor ozone levels in the lower atmosphere and study their effects on plant growth and human health.

Planet **Earth** is a complex environmental system with constant interactions between the atmosphere, the oceans and the land. A better understanding of these interactions will help us more accurately predict the effects of human activity. Better predictions can help us manage natural resources in a way that will minimize the impacts of human activities on the environment.

Biomes—Climatic Zones of Life

When viewed from space, the biosphere appears to be a giant puzzle. But the pieces of the puzzle do not represent political regions. They represent biomes. A **biome** is a large geographic region determined by the climate and soil type. Each biome has a distinctly different type of plant life. Major biomes are Arctic tundra, northern coniferous forest, temperate deciduous forest, prairie, desert, tropical savanna and tropical rainforest (see pages 4 and 5).

The **climate** of a region refers to its average weather pattern over a long period of time. The amount and pattern of precipitation and the normal range of temperatures describe the climate. The climate affects both the soil type and the plant life. The existing plant life creates an environment that supports a characteristic group of animals.

Can you find the two ecosystems in this scene?

Ecosystem—a Functional Unit

While it is easy to identify biomes, a biome is too large an area to conduct research. The functional unit of a biome that ecologists study is the ecosystem. An **ecosystem** is a group of organisms that live together and interact with each other and their environment. Ecosystems may be natural or human-made.

The Sonoran Desert, in the southwestern United States, is an example of a natural ecosystem. Equally famous ecosystems include the Ozarks, the Everglades, Yellowstone, the Badlands, the Amazon River, Chesapeake Bay, and the Great Barrier Reef. You can think of others.

Natural ecosystems tend to be self-sustaining environmental systems. With the exception of water (precipitation) and energy (sunlight), the environment of a natural ecosystem contains all resources needed to support its organisms. Of course, natural disasters and human activities can destroy natural ecosystems. Humans consider fires disasters. But they are essential to the maintenance of some forest and grassland ecosystems.

Human-made ecosystems include farms, cities, flower gardens, terrariums and aquariums. Unlike natural ecosystems, ecosystems created by humans are seldom self-sustaining systems. They usually require huge inputs of resources and energy.

The Myriad Gardens Crystal Bridge in downtown Oklahoma City is a human-made tropical ecosystem. Inside this large cylinder, scientists have created both wet and dry tropical environments.

Relationships within an Ecosystem

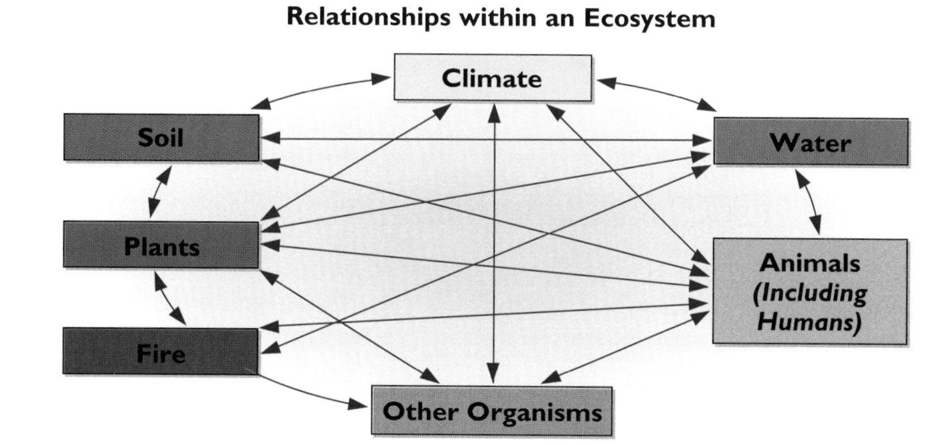

WWW

Biosphere 2 is a 3-acre building in the Sonoran desert that contains 7 ecosystems. For a virtual tour of this model biosphere, visit www.bio2.edu.

Biome			
Arctic Tundra	**Northern Coniferous Forest or Taiga [TIE-guh]**	**Temperate Deciduous Forest**	**Temperate Grasslands or Prairie**

Temperature			
very low temperature cold winds only surface of soil thaws growing season 60 days or less	short summers; long, cold winters above freezing for only 2–4 months	-30°C to +30°C distinct seasons growing season, 5 months in North	distinct seasons moderate seasonal temperatures hot summers and cold winters continuous winds
Precipitation			
often less than 10 in/yr. (25 cm/yr.) falls mostly during summer months	14–39 in/yr. (35–100 cm/yr.) falls mostly during summer months	29–59 in/yr. (75–150 cm/yr.) snow in North evenly spaced throughout year	10–39 in/yr. (25–100 cm/yr.) mostly in spring and early summer growing season limited by rainfall periodic droughts
Soil Type			
thin, acidic few nutrients permafrost—layer of permanently frozen soil	thin, acidic soils little **humus**—decayed matter lacks nutrients no permafrost	rich in humus medium nutrient level more decomposers than tundra	ten times more humus than deciduous forest very rich in nutrients deep topsoil

Biome

	Desert	Tropical Savanna	Tropical Rain Forest

Temperature	cold, temperate, or tropical daily temperature variation may be greater than seasonal variation	cool and hot dry seasons separated by warm and rainy seasons no cold season	tropical daily variation 9°F(5°C) is greater than seasonal continuous growing season
Precipitation	usually less than 10 in/yr. (25 cm/yr.) years of drought dry winds; high evaporation rate flash floods	39–59 in/yr. (100–150 cm/yr.) wet spring and fall long dry spells during hot months heavy thunderstorms	more than 78 in/yr. (200 cm/yr.) seasons determined by amount of rain
Soil Type	sandy little ability to hold water some rich in nutrients; others nutrient-poor	fertile soils deep layer of topsoil grasses prevent erosion	thin soils few nutrients if exposed to sun, forms cement-like layer rapid leaching

Environmental Challenge:

Human Population

The population of planet Earth is 6 billion and growing. It took about one million years for the human population to reach 1 billion. At the current rate of growth, an additional 1 billion people are added every twelve years. Think about the following questions in terms of the human species—Homo sapiens.

- At the current rate of growth, what will the earth's human population be when you are 30 years old? 60 years old? 90 years old?
- Scientists predict that the human population could be near 10 billion by the year 2050. What is the carrying capacity of the earth for Homo sapiens? Can the earth support 10 billion people?
- What limiting factors control the growth of the human population?
- How have these limiting factors changed since 1800 when the earth's population was only one billion?
- How does the increase in the human population affect the carrying capacity of the planet Earth for other species? For the human species?

Habitat—a Place to call Home

The difference between this hairy woodpecker and the downy woodpecker is the downy is smaller with a shorter bill.

It is important to remember that the biotic (living) and abiotic (non-living) parts of an ecosystem are dependent upon one another. "Nothing can live alone." Each living organism requires a certain set of physical and chemical conditions. Climate and soil conditions determine the types of plants that grow in an ecosystem. The plants determine the kinds of animals that live there.

If the correct sets of physical and chemical conditions exist, organisms thrive. Large herds of grazing animals exist only where grasses are abundant. If trees invade the area, animals that prefer trees become more common. Where trees produce too much shade, the growth of grasses is limited, and the number of grazing animals declines.

Although large animals are more obvious, an ecosystem includes many different kinds of organisms. Each organism has its own special "home" within the ecosystem. The place in an ecosystem where an organism prefers to live is its **habitat**. You might think of a habitat as the organism's address. It describes where the organism lives, but a habitat is more than just a place to live. It must meet all of the needs of the organism. A good habitat provides enough food and water, suitable living space, and cover.

Cover describes those places where animals hide to escape predators or where the young are protected from harm. Cover also provides the animals with shelter from harsh weather. If the cover disappears, the wildlife will also disappear. The disappearance of cover may be due to natural changes in an ecosystem, or it may be due to human activities.

POPULATION LINK

Populations of Woodpeckers

Similar organisms that breed to produce fertile offspring in their natural environment are members of the same **species**. Differences in structure or behavior usually prevent members of different species from breeding with each other. The downy woodpecker and the hairy woodpecker are members of the same family, but they are different species. Twenty different species of woodpeckers breed in North America.

The total number of a species living in a defined region is the species' **population**. We frequently refer to the population of one species—humans, but the term population can refer to any species of plant or animal. The number of hairy woodpeckers in the forest is one population. The number of downy woodpeckers in the area is another population.

Both the downy and the hairy woodpeckers are **cavity nesters**—birds that build nests in holes within trees. Even though these two species of woodpeckers make cavities for nesting, they do not compete for housing. The preferred habitat of the hairy woodpecker is the interior of the forest. The downy woodpecker often chooses a tree at the edge of the forest or a tree along a road.

Even if downy and hairy woodpeckers are found in the same area of the forest, it is unlikely that they will choose the same tree. The hairy woodpecker, with a longer and stronger beak, prefers to make its cavity in live wood or hard dead wood. The downy woodpecker always chooses soft dead wood.

Did You Know?

In most of the U.S. the populations of hairy woodpeckers are stable or increasing, but in Florida and Georgia they have become rare. In this region hairy woodpeckers prefer a recently burned area of mature pine forests. Because of the suppression of fires, many species — including the hairy woodpecker — are now threatened.

More Cavities Needed

Bluebirds are cavity nesters, but they can't make their own cavity. Like the downy woodpecker, bluebirds prefer trees in open areas. The best habitat for bluebirds is an open area with scattered trees such as an old orchard. By clearing sections of forest to create fields and orchards, early settlers improved the bluebird habitat. Bluebirds feed on insects on the ground, and insects were abundant in the fields and meadows.

Bluebird.

In the early 1900s, eastern bluebirds were one of the most common songbirds, but by 1969 fewer than 100 bluebirds nested in Minnesota. Other states also reported severe declines in bluebird populations. All three species—eastern, western, and mountain—declined nearly 90% between 1935 and 1985.

One factor causing the decline in bluebird populations may have been the widespread use of insecticides, but the most important factor was the loss of habitat. At first, fences were built with wooden posts, and wooden posts develop cavities. While bluebirds like fence posts with cavities, farmers don't. Cavities make the fence posts weak, and cattle escape through weak fences. After World War II, most farmers replaced wooden posts with new posts made of steel.

Destruction of habitat occurred at a rapid pace. The invention of the chain saw made cutting of trees easier, and cattle often destroyed the trees that were not cut. As the size of the farm machinery increased, farmers removed trees in fencerows to make larger fields. Other trees disappeared during the construction of highways, shopping centers and developments.

With less suitable habitat, the bluebirds had to compete with other birds for the few remaining nesting sites. More aggressive birds such as the tree swallow and house wren often drove the bluebirds from their nests. Starlings and house sparrows—both introduced to this country from Europe—also competed with the bluebirds for nesting sites.

The North American Bluebird Society and others are working to increase the number of bluebirds across the United States. The most

For more information on bluebirds, visit the North American Bluebird Society Website: www.nabluebirdsociety.org. To learn more about wood ducks, visit: www.onwis.com/outdoors/wildlife/woodduck.stm.

Properly placed nesting boxes like this one provide much needed habitat for Eastern bluebirds.

Although the cavity is now too large, this old wooden fence post has provided a home for many bluebirds. Now it may provide protection for other cavity nesters.

This box is prime habitat for a female wood duck looking for a home.

Grouse depend on young forests. Brushy growth provides both protection and food.

Wood Duck.

Young Turkey.

successful way to improve the habitat is by providing the bluebirds with nesting boxes near an open area where food is available. Today individuals interested in helping the little bird that Henry Thoreau once said, "...carries the sky on its back," are monitoring thousands of bluebird boxes.

Another nesting box program aids the wood duck population. When house hunting, the female wood duck looks for a cavity in a tree in or near the water. Often she chooses a cavity, excavated by a pileated woodpecker, with a hole too small for a raccoon to enter. Human activities—logging mature trees, draining ponds and hunting—threatened the wood duck population. In 1918, the United States and Canadian governments banned the hunting of this species. Groups of citizens and conservation organizations built nesting boxes and placed them on poles or in trees in or near the water. Today the wood duck population exceeds one million, and regulated hunting is permitted.

Finding the Right Neighborhood

When the settlers came to America, much of the area east of the Mississippi River was mature forest. The large trees in a mature forest ecosystem provide too much shade for many low-growing plants. Due to the shade, mature forests do not provide suitable food or cover for a number of species including rabbits, ruffed grouse and white-tailed deer.

By clearing sections of the forest, the early settlers improved the habitat for these species. As the forests were cut, new growth in the clearings provided plenty of food and good cover. The settlers not only improved the habitat, they also killed many of the natural predators. With better habitat, fewer predators, and restricted hunting, the populations of these species increased.

Today many of Pennsylvania's forests are once again mature. The shade of the mature trees and a large white-tailed deer population have reduced the low-growing plants that provide cover and food for rabbits and young grouse. Where housing developments have created openings that allow more sunlight to enter, there is more brushy growth. In these areas the rabbit population may increase, but the eastern ruffed grouse is shy and avoids areas where there is human activity. As a result, Pennsylvania's ruffed grouse population is declining.

Do Not Disturb

One species that does benefit from human activity is the woodchuck, also called the groundhog. Groundhogs create their own cover by digging burrows, and agriculture ensures an abundance of food. Groundhogs are mainly vegetarians, feeding on grass, leaves and flowers. They are especially fond of alfalfa, clover and soybeans, but they may also find a meal in the garden or orchard.

Unlike the groundhog, many species do not benefit from changes in the landscape. Agriculture, urban development, the construction of roads, pipelines, and power lines all disturb habitats. All of these activities cause **habitat fragmentation**—the breaking of habitats into smaller isolated pieces.

Islands of habitat are sometimes too small or too far apart to support self-sustaining populations. Some species require large tracts of unbroken habitat for successful reproduction. Researchers found the nesting success rate for the wood thrush was 86% in a 25,000-acre (10,100-hectare [ha]) forest, but only 43% in 20-acre (8-ha) plots.

Fragmentation of large tracts of forests is one factor responsible for the declining populations of songbirds. Habitat fragmentation creates an abundance of **edges**. While some species thrive near the edges of the habitat, others cannot tolerate the disturbances that occur there. Even narrow openings, such as logging roads, create highways for many predators. Bird's nests are more accessible to housecats, snakes, blue jays, and cowbirds. Nests near the edge of a forest are also exposed to stronger winds and greater temperature changes.

Human activities break habitats into isolated pieces.

In summary, to survive, animals need a suitable habitat. Habitat is more than just a place to live. Good habitat provides enough food, cover, water and living space. The most critical threat to animals is often not a direct physical assault by humans. The greatest threat to most species of wildlife is the destruction of their habitat.

Limits to Population Growth

An ecosystem's **carrying capacity** is the maximum size of a population existing in the ecosystem at any given time without damage to the ecosystem. There are a number of factors limiting the ability of the ecosystem to support a species. Anything preventing the growth of a population is a **limiting factor**. Limiting factors are:

Farming and other activities create an abundance of edges. Some species will thrive at the edges where they find food in the open field with cover nearby.

Space:

Many species of animals establish territories for breeding. This includes most songbirds, as well as many mammals and fishes. Even species that do not establish territories often have fewer offspring when species are crowded.

When the population becomes crowded, individuals may **emigrate** or move to other areas. The lemming, a small Arctic rodent, emigrates every four or five years. During an ordinary winter, lemmings are protected from their enemies by the snow, and if plenty of food is available, they continue to breed during the winter. As they become crowded, they move up or down the mountainside in search of food. Contrary to popular belief, they do not march to water to commit suicide.

Clean water, supporting fish and other aquatic life in an area free from too much human activity, is a good habitat for the river otter. As we develop wild areas, we destroy good otter habitat. In Pennsylvania the otter has been protected since 1952, but laws to protect a species cannot save it if it has no space to live.

What are the limiting factors for the plants and animals in this ecosystem?

Food:

When food supplies decrease, the size of the population depending on that source of food becomes smaller. In the tundra ecosystem of northern Canada, the only food for the lynx (lingks) is the snowshoe hare. When the

Because it helps control the population of Mexican bean beetle larvae, the large spined soldier bug is a "good bug."

number of hare decreases, the number of lynx also decreases. In the Florida Everglades, the snail kite population fluctuates with availability of its only source of food—the apple snail. Organisms that depend upon one food source are most vulnerable to population crashes.

In the garden, "good bugs" eat "bad bugs." If pesticides are sprayed to kill the "bad bugs," the population of "good bugs" also decreases. While some bugs—both good and bad—survive the spray, others move into the area from nearby gardens. The population of "bad bugs" must recover before there is enough food to support a large population of "good bugs."

Climate and Weather:

Why is the coniferous forest biome in the northern reaches of the planet? Coniferous trees can tolerate extreme cold. Climate plays a major role in the distribution of plants and animals.

Fewer animals survive when the winter weather is unusually cold, and the snow is deep. For certain species, such as rabbits, a cold and wet spring may decrease the number of young that survive. For other species, such as mosquitoes, an unusually wet spring provides ideal conditions for breeding and can result in a population explosion.

These native grasses provide excellent cover for white-tailed deer and many other species.

Cover:

If the habitat does not provide a good place to hide, organisms may become easy food for predators. On modern farms, the quail and rabbit populations are often limited due to a lack of brushy fencerows that would provide good cover. Farmers can improve the habitat by not mowing or harvesting certain sections of land.

Most species do not travel far from home in search of food. One study showed that quail would not travel to a food supply that is more than two hundred yards (180 m) from their cover. When there was cover on only one side of a square forty-acre (16-ha) field, the quail fed in only one half of the field. When there was cover on both sides of the field, the quail used the entire field.

Disease:

Organisms spread disease more readily if they are crowded. As the **population density**—number of a species per unit area of living space—increases, the distance that a diseased organism must travel to reach its next victim is reduced. More organisms are infected with the disease. If the population density increases until the supply of food is limited, the weakened animals may die from diseases they would normally survive.

Human activity:

As wild areas become developed, the populations of those species that do not tolerate human activity will decline. Loons abandon their nests when disturbed by human activity. Bobcats and river otters leave the area in search of a more peaceful habitat. Successful breeding may depend upon the availability of a habitat without human disturbance.

Environmental Challenge: Ecosystems

Choose an ecosystem that you would like to visit, and find the following information:

- What are the prominent plant species?
- What animals are unique to this ecosystem? What adaptations help them survive?
- How have human activities affected species in this ecosystem?

Shade:

The tops of the mature trees in a forest make a roof or **canopy**. The shade created by a canopy of mature oak trees becomes a limiting factor. It prevents other trees of the same species from growing. Shade-tolerant species, such as maple and beech, are more successful, and eventually become the dominant trees in the forest.

Population Explosions

In the absence of limiting factors, population explosions occur. This frequently happens when a new species is introduced to an ecosystem. When Thomas Austin immigrated to Australia from England, he missed the sport of hunting, so in 1859 he imported two dozen rabbits and released them on his estate. Six years later 10,000 rabbits were destroying his grasslands. Even hired guns could not effectively reduce the population.

By 1995 the estimated population of rabbits in Australia was over 300 million. Rabbits invaded the habitat, eating all the native plants. This reduced the food supply available to the native birds and mammals. The rabbits also competed with livestock and caused erosion. It is estimated that they cost Australian agriculture $600 million each year.

The European rabbit is the most serious animal pest in Australia. Rabbits are a problem in Australia but not in England. In England there were both predators and diseases that controlled the rabbit population. When rabbits were introduced in Australia, they readily adapted to the new environment without natural predators or diseases.

Population explosions also occur when limiting factors are removed from an isolated ecosystem. A classic example is the story of the Grand Canyon National Game Preserve. In 1906 President Theodore Roosevelt created the game preserve on the Kaibab Plateau in northern Arizona. The purpose of the preserve was to protect mule deer from predators and from unregulated hunting.

The management plan called for removal of animals that would compete with or prey upon the deer. In 1906, ranchers began removing thousands of sheep and cattle from the preserve, and government officials intensified their efforts to eliminate wild horses and all major predators. Hunters and trappers killed 1310 wild horses, 816 cougars, 30 wolves, 7,388 coyotes and 863 bobcats. There were about 4,000 mule deer on the plateau when the intensive predator control began. In 1918, an estimate of the herd size was 40,000 deer. A census taken six years later reported nearly 100,000 deer. The following winter, approximately 60,000 deer died of starvation and disease.

The government replaced the predator control program with a mule deer "killing program." At its peak, the population density was one mule deer per 7 acres (3 ha). The deer had destroyed much of their habitat and reduced the carrying capacity of the land. Since 1939, the size of the herd has been controlled at about 10,000—one deer per 68 acres (27 ha). Controlling the population of mule deer has allowed the ecosystem to recover.

Environmental Challenge: Rabbit Control

Find out what methods are currently being used to control the rabbit population in Australia. How successful are these methods? To find out, visit: www.agric.wa.gov.au.

www

If there are no predators or diseases to prevent a population explosion, rabbits will destroy their habitat.

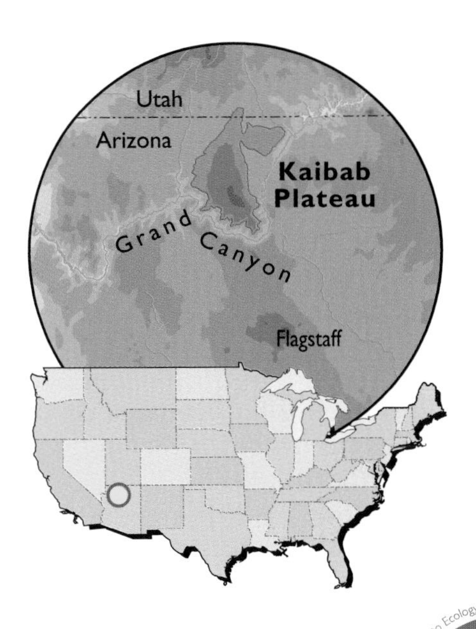

1.1 QUESTIONS FOR STUDY AND DISCUSSION:

1. Define the following terms: VOCABULARY

abiotic	cover	emigrate	rain forest
biome	deciduous forest	habitat	savanna
biosphere	desert	habitat fragmentation	sensors
biotic	earth	humus	species
canopy	ecologist	limiting factor	tundra
carrying capacity	ecology	permafrost	TOMS
cavity nesters	ecosystem	population	
climate	edges	population density	
coniferous forest	electromagnetic radiation	prairie	

2. What is ecology? What do we call a scientist who studies ecology?
3. Describe the biosphere.

Viewing planet Earth from Space

4. Describe how spacecraft gather data from planet Earth?
5. What are some advantages of studying planet Earth from space?

Biomes—Climatic Zones of Life

6. Describe a biome and identify the factors that determine the type of plant life that exists in a biome.
7. Give three examples of biomes and identify unique characteristics of each.

Ecosystem—a Functional Unit

8. Describe an ecosystem and give examples of ecosystems where you live and ecosystems that you would like to visit.
9. Compare a natural ecosystem to a human-made ecosystem.

Habitat—a Place to Call Home

10. Explain the statement: "Nothing can live alone."
11. List the physical factors which affect an organism's environment.
12. Explain how plants change the chemical and physical environment.
13. Give three reasons why animals need cover.

Populations of Woodpeckers

14. What prevents members of different species from breeding with each other?
15. Compare the habitat of the downy woodpecker to the habitat of the hairy woodpecker.

More Cavities Needed

16. Describe how changes made by the early settlers caused the bluebird population to increase.
17. What caused a decline in bluebird population?
18. How are some people trying to increase the bluebird population? Explain.
19. Compare the habitat requirement of the bluebird to the habitat requirement of the wood duck.

Finding the Right Neighborhood

20. Identify three species that benefited from the activities of the settlers and explain why these populations increased.
21. In a development in Pennsylvania's Pocono Mountains, trees are being cut and areas are being cleared for roads and houses. Will the clearing and development cause the grouse population to increase or decrease? Why?

Do Not Disturb

22. How did the coming of the settlers affect the groundhog population?
23. Give two reasons why some bird populations decline when their habitat is fragmented.
24. Identify the four factors that are necessary for a good habitat.
25. Complete the following sentence: The greatest threat to many species is the…

Limits to Population Growth

26. Define carrying capacity. How do limiting factors affect the carrying capacity of an ecosystem?
27. Give examples of limiting factors that affect four of the following species: quail, rabbits, lynx, loons, bobcats, river otters, ruffed grouse, white-tailed deer, bluebirds, or oak trees.

Population Explosions

28. Why do population explosions occur?
29. What limiting factors were missing when Thomas Austin introduced the rabbit to Australia?
30. What limiting factors controlled the population of mule deer on the Kaibab Plateau prior to 1906? In 1925? Since 1939?

Food Chains and Food Webs

1.2

OBJECTIVES

- ✔ **Identify** the source of energy for ecosystems.
- ✔ **Identify** the niche of an organism in a food chain or food web.
- ✔ **Evaluate** the stability of an ecosystem on the basis of its food web.
- ✔ **Predict** the effects of human activities on a food web.

One of the most important relationships that exists between living organisms is based on their need for energy. Plants cannot make energy, but they can make their own food. To get energy they must compete with other plants for sunlight. Plants trap the sun's energy and use it to make food in a process called **photosynthesis**.

Green plants or algae are the foundation of nearly all ecosystems. They are producers. A **producer** is an organism that can use the sun's energy to make its own food. Mushrooms are not producers. Since they lack chlorophyll, they cannot capture the sun's energy to make or "produce" food.

The word "producer" is used only when we speak of an organism that uses sunlight to create food molecules (sugar) from nonfood molecules (water and carbon dioxide). Producers are vital to the ecosystem because they make food for all other species. We say that a cow produces milk, but cows are not classified as producers because they cannot make food from nonfood molecules. In fact, no animal can make food from nonfood molecules.

Eat and be Eaten

All organisms must have food. Organisms are classified as producers or consumers. **Consumers**—organisms that cannot make their own food—depend upon producers. There are several types of consumers. Those consumers that eat plants are called **herbivores** or "plant eaters." Consumers that feed on animals instead of plants are **carnivores** or "meat eaters."

Some consumers eat both plants and animals. They are **omnivores**. Bears and coyotes are omnivores. Their digestive systems are not adapted for large amounts of plant material. However, when their food supply is limited, they can digest plants well enough to keep from starving.

A special type of consumer is a decomposer. A **decomposer** feeds on the waste products or bodies of other dead organisms. Most decomposers are small. They include bacteria, fungi and a few flowering plants, such as Indian pipes, that lack chlorophyll. Decomposers have a very important role in any ecosystem. They recycle nutrients by breaking down dead organisms and animal waste.

An organism's **niche** is its role or job in the ecosystem. The niche describes the position of the organism in the food chain. While an organism's habitat can be compared to a person's address, the organism's niche can be compared to a person's occupation.

Some organisms have a very specialized niche. An example is the koala bear. They are herbivores feeding only on the tender shoots and leaves of eucalyptus trees. They can be compared to a surgeon who only performs heart surgery. Other organisms, such as brown bears, have a broader niche. Their varied diet includes both plants and animals. They

Did You Know?

Deep within the ocean where there are thermal springs on the ocean floor, unique ecosystems exist. The producer in these ecosystems is not algae, but a type of bacteria that can make food from hydrogen sulfide dissolved in the hot water that flows from the springs. This food-making process is called **chemosynthesis**.

Indian Pipes.

can be compared to a farmer who may fill the roles of mechanic, heavy equipment operator, laborer, and businessman on any given day.

All animals classified as carnivores do not fill the same niche. Some carnivores are predators. A **predator** is an organism that feeds on other animals, but first it must hunt and kill the animal. The animal that is killed is the **prey**. Carnivores that feed on animals that either died naturally or were killed by other organisms are **scavengers**. Vultures, flies and crows are examples of scavengers.

Those consumers that feed on organisms that are still living are called **parasites**. The organism that is "eaten" is the **host**. During the summer, you may be the host for a mosquito or tick. Your dog may be the host for several fleas. Mosquitoes and fleas are parasites. Since their host is an animal, they are also carnivores. If their host were a plant, they would be classified as herbivores.

Rocky Mountain Elk.

Energy Maps

A **food chain** is a diagram that shows the flow of energy from green plants or algae to consumer organisms. The food chain also shows the niche of each organism. The first step in any food chain is always a producer. The second step is always a herbivore. Since the herbivore is the first consumer, it is sometimes referred to as the first-order or **primary consumer**.

The second consumer in a food chain is a second-order or **secondary consumer**. The second-order consumer is always a carnivore. It may be a predator, a scavenger, or a parasite. The third consumer is called a third-order consumer or a **tertiary consumer**. In some food chains there is a fourth-order consumer. Decomposers may be at any step except the first, for like any other consumers, they ultimately depend upon producers.

The arrows in a food chain show what eats what. The arrow replaces the phrase "is eaten by." The direction of the arrow is very important. The arrow must point toward the "eater." "Grass is eaten by a grasshopper" would be shown as: Grass → Grasshopper.

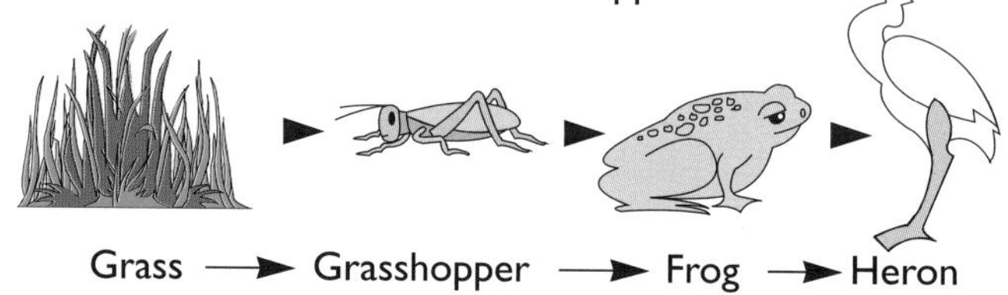

Louisiana or Tricolored Heron.

The relationships in an ecosystem are more complex than the relationships shown in a single food chain. Grasshoppers do not always eat grass and frogs do not always eat grasshoppers. A **food web** shows the many possible food chains that exist in an ecosystem.

An ecosystem with a very simple food web is not a very stable ecosystem. Ecosystems with a complex food web—a web made of many chains—is more stable than an ecosystem with a simple web. This is due to the fact that the organisms have more choices of things to eat. If the population of one food source declines, the animal can feed on other organisms.

Can you identify the niche of these organisms?

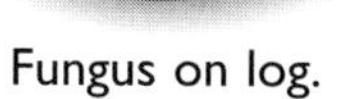

Fungus on log.

Herring Gull.

Eastern Tiger Swallowtail on red clover.

Black-and-yellow Argiope.

A food web showing some of the food chains in and near a pond.

1.2 Questions for Study and Discussion:

1. Define the following terms: **VOCABULARY**

carnivore	food chain	parasite	scavenger
chemosynthesis	food web	photosynthesis	secondary consumer
consumer	herbivore	predator	tertiary consumer
decomposer	host	prey	
environmental impact statement	niche	primary consumer	
	omnivore	producer	

2. Green plants "make" food. You might "make" a cake. Explain the difference between what a plant does and what a cook does in the kitchen.
3. Why are producers said to be the foundation of all ecosystems?

Eat and be Eaten

4. Why are decomposers essential to an ecosystem?
5. What is the niche of each of the following organisms?

brown bear	coyote	fungus	grass
house fly	koala bear	mosquito	vulture

Energy Maps

6. What information can you learn from a food chain?
7. What phrase replaces the arrow when describing a food chain?
8. Identify the niche of each organism in the food chain and food web shown on pages 14 and 15.
9. Predict what will happen at the pond. Is the food web shown a stable ecosystem? Explain.

Environmental Challenge: Goldenrods

There are about 100 species of goldenrods in the United States. Although goldenrods are not an important source of food for birds and mammals, they do provide valuable cover. The birds feed on the insects that feed on the goldenrods. Every part of the goldenrod provides nutrients and energy to insects. The herbivores are specialists. There are flower eaters, foliage eaters, pollen eaters, nectar sippers, and sap suckers. In turn the herbivores provide food for a variety of insect and arachnid predators that also provide food for the birds.

You may think that the goldenrod is causing your allergies. The cause of your allergies is probably not goldenrod but common ragweed. The pollen of common ragweed is light and easily blown by the wind. The pollen of the goldenrod is heavy. The goldenrod needs the insects for pollination as much as the insects need the goldenrod for food.

A weed is any plant that grows in a place where it isn't wanted. In many human-created ecosystems the goldenrod is considered a weed.

- Write an environmental impact statement that describes the changes in the food web that occur in areas where herbicides are used to eliminate weeds. These areas might be lawns, gardens, golf courses or farm fields.

Predators—a Natural Balance?

OBJECTIVES

- **Explain** why predators are an important part of a balanced ecosystem.
- **Evaluate** the role of humans in the control of predator populations.

Killing and eating other animals: that is how predators survive. Some animals must die so that others may live. Many animals, including humans, get at least part of their food this way. We don't often think of robins as predators, yet they prey upon insects and earthworms. Living things consume other living things; that is how the world works.

It is the **niche** of some animals to be predators, but for some it is a part-time job. Foxes sometimes eat grasses, berries and grapes. It is easier than catching a rabbit or ruffed grouse. But the farmer needs to keep the door to the chicken house closed. If chickens are easier for predators to catch than their natural food, they will eat chickens.

Predators are valuable to us most of the time. We need them to balance the reproductive power of most animals. Predators are nature's mousetraps. Without predators to control the populations, certain species like mice would crowd out other species. They would also destroy their habitat.

Predators not only control the size of pest populations; they also get rid of the weak, the crippled, the stupid, the stunted and the diseased organisms. They often kill the unfit before they can breed or spread disease. Those organisms that escape predators and breed make the population stronger.

Research has shown that predators do kill **game species**—species that humans can legally hunt. To control such predators, people were paid money, called a **bounty**, to kill them. Bounties were put on wolves as early as 1850, and by 1900 about 2 million had been killed. During the 1940s, people were paid for killing bobcats, weasels, foxes, hawks, owls and coyotes. Bounties were paid for predators in an effort to increase certain game species, but the populations of game species did not increase as expected.

The surplus animals died of other causes, mainly lack of food or cover. When farmers removed the brushy fencerows and created bigger fields, they destroyed the cover for rabbits, quail and other wildlife. Without sufficient cover, the surplus animals became easy prey for the remaining predators. When the surplus was gone, the predator usually turned to other, easier-to-get food sources.

Predators prevent successful breeding of certain birds. Destruction of habitat gives predators greater access to nesting sites. In the **Mississippi Flyway**, fewer than 15% of the waterfowl nested successfully. Where the prairie grasses once provided extensive cover for nesting birds, farming has allowed foxes, raccoons, skunks and even domestic cats to move in.

Researchers in North Dakota trapped nearly 300 foxes, skunks and raccoons on one 61-square mile study plot. Why are there so many of these small **predators**? One factor is that the settlers wiped out these predators' predators—the large carnivores. After the loss of the large carnivores, trappers who marketed the furs, controlled their populations. Now because of their low market value, trappers are taking fewer of these fur-bearing predators.

From its perch on the big bale, the red-tailed hawk scouts the hay field for rodents.

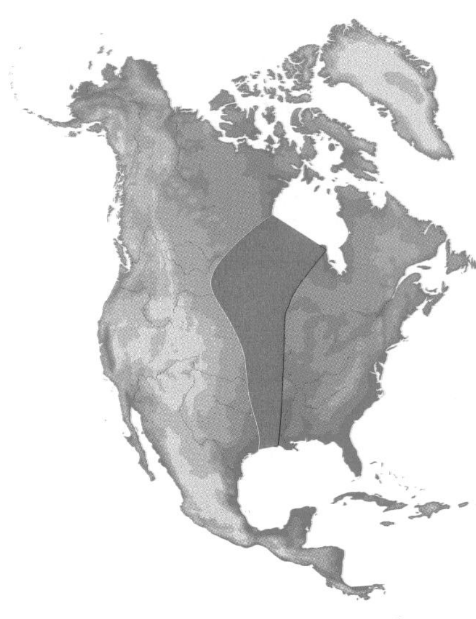

Mississippi Flyway (area in red).

Without larger carnivores to control their populations, raccoons become a destructive predator.

Where a habitat is destroyed and predators are abundant, hunting or trapping of predators may be necessary to protect certain species of wildlife. But we must remember that predators are not the only animals that cause damage. The animals that predators kill may be more destructive than the predators. These include rabbits, deer, crows, mice and many insects. Any animal may be destructive if it becomes too abundant. The plant-eaters may be the most destructive of all. The animals we call predators are still the best protection we have against an overpopulation of plant-eating pests.

Environmental Challenge: House Cats

A biologist and an ecologist conducted a survey of the hunting habits of 77 house cats in a small village in Britain. With the cooperation of the owners, they collected and identified the remains brought home by the cats during the year-long study. Of the 1100 prey, 64% were small mammals (mostly wood mice, field voles and common shrews). The remainder were songbirds. They estimated that cats kill at least 20 million birds each year.

The 1990 U.S. Census shows that there are 60 million cats kept as pets. A study at the University of Wisconsin-Madison found up to 114 free-ranging cats per square mile. This is several times greater than all other native predators of similar size, including foxes, skunks, opossums and raccoons.

- What is the impact of the house cat population?
- What can/should be done?

1.3 Questions for Study and Discussion:

1. Define the following terms: **VOCABULARY**

   bounty
   game species
   niche
   Mississippi Flyway
   predator

2. In what ways are most predators valuable to us? To other species?
3. How do game species differ from nongame species?
4. Make the connection between bounties, game species and predators.
5. Did the bounty system work?
6. How do humans sometimes help predators kill more of a certain species?
7. Predict how your life would be different if there were no predators.

The Case of the Missing Hawks

OBJECTIVES

- ✔ **Draw** a food web showing the niches of organisms in the pine grove.
- ✔ **Evaluate** the advantages and disadvantages of protecting populations of predatory birds.

In 1724, the colony of Pennsylvania offered a bounty for crows. Later hawks and owls were added to the list. In the 1930s, the state of Pennsylvania offered a bounty for goshawks, a species that preys on birds. Farmers were concerned because goshawks also killed some chickens.

Most people cannot tell a goshawk from a red-tailed hawk. The bounty resulted in the killing of 76 goshawks and 295 other hawks. The farmers were the real losers since many of those hawks would have killed many thousands of rodents that feed on their crops.

In 1935, a large pine grove surrounding the reservoir of Reading, Pennsylvania, was dying. At least 40% of the 2 million small pine trees had turned brown and died. Close inspection showed that each tree had a ring, near the base, where the bark had been chewed off. All of the trees with a complete ring of missing bark died. It was later discovered that meadow mice had eaten the bark. Why did this happen?

Around this time, a deputy game warden had shot a large number of hawks. He may have been trying to protect the rabbits and pheasants—important game species. He may have had a dislike for predators. Some people feel that predators are our enemies. But his actions caused an unfortunate chain of events.

The grass in the meadow area between the trees provided cover for rabbits, pheasants, meadow mice, groundhogs, weasels, and other small animals. The meadow mice were the most important primary consumer in the meadow ecosystem. They were the major item in the diet of many predators: rough-legged hawks, short-eared owls, weasels, snakes, and sometimes crows.

A pair of meadow mice might have 17 litters in one year. Each litter could have between two to nine young. The young begin to breed when they are 25 days old. In just one year, one pair of mice could produce one million offspring! So in order for the population of meadow mice to remain the same, 43 mice must be destroyed each year for every mouse that survives. It was the job, or niche, of the predators to keep the population of meadow mice in balance.

Removal of the rough-legged hawks by the warden caused a **population explosion** of meadow mice such that there was a shortage of their normal food supply. In order to survive the winter, they fed on the bark of the pine trees, thus causing the trees to die.

How do we know the rough-legged hawks ate meadow mice and not pheasants or rabbits? The hawks shot by the game warden were sent to the Reading Museum. Examination of their stomach contents showed only the remains of meadow mice. No remains of pheasant or rabbit were found.

Kestrel feeding on a meadow mouse.

www

For more information about and photographs of birds of prey found in North America, visit www.buteo.com.

Can you identify these hawks?

1.4 Questions for Study and Discussion:

1. Draw a food web using at least six of the organisms found in the area around the Reading Reservoir.
2. How is the population of meadow mice normally controlled? What evidence do we have to prove this?
3. Meadow mice do not normally feed on pine trees. Why did they eat the bark of the pine trees at the Reading Reservoir?
4. How does the offer of a bounty for killing predators affect the farm ecosystem? Explain.

Environmental Challenge: Owls

Legal protection of predatory birds has resulted in high populations of certain species at some locations. The great-horned owl population in New York and Pennsylvania has increased so much that they are preying on animals that are not normally a part of their diet. In addition to their normal diet of small mammals such as mice and rabbits, they sometimes raid the nests of other birds of prey. The remains of fledgling hawks and wild turkey poults have been discovered in their nests. They sometimes kill and eat small dogs and house cats.

- What do you think—are there too many great-horned owls?
- Should the protection from hunting be removed for this species?
- Predict what would happen if the great-horned owl could be hunted legally?

A CLOSER LOOK 1.5

Coyotes—Opportunistic Omnivores

"Coyotes howling, yipping, barking, chanting in the brush this morning—that thrilling call of the wild. Like a loon's cry in the lake country, the song of the coyote... is the voice of the desert... ."
EDWARD ABBY

OBJECTIVES

- **Compare** the niche of coyotes to other large predators.
- **Evaluate** the effectiveness of methods used to control coyote populations.
- **Predict** how coyote populations will change over the next 50 years.

Many people associate coyotes with the West, but remains in prehistoric Indian villages tell us that they lived in the East during the Ice Age. Coyotes vanished from the East perhaps 10,000 years ago. Their disappearance is probably related to the changing habitat and the presence of a larger predator—the wolf.

When the first settlers from Europe came, the Northeast was covered with forests. They found no coyotes, only timber wolves. Since the days of the first human settlements, the populations of large predators, including wolves, have decreased due to uncontrolled hunting and the loss of habitat.

Return of the Coyote

Coyotes are not like most predators; the coyote population is increasing in the Northeast. The return of the Eastern coyote is thought to be due to the massive clear-cutting of forests and the disappearance of the eastern timber wolf. Unlike the wolf, the coyote thrives in open spaces. They are very adaptable and can usually avoid humans. The coyote is filling an ecological niche that was left vacant in areas where the wolf and the mountain lion were eliminated.

The coyote is very adaptable and can usually avoid humans.

The Eastern coyote is about the size of a German Shepherd, slightly larger than its western cousins. They are smaller than wolves but larger than foxes. They make their nest in a room at the end of a long tunnel, often enlarging a burrow abandoned by a groundhog, skunk or fox. They are opportunistic **omnivores**—eating almost any kind of plant or animal.

By studying coyote **scat (feces)**, we know that they eat a wide variety of foods. They prefer rodents—voles and mice. But they also eat snakes, lizards, frogs, turtles, raccoons, squirrels, foxes, and porcupines. If grasshoppers are plentiful, they eat grasshoppers. They also eat watermelon, berries and corn. In the cities they eat rats, house cats and garbage. They usually eat whatever gives them the most nutrition with the least output of energy.

The population of coyotes in Pennsylvania is small compared to the population in New York. This may be due to Pennsylvania's larger population of white-tailed deer. Deer feed on the low-growing plants that snowshoe hares need for food and cover. When there is a large white-tailed deer population, there is a small snowshoe hare population. The snowshoes are an important winter food source for the coyote. The snowshoe hare population may be a **limiting factor** that determines the size of the coyote population.

For more information on coyotes, search for "eastern coyote" or visit www.wildtexas.com/wildguides/coyote.htm or www.state.pa.us/PA_Exec/PGC/coyote.htm.

Environmental Challenge: Sea Otters

Sea lions and seals are the preferred foods of killer whales. Sea lions and seals eat fish; the same fish that humans eat. Overfishing in the Bering Sea has caused a decline in fish populations. Fewer fish means less food for sea lions and seals. With fewer sea lions and seals to eat, the killer whales are now dining on sea otters. The sea otter populations in Alaska's Aleutian Islands have declined by 90% since 1990. Sea otters eat sea urchins that dine on kelp (seaweed).

- Draw a food web that shows the relationships described here.
- Predict the effects of these changes on the food web in the coastal kelp forests.

Sea Otters.

The Persistent Predator

Ranchers have declared war on the coyote because of its reputation for killing livestock. According to the National Agricultural Statistical Service, coyotes eat as many as 250,000 lambs and sheep each year. In an effort to reduce losses of livestock, thousands of coyotes are poisoned, trapped, and shot each year. The Wildlife Services Division of the United States Department of Agriculture exterminated 82,261 coyotes in 1996. Almost all of the killings took place in 17 western states. The cost of coyote control is approximately $20 million each year.

In spite of the efforts to reduce the population, the western coyote population remains stable. Unlike wolves, coyotes have survived the war by adjusting their reproductive rate. When the population reaches the **carrying capacity** of their habitat (the maximum number of animals the land can support), the average size of a coyote litter is two or three. When the population is below the carrying capacity, the litter size increases and more offspring survive to adulthood. As a result, ranchers are faced with the same problem year after year.

It is true that coyotes sometimes kill large animals, but research shows that they are a much greater threat to the smaller ones. Examination of stomach contents from several thousand dead coyotes in the Western U.S. has shown their diet to be mainly rabbits, mice, voles, and other small rodents. Many other foods are eaten: insects, birds, fish, beaver, skunks, grass, and nuts. Poultry and livestock make up only 1/8 of the stomach contents.

The coyote's bad reputation is probably due to the fact that they often eat **carrion**—dead animal carcasses. If coyote tracks are seen around a half-eaten sheep or deer, the coyote gets credit for killing the animal. The animal may have already been dead or was weakened before the coyote found it.

Stomach contents of 37 coyotes and 7 coydogs (coyote-dog hybrids) killed in Pennsylvania were examined. The stomachs of 15 contained the remains of deer. All but two of these were killed during or shortly after the legal hunting season. These coyotes had probably eaten the remains of deer left by hunters, or wounded deer that had not been found by the hunter.

Maggots found in one stomach proved that the coyote had been dining on the carcass of a deer. One stomach contained hide from a Holstein cow and another contained hair from a pig. Both coyotes were probably acting as scavengers.

Coyotes eat whatever is available. If the watermelon is ripe, it is an easy dinner. If rabbits and rodents are plentiful, lambs or chickens are not bothered. If lambs or chickens are more available, the coyote will not pass up the opportunity. Coyotes are most frequently predators or scavengers, but they may also be the prey, hunted by wolves, golden eagles, and large cats, such as mountain lions.

A New Approach

Coyotes remain the number one problem for the sheep industry. Killing coyotes has not solved the problem. Realizing this fact, some farmers and ranchers are now turning to nonlethal methods to reduce their losses. Putting the sheep in corrals at night or fencing the pastures is effective, but not foolproof.

Keeping sheep in—and predators out—requires an expensive eight-strand high tensile wire fence, with two electrified wires. Fencing 5000 acres (2020 ha) of land on a western ranch is prohibitively expensive. Rounding up sheep to pen them at night may not be practical. If fences are not an option, losses can be reduced with a few good security guards.

Certain breeds of European guard dogs—Great Pyrenes, Komandor, and Maremma—have been bred to herd sheep. When the dogs are raised with the sheep, they bond to them and protect them from coyotes. Guard dogs are effective, but they are costly and they require care.

When raised with another animal, sheep become attached to the animal and follow the animal wherever it goes. Some farmers are bonding sheep with young donkeys. They require less care than guard dogs because they eat the same food as the sheep. Donkeys herd sheep like guard dogs, and they will attack coyotes if they get too close. Cattle don't herd sheep, but they instinctively charge coyotes.

Researchers trained sheep to graze among cattle by penning newly weaned lambs with young cattle for two months. Once a bond is established, the sheep graze among the cattle. The scientists put bonded sheep and cattle in one pasture, and unbonded sheep and cattle were put in another pasture. To be sure that the coyotes did not prefer one pasture to the other, the animals were switched each time a sheep was killed. The researchers stopped the experiment when 50% of the unbonded sheep had been killed. All of the bonded sheep survived.

Bonding sheep with cattle provides another advantage for ranchers. Cattle eat grasses and sheep prefer broad-leaved plants. The **carrying capacity** of the land—the number of animals the land supports—is greater for a mixed herd than it is for a single-species herd. The rancher's income is increased by a combination of two factors: the larger number of animals that the land can support, and the greater number of sheep that survive.

Coyotes take advantage of an easy food source. Farmers and ranchers make life easy for a coyote by providing an easy source of food for them. When a guard dog, donkey, cow, or an electric fence makes it more difficult for the coyote to prey on sheep, they begin to hunt rodents and jack rabbits.

If the farmers and ranchers win the war with the coyote, the cattle and sheep would then have to compete with the herbivores that were the coyote's prey. It seems unlikely that this will happen. The coyote appears to be the ultimate survivor.

Environmental Challenge: Coyotes

The local newspaper reports that the game commission is planning a predator control program for your area. The controls will focus on the increasing population of coyotes.

- Predict the reaction of an orchard owner to this announcement.
- Predict the reaction of the owner of a Christmas tree farm.
- Would you be in favor of this program? Why or why not?

Dog guarding sheep.

1.5 QUESTIONS FOR STUDY AND DISCUSSION:

1. Define the following terms: **VOCABULARY**

carrion	limiting factor
carrying capacity	omnivore
environmental impact statement	scat

2. What may have caused the coyote's disappearance from the East more than 10,000 years ago?
3. Have the populations of most predators increased or decreased? What are the two major reasons for the changes?

Return of the Coyote

4. What two changes have made the eastern part of the U.S. more suitable for coyotes?
5. Draw a food web that includes the coyote as a herbivore, predator, scavenger, and prey. Write the niche in parenthesis ( ) beside the name of the organism.
6. Describe the relationships that exist between the snowshoe hare, white-tailed deer and coyote populations.

The Persistent Predator

7. What means have ranchers used to control the coyote populations?
8. Describe the impact attempts to eliminate the western coyote have had on the coyote population?
9. Do you think that coyotes deserve their bad reputation? Explain.
10. The term "opportunistic omnivore" is used to describe the coyote. Explain why this term fits the "niche" of the coyote.

A New Approach

11. What methods are ranchers using to protect their flocks of sheep from the coyote?
12. Give two advantages of "bonding" sheep to cattle.

www

Wolves were eradicated from most of the United States by the 1930s. In 1995 the National Park Service released a group of Canadian wolves into Yellowstone. To find out how the reintroduction of this large carnivore is affecting the food web, visit www.idahonews.com/wolf/wolfpage.htm and www.timberwolfinformation.org.

Environmental Challenge: Wolves

Between 1904 and 1935, 121 mountain lions, 132 wolves and 4,352 coyotes were killed in Yellowstone National Park. When predators were finally protected in 1940, only the coyotes were left. For more than 50 years, the coyote has been the major predator in the park. The park also is home to a small population of red foxes as well as many herbivores including elk and bison.

- Write an environmental impact statement describing how you think the reintroduction of the wolf to Yellowstone will affect the food web in the park.
- Do some research to find out what has happened to the coyote population in Yellowstone.
- Do you think a predator should be reintroduced to an ecosystem once it has been eliminated?

The settlers exterminated the wolf from much of its natural range. With the wolf gone, smaller predators filled its niche.

The Flow of Energy through an Ecosystem

OBJECTIVES

- **Describe** how energy moves through an ecosystem.
- **Compare** food chains for the human population of the United States with food chains for the human populations of other countries.

- **Compare** the productivity of different ecosystems.

When the sun shines on a grain of sand, it may make it so hot that you cannot walk on it with bare feet. Yet when sun strikes a green leaf, it does not become hot. Why?

When sunlight—solar energy—strikes an object, the object either reflects or absorbs the energy.

Reflected:

Approximately 30% of solar energy reaching the earth's surface is reflected from the surfaces of water, land, clouds, air, plants and human-made structures.

Absorbed:

Approximately 70% of solar energy reaching the earth's surface is absorbed by water, land, clouds, air, human-made structures, and plants.

Most of the energy that is absorbed by objects, living or nonliving, is changed to heat energy. If the object is a dry grain of sand, all of the heat energy is radiated back into the air or, in the case of the sand particle, to your bare foot. If the sand is wet, it will probably not be uncomfortable because much of the heat energy is used in the process of **evaporation**.

The leaf is like wet sand. It is not hot to the touch, because most of the heat is used in the evaporation of water that is inside the leaf. The water vapor then diffuses through openings in the leaf. This process is called **transpiration**.

Very little—between one and two percent—of the solar energy that reaches the earth is absorbed by plants and trapped by chlorophyll. Once it is trapped by chlorophyll, solar energy is changed to chemical energy. In the process of photosynthesis, low energy molecules—carbon dioxide and water—are combined to make a high-energy molecule—sugar. The sugar may be changed into other chemicals that form the structure of the plant (DNA, protein, and cellulose), or it may be stored in energy-rich molecules (sugars, starch, and oil). The energy, trapped in these molecules, is the foundation for the flow of energy through the ecosystem.

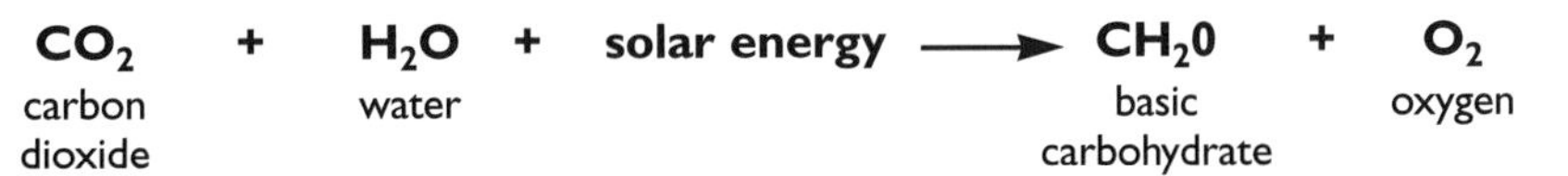

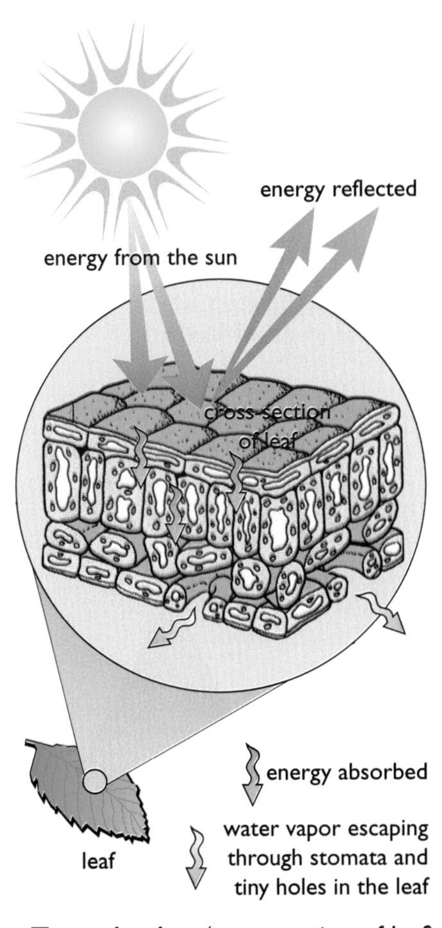

Transpiration (cross-section of leaf)

Building a Pyramid

The total amount (mass) of all organic matter at any level in a food chain is the **biomass**. To determine the biomass of the producers in an ecosystem, it is necessary to collect all plants in one unit area (one square meter), dry the plants and weigh them. Although it is a more difficult task, the biomass of herbivores and carnivores can also be calculated.

The biomass of the producers is always greater than the biomass of the herbivores, and the biomass of the herbivores is always greater than the biomass of the carnivores. The biomass decreases with each

Total Mass of Carnivores
(second-order consumers)
Total Mass of Herbivores
(first-order consumers)
Total Mass of Producers

additional step in a food chain. A diagram that shows this decrease in biomass is a **pyramid of biomass**.

The biomass of organisms in a food chain always forms a pyramid. To carry on its life processes, the plant uses most of the energy trapped during photosynthesis. Only a small part of the energy trapped by the plant remains stored in the plant when it is harvested. This is energy available to the herbivores.

If a plant receives 1000 Calories of energy from the sun, about 5 Calories will be stored in the plant and be available to herbivores. If a deer eats the plant, less than one Calorie (less than 20% of the energy stored in the plant) will be converted to body tissue. About 25% of the energy in the plants eaten by the deer is not digested and remains in the waste. More than half of the energy is changed to heat energy.

William C. Schultz kept 450 rabbits in a building next to his greenhouse. Rabbits give off excess body heat through their ears. Mr. Schultz designed a system to withdraw the warm air from the cages and blow it through plastic tubes on the greenhouse floor. He reduced his fuel bill by 13%—650 gallons (2,500 L) of liquid propane per day. He estimated that he could heat the greenhouse completely with 4,500 rabbits.

In its daily activities, the animal uses most of the energy that is not converted to heat. The need for energy increases when the animal is more active. Energy is used for digestion of food, making new cells, repairing injuries, mating and reproduction. Every activity, even eating, sleeping and breathing, requires energy.

Only 10% of the grass will be converted to rabbit biomass.

The pyramid of biomass reflects the energy loss occurring at each step in the food chain. Only a small portion of what is eaten at one level in the food chain is passed on to the next level. Generally only about 10% of the biomass at one level is converted to biomass at the next level. Rabbits are only able to convert about 10% of the grass they eat into rabbit biomass. The other 90% is undigested, given off as heat, or used in rabbit activities. The energy that remains trapped in an animal's wastes, or in uneaten parts of plants or animals, will provide energy for decomposers.

Numbers in a Pyramid

Usually large numbers of organisms at the base of a food chain are required to support the smaller number of organisms at the top. This makes a

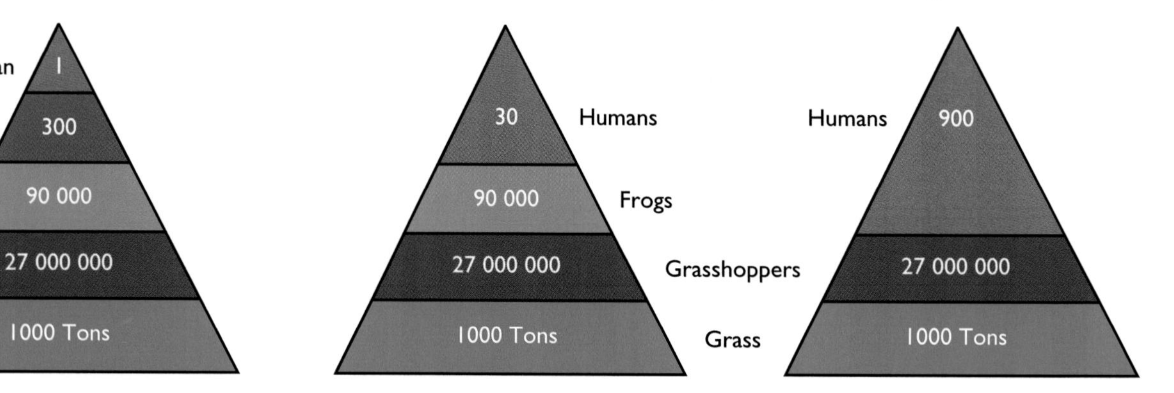

pyramid of numbers, but the number of organisms at each level in a food chain does not always form a pyramid.

While the biomass of a food chain always forms a pyramid, the number of organisms does not. If the producer is very large, there may be a small number of organisms at the base of the food chain. For example, a large number of gypsy moth larvae can feed on one large oak tree.

Plants or algae form the base of the food pyramid. The producers are frequently eaten by insects.

The Population Connection

The number of organisms at the highest level in a food chain is directly related to the number of levels in the chain. More people can be supported if the food chain is shortened. If trout were eliminated from the food chain above, each person could live on 10 frogs per day. The ecosystem would then support 30 people. But who wants to eat 10 frogs a day?

If we eliminate the frogs and eat grasshoppers, nine hundred people could be supported by the ecosystem. They would each be allowed 100 grasshoppers per day—probably more than they would want.

Even more people could live off the land if they ate plants instead of growing plants to feed other animals. About 2,000 people, each eating three pounds of plants per day, could live on land that supports only one person eating a diet including meat.

In America we produce 27,000 pounds (12,150 kg) of alfalfa to produce 3,300 pounds (1,485 kg) of beef. The 3,300 pounds (1,485 kg) of beef will produce 150 pounds (67.5 kg) of human tissue. Countries like India and China cannot support their large populations with this food chain. This explains why the main ingredient in traditional Chinese cooking is rice. The Chinese eat only small amounts of meat. By using the land to grow plants that people eat, the land can support more people.

How many insects will it take to support this fisherman?

Corn Fields and Coral Reefs

Ecosystems vary in the amount of plant matter they are capable of producing. **Productivity** is the amount of biomass (plants, animals and microbes) created in an ecosystem over a period of time, usually a year. The most productive ecosystem is an aquatic ecosystem. Coral reefs produce 70,000 pounds of algae per acre (78,750 kg/ha) each year. Some of our best cultivated farm lands produce only 13,000 pounds of corn per acre (14,625 kg/ha) in a good year. Mountain meadows produce only one or two pounds of plants per acre (1.125–2.25 kg/ha) in a year.

The biomass of producers that an ecosystem can grow per unit area (acre/hectare) depends upon the solar energy that reaches the ecosystem, the nutrients and water available and the length of the growing season. The biomass of producers available is a limiting factor for the consumers in an ecosystem. Energy is not recycled. It is lost at each step in the food chain. This means that there will be smaller populations of those organisms at the higher levels in the food chain.

Environmental Challenge: The Eel River

One food chain that exists in California's Eel River looks like this:

filamentous algae → midge larvae → damselfly nymphs → steelhead trout → humans

One ecological theory says that the biomass of producers (algae) will be limited when the food chain has an even number of levels and more abundant when there is an odd number of levels in the food chain.

- Predict what will happen if fishing is not permitted in the Eel River.
- Predict what will happen if trout can no longer live in the river.
- Can you think of a way to prove that this theory is correct?

1.6 Questions for Study and Discussion:

1. Define the following terms: **VOCABULARY**

biomass	pyramid of biomass
evaporation	pyramid of numbers
productivity	transpiration

2. What happens to solar energy when it strikes an object?
3. Explain why the air temperature on a golf course is cooler than the temperature in the center of the city a few miles or kilometers away.
4. What part of the solar energy reaching the earth is absorbed by plants and trapped by chlorophyll?

Building a Pyramid

5. Describe how to determine the biomass of your lawn.
6. Why does the biomass of the organisms at each level in a food chain always form a pyramid?
7. Very little of the energy received by a plant becomes available to the organisms at the next level of the food chain. What happens to the rest of the energy?
8. Explain why food chains are usually limited to three or four levels.

Numbers in a Pyramid

9. All food chains don't form a pyramid of numbers. Why?

The Population Connection

10. How do food chains in China and India differ from food chains in the United States? Why?

Corn Fields and Coral Reefs

11. What factors determine the productivity of an ecosystem?
12. Rank the following ecosystems in order from most productive to least productive: field of corn, coral reef, mountain meadow.
13. What is the limiting factor for the biomass of consumers in an ecosytem?

Environmental Challenge: Snow Geese

The population of snow geese that nest in the eastern and central Arctic and sub-Arctic regions of Canada exceeds 5 million birds. The population has increased 5% each year for the past 10 years.

Plants grow slowly on the cold nesting grounds, and the geese are removing more plant material than can be produced before the next breeding season. This is a problem for the snow geese and for other species that share their habitat. The populations of a number of bird species that nest in the same area are declining. The caribou population may also decline if they can't find enough food.

There are several factors that are responsible for the increase in the population of snow geese. One of these factors is directly related to changes in land use in the areas where the geese spend the winter. The original habitat for the snow geese was the wetlands along the Gulf of Mexico. Humans have drained and developed many of these wetlands, and the geese have adapted to the changes.

The snow geese have expanded their range as they have found that farm fields provide an abundant supply of food. Waste grain in farm fields along the migration route provide plenty of food as they return to the breeding grounds. The good nutrition allows more geese to survive and produce offspring.

- What suggestions do you have to address this problem?
- Why isn't this problem easily solved?
- What will happen if nothing is done?

Cycles in the Ecosystem 1.7

OBJECTIVES

- ✔ **Compare** the movement of energy and the movement of matter in an ecosystem.
- ✔ **Compare** the movement of matter in natural ecosystems and human-made ecosystems.
- ✔ **Create** models or illustrations showing the relationships between the biotic and abiotic components of the biogeochemical cycles.

All ecosystems consist of biotic (living) and abiotic (nonliving) components. Interactions occurring between the biotic and abiotic parts of an ecosystem are essential to make it function as one unit or system. As we learned in Section 1.6, solar energy is an important abiotic component of nearly every ecosystem.

Once the solar energy is converted to chemical energy, it may be used for essential life processes. Much of it is lost as heat. Energy passes through an ecosystem in much the same way that cars travel on a one-way street. It travels in only one direction—from sun to producer to consumer. The process of photosynthesis must constantly replace the energy that is lost from the ecosystem.

Unlike energy, matter can be recycled within an ecosystem. **Matter** may be defined as anything that takes up space and has mass. Matter refers to all of the chemicals that make up the earth, the air and the organisms in an ecosystem. The chemicals cannot be created or destroyed, but they can be changed from one form to another.

Nature Recycles

Imagine an aquarium that doesn't require someone to feed the fish. In a closed ecosystem, matter is never gained nor lost. Working for NASA, Dr. Joe Hanson developed a totally closed aquatic ecosystem. Dr. Hanson carefully selected species of shrimp, algae and microorganisms, and then he sealed them in glass containers. No one ever needs to feed the shrimp or change the water in the aquarium.

With controlled light and temperature conditions, the sealed ecosystems continue to function without the loss or gain of any matter. The light provides the energy, and the microorganisms recycle the chemicals. Most human-made ecosystems are not closed ecosystems. They usually require huge inputs of matter and energy. Zoos are an excellent example of an unnatural ecosystem where matter is not recycled within the system.

Ecosphere — A totally enclosed ecosystem.

In natural ecosystems, some matter is gained or lost, but most matter is recycled. Although it is unusual, meteors and debris from outer space sometimes inject matter into an ecosystem. It is far more likely that matter entering an ecosystem was removed from another ecosystem by wind or water. Water sometimes removes large amounts of soil from an ecosystem and deposits it in an aquatic ecosystem. Wind picks up and carries small particles and gases great distances. Rain cleanses the air and deposits the matter in a distant ecosystem.

Human activities sometimes disrupt the normal flow of matter and threaten the continued existence of an ecosystem. The **biogeochemical cycles**, the flow of chemicals between the environment and organisms in it, are essential to the survival of all ecosystems. As you study each cycle, give particular attention to the potential environmental impacts of technology.

A zoo is not a closed ecosystem because it requires huge inputs of resources.

Smokestacks at coal-burning power plants and industries release huge amounts of carbon dioxide and water vapor into the atmosphere.

Algae, such as this seaweed clinging to the rocks and microscopic algae (phytoplankton), produce most of the oxygen in the atmosphere.

The Carbon-Oxygen Cycle

Plants use carbon dioxide (CO_2) from the atmosphere in the process of **photosynthesis**. Using light energy, plants combine carbon dioxide and water to form sugar. The sugar is both a source of energy and a building block for other compounds such as proteins, oils and starches. The compounds produced by plants contain carbon and are called **organic compounds**.

Plants give off oxygen (O_2) as a waste product. Although algae in the ocean produce most of the oxygen in our atmosphere, trees are also an important source. Plants, animals and microorganisms use oxygen in the process of respiration. In **respiration**, the compounds containing carbon—the organic compounds—are broken down, and carbon dioxide is released. When respiration occurs without enough oxygen, the organic chemicals are not completely broken down, and the organic compounds released often have offensive odors.

The Carbon-Oxygen cycle is out of balance. There is more carbon dioxide being released into the atmosphere than is being removed from it. Most of the carbon dioxide is produced during the process of burning—**combustion**. When compounds containing carbon (coal, oil, or wood) are burned, the carbon is chemically combined with oxygen, and carbon dioxide is released. In a short period of time, combustion releases carbon dioxide into the atmosphere. The use of carbon dioxide by plants during photosynthesis is a much slower process. As a result of the imbalance between these two processes, the level of carbon dioxide in the atmosphere is increasing. In Unit 2, pages 111, 119, and 124, we will examine the possible effects of the increasing levels of carbon dioxide.

When organisms die, decomposers break down the carbon compounds in their bodies, and carbon dioxide is returned to the atmosphere. During decomposition (decay), other chemicals are also returned to the soil or released into the air. One of these chemicals is nitrogen.

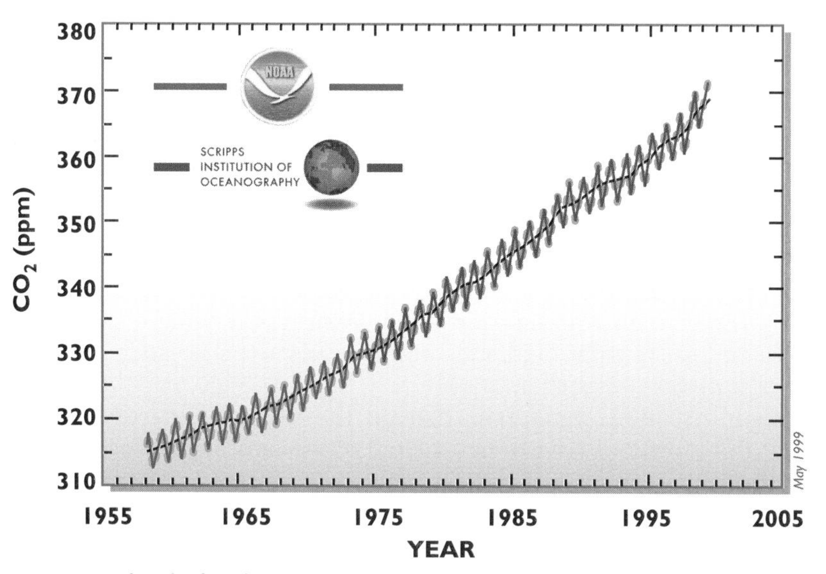

The increasing level of carbon dioxide over time is due to the burning of fossil fuels.

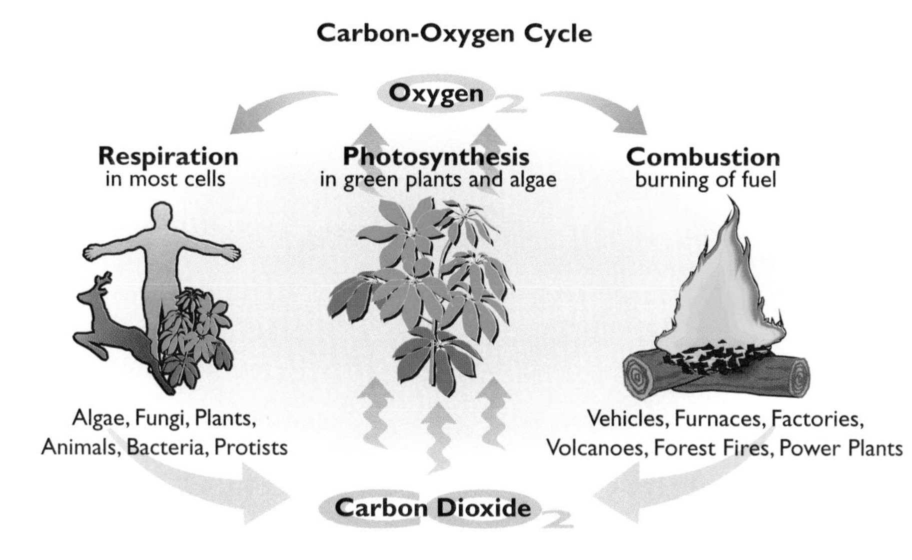

The Nitrogen Cycle

Without plants and decomposers, the carbon—oxygen cycle would stop. Plants and decomposers are also important in the nitrogen cycle, but a certain group of bacteria is essential to this cycle—the nitrogen "fixers." Plants and animals need nitrogen to make protein. The air is about 78% nitrogen, but plants and animals cannot use nitrogen (N2) directly from the atmosphere.

Special bacteria, in the soil and water, must change or "**fix**" nitrogen gas (N_2) into nitrogen fertilizers {nitrate ions (NO_3^-) or ammonium ions (NH_4^+)} that plants can use. These bacteria are called **nitrogen fixers**. Most nitrogen-fixing bacteria live in little houses, or **nodules**, on the roots of plants called legumes. **Legumes** are members of a large family of plants that includes peas, beans, alfalfa, clover, **vetches**, and locust trees. The plants provide food and cover for the bacteria, and the bacteria convert nitrogen gas into fertilizer for the plant.

Animals get nitrogen from plants or from other plant-eating animals, in the form of protein. The nitrogen is recycled by special bacteria that break down the nitrogen compounds (proteins) in dead plants and animals, and in animal wastes. If plants do not use the nitrogen compounds as fertilizer, special forms of bacteria may recycle it. These bacteria convert the unused fertilizer into nitrogen gas and release it into the atmosphere. All natural ecosystems depend upon bacteria to keep the nitrogen cycle going.

Lightning plays a small role in the nitrogen cycle. The huge amount of electrical energy, called lightning, combines nitrogen and oxygen in the atmosphere. Dissolved in the rain, the "fixed" nitrogen enters the soil where bacteria convert it into nitrate fertilizer. But nature is no longer in total control of the nitrogen cycle. Human activities are dramatically increasing the nitrogen available to ecosystems.

To grow crops that require large amounts of nitrogen, farmers add commercial fertilizers. Fertilizer manufacturers take nitrogen from the air

WWW For information on the global carbon cycle, visit www.whrc.org/carbon/carbon.htm.

Crown vetch has been planted along highways to control erosion. It needs no fertilizer because bacteria on its roots can "fix" nitrogen from the air.

Bacteria in the nodules on the roots of soybeans and other legumes can "fix" or change nitrogen gas into fertilizers.

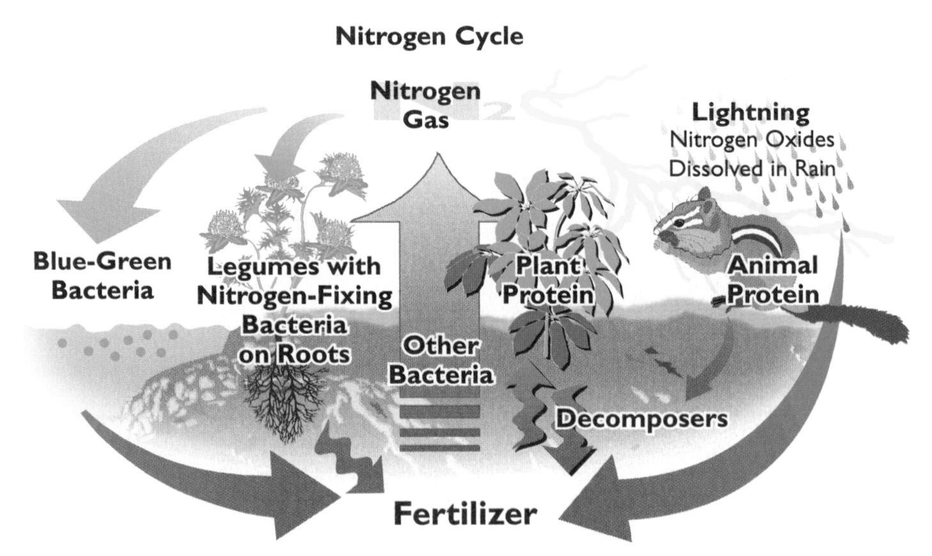

and hydrogen from natural gas and combine them in a high-pressure, high-temperature environment. Since this process is very expensive, farmers often plant legume crops to take advantage of their natural abilities to fix nitrogen. There is also a large demand for some legume crops such as soybeans.

Another major source of nitrogen comes from burning fossil fuels. The atmosphere contains 78% nitrogen and nearly 21% oxygen. The high temperatures created during combustion cause nitrogen and oxygen to combine creating nitrogen oxides (NOx). Motor vehicles, factories, power plants, forest fires, fireplaces and even grills are all sources of nitrogen oxides. The gases dissolve in the rain and are carried to an ecosystem somewhere downwind from where they were created. While their fertilizing effect may benefit some crops, there are some disadvantages. These are discussed in Unit 2, page 123.

The Mineral Cycle

Most of the minerals (such as calcium and phosphorus) in an ecosystem are stored in rocks. They are released from the rocks by the action of wind, water and changes in temperature. The process of physical and chemical forces releasing minerals from rocks is called **weathering**.

Wind sometimes acts as a sand-blaster, breaking off small particles of the rock. Rocks are broken into smaller pieces when water freezes and thaws. Rocks are also broken by the action of the roots. Plant roots exert a great amount of force as they grow. This can be seen when walking along a sidewalk on a tree-lined street. The tree roots often cause sections of concrete to crack. The foundations of buildings and underground pipes are sometimes cracked by the growth of tree roots. This is physical weathering.

At Mammoth Springs in Yellowstone National Park, hot water evaporates leaving behind an impressive deposit of minerals.

Chemical weathering occurs when acidic rain dissolves minerals in the rocks. Roots also produce chemicals that dissolve minerals in the rocks. The trees absorb some of the minerals. Others are carried away by water moving through the soil. This process is known as **leaching**.

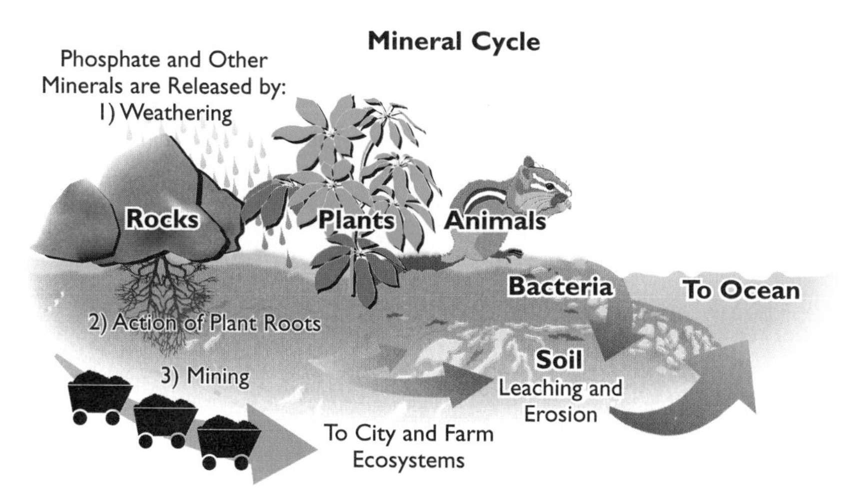

What forces will cause weathering of the rocks shown in this picture?

Due to leaching and mining, the mineral cycle is a leaky cycle. **Mining** is the process of removing a natural substance from an ecosystem faster than it is replaced. Humans mine many ores for the minerals they contain—aluminum, zinc, lead, gold and phosphorus. You can think of others. We often remove these materials for use in our human-made ecosystems. Some of the minerals will be recycled and used over and over again. Others will be discarded in a landfill.

Mineral particles are also removed from an ecosystem by the action of wind and water. This process is called **erosion**. The mineral particles carried away by the flowing water may become a part of a sand bar in a large river or they may be deposited in the ocean. Whether they are removed from the cycle by leaching, mining or erosion, the minerals are no longer available to the ecosystem.

For information on the hydrologic cycle, visit www.epa.gov/seahome/groundwater/src/cycle.htm and utility.co.pinellas.fl.us/hydro.html.

The Hydrologic Cycle

"Hydro" means water. The hydrologic or water cycle describes the movement and storage of water on planet earth. The total amount of water doesn't change. Its movement is influenced by the earth's surface. Winds transport water vapor in the atmosphere and influence climate. The sun provides the energy for the water cycle.

Water re-enters the atmosphere by one of two processes—evaporation or transpiration. Water is lost from the soil and all surface water—rivers, lakes, streams and oceans—through the process of evaporation. Since the oceans cover more than 70% of the earth's surface, most water enters the atmosphere through the process of evaporation. **Evaporation** occurs when the sun's energy heats the water, changing it from its liquid state into its gaseous state known as **water vapor**.

Water taken up by the roots of plants travels to the leaves. Some of these water molecules move by the process of osmosis through the cell membranes and into the microscopic spaces within the leaf. The water vapor then diffuses out of the leaf through openings called **stomata**. This loss of water vapor from the leaves of plants is called **transpiration**. During the growing season, as many as 500,000 gallons (2 million L) of

Did You Know?

The average water molecule resides in the atmosphere for 10 days where it may travel thousands of miles before returning to the earth as precipitation.

The tiny water droplets in these clouds are formed by the process of condensation.

water vapor may re-enter the atmosphere through transpiration from one acre (0.4 ha) of corn.

As warm humid air rises, it loses energy. As the air cools, the water vapor collects on small particles in the atmosphere called **condensation nuclei**. The tiny droplets that form on the surface of these particles form clouds. This process of water vapor changing into its liquid form is called **condensation**. When the water droplets become too heavy to remain in the atmosphere they begin to fall. The temperature of the air determines the form of moisture—rain, snow, sleet or hail. All moisture falling from the atmosphere is collectively called **precipitation**.

Some precipitation falling through a warmer mass of air will re-evaporate before it reaches the earth's surface. Since most of the earth's surface is covered by water, most precipitation falls into the oceans or into other bodies of water. If the precipitation falls on land, it may enter the soil or flow over the surface as **runoff**. The runoff flows into streams or lakes where the water may begin its journey back to the ocean. Along the way it may evaporate or be withdrawn for many uses.

Infiltration is the process of precipitation entering the ground. Plants may take up water that enters the soil, or it may move or **percolate** through the soil and rocks until it reaches a layer of impermeable rock or clay. This layer of water is called **groundwater**. The layer of permeable (porous) rock where the water is stored is an **aquifer**. **Seepage** occurs when groundwater flows naturally from the ground at a **spring**. More often it is pumped from a well drilled into the aquifer.

The amount of precipitation is an important factor in determining the type of ecosystem and the populations of organisms it can support. Unit 4 investigates the role of water in much more detail.

Did You Know?

Morning dew is formed when the night air is cooled below a temperature called the "dew point." The water vapor in the air condenses into tiny droplets. The droplets form on the surface of the soil, and on plant leaves and stems. These droplets of condensed water vapor are called dew. They will remain on plant surfaces until the warmth of the sun evaporates them. You may want to check the newspaper's daily weather report for further information.

Think About It

What happens when you take a soda can from the refrigerator on a hot summer day? Can you explain what actually happens when the can "sweats"? What process in the hydrologic cycle is occurring on the surface of the can?

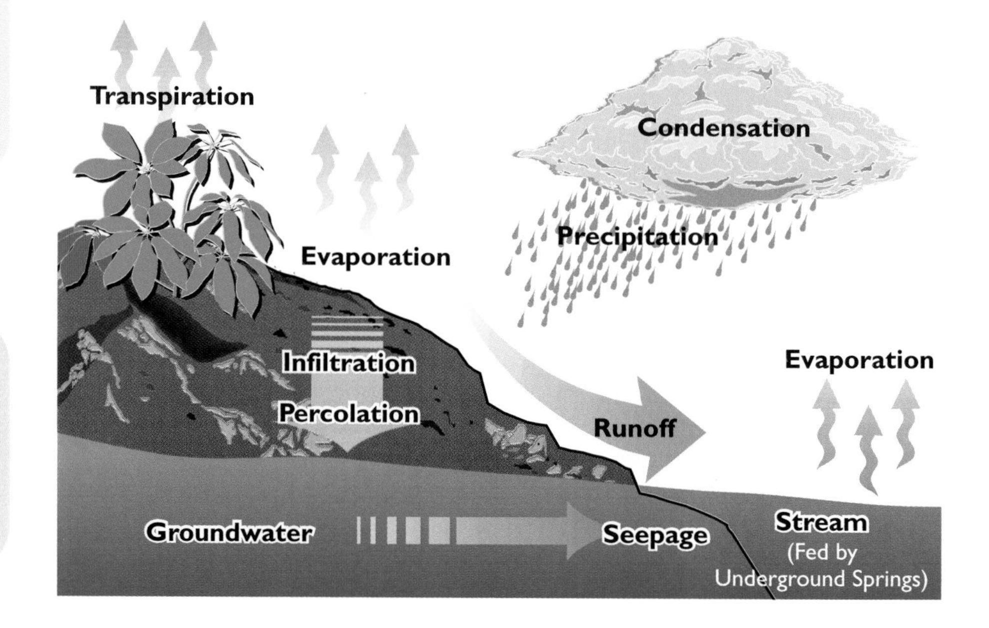

1.7 Questions for Study and Discussion:

1. Define the following terms: **VOCABULARY**

abiotic	erosion	mining	runoff
aquifer	evaporation	nitrogen fixers	seepage
biogeochemical cycles	groundwater	nodules	spring
biotic	infiltration	organic compounds	stomata
combustion	leaching	photosynthesis	transpiration
condensation	legumes	precipitation	water vapor
condensation nuclei	matter	respiration	weathering

2. Compare the flow of matter and energy through an ecosystem.

Nature Recycles

3. How did Dr. Hanson's ecosystems differ from most human-made and natural ecosystems?
4. Compare the recycling of matter in natural ecosystems and in human-made ecosystems.

The Carbon-Oxygen Cycle

5. What process uses carbon dioxide and produces oxygen?
6. What kind of organism produces most of the world's oxygen supply?
7. What two processes produce carbon dioxide? What process produces most of the carbon dioxide in the atmosphere?
8. By what process do decomposers return carbon dioxide to the atmosphere?

The Nitrogen Cycle

9. What kinds of organisms are essential for the nitrogen cycle?
10. Identify plants that are legumes and explain how they are important to the nitrogen cycle.
11. In what way is lightning important to the nitrogen cycle?
12. Why do farmers plant legume crops?

The Mineral Cycle

13. How are minerals removed from rocks?
14. Identify three processes that create "leaks" in the mineral cycle.

The Hydrologic Cycle

15. Identify the two processes that return water to the atmosphere. Most water enters the atmosphere by which of these processes?
16. What is the process in which water vapor collects to form tiny droplets?
17. What is the term that describes all forms of moisture leaving the atmosphere?
18. What term describes the layer of porous rock which is filled with water? What two processes are necessary to maintain water in this layer.

1.8 Succession—Changing Ecosystems

OBJECTIVES

- ✔ **Identify** the stages of succession that occur in a pond or lake.
- ✔ **Compare** the types of plants and animals that are found in early stages of succession with those found in later stages.
- ✔ **Describe** how human activities and natural events alter the process of succession.

Grass sprouts along the bank of this newly dug pond. What stage of succession is it?

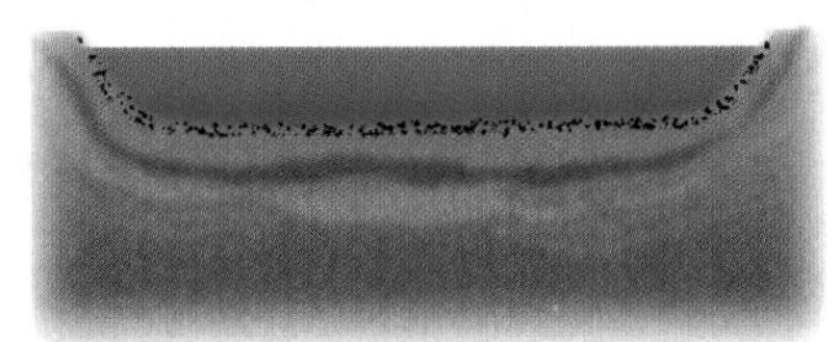

When first formed, a pond has a sandy or muddy bottom. This is the pioneer stage.

What would you see if you studied the same ecosystem year after year for say one thousand years? You would see groups of organisms being replaced by others. This series of changes in which the original species are replaced by new species that immigrate into an ecosystem is **ecological succession**. It is the natural "aging" of the ecosystem.

Why does an ecosystem change with age? Organisms change the environment in which they live. The new environment is no longer a suitable habitat for the organisms that first lived there. New species enter the ecosystem and, if they find the conditions suitable, they crowd out the original inhabitants.

If a field is not mowed, trees begin to grow. As the trees get larger, they shade the ground below. The grasses that grew well in the full sunlight will not survive in the shade. The animals that lived in the field, and fed on the grasses, will move to a new area in search of a better food supply. Those organisms that cannot move will die as the environment changes.

Succession occurs in all ecosystems. In cold or dry climates, the rate of succession may be extremely slow. The rate of succession may also be altered by human activities. Ecologists have studied the changes that occur in various ecosystems. Sometimes they interrupt the process in order to maintain the habitat for a rare or endangered species. One example of this is managing a forest for the red-cockaded woodpeckers and Kirtland's Warblers. See Sections 1.12 and 1.14 on pages 57 and 74.

Ponds provide a particularly good example of succession. A pond is not a pond forever. As it grows old, it gets drier and drier. If you conduct a survey of ponds in your community, you may be able to locate ponds in each of the stages of succession described below.

When first formed, a pond has a sandy or muddy bottom. This "bare bottom" stage is the **pioneer stage**. The species of animals that live in the pond depend upon the "bare bottom." Mussels, a type of fresh water clam, cannot move across the bottom of the pond if plants are growing there. The species of caddisfly larvae that live in a pond in the pioneer stage will not remain in the pond when the bottom is covered with plants. They use sand from the bottom of the pond to build the case or "house" in which they live.

Some species of fish make nests on the muddy bottom of the pond. These fish will stop reproducing when the bottom becomes covered with

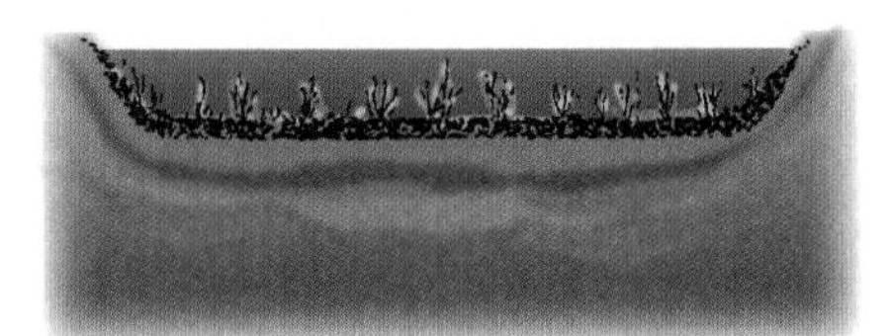

Pond weeds grow in the humus, but they don't reach the surface. This is the submerged plant stage.

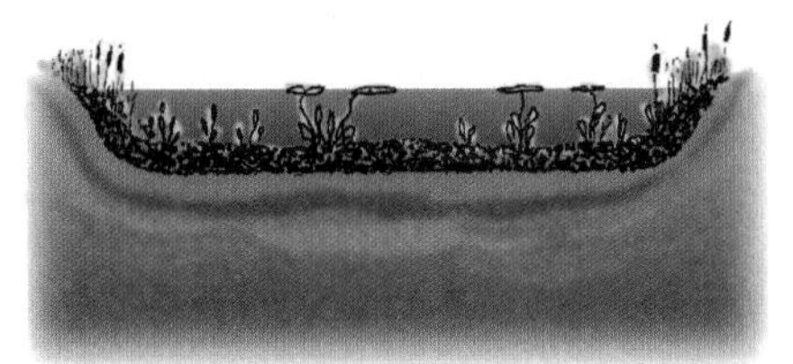

Cattails, bullrushes and water lilies are found growing in ponds which are in the emerging plant stage.

There are no large areas of open water. The pond has now become a marsh.

plants. Animals that live in the pond during the pioneer stage feed on the small floating organisms—algae, protozoa, bacteria, and crustaceans.

In time, the death and decay of organisms form a layer of organic matter that covers the bottom of the pond. This layer of **humus** allows larger algae and small aquatic plants (pond weeds) to grow on the bottom of the pond. Since the plants do not reach the surface of the water, this stage is called the **submerged plant stage**.

The original fish are replaced by other species that lay their eggs on the leaves of the plants. Dragonfly and mayfly nymphs burrow in the muddy bottom. New species of mussels and caddisfly larvae replace the species found in the bare-bottomed stage. The submerged plants and algae provide new habitats for organisms found in this stage.

As the pond continues to fill in, the thicker layer of humus on the bottom allows larger plants to become rooted. Cattails and bulrushes grow near the edge of the pond, and water lilies may be seen floating near the middle. This is the **emerging plant stage**.

The emerging plants provide stems for those air-breathing organisms that need to climb to the surface for a breath of oxygen. Organisms found in the pioneer stage are entirely gone. The burrowing dragonfly nymphs are replaced by a new species that climbs on the submerged parts of the bulrushes. Lung-breathing snails replace the gill-breathing snails.

Diving spiders rest on the exposed bulrushes and cattail stalks and feed on the abundant mayfly and dragonfly nymphs. The nymphs cling to the submerged stalks, then climb to the surface, shed their **exoskeleton**, and fly away. A species of caddisfly larvae, that is new to the neighborhood, makes its "house" from parts of aquatic plants.

The stagnant water in the plant-choked pond has a low level of oxygen. Organisms that require a high oxygen level cannot survive. Crayfish solve this problem by carrying their eggs and young with them. Worms live in the bottom mud, and aquatic insect larvae provide food for diving beetles. Frogs, turtles and salamanders find plenty of food and places to rest. A few fish, such as catfish, may be found scavenging on the bottom. Leeches may feed on the fish or on an ecologist who wades in to study succession.

As more years pass, the pond is filled with plants, waste products and bodies of dead organisms. When there are no longer any large areas of open water, the pond has become a **marsh**. It is now an area of shallow water with grasses and other rooted plants.

Can you identify the stages of succession?

www

To learn more about ecological succession, visit http://hyperion.advanced.org/17456/.

Drier than a marsh, the swamp supports the growth of trees that don't mind having wet "feet."

Soil carried by floods is deposited in the swamp. The drier ground supports a beech-maple forest.

On the prairie, flowers bloom in spring. Fires prevent the growth of trees.

Environmental Challenge: Fire

The Greater Yellowstone Ecosystem has been shaped by wildfires. Fire can be an enemy or a friend. The early European explorers regarded fire as an enemy. Ecologists have a different view. Between 1972 and 1986, Yellowstone's fire policy allowed natural fires (fires caused by lightning) to burn. Then in 1988 fires caused by humans and lightning burned 1.2 million acres. Fire policies were re-evaluated.

Research the effects of fire in Yellowstone and other National Parks. Find out:

- How the Native Americans viewed fire?
- What effect fires have on trees? On other plants?
- What effect fires have on small animals? Birds? Fish? Large mammals?
- What do you think? Should natural fires be allowed to burn?

To learn more about the role of fire in ecological succession at our national parks, visit:
www.nps.gov/htdocs4/yell/nature/fire/wildfire.htm;
www.nps.gov/htdocs1/pub aff/issues/fire.html.

WWW

The truly aquatic animals die in the shallow, muddy water of the marsh. Frogs, salamanders, crayfish and leeches remain, but fish cannot survive. Turtles and snakes may feed on the frogs or on dying fish. Even though the adults cannot survive, the eggs of many small aquatic organisms survive the summer and winter months and produce the species the following spring. This is why we find many small organisms in temporary ponds each spring.

The water in a marsh may come from springs or from a stream or lake. Some marshes are entirely dependent upon rainfall for their supply of water. The marsh may dry out completely during the summer. Salt-water marshes depend on the tides to bring in water with a supply of food and oxygen. Only animals that can burrow in the mud or move with the tide can survive in a salt-water marsh.

The marsh becomes drier as the organic matter continues to build up. Trees, like the red cedar and red (swamp) maple begin to invade the area. The marsh has now become a **swamp**. The swamp will be wet, maybe flooded, during spring and fall. The floods will deposit soil in the swamp. As the area continues to fill in, more trees invade; and the ecosystem eventually reaches the final stage in succession or the **climax community**; in this case a **beech-maple forest**. Although there will be changes in the climax community, it will remain until it is disturbed by some natural event or human activity.

On the western plains a marsh may not reach the swamp and forest stages. Instead, the marsh becomes a grassland or **prairie**. Why don't trees invade? Fires swept by strong winds frequently spread across hundreds of miles on the Great Plains. Where natural fires are allowed to burn or farm equipment cultivates the land, trees are not given a chance to grow. In areas that are not disturbed, the process of succession will reach the forest stage unless there aren't enough nutrients in the soil or enough rainfall to support the growth of trees.

1.8 Questions for Study and Discussion:

1. Define the following terms: VOCABULARY

beech-maple forest	emerging plant stage	marsh	submerged plant stage
climax community	exoskeleton	pioneer stage	swamp
ecological succession	humus	prairie	

2. The kinds of organisms found in an old ecosystem are not the same as those found in a younger ecosystem. Why do some organisms disappear and others flourish in the same area?
3. How does a pond in the pioneer stage differ from older ponds?
4. Arrange the stages of succession listed in question 1 in the order in which they occur, and describe the predominant type of plant associated with each stage.
5. Explain how emerging plants are important to some animals in the pond.
6. Describe how human disturbances and natural fires alter succession.

Ten thousand years ago, in much of the northern United States, snow would not stop falling. Summer never came. Large masses of ice were formed, and today we call them **glaciers**. A glacier is very heavy and slides very slowly along the ground. As it moves over land, it scrapes the rock and/or soil below. Pieces of rock break off. Glaciers sometimes act as snow plows or bulldozers pushing ridges of rock in front of them. This is how large rocks can end up on top of hills.

OBJECTIVES

- **Contrast** the physical structure of kettle lakes and other lakes.
- **Explain** why the process of succession in kettle lakes differs from succession in other lakes.
- **Compare** the role of succession with the role of human activities in the extinction of species.

Kettle Lakes

Eventually, temperatures began to rise, and the glaciers started to melt. Rocks that had been carried or pushed by the glacier were left behind. The glaciers that pushed rocks in front of them left a ridge of rocky debris. While some deposits formed small ridges, other ridges were large enough to create dams. Behind some dams, a deep hole with steep sides had been gouged out of the rock. When the ice in this hole melted it formed a kettle lake.

Kettle lakes are different from other lakes; they have no entrances or exits. There are no streams that bring water to the lake. The water in the original lake came from the melting block of ice. Now the only sources of water are precipitation that falls into the lake and runoff from the surrounding land—the **watershed**. Since there are no streams that allow water to flow from the lake, the water that leaves the lake is mainly lost through evaporation.

Like any other lake, the kettle lake begins to "age." The leaves on the forest floor filter the runoff from the lake's watershed. Without mud and nutrients carried by a stream, the "aging" of a kettle lake is a very slow process. Without flowing water, there is little oxygen mixing with the water in the lake. As the organisms in the lake use oxygen, the level of dissolved oxygen decreases. Eventually the low level of oxygen becomes a limiting factor for organisms living in the lake.

Without flowing water, the carbon dioxide produced by the organisms in the lake is trapped there. It chemically combines with water to form carbonic acid (H_2CO_3). As the bacteria work to decompose the dead plants, they produce more and more carbon dioxide. The bacteria also produce another waste product.

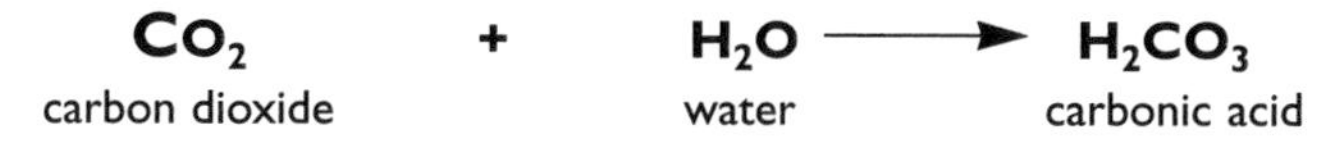

$$\underset{\text{carbon dioxide}}{CO_2} + \underset{\text{water}}{H_2O} \longrightarrow \underset{\text{carbonic acid}}{H_2CO_3}$$

The bacteria must work in an environment without a good supply of oxygen. When your muscle cells work without enough oxygen, they produce a waste product called **lactic acid**. When bacteria break down plant material, the waste product is **tannic acid**. Tannic acid is an amber color, the same color as iced tea. The increasing concentrations of carbonic and tannic acids make the water too acidic for most organisms.

Sedges, ferns and woody plants grow along the boardwalk at the edge of this bog.

A peat mining operation in Ireland.

A Floating Mat

A pond or lake with a flow of water eventually succeeds to a marsh, then a swamp. In ponds and lakes without a good flow of water, the marsh and swamp stages are replaced by a stage of succession called a **bog**. Limiting factors determine which plants and animals will survive in the bog ecosystem. These include the lack of oxygen and the increasing acidity. Only a few species of plants can live in this harsh environment.

Sedges and other grasses invade the water at the edge of the lake. Sphagnum moss (an evergreen plant) begins to grow around the sedges and other rooted plants near the shore. It continues to grow at the top, and as it grows, it extends outward, floating on the surface like a green raft.

This raft gradually begins to sink as its weight increases. As it sinks, the lower parts of the moss die and begin to decay, but decomposition is not complete. The highly acidic water prevents the growth of fungi and bacteria that are responsible for the decay.

The mat of partly decayed moss is called **peat**. It becomes many feet thick and will eventually fill the entire lake. In countries like Ireland and Denmark, peat is used for fuel. In other countries where there is a better fuel supply, peat is sold at garden centers for mulching and potting mixes.

In a bog, the sphagnum mat acts as a gigantic sponge. It can absorb as much as 25 times its weight in water. It is said that the Native Americans used the sphagnum to line their backpacks. Perhaps it was a **papoose**, an American Indian baby, who had the first disposable diapers!

Sphagnum was also important as a bandaging material. It made a clean dressing for wounds because its acidity did not allow bacteria to grow. Native Americans and American soldiers used it for bandages.

Plants can easily absorb water from the sphagnum moss. Pitcher plants have adapted to the mineral-deficient environment of the bog by digesting insects.

The "Eye" of the Bog

As the sphagnum mat increases in size, the lake becomes more like land rather than a lake. The last remnant of the lake is an area of open water called the **eye of the bog**. Here the water is still deep enough to support the floating lily pads. While the lilies may be the dominant plants in the emerging plant stage, sphagnum moss is the dominant plant of the bog. The thick mat provides a place for other plants to grow. Eventually the sphagnum mat closes in on the eye, and the lilies are replaced by bog cotton, orchids and other plants that like to live in a slightly drier habitat.

Few kinds of plants can tolerate the high level of acidity and the low level of oxygen in the sphagnum mat. For those plants that can survive, the rate of growth is very slow due to the lack of nutrients. A few plants compensate for the lack of minerals by capturing and digesting insects. The sundew and pitcher plants are found in northern bogs. The Venus flytrap is common in bogs in the South where the temperatures are warmer.

The Invasion of Woody Plants

Several types of shrubs, including leatherleaf, blueberry, cranberry, bog rosemary and bog laurel, begin to grow on the sections of the mat that are more solid. Larger shrubs like witch hazel and poison sumac replace these plants. Poison sumac is a shrub with a distinctive branching pattern, but it is easiest to identify after it has formed its white berries.

One of the chemicals in the bark of poison sumac is far more irritating to the skin than poison ivy. Anyone planning to hike through a swamp or a bog should first learn to identify poison sumac. Poison sumac only grows in wet areas. Many people confuse poison sumac with the staghorn sumac. Since staghorn sumac likes to keep its feet dry, it is never found in a swamp or bog. Its bright red seed clusters distinguish it from poison sumac, which has white berries.

Surrounding the zone of shrubs, nearer to the original shoreline, trees begin to grow in the sphagnum mat. The type of tree is determined by the location of the bog. In addition to rocks, the glaciers also carried seeds. The constant evaporation of water from the bog makes it cooler than the surrounding area. The plants of the bog may be species found usually in northern regions. Black spruce and tamarack, also known as larch, are species native to Canada, but they are found in **boreal** (northern) **bogs** in the northern United States.

The species of trees found in bogs are those tolerating the highly acidic and extremely wet conditions. The tree roots grow near the surface of the sphagnum mat. They do not provide the support of deeper roots, and the trees are easily blown over by the wind. Tree rings show that the trees growing in the bog are hundreds of years old, yet they are only a few inches in diameter. While the lack of nutrients in the moss mat doesn't prevent a tree from growing in a bog, it is the major limiting factor for the rate of growth.

Blueberry shrubs growing in bogs provide food for bears and other animals.

The bog is not a bog forever. The hardwood forest along the edge is invading.

Black spruce are one of few types of trees that can grow in a bog. Their small size is due to the lack of nutrients in the bog.

Unlike most conifers, the tamarack is a deciduous tree. It will lose the clusters of soft, flat needles in the autumn. The cones may cling to the tree for several years.

Environmental Challenge: Mount St. Helens

On May 18, 1980, Mount St. Helens erupted violently. Almost 150,000 acres of forest was devastated. What does Mount St. Helens look like today?

- Find out how succession has changed the mountain during the last 20 years.

The bog is home to many animals including this small snake and moth.

Some birds, reptiles, amphibians, and insects make their home in the bog. Some species, such as the bog turtle, are only found in bogs. As succession continues in the bog, the bog becomes drier and less acidic. The hardwoods—beeches, red maples, hickory and oaks—that grow in the woods nearby replace the trees of the bog. Land-loving animals replace those that live in the bog. In time, the bog changes into a hardwood forest.

1.9 Questions for Study and Discussion:

1. Define the following terms: **VOCABULARY**

bog	glacier	lactic acid	tannic acid
boreal bog	kettle lake	peat	watershed
eye of the bog			

2. How do glaciers change the land?
3. How are kettle lakes formed? How do they differ from other lakes?

Kettle Lakes

4. Why does a kettle lake "age" more slowly than other lakes?
5. As the lake "ages," how do the levels of oxygen and carbon dioxide change?
6. Describe the appearance of water that contains tannic acid.

A Floating Mat

7. Compare the process of ecological succession in lakes with a flow of water to lakes with no flow.
8. What are two important limiting factors for the growth of plants in a bog?
9. Describe how sphagnum moss grows and what happens when it dies.
10. Describe at least three ways that sphagnum or peat moss has been used.

The "Eye" of the Bog

11. Describe the "eye of the bog."
12. Why do some of the plants in the bog "eat" insects? Name some of the insect-eating plants you may find in a bog.

The Invasion of Woody Plants

13. What species of shrub grow in a bog?
14. Explain why some species of trees, such as oak and hickory, aren't found in the bog?
15. How does the size of a spruce tree growing in the bog compare to the size of a spruce tree growing outside the bog? What causes this difference?
16. What is the final stage of succession for a bog ecosystem?
17. Name one species of animal that lives only in a bog.

Environmental Challenge: Bog Turtles

The U.S. Fish and Wildlife Service has designated the bog turtle (*Clemmys muhlenbergii*) as threatened. A species qualifies for protection under the Endangered Species Act if it is likely to become endangered and may face extinction in the near future. Illegal collections, mostly for the national and international pet trade, and loss of habitat are the major reasons for the decline in the bog turtle populations.

There are two populations of bog turtles. The northern population has declined by 50%, mostly during the last 20 years. The range for the northern population extends from Massachusetts and New York south to Maryland. The southern population, in Virginia and Georgia, is also protected because it is so similar in appearance.

The bog turtle can be easily distinguished from other turtles by the large, conspicuous bright orange, yellow or red blotch found on each side of the head. The shells of the adult turtles are 3 to 4-1/2 inches in length and are light brown to ebony in color.

Bog turtles are found at fewer than 200 sites in the northern range. Most bog turtle habitats are on private land. Scientists think that in the future there may be only 35 of these sites supporting a healthy population of bog turtles.

- What do you think the future holds for the bog turtle?
- If humans stop the illegal collections of these turtles and the modification of turtle habitats, will the turtle survive?
- What effect will ecological succession have on the turtle population?

Once this bog has become a forest it will no longer be suitable habitat for the bog turtle.

A kettle lake that has no outlet (exit) will eventually become a bog.

More than Trees—an Old-Growth Forest Ecosystem

OBJECTIVES

- ✔ **Compare** virgin or old-growth forest ecosystems with other forest ecosystems.
- ✔ **Relate** the roles of organisms in an old-growth forest ecosystem.
- ✔ **Explain** the relationship between biodiversity and stability of an ecosystem.
- ✔ **Identify** criteria that you would use to assess an old-growth forest ecosystem for purposes of logging old-growth trees.
- ✔ **Discuss** the sustainability of old-growth forest ecosystems.

Majestic trees grow in a virgin stand of timber in the Olympic National Forest.

"... two hundred fifty years at least. That's old-growth bark; all kinds of animals can live in it. That's habitat!"
CHRIS MASER
Forest Consultant

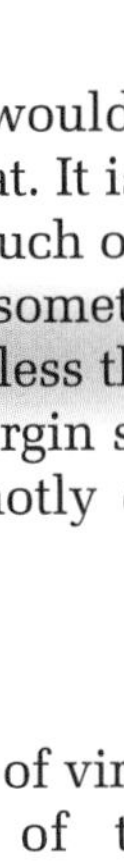

Most people, when asked to define a forest, would probably say "a place with trees," but a forest is much more than that. It is a complex ecosystem. When settlers came to America, they found much of it covered with **virgin forest** ecosystems. The word virgin refers to something that has not been altered by human activity. It is estimated that less than 10% of the original forests remain. The future of the remaining virgin stands of timber, whose ancient trees have never been logged, is a hotly debated issue. Perhaps there is a lesson to be learned from the past.

Penn's Woods

There were 29 million acres (11.6 million ha) of virgin forest in the colony founded by William Penn. The name of the Commonwealth—Pennsylvania—means "Penn's woods." The largest tract of virgin woods that remains in eastern Pennsylvania today is the 649-acre (260-ha) Woodbourne Forest and Wildlife Sanctuary. **The Nature Conservancy**, an organization whose goal is to preserve the best examples of a wide variety of unique ecosystems, owns the sanctuary.

Native Americans saw the virgin forest as a source of food and a dwelling place of their God. The colonists feared the forest and the animals that lived in it. This fear is reflected in Little Red Riding Hood and other popular children's stories. The colonists viewed the forest as an obstacle to agriculture, and they began clearing the land. Clearing was often accomplished with fire, and thousands of acres of forest burned when fires got out of control.

For the first 200 years logging was primarily done to clear land for crops. The first sawmills were water-powered, and only a few existed. More than two-thirds of Pennsylvania was still covered with virgin forest in 1820. With increased demand for wood and improved technology, the rate of logging increased. By 1860 Pennsylvania had become the lumber-producing capital of the world.

Much of the wood was wasted. Frequently loggers removed only the prime log, and the remaining portion of the tree was left to decay. Hemlock was cut only for its bark. The bark, rich in tannic acid, was used in the tanning of leather. The log itself was not valuable, so it was left to decay on the forest floor. When owners sold the land, they often kept **bark rights** that allowed them to continue cutting trees and selling bark.

By 1900 the boom was over, and many towns became ghost towns. Hillsides were bare and gullies were filled with logs and branches. The young forests that grew would once again be cleared by forest fires and logging. Today the State of Pennsylvania owns and manages some two million acres of forest, but there are only a few isolated stands of virgin woods.

As the large stands of ancient trees disappeared in the East, the timber industry expanded westward. Today the lumber capital is somewhere in the Pacific Northwest—Washington, Oregon or perhaps British Columbia. The logging communities in the Pacific Northwest are at the center of a national debate over the issue of logging the remaining old-growth forests.

Old-growth forests in the Pacific Northwest are noted for the huge majestic Douglas fir trees. Should this tree be cut?

Old-Growth Forests

An **old-growth forest** generally has some trees that are at least 250 years old, a multi-level **canopy**, standing dead trees and fallen logs. The old-growth forests of the Pacific Northwest are noted for the many huge Douglas fir trees that are hundreds of years old, but within the old-growth forest there are trees of all sizes and ages. While Douglas fir is the dominant species of tree, it is not the only species.

The variety of tree species and the different sizes and ages of trees in an old-growth forest help to make it a healthy ecosystem. A forest needs healthy mature trees to produce seeds to grow new trees or provide food for wildlife. Dead and dying trees also play important roles in the ecosystem. The standing dead trees or **snags** create habitats for insects and small mammals.

When a huge old snag topples during a storm, it opens up the canopy letting sunlight reach the forest floor. Fallen trees provide habitats for insects, amphibians, and other small animals. Decomposers eventually return the nutrients to the soil. Some downed logs become **nurse logs** where young seedlings take root and grow. Nurse logs provide evidence of the natural recycling processes that occur in an ecosystem.

Nurse logs provide the moisture and nutrients needed by these young hemlock seedlings.

The old-growth forest is a rich and diverse ecosystem. **Biodiversity**—the variety of plant and animal species in an ecosystem—determines the stability of the ecosystem. The greater the biodiversity of an ecosystem, the more stable the ecosystem will be. Ancient forests provide the unique habitats required by more than one hundred species of vertebrates. One massive tree supports an estimated 1,500 species of invertebrates—that's biodiversity!

Some species that need old-growth habitats are in trouble. The U.S. Forest Service studies of California's Sierra Nevada forests found that the fisher, the Sierra Nevada red fox, the pine marten and the wolverine are at risk. All of these species are carnivores and need large areas of old-growth forest for hunting.

Some birds are also threatened with extinction. The marbled murrelet, a seabird that nests in the old-growth forest, and the northern spotted owl are listed under the Endangered Species Act as federally threatened species. The northern spotted owl is an **indicator species**—a species whose presence indicates a healthy ecosystem. This owl needs large tracts of habitat like those found in old-growth forests for foraging and protection. One study indicated that a nesting pair of owls used 3000 acres (1,200 ha).

To learn more about the marbled murrelet, visit www.sei.org/murrelet.html and www.fws.gov.

Streams in old-growth forests are among the cleanest streams in the world.

Can the old-growth forest survive without the owl? The owl is an important limiting factor for small mammal populations. One of the owl's favorite foods is the northern flying squirrel, but it also feeds on red-backed voles and other small mammals. Although remote cameras placed near the nest of the marbled murrelet have recorded flying squirrels eating the young chicks, their diet is mostly fungi that grow on the old-growth trees. One of the favorite foods of red-backed voles, flying squirrels, and other small mammals is the truffle.

A **truffle** is a kind of fungus that produces a massive network of filaments that grow through the soil and penetrate the outer cells of the tree roots. The fungi help the tree absorb minerals, nitrogen and water from the soil. In turn, the root cells provide the fungi with food. The fungi also produce a chemical that stimulates the growth of the new root tips.

Scientists say that truffles are absolutely essential to the survival of trees. Unlike mushrooms, the spore-filled reproductive structure of the truffles remains below ground. When the spores are ripe, the truffles give off an odor. Small mammals detect the odor, and dig for these golf ball-sized fungi that grow beneath the forest floor.

When squirrels, voles, and mice feed on these fungi, they carry the spores to new sites. The spores travel through their digestive system unharmed and are deposited with their wastes. Some animals deposit the spores nearby while others carry the spores to areas where trees have been cut. Here the fungi stimulate the growth of new trees. The relationships between truffles, flying squirrels and the northern spotted owl are examples of the many interactions that occur in old-growth forests.

Streams in old-growth forests are among the cleanest streams in the world. They are ideal habitats for trout and salmon. The thick mat of decaying material on the forest floor holds and filters the water entering the streams. Streams in logged areas become choked with silt and woody debris. The fish populations of the northwest rivers have suffered from the effects of logging.

The northern spotted owl is an indicator species — a species whose presence indicates a healthy ecosystem.

The flying squirrel is one of the favorite foods of the northern spotted owl.

Multiple Use Management

Most old-growth timber on private land is already gone. Nearly all remaining old-growth wood is in National Forests and is managed by the federal government. Only those old-growth forests in National Parks or designated Wilderness Areas are protected. The U.S. Forest Service can sell permits to log most of the remaining old-growth forests.

There are 191 million acres (77 million ha) in our National Forests. The law requires the 156 National Forests and other federal lands to be managed for **multiple uses**—timbering, mining, watershed protection, grazing, recreation, and fish and wildlife habitats. The local economy is often based on the "uses" permitted on the federally owned land. The Allegheny National Forest, in northwestern Pennsylvania, provides an example of "multiple use" forest management.

A logger would say that this tree was overmature. What would an ecologist say?

The Economic Impact of the Allegheny National Forest

Use	Jobs Created	Value of Use
wood-products	970	$48,400,000
oil and gas	950	$30,000,000
recreation	2,700	$91,000,000
Total	4,620	$169,400,000

Managing land for multiple uses isn't easy, and conflicts often occur. Pennsylvania Fish Commission data shows that the water quality of streams is being damaged by improper disposal of wastewater from oil-and-gas production. The Forest Service admits that protecting ospreys and bald eagles during their breeding season is possible only "if the oil and gas operator is willing."

Declines in the populations of bald eagles, black bears, river otters, pine martens and Sitka black-tailed deer could occur if there is excessive logging in Alaska's Tongass National Forest. Critics of the Forest Service say that too often timber harvest is given priority over other uses. The Forest Service is quick to point out that Congress makes the final decision on how much timber will be sold each year.

Advances in technology have reduced the number of workers needed in the logging industry.

Conflict in the Northwest

The issue of logging old-growth forests is the most controversial environmental issue in the Pacific Northwest. Environmentalists are fighting to save the disappearing old-growth ecosystem. Ecologists believe the wood should stay in the forest. From an ecological point of view, there is no such thing as waste in a forest. The death and decay of a Douglas fir tree provide for the life of many other organisms.

Foresters, hired by commercial timber companies, consider the old growth forest "overmature." To the forester, timber is a crop, and the crop is ready for harvest. Because of their size and mass, the old-growth trees provide valuable lumber. The clear, straight, tight-grained wood of an old-

Erosion from treeless hillsides carries silt into the streams.

growth tree is far superior to wood from younger trees. Foresters hired by the timber industry believe it is wasteful to allow this valuable wood to decompose on the forest floor. They view the 200 year-old trees in terms of the board-feet of lumber the tree will yield (i.e., their commercial value).

Loggers and millworkers are fighting to save their jobs and the region's economy. Money from the sale of logging permits supports schools, libraries and local governments. Some timber companies own no land and are totally dependent upon logs from National Forests. Some mills are designed for old-growth logs and cannot process smaller logs. Without permits to log, these mills must close. If loggers and millworkers are unemployed, every business in a logging town suffers.

While the spotted owl was an easy target for the loggers' frustrations, many other factors are working against the timber industry in the Pacific Northwest. The list below demonstrates why the logging industry in the Northwest is an endangered way of life:

- For many years, trees were logged but not replanted. In British Columbia, more than one million acres are listed as "not sufficiently restocked."
- Advances in technology have reduced the number of workers needed; additional jobs will be lost to automation in the future.
- The export of logs to Japan and China has reduced the number of jobs in local mills.
- Some timber companies are moving south to take advantage of cheaper land, better soil and a longer growing season.
- Products must compete with cheaper imports.

The timber industry is concerned about the loss of jobs because trees are "locked up." But the commercial fishing industry is concerned that poor logging practices will cause a critical decline in the salmon runs. Erosion of treeless hillsides carries silt into the streams where it suffocates young fish and fish eggs. The lack of forest cover also increases the sunlight reaching the water, and the fish suffer when water temperatures are warmed.

How Much is Enough?

Congress passed the **National Forest Management Act** in 1976. This law requires that management plans be made for all national forests. The plans must provide sufficient habitat for all native vertebrate species. In 1992 the court ruled that the U.S. Forest Service plans for the Pacific Northwest were inadequate and extended a ban on logging a tract of old-growth forest.

According to the National Audubon Society, timber companies were logging old-growth timber at a rate of 60,000 acres (24,000 ha) per year, in 1987. If logging had continued at that rate, the unprotected old-growth forests would be gone by 2010. Today the logging continues, but at a slower rate. Since a new plan was adopted in 1994, there has been a significant decline in logging on the 24 million acres (10 million ha) of federally owned land covered by the plan. About 80% of the area inhabited by endangered species is protected. At recent logging rates, old-growth forests outside of protected areas could disappear in 30 to 40 years.

Sustainability is the ability to keep in existence or maintain. Are old-growth forest ecosystems sustainable? How many more acres of old-growth forest can we safely cut and still sustain the virgin forest ecosystem? The problem is that we do not know how many acres of old-growth forest are necessary for the ecosystem to be maintained.

What we do know is that if we want old-growth forest ecosystems for our children and our children's children, we must protect these forests now. Satellite images of forests in the Pacific Northwest show a disturbing image. Habitats are being severely fragmented by logging, roads and development. A NASA research team warned that the Northwest forests are losing their "biological vitality." New management plans must protect sections of ancient forest large enough to maintain biodiversity.

The U.S. Forest Service is implementing a policy to establish a balance among demands for timber, wildlife habitats, recreational opportunities, and long-term stability of the ecosystem. How many of the remaining old-growth forest ecosystems are **viable** ecosystems—able to survive with all of their functioning parts? Only time will tell how many of these unique forests will survive and support healthy populations of endangered species.

Whether the goal is to sustain old-growth ecosystems or continue timber production, we cannot continue to manage our National Forests as we have in the past. Tough decisions lie ahead because tough decisions were avoided in the past. Past decisions regarding the use of federal lands have too often been made on the basis of politics rather than science. Too many management decisions have favored short-term profits rather than long-term investments.

Forest fragmentation threatens the stability of the ecosystem.

Environmental Challenge: Sustainability

The Canadian Council of Forest Ministers defines environmental sustainability as "A healthy ecosystem that is productive and renewable."

- Based on this definition, is an old-growth forest ecosystem a sustainable ecosystem?
- Defend your opinion.
- Suggest alternatives to the logging of old-growth timber.

1.10 Questions for Study and Discussion:

1. Define the following terms: **VOCABULARY**

bark rights	multiple use	sustainability	truffle
biodiversity	nurse log	The National Forest Management Act	viable
canopy	old-growth forest	The Nature Conservancy	virgin forest
indicator species	snag		

2. How does a virgin forest ecosystem differ from other forests, and how much of the original virgin forest remains?

Penn's Woods

3. What is the goal of the Nature Conservancy? Why did the Conservancy buy the Woodbourne forest?
4. Describe the change in the landscape that you would have noticed if you had visited Pennsylvania in 1820 and then again in 1920. What about the year 2020?

Old-Growth Forests

5. What is the dominant species of tree in the old-growth forests in the Pacific Northwest? How old are the trees in an old-growth forest?
6. What is the relationship between the biodiversity of an ecosystem and the stability of the ecosystem?
7. Is an old-growth forest ecosystem a stable ecosystem? Defend your answer.
8. Identify six species dependent on old-growth habitat. Which of these species is considered an indicator species? What is the niche of each of these species?

9. List the changes that might occur in the forest as the populations of owls and other small predators in the forest decline.

Multiple Use Management

10. Who is the largest owner of the remaining virgin forests?
11. Can trees in a National Park be legally cut? Can trees in a designated Wilderness Area be legally cut? Can the trees in a national forest be legally cut? List other possible uses of national forests.
12. Who makes the final decision on the amount of timber sold from federal lands each year?

Conflict in the Northwest

13. "Should trees in the old-growth forests be cut?" Give the position of each of the following groups on this issue and list the reasons for their position:
conservationists, loggers, foresters, fisherman, and ecologist.
14. The northern spotted owl is a "threatened species." List several reasons why logging in the Pacific Northwest is a "threatened career."

How Much is Enough?

15. Does the National Forest Management Act protect the northern spotted owl?
16. Outline a management plan to protect the "biological vitality" of a forest.

Environmental Challenge: Life-Saving Drugs

Nearly 20,000 women in the United States are diagnosed each year with ovarian cancer. In 1966 the National Cancer Institute conducted a screening of 35,000 species in a search for chemicals that could be effective in the treatment of cancer. A chemist in North Carolina discovered one compound—"Taxol"—that had an outstanding ability to suppress the growth of tumor cells.

Taxol, a compound originally extracted from the bark of the Pacific yew (*Taxus brevifolia*), is a potent chemotherapeutic agent used in the treatment of breast, ovarian and other cancers. The Pacific yew grows in the shady old-growth forests. Loggers consider the tree a weed species, and they destroy it when they clear-cut the forest.

The yew tree is rare, and it is a slow-growing species. The bark from at least three 100-year-old trees is required to extract enough chemical to treat one cancer patient. The forest cannot produce enough of the chemical to treat the patients who need it, but hopefully scientists can.

Chemists have synthesized taxol in the laboratory. But taxol's molecular structure is so complex that commercial production of synthetic taxol is not possible. Scientists have created semi-synthetic versions of taxol by extracting chemicals from needles and twigs of other yew species grown on tree farms.

Scientists are using biotechnology techniques to extract taxol from cell cultures of the yew tree. Donna M. Gibson, a plant physiologist with the Agricultural Research Service, has applied for a patent. Her process can identify which cell cultures are better producers of paclitaxel (the generic term for taxol).

The issue of saving or logging the old-growth forest is far more complex than saving jobs or saving spotted owls. We do not know what other life-saving drugs are in the forest.

According to the U.S. Forest Service, there are nearly 4.5 million acres of old growth in the Northwest. Nearly all of the old growth is owned by the public. Most of the remaining old growth in the Northwest will not be harvested because it has been declared "critical habitat," or preserved in National Parks or designated Wilderness Areas.

- What is your opinion about harvesting trees in old-growth forests to produce life-saving drugs?
- What factors should be considered in the logging plan?

Logging—Making Clear-cut Decisions

Economic activities of man, such as logging can—if pursued relentlessly without regard for other forest values—do great harm to nature and her creatures.

THE LIVING FOREST

—a report from MacMillan Bloedel Limited, Vancouver, British Columbia

OBJECTIVES

- ✔ **List** possible goals of a forest management plan.
- ✔ **Compare** the biodiversity of managed forests to the biodiversity of unmanaged forests.
- ✔ **Describe** different methods of logging.
- ✔ **Evaluate** the impact of a logging procedure selected for a given situation.

It looks terrible. They go in with big equipment and log off all the beautiful old trees. The **felling** or cutting of every tree in a specific area of a forest is called clear-cutting or **clear-cut logging**. There is nothing left but big ruts and dead branches. The next spring brushy growth begins to appear. People who care about what happens to the land see changes, sometimes drastic ones, and they may get upset. A forester may see these changes as forest management.

Clear-cut in a Mixed-Oak Forest

A hunter may see a large section of old white oaks as a great place to hunt squirrels. It is also a place where wild turkeys may roost. To the squirrel, the turkey and the hunter, this is good wildlife habitat. As the loggers move in, the squirrels, turkeys and other species needing mature trees for food and cover, crowd into the sections of forest left uncut.

In the spring new growth occurs, and the area becomes a tangle of brush. The adult turkeys will not find a place to roost, but the hen turkeys find the area an ideal habitat for nesting. Ruffed grouse and rabbits are more plentiful. The young thrive in the dense tangles of brush where they find plenty of food and cover. Although there is no place for the hunter's tree stand, the young sprouts and grasses become favorite deer food.

As time passes, much of the low "brush" grows into young trees. After 10 years or so, the clear-cut area supports a thick stand of young saplings. Later—in 60–100 years—some saplings might become mature trees to be sawed for logs. The forester explains that, with proper management, this new stand of trees will be in a better condition than the old stand.

The management of a forest should include production of quality wildlife habitat. Other goals for the same forest may include harvest of timber, protection of unique areas, protection of streams or lakes, outdoor recreation, and the mining of minerals.

Some people think there are too many logging trucks on our highways; others think there are too few.

Managing for Wildlife

In a forest where trees have reached maturity, some trees begin to die. Sometimes a whole tree dies during one growing season. More often the top of the tree dies leaving hollow sections in the trunk. These old trees provide homes for the cavity nesters and habitat for other species to nest and feed high within the **canopy**. More than 80 species of birds nest only in dead or dying trees. Some birds found in old-growth forests are not found in younger forests. To provide homes for these species, at least 10% of a forest should be old growth.

Is this good forest management?

It will be 60 to 100 years before this brushy growth develops into a mature forest with sawlogs, but it provides quality habitat for certain species of wildlife.

Mast on the forest floor provides food for wildlife.

At least 40% of a forest should have trees that are capable of producing mast. **Mast** refers to acorns and other nuts and seeds that lie on a forest floor. Mast supports a large variety of wildlife, especially during winter when other foods are not available. Wildlife management plans often allow one-half of the forest to remain in the mature mast-producing stage.

Another 20% of the forest must be capable of producing **forage**—those plants that are eaten by grazing or browsing animals. Clear-cutting creates openings in the forest that allow sunlight to penetrate. Clear-cutting is beneficial to certain species. Populations of rabbit, elk, deer and other species that depend upon forage increase. Although bobcats are forest creatures, they thrive in areas with clear-cuts. If the clear-cuts are not too large, the forest provides plenty of cover while the clear-cuts provide their preferred food—the rabbit.

A forest with all stages of growth ensures a diversity of wildlife. Timber companies can make a profit managing their forest lands for the production of wood and, at the same time, protecting other resources. If the management of a forest is well planned, it can provide both benefits for wildlife and resources for humans.

If a Little is Good, is More Better?

While clear-cutting destroys the habitat for some species, it improves the habitat for others. Clear-cutting a forest creates **edges** — places where one ecosystem meets another. Clear-cutting some areas within a forest produces an **edge effect** — an increase in the population of those species that depend upon the forest for cover and the clearings for food. But it is not always desirable to create an edge effect. The populations of **"deep forest" species**, species that live in the interior of the forest, decline as clear-cutting creates more edges.

The size of clear-cuts must be kept small, and the location must be carefully chosen to prevent fragmentation of the ecosystem. **Habitat fragmentation** refers to the carving of an ecosystem into small isolated tracts. Activities that cause fragmentation include logging, road-building, development and agriculture. These activities may create islands of plants and animals. If there are no corridors or passageways between islands, it can spell trouble for the ecosystem. If passageways are too narrow, animals may not use them.

POPULATION LINK

Species unwilling to move across large open areas become genetically isolated populations. Inbreeding occurs in small isolated populations, and the species is threatened by a loss of genetic diversity. Some species may stop breeding because of an inadequate food supply or lack of space. With fewer species—less biodiversity—the stability of the ecosystem is threatened.

The Forest Cycle—Managing for Timber

In some regions, the number-one agricultural crop is trees. When a forest is managed to produce a "crop of trees," the biodiversity is greatly reduced. In Canada's natural forest ecosystems there are 131 tree species, but only a few of these are considered commercially valuable. Both farmers and timber companies plant and manage large tracts of land for the commercial production of a single species—a **monoculture**.

How does the management of this forest affect "deep forest" species?

The planting-to-harvest is measured in years at a tree farm.

In many ways growing trees for harvest is much like growing and harvesting vegetable crops. The biggest difference is that a farmer planting a field of corn will harvest the crop in 80 to 120 days while a tree farmer planting a forest will wait 20 to 60 years.

To Log or Not to Log—That is the Question!

When converting a forest to a tree farm, the first decision is how and when the existing trees should be harvested. All areas are not suited for logging. In some places the ecosystem may be irreparably damaged if any logging is allowed. In these areas the management plan must read "logging prohibited." The decision regarding logging and the method of cutting chosen should be based on an analysis of the factors listed below:

- Type and ages of trees—Does the "taking" of these trees threaten the sustainability of the species? Is the wood that is "taken" replaced by new growth?
- Slope of the land—Is the land too steep for replanting? Can erosion be controlled and water quality protected?
- Type of soil—Will the soil support the regrowth of trees? The soil in the rain forest is baked into a hard, concrete-like surface when logging exposes it to the sun.
- Climate—Is there enough rain to support the recovery of the ecosystem? Is the amount and pattern of rainfall likely to cause severe erosion and flooding problems? Is the temperature too cold or too hot for germination and growth of seedlings?
- Wildlife—Are there endangered or threatened species that will be affected by the logging? Is the ecosystem sustainable?

Think About It

In 1945, Smokey Bear first said: "Care will prevent 9 out of 10 forest fires." The creation of Smokey as a messenger was a part of the USDA Forest Service effort to protect the wood supply needed for the war. For 50 years, Smokey's message has helped to prevent accidental human-caused forest fires. While fire is essential for the regeneration of some plant species, accidental fires are potentially disastrous. With more people living in or near forests, Smokey's message is still an important one.

Tree farmers and timber companies often plant a single species of tree like these Douglas fir trees growing in Washington. What are the advantages and disadvantages of growing a single species — a monoculture?

Clearcut logging is the method often used to harvest stands of even-aged trees.

Environmental Challenge: Buffer Zones

It's the law in Oregon. All logging operations near streams must comply with comprehensive **riparian** (streamside habitat) protection rules for all streams that support fish populations. In most situations, a 20-foot no-harvest buffer is required on each side of the stream. Live trees and other vegetation must be retained. The goal is to increase biodiversity, cover, and shade, and to protect the stream bank. The shade will help maintain the stream temperature. In the future when the trees fall into the water, they will create fish habitats.

- Find out if your state has passed laws that protect streams and their riparian habitats.
- Does the law require a buffer zone? If so, is it a no-harvest buffer zone? How wide is it?

- Location—Will logging fragment the ecosystem endangering whole groups of species? Are the trees near a stream bank that will erode?

The Harvest: Which Trees to Cut?

Clear-cut logging—this method removes all timber regardless of size and condition. It is usually chosen for old-growth forests with many huge mature and "overmature" trees. It is often the preferred method of harvesting stands of **even-aged trees** where all trees are mature and ready for harvest at the same time. Clear-cutting is also used in sections of forest damaged by wind, fire or insect infestations.

Clear-cutting is necessary for the regeneration of certain tree species used in a large number of wood and paper products. In some regions, oaks are the most economically valuable species. In other regions timber companies grow pine, spruce or fir. Without clear-cutting, there would be fewer of these economically valuable shade-intolerant species. Clear-cutting prevents maples and other less commercially valuable species from reproducing under shaded conditions and taking over an area.

Selection logging—also called selective cutting, this method is used to harvest mature trees in a stand of **uneven-aged trees**. The logger may remove individual trees or small groups of trees. Mature high-quality trees are removed for sale as **sawlogs**. Lesser quality and smaller trees may be removed to improve the growing conditions for the remaining trees.

When selectively cutting trees, care must be taken to protect the remaining trees. A University of Idaho study compared the use of horses and tractors as power sources in logging operations. The study found that tractors caused 91% of the damage to standing trees. Mules and horses remove logs from selectively logged areas with less environmental impact than heavy equipment.

Seed-tree logging—this method is much like clear-cutting except that selected mature trees are left to provide seed for regeneration of the cut area. This method is used for sun-dependent species. It eliminates the need for replanting.

Shelterwood logging—in this method, mature trees are harvested in a series of cuts over several years. The remaining trees provide a seed source and protection for shade-tolerant species such as the Douglas fir.

After the Harvest: Planning for the Next Crop

The forest is restored by **natural regeneration** or germination of seeds from remaining trees after seed-tree, shelterwood, or selection logging. Small clear-cut areas may recover with natural regeneration or by planting. Natural regeneration costs less than planting, but it requires more years until harvest. Planting may be necessary to grow a selected species. Preparation for planting often includes:

Mechanical preparation—Debris on the forest floor makes replanting difficult and expensive. If the **duff**—blanket of twigs and needles—is too thick, the roots of the seedlings may die before they reach the moisture and nutrients in the soil below. The **slash**—limbs, tree tops, and other waste—and duff may be removed by heavy equipment. Slash and duff are sometimes piled in rows and burned.

Slash burning clears the planting sites of brush and duff, making it easier to plant seedlings.

Slash burning—clears planting sites of brush and duff. The advantages of slash burning are low cost and suitability for steep slopes. It may be detrimental in sites where soil is thin and there is only a shallow covering of duff.

Herbicides—are used to kill the undesirable species. Though these species are a part of a natural forest ecosystem, the tree farmer considers them "weeds." Competition for nutrients and water slows the growth of the commercially valuable trees. Herbicides are an efficient and effective way to remove weeds, but there are some concerns about their use. They destroy vegetation that could feed and shelter wildlife.

Herbicides reduce the competition of "weed species," and the young trees grow faster.

Planting—More and more forests are restored by planting genetically improved seedlings or plantlings. **Plantlings** look like seedlings, but they are produced by tissue culture from a few selected parent plants. Large areas in New Zealand have been re-forested using plantlings.

Thinning—Forests with the greatest commercial value contain trees that are tall and straight. After trees grow to pole size, 6–10 inches (15-20 cm) in diameter, they are examined to see which trees should be removed. The best trees are given space to grow by removing poorly formed and overcrowded trees.

Fertilization—Many soils do not provide enough nutrients for trees. Applying fertilizers using helicopters or airplanes increases the growth rate.

Protection—Forests need protection from fire and from pests. Protection from forest fires is an important part of forest management. Netting may protect seedlings from browsing deer and elk. Pesticides are used to control outbreaks of pests and diseases. The problems caused by pests and diseases increase in areas with large monocultures. This increases the need for pesticides. Both chemical and biological controls are used. There is concern about the use of herbicides and pesticides. Researchers continue to look for more biological controls.

Forests Forever

We cannot meet our increasing demand for wood and wood products without intensively managed forests. **Intensively managed forests** can produce nearly twice as much timber as unmanaged forests. High-quality seedlings are promptly planted. Competition from "weed" species is controlled. Growth is enhanced by thinning and adding fertilizers. And trees are protected from fire and insects. Our lifestyle depends upon intensively managed forests or tree farms, but there is a lot more than lifestyle at stake.

Did You Know?

According to the World Resources Institute, the average American uses 700 pounds of paper products each year — triple the amount used 30 years ago.

The days of "cut-and-run" are long gone. "Forests forever" is a slogan of the British Columbia forest industry. The life of the industry depends upon sustainable timber production. The life of the planet is more important and depends upon sustaining our forest ecosystems. Sustaining planet Earth requires careful and intelligent decisions concerning clear-cuts and other forest management practices.

1.11 Questions for Study and Discussion:

1. Define the following terms: **VOCABULARY**

canopy	even-aged trees	mast	seed-tree logging
clear-cut logging	felling	monoculture	selection logging
deep forest species	forage	natural regeneration	shelterwood logging
duff	habitat fragmentation	plantlings	slash
edge	herbicides	riparian	slash burning
edge effect	intensively managed forest	sawlogs	uneven-aged trees

Clear-cut in a Mixed-Oak Forest

2. Why do foresters consider it necessary to clear-cut some areas of a forest?
3. Give two species whose populations will increase if certain areas of the forest are clear-cut.
4. What should be the primary goal of forest management? List three additional goals.

Managing for Wildlife

5. When good forest management is practiced, what is the minimum percentage of the forest in each of the following conditions: old-growth, healthy mature trees, and young brushy growth?
6. List or describe the type of wildlife that will benefit from each of the stages of growth listed in the previous question.

If a Little is Good, is More Better?

7. Explain why the edge effect is not always a "good" effect.
8. What are the effects of habitat fragmentation?

The Forest Cycle—Managing for Timber

9. How does the biodiversity of managed forests compare to the biodiversity of unmanaged forests?
10. List at least three examples of forest conditions where logging should be prohibited.
11. Identify the harvest methods often chosen for even-aged and uneven-aged trees. Explain the reason for choosing each harvest method.
12. Give an advantage and a disadvantage of growing a forest by natural regeneration.
13. Describe the process used to prepare the forest for planting young trees.
14. How do "tree farmers" increase the growth rate of trees?
15. Why are pests and diseases a greater problem in commercial forests than in unmanaged forests?

Forests Forever

16. Can we maintain our lifestyle without intensively managed forests? Explain.
17. How has the philosophy of the forest industry changed?

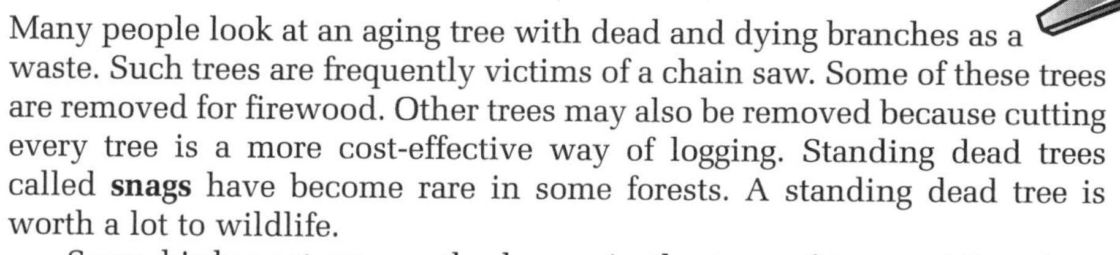

Spare that Snag!

A CLOSER LOOK 1.12

OBJECTIVES

- ✔ **Explain** why snags are an important part of a forest ecosystem.
- ✔ **Compare** different species of woodpeckers and **explain** why some are common while others are endangered.
- ✔ **Describe** the design and results of an experiment which shows that trees need birds.

Many people look at an aging tree with dead and dying branches as a waste. Such trees are frequently victims of a chain saw. Some of these trees are removed for firewood. Other trees may also be removed because cutting every tree is a more cost-effective way of logging. Standing dead trees called **snags** have become rare in some forests. A standing dead tree is worth a lot to wildlife.

Some birds nest among the leaves in the tops of trees while others prefer a nest with a view. The dead branches at the top of an aging tree provide an ideal nesting site for eagles and ospreys. Some birds prefer to nest in cavities. About one of every 10 bird species in the United States is a **cavity nester**. Each cavity nester plays an important role, and has a specific **niche** or job to do in the ecosystem. Woodpeckers are the **excavators**.

Many woodpeckers make cavities in dead or dying trees. Some cavity nesters are very demanding. The American ivory-billed woodpecker needed large tracts—several hundred acres—of old-growth forest. The snags provided both cover and food. The large birds fed by removing large pieces of bark in search of insects. As their habitat disappeared, so did the ivory-billed woodpecker. It has not been seen since the late 1940s. The U.S. Fish and Wildlife Service declared the species extinct in 1986.

Another large woodpecker, the pileated, has become more common because it can survive in smaller tracts of about 160 acres (64 ha) of less mature forests. The pileated also uses snags for "drumming boards" to announce their presence to other birds intruding on their territory. The U.S. Forest Service considers the pileated woodpecker an **indicator species**. When a forest with a suitable habitat for a pileated woodpecker is a healthy ecosystem, it provides for the needs of many other species including smaller woodpeckers.

Although some cavity nesters adjust to changing conditions, others are in trouble. The common flicker has been known to nest in utility poles, and even in burrows made by other animals. The red-cockaded woodpecker nests exclusively in living longleaf or loblolly pine trees in the southeastern part of the United States. Though the trees are living, they must be at least 80 years old with a center weakened by a fungus called red-heart disease.

There is an advantage to choosing a live pine tree for a home. Pecking holes in the bark near the entrance starts the flow of sap. The sticky sap running down the tree keeps rat snakes away from the nest cavity. But it can take the red-cockaded woodpeckers as long as two years to make a cavity in a loblolly pine tree or 6 years to make a cavity in a longleaf pine. The Forest Service is trying to help the woodpeckers by drilling artificial cavities in trees where suitable habitats remain.

Should this snag be cut for firewood?

Pileated Woodpecker (male).

Pileated Woodpecker with young.

For information on the red-cockaded woodpecker population in eastern Texas, visit the Texas Parks and Wildlife Website at: www.tpwd.state.tx.us.

The red-cockaded woodpecker is an endangered species. Most of its habitat has been converted to pine plantations with younger, smaller pines that are clearly not suitable habitat. Due to habitat fragmentation, the remaining old-growth pine habitats are located in small isolated patches. Fire-fighting policies have prevented the spread of natural fires. Fires do not harm the pine trees, but are necessary to prevent the brushy growth and keep the pine forest open. The red-cockaded woodpecker will not nest where there is brushy growth.

Life in the Old Hemlock

During its long life, the 100-year-old hemlock tree has held the nests of a few species of birds. It has contributed its share of food and cover for the animals in the forest. Now it is showing its age, but the old tree still has much more to give before it is taken down by a winter storm. As a huge old dying tree, it is worth a lot to wildlife.

Boring insects attack the aging tree. They create tunnels that allow water, fungi and other insects to enter. As the wood begins to soften, new bird species are attracted to the tree. An eagle may choose the top of the old tree as a site for a nest. As branches die and lose their needles, they provide places for birds to sit and watch for flying insects. Bats also feed on insects near the tree.

As the bark becomes loose and the wood becomes softer, other species of birds can find food more easily. A brown creeper may nest behind loose pieces of bark. Insects that prefer solid wood move to a younger, firmer snag. Woodpeckers move into the old hemlock.

The pileated woodpecker selects a dead tree and makes a new nest each year. The perfect tree is 80–100 years old and about 12 inches (30 cm) in diameter. The snag needs to be somewhat decayed, but not spongy.

Some cavities are suitable for birds while others are just right for a swarm of bees or a small mammal.

Wood ducks, salamanders, flying squirrels, raccoons and screech owls are a few of the animals that may move into old woodpecker homes. Larger birds such as great-horned owls will follow them. The neighbors are constantly changing.

Eventually the tree falls and becomes a log where insects, snails and other small animals find food and a place to hide. Birds, that prefer life on the forest floor to life in the canopy, feed on the organisms living in the log. The rotting log continues to break down into **humus**—partly decayed plant material. Seeds fall on the rotted log. The moisture and nutrients in the humus provide the ideal conditions needed for the seeds to sprout. The log becomes a **nurse log**—a nursery for new trees. The life cycle begins again.

When there are not enough snags, some species will use nesting boxes.

The U.S.F.S. Policy

Most woodpeckers and other cavity nesters are insect eaters and provide an important pest control service that protects the forest. It is the policy of the United States Forest Service (U.S.F.S.) to save some trees for the insect-eating woodpeckers and other cavity nesters. In Missouri's Mark Twain National Forest, portions of the forest have been left uncut for 200 years.

California now leaves all snags that are not a fire or safety hazard. U.S.F.S. biologists recommend that two or three snags per acre (0.4 ha) be protected from cutting. Some **cull trees**—trees that will not yield high quality lumber—are left to become future snags. Timber companies complain that the Forest Service leaves too many good trees standing on federal land.

We need to leave some good trees in the forest. It takes nearly 100 years for a tree to reach maturity, die and become a snag. If all mature trees are removed, soon there will be no snags. Woodpeckers and other birds that thrive on tree-killing bark beetles and other forest pests may disappear if logging operations remove all dead and dying trees. Foresters now believe that leaving snags for woodpeckers provides a forest with better insect protection. They also agree that it is possible to meet fire, safety and timber management goals and, at the same time, preserve the habitat of the cavity nesters.

A naturalist discusses the importance of a nurse log to a group of students.

Do Trees Need Birds?

We know that birds need trees, but scientists wanted to know if the trees need the birds. At the Tyson Research Center in Eureka, Missouri, researchers designed an experiment to study the impact of birds on the trees in a forest. They marked 90 white oak saplings arranging them into groups of three. One sapling was the control. It received no treatment. Another sapling was covered with a net cage with openings large enough for insects but too small for birds. The third sapling was treated with an insecticide, and insects were removed by hand.

Every few weeks, through the growing season, the researchers counted the insects on each sapling. As expected, the saplings that were sprayed

How does this tree provide protection for the forest?

had few insects. When they counted the insects on the caged saplings, which the birds could not reach, they found twice the number of insects on their leaves as on the control saplings, which the birds visited.

The experiment provided evidence that trees do need birds. The caged saplings lost twice as much leaf biomass as the sprayed or control trees. The caged saplings also grew less (one-third less biomass) than the other saplings. By eating leaf-damaging insects, the birds improved the growth of the young trees.

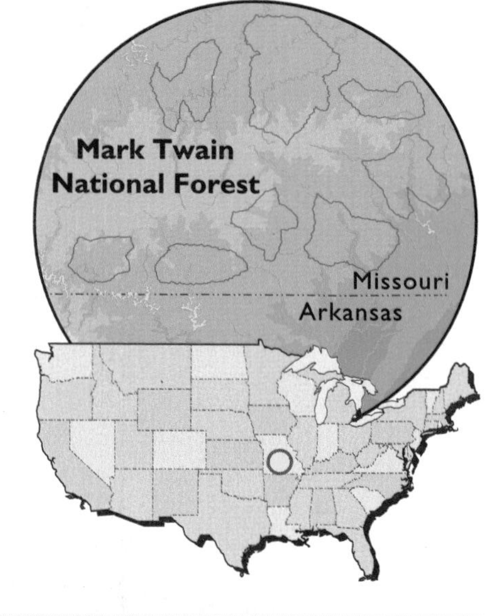

1.12 Questions for Study and Discussion:

1. Define the following terms: **VOCABULARY**

cavity nester	indicator species
cull tree	niche
excavator	nurse log
humus	snag

2. Why are snags becoming rare?
3. What niche do woodpeckers fill?
4. Draw a food chain including one of the woodpeckers discussed, and give the niche of each organism.
5. On a walk through a forest, you see a pair of pileated woodpeckers. What does this chance sighting tell you about the forest ecosystem?
6. Compare the habitat requirements of the ivory-billed, the red-cockaded woodpecker and the common flicker. Explain why the common flicker is so common.

Life in the Old Hemlock

7. What relationship exists between the woodpeckers and the great-horned owls?
8. Explain how a healthy forest is dependent upon the presence of dead and dying trees.

The U.S.F.S. Policy

9. Do timber companies agree with the U.S. Forest Service policy concerning snags? If not, explain how their policy differs.
10. Why is it important to allow some cull trees to grow and not remove them for firewood?

Do Trees Need Birds?

11. Create a visual display showing the results of the experiment conducted at the Tyson Research Center, and supporting the hypothesis, "trees need birds."

"The invasion of noxious alien species wreaks a level of havoc on America's environment and economy that is matched only by the damage caused by floods, earthquakes, mud slides, hurricanes, and wildfire."

BRUCE BABBITT
Secretary of the Interior

OBJECTIVES

- ✔ **Identify** species that have been introduced to the United States and **describe** the ecological impacts of their introduction.
- ✔ **Identify** the traits and/or conditions that permit an introduced species to become an invasive species.
- ✔ **Evaluate** the economic impact of introduced species.
- ✔ **Describe** methods used to control the spread of introduced species.
- ✔ **Evaluate** methods used to prevent the introduction of a new species.

Bioinvasion describes the introduction of species, by direct or indirect human actions, to areas where they did not previously exist. Species introduced to areas beyond their historic natural range are **non-native species**. Other terms often used to describe non-native species are alien, **exotic**, foreign, introduced or non-indigenous species.

Some **introduced species** are **invasive species** because they are aggressive and spread over large areas, disrupting natural ecosystems and interfering with human activities. Invasive species are costly. According to the U.S. Department of the Interior, the cost to our Nation's economy is $123 billion each year. After destruction of habitat by human activities, invasive species are the worst threat to endangered species and biodiversity.

POPULATION LINK

The Birds

Did you ever see a large flock of very noisy black birds? The birds are probably European starlings, imported from England in 1890. Starlings were intentionally released in New York City's Central Park by literary societies who thought that America should have all of the birds mentioned in Shakespeare's literature. Since their release, these aggressive black birds have spread throughout the United States and into Canada.

Starlings are now our most common, but not our most loved, bird. They congregate in large flocks, making noise and messing the sidewalks and buildings. Their droppings contain a fungus that causes **histoplasmosis**, a respiratory disease in humans. They drive native birds from their nesting sites and compete with them for food. They are omnivores that feed on insects, but they also eat large quantities of farm crops.

Now there are special rules for importing birds. The transportation of birds is regulated for two reasons:

- Some birds are protected by the Convention on International Trade in Endangered Species (CITES), and
- Birds carry serious diseases.

Intentionally introduced to New York City, the starling is an aggressive bird that competes with native species.

This Fischer's Lovebird lives in a cage at the Crystal Bridge in Oklahoma City. Its native habitat is the tropical forest surrounding Lake Victoria in Africa, where it lives in small flocks.

Escaping cultivation, the water hyacinth has become a weed that is choking the life out of wetlands and filling in waterways.

Exotic Newcastle disease is a fatal viral disease that affects all species of birds. Parrots from South America probably carried the virus that caused an outbreak of Exotic Newcastle disease in southern California's commercial poultry flocks. Since the virus is highly contagious, 12 million birds—mostly laying hens—had to be destroyed. The cost to eradicate the 1971 outbreak was $56 million. Deadly strains of Newcastle disease have been detected in pet birds in all but 3 years since 1974. The United States Department of Agriculture still considers smuggled pet birds, especially Amazon parrots, a serious threat.

The importation of birds, both legal and illegal, creates two major problems. There is a big demand for pet parrots in North America, Europe and Japan. Together with habitat loss, the "taking" of birds from the wild is causing serious declines in populations of the most popular species. Although many parrots enter the country through legal channels, each illegally imported bird is a potential threat to poultry flocks and native bird species because it can carry communicable diseases without appearing sick.

Alien Plants

Plants growing in North America come from as many countries as the people do. Hundreds of plants were brought intentionally for food, medicine or ornamental uses. Other plants were brought accidentally in grain, or straw, or soil. Whether the introduction was intentional or accidental, these "naturalized" plants have changed the landscape forever. Some invasive species are causing monumental problems.

Introduced to the northeastern U.S. and Canada in the 1800s, purple loosestrife was valued both as a medicinal herb and an ornamental plant. It is still widely used as an ornamental plant though several states now prohibit propagation, sale and transport. Plants native to North America cannot compete with invasive species, like purple loosestrife.

Purple loosestrife has eliminated native plants from 1.5 million acres (600,000 ha) of wetlands. A mature plant may produce two to three million seeds each year. It also reproduces by rapid growth of underground stems. The dense stands of loosestrife are displacing the normal food supply of many wild animals. Very few animals feed on the loosestrife plant or its seeds. Some animals do use the loosestrife for cover, but others, including many songbirds and waterfowl, avoid it.

Hopefully, purple loosestrife populations can be controlled. A search in Europe found two leaf-eating beetles, one flower-feeding beetle, and a root-mining weevil that feed only on loosestrife. After years of testing, the U.S. Department of Agriculture has approved these **exotic species** (non-native species) for use as biological control agents. A Cornell University laboratory is rearing and releasing the insects in the United States and Canada. Results look promising; at several sites loosestrife was reduced by 95%.

Possibly the most troublesome aquatic plant in the area bordering the Gulf Coast is water hyacinth, a native to South America. Sold in the 1800s

Accidentally introduced into this country from Europe, the purple loosestrife is a favorite in some flower gardens due to its tall, brightly colored spikes of flowers. It is readily pollinated by bees and other insects that feed on the nectar, but it is devastating to wildlife when it invades wetlands.

as an ornamental plant, water hyacinths were praised for their beauty and easy care. It escaped cultivation, and now it is a **weed**—a plant growing where it is not wanted.

The water hyacinth turned open waterways into wetlands and choked the life out of wetlands. Scientists imported a South American weevil that feeds on the plant's juices. Weed-eating boats and herbicides are also used to control the aggressive plants. Florida has reduced water hyacinth infestations from 120,000 acres (30,000 ha) to less than 2,000 acres (800 ha).

The Little (but Mighty) Mollusk

If a movie was written about the zebra mussel, it might be portrayed as a giant human-eating clam. In real life it is tiny, no bigger than your thumbnail, but it's probably a good idea to wear shoes when you go walking on a beach where they wash ashore. The shells are sharp, and they aren't kind to bare feet. The decaying mussels also create a very unpleasant odor. These are only two of the problems caused by this tiny invader.

The zebra mussel is native to the Caspian Sea region of the former Soviet Union. Sometime before the industrial revolution, the little mussel made its way to western Europe. In 1988 zebra mussels were first spotted in Lake St. Clair, between Lake Huron and Lake Erie. Scientists believe the mussel probably came as a stowaway aboard a European freighter.

The zebra mussel is only one of many species that enter the Great Lakes when ocean-going ships dump **ballast** water taken in at other ports. In 1981, scientists (commissioned by Environment Canada) examined the potential problems that might result from foreign organisms in the water held in ship's ballast tanks. They examined the water in the ballast tanks of 30 ships and found living organisms in every tank. The zebra mussel was one of the organisms identified, and the scientists predicted that they would cause problems.

Did You Know?

When cargo is unloaded from a ship, its weight must be replaced to keep the ship upright and stable in the water. Ballast is added by taking on water to keep the ship upright. When an empty ship has cargo loaded, the ballast is pumped out. Ships originally used solid materials like soil and rocks for weight (ballast). The invention of motorized pumps and metal hulls on ships led to the use of water as ballast.

A large tanker can hold enough ballast water to fill 2,000 Olympic-sized swimming pools. In the water are many tiny stowaways. Some of them become invasive species.

www

To learn about other species of alien plants, visit www.nps.gov/plants/alien/.

How to stop zebra mussels? Boats transported from one lake to another, need to be inspected for fingernail-sized adult zebra mussels. If the boat's hull feels like sandpaper, it may be covered with zebra mussel larvae.

Environmental Challenge: Gerbils

Gerbils are not native to the United States. They are imported from Africa or Asia where they normally live in a desert ecosystem. They are rodents that eat seeds and breed rapidly.

- What do you think would happen if a gerbil owner released one or more pairs of gerbils in Southern California?
- Would the result have been different if this gerbil owner had lived in the Northeastern U. S. or in Canada? Explain.

Since they were released in Lake St. Clair, there has been a massive **population explosion**. A mature female zebra mussel can produce between 30,000 and 40,000 eggs each year. A zebra is sexually mature and reproducing by the following spring. The eggs hatch into free-swimming larvae that eventually develop adhesive threads and attach to a solid surface. They attach themselves to boats and barges and are transported upstream or carried to other bodies of water.

The fast-multiplying mussels have spread into all of the Great Lakes and are expected to spread to all bodies of water connected to them. Even distant bodies of water are threatened. Zebra mussels can stay alive for several days out of water. Live zebras have been found by inspectors at agricultural inspection stations and on several trailered boats entering California. Birds and other animals can transport the larvae. As many as 200 larvae have been found on the suits of scuba divers.

The zebra mussel is not the first organism to invade the Great Lakes and spread into other waterways, but it may cause the greatest economic and ecological problems. Zebra mussels are creating enormous problems and huge expenses for cities and industries that use water from the Great Lakes. Mussels are filter feeders that prefer moving water. The larvae attach inside the water intake pipes of industries and power plants. The mass of mussels blocks the flow of water much like the buildup of plaque blocks the flow of blood in arteries.

Zebra mussels may damage the fishing industry in the Great Lakes. Although early studies show that the zebra mussels are having a minimal effect on fish populations, it may be too soon to determine some of the biological impacts. Zebras form large colonies with thousands of organisms per square meter. The colonies may completely cover the hard rocky surfaces that some fish use for spawning. No one knows how this will affect the development of the fish eggs.

Mussels feed on plankton that they filter from the water. A large colony of mussels filters a vast quantity of water. By removing algae and chemical pollutants, the mussels do improve water quality, but they may make it too clean for fish. If too many algae and other microscopic organisms are filtered from the water, zebra mussels may deplete the food supply of fish larvae. So far the cleaner water has allowed light to penetrate deeper, having a positive impact on the growth of plants. The beds of plants are good nurseries for some species of fish.

Although humans do not consider the zebra mussel edible, diving ducks, crayfish and some species of fish (freshwater drum, carp and sturgeon) do eat them. It is unlikely that the native fish will significantly decrease the population, but new exotic species of fish, the round goby, have entered the Great Lakes. Its peg-like teeth are well suited for feeding on zebra mussels. We do not know what effect this new predator will have on the food chain.

An isolated stand of American chestnuts in northern Michigan have so far escaped the blight.

Trees like this once dominated the eastern forest.

The living roots of the American chestnut continue to produce sprouts, but like the tree that once stood here, they, too, soon die.

Dreaded Diseases

Diseases have attacked two of the most valuable native trees in the United States—the American chestnut and the American elm. In the 1800s, one out of four hardwood trees, in forests from Maine to Georgia, was an American chestnut. It was probably the most valuable tree in the forest. Its beauty was described in poems, its lumber used for building, and its nuts provided food for both humans and wildlife.

Chestnut blight—a fungus that grows beneath the bark and cuts off the flow of nutrients and water—was first seen in American chestnut trees in the New York Zoological Park, in 1904. It probably entered the United States on chestnut trees imported from Asia. The spores of the blight are spread by the wind and carried by insects and birds. All efforts to stop the spread of the disease failed. By 1950, the disease had spread throughout the chestnut's natural range, and 3.5 billion trees had fallen victim to the disease.

The disease doesn't kill the roots, and new sprouts develop, but soon the fungus infects them. Within a few years they die. Only isolated stands of the American chestnut remain. Scientists have discovered a non-lethal **hypovirulent** form of the fungus. Trees infected with this form of the disease seem to be recovering. Scientists still hope to develop a biological control for the disease. Even if the species is saved from extinction, the American chestnut will never again be the dominant tree that it once was in the eastern forests.

Another fungus, Dutch elm disease, produces a poison that clogs the sap-carrying tubes of the American elm. It is carried from tree to tree by the European elm bark beetle. Both the fungus and the beetle were probably imported from France with a shipload of elm burl logs sent to Ohio furniture makers.

Dutch elm disease was first reported in Ohio in 1931. By 1980 it had reached California. Though the elm isn't considered an important forest tree, 90% of the trees lining the streets of some towns were elms. Tree surgeons continue their efforts to save the few remaining trees by

At one time many city streets looked like this. The citizens of Westmont, PA, spend thousands of dollars each year to protect this stand of American elm trees on Luzerne Street.

Many American elms are still found on college campuses. This majestic tree stands in front of the church on the campus of Hope College in Michigan.

Tree surgeons inject fungicides to protect the American elms from Dutch elm disease.

injecting fungicides in the tree and the soil. They also remove the dead branches to prevent the beetle from breeding in the soft wood.

Scientists have been working for many years to develop chestnut and elm trees that are resistant to disease. Blight-resistant American chestnut trees have been planted at a test site in the Moshannon State Forest in Pennsylvania. American elm trees that are clones of two trees with a high level of tolerance for Dutch elm disease (DED) are now available at retail nurseries. While these trees are resistant to DED they are not **immune** to the disease.

Like the populations of American chestnut and American elm trees, the human population of Native Americans was also reduced by the spread of disease. Blankets and other items traded to the Indians carried bacteria. The American Indian had no resistance to the diseases of the European settlers. History repeats itself. During the 1980s, gold miners who entered Brazil's Amazon region introduced diseases to the Yanomami people. Within three years, 15% of the population had died of tuberculosis, influenza, mumps, malaria and the common cold.

The Hitchhiker

The gypsy moth is one of the most devastating insect pests in the forests of the Northeastern United States. E. Leopold Trouvelot, an artist with an interest in silk production, brought gypsy moth egg masses to Massachusetts from France in 1868 or 1869. He had hoped to breed a better silk-producing insect. When some of the larvae escaped from his backyard, he notified authorities but nothing was done.

The first outbreak occurred in Mr. Trouvelot's neighborhood in 1882. By 1902 they had spread throughout the New England States. They continue to spread south and west at a rate of about 13 miles (21 km) per year. The larvae are carried long distances by strong winds, but the prevailing wind direction has worked against the spread. The USDA Forest Service has begun a national project to slow the spread. Traps are set along the expanding front, and steps are taken to wipe out isolated colonies.

Hitchhiking gypsies have traveled to California, Utah, Oregon and many other states. One moth found in Sequoia National Park in 1983 probably hitchhiked from New England on a camper. Other moths have been transported on cars, firewood, nursery plants, and other personal possessions. Federal regulations now require movers to check for gypsy moths before moving outdoor equipment.

The gypsy moth prefers to breed on oak trees. As the population increases, the larvae feed on as many as 500 species of plants. A record 12.9 million acres (5.2 million ha) of forests, in the Northeastern U.S., were stripped of their leaves in 1981. This was followed by 8.2 million acres (3.3 million ha) in 1982 and 2.4 million acres (1.0 million ha) in 1983. During the last 20 years, millions of acres have been sprayed with pesticides to reduce damage from gypsy moths.

Egg masses on this tree indicate trouble for this mixed-oak forest.

Once the oak leaves are gone, the gypsy moth caterpillar turns to other species of plants including grasses.

This male gypsy moth is attracted to a chemical emitted by a female that is ready to deposit her eggs. After the eggs are deposited, both adults die.

Hemlocks when completely stripped of their needles will die in one year. After two years of defoliation many hardwood trees die. Without new leaves, gypsy moths cannot find enough food to support the population. As food becomes a limiting factor, many larvae die of starvation. Cold and wet weather also reduces gypsy moth survival.

When insects immigrate to this country, they usually leave their natural enemies behind. Without this limiting factor and with plenty of food, the population quickly reaches epidemic numbers. Limiting factors for gypsy moths in Europe included more than 100 parasites and predators. Few of these limiting factors were present in the United States.

Some of the gypsy moths' natural enemies have become important factors limiting the size of the gypsy moth population. Wilt disease caused by a virus is the most effective of the natural diseases. Many animals have learned to eat gypsy moths. Small woodland mammals such as white-footed mice and shrews are important predators when gypsy moth populations are low. Birds, beetles and ants also eat them, but not in numbers that will control the population.

How has the introduction of the gypsy moth affected the northeastern forest ecosystem? As the larger trees die, the forest canopy is opened. With the additional sunlight, the low-growing plants in the forest become denser. This increases the cover and food supply for some animals such as rabbits, grouse, and turkey.

The loss of acorns and other nuts does cause an immediate food shortage for some species, especially squirrels. Due to the increased growth of young woody plants, the white-tailed deer soon have an increased food supply. Gypsy moth damage results in an increase in the carrying capacity of the forest for some species and a decrease for others.

www

For maps that show the current distribution of the gypsy moth, visit www.nbii.gov/invasive/GypsyMoth/GypsyMothpub.html.

Environmental Challenge: Exotic Species

Trees in our forests and cities are under attack by insects introduced from Europe and Asia. They may have devastating economic impacts. Try to find out more about one of these exotic species: (1) the balsam wooly aphid; (2) the wooly adelgid; or (3) the Asian longhorned beetle.

- How did they get here?
- Where have they been found?
- What trees do they prefer?
- How are populations controlled?

Except for their behavior, it is difficult to distinguish Africanized bees from European honeybees. The African bee is slightly smaller than the European honeybee but it is much more aggressive.

For more information on Africanized honeybees, visit www.cdfa.ca.gov/pests/honeybee/honeybee.html and www.stingshield.com.

The Flight of the Bees

Warwick E. Kerr, a bee geneticist, imported southern African queen bees to Brazil in 1956. He hoped that breeding them with European honeybees would produce a more productive bee that was better suited to the tropics. When someone visiting the laboratory removed the cover, 26 Africanized bee queens escaped and bred with wild European honeybees. The Africanized hybrid bees extended their range northward through Central America arriving in Hidalgo, Texas, on October 15, 1990.

Africanized bees have been found in Texas, New Mexico, Arizona, Nevada and California. Although scientists knew that the bees would eventually enter the United States, they have slowed their natural migration by trapping swarms in baited hives. Still the bees continue to extend their range by more than 200 miles (320 km) per year. Many scientists think that the Africanized bees will continue to expand their range throughout the southern states, but there is no agreement on the northern limit of the range.

Ship's crew members and dock workers have been alerted by the U.S. Department of Agriculture to look for bee swarms that might be hitchhiking on ships coming to U.S. ports from Latin America. Nearly 20 swarms of Africanized bees have been discovered at ports in Florida since 1983. The agricultural department regularly checks more than 500 baited hives located at ports and along Florida's interstate highways.

Most honeybees that are frequently seen visiting flowers are not natives, but they have been in North America nearly 400 years. The European honeybee was intentionally introduced into the U.S. nearly 400 years ago. Only an expert can correctly identify a bee as an Africanized or a European honeybee. The Africanized bee is slightly smaller, and scientists can use wing measurements for a fast identification. A DNA analysis confirms the identification.

Although Africanized honeybees are not the "killer bees" that movies describe, they are more defensive than the European honeybees. When disturbed, they react more quickly, and many more bees respond. The venom of the Africanized honeybee is no more poisonous than the venom of the European honeybee. But they sting 8 to 10 times more often and follow the intruder farther. As of June 1999 seven fatalities had occurred in the U.S. The victims were elderly people with limited mobility.

We do not know how the Africanized intruders will affect the existing bee population. The unpredictable and aggressive behavior of the Africanized bees may make it more difficult for beekeepers to manage the hives. Even if behavior is not a problem, there may be less honey for the beekeeper. European honeybees store large amounts of honey. Africanized bees use more of the honey they produce. European bees produce a surplus 200 million pounds (91 million kg) of honey worth $125 million each year.

More important than the loss of honey may be the effect on pollination. Farmers depend upon bees to pollinate over 100 crops (including fruits, vegetables and nuts) worth about $10 billion each year.

One third of the food we eat comes directly or indirectly from crops pollinated by European honeybees. We do not know how the presence of Africanized bees will affect pollination.

Africanized bees are not the only threat to the European honeybees. Diseases and parasites introduced to North America also threaten bee colonies. An Asian mite attacks bee larvae and pupae. A small European mite that lives, feeds, and reproduces inside the bee's breathing tubes was first found in Texas in 1984. It has spread to bee colonies throughout the country. The tracheal mite blocks the flow of oxygen and eventually kills the bee.

Chemicals used by beekeepers to control the mites are effective but expensive. In four states mites have developed resistance to the only approved pesticide. Scientists have imported honeybees from Russia that are resistant to mites. After several years of research, mite-resistant Russian queens may be available to beekeepers.

An adult mite feeds on a developing worker bee.

The Medfly Attack

The Mayflower may have imported more species of pests than the number of humans it carried. The threat of introduced pests and diseases continues today with each illegal plant or animal that someone brings into the United States. The Mediterranean fruit fly, commonly called the Medfly, is a native of tropical Africa. It has become a serious pest in the Mediterranean area and in other countries. The small fly attacks more than 250 varieties of fruits, vegetables and nuts. A female fly deposits one to ten eggs beneath the skin, and the fly larvae feed on the fruit pulp causing soft spots where the fruit begins to rot.

First introduced to the Hawaiian Islands in 1910, the medfly continues to be a serious threat. The fly has been discovered in Texas, Florida and California, but so far controls have been successful. The discovery of one wild medfly near Dodger Stadium in Los Angeles, and the subsequent discovery of more than 200 flies at other locations, initiated an eradication program that involved 5 counties and cost $60,600,000. State and federal agricultural officials are required by law to keep the Mediterranean fruit fly out of this country to protect the multibillion dollar agricultural economy.

Mediterranean fruit flies, introduced to this country in just one orange carried by a traveler, can cost millions of dollars to eradicate.

Environmental Challenge: Green Iguanas

It appears that humans were not responsible for the appearance of 15 green iguanas on the Caribbean Island of Anguilla in 1995. A researcher who studies iguanas on the island thinks that they were stowaways on tangles of huge trees that washed ashore several weeks after hurricanes Luis and Marilyn passed through the area. The debris came from Guadeloupe some 200 miles (320 km) away.

- Is this bioinvasion?
- Are the green iguanas exotic species?
- Will they be an invasive species? What will happen if they are?

WWW

To learn more about the methods used to control medfly infestations, visit www.cdfa.ca.gov/pests/medfly/mediterranean_fly.html.

Did You Know?

During fiscal year 1998, APHIS officials intercepted more than 52,000 plant pests and diseases identified as dangerous to the U.S. agricultural industry. Also intercepted were 1.8 million illegal plants, animals, and plant and animal byproducts.

With the supervision of their handlers, beagles inspect baggage of passengers arriving on international flights. They are doing their part to defend the country against foreign pests.

Did You Know?

The U.S. Fish and Wildlife Service has listed 244 species that have been transported by the aquarium trade and released into U.S. waters outside their natural range. In many cases these introduced species have endangered native species.

USDA Animal and Plant Health Inspection Service (APHIS)

Every year, taxpayers spend billions of dollars to control imported pests. In addition, billions of dollars worth of crops are lost because of these pests. The U.S. Department of Agriculture restricts items brought to the U.S. from foreign countries as well as items brought to the mainland from Hawaii, Puerto Rico, and the U.S. Virgin Islands.

The Animal and Plant Health Inspection Service (APHIS) is responsible for guarding against the introduction of foreign plants and animals into this country. Anyone entering the country is required to declare any meat, fruits, vegetables, plants, animals, and plant and animal products they are bringing into the country. APHIS inspectors search luggage for undeclared products. In airports at the border, inspectors use beagle dogs that are trained to "sniff out" contraband items. At other airports, low-energy x-ray machines scan luggage for fruits and meats.

Potted plants and soil from overseas cannot be imported because the soil might carry pests and diseases. Many plants and animals can be imported safely if the correct procedures are followed. Most fruit and lumber trees must go through inspection and testing procedures in quarantine. For some trees it may take as long as five years, because certain diseases aren't apparent until the tree begins to produce fruit.

Although quarantine procedures are good, they are never totally effective. Why do we take the risk of a disease or pest hitchhiking on a plant and being accidentally released into this country? Few of the plants that are important food sources are native to North America. The only way to get new genes that might improve the varieties we grow here is to import plants from the mother country.

Know Before You Go

When you plan a trip, check the U.S. regulations and make the proper arrangements. The U.S. Department of Agriculture has a publication called "Know before you go." You should also know the import and export restrictions for the country you are visiting. Until recently, if you took your dog with you to England, the dog would have been quarantined for six months to ensure it did not have rabies.

The disease rabies is not present in England, but a rabid dog or cat could easily introduce it. A six-month bill for keeping your dog in quarantine is very expensive and some pets die while quarantined. After a long campaign against the 100-year-old law, it was recently changed. New regulations require pets to have a passport that certifies the pet has a tiny microchip implant to verify its identity, vaccination against rabies, and treatment for ticks and tapeworms. The regulation does not apply to all countries, so it is best if you "Know before you go."

1.13 Questions for Study and Discussion:

1. Define the following terms: **VOCABULARY**

ballast	immune
bioinvasion	introduced species
exotic species	invasive species
histoplasmosis	non-native species
hypovirulent	weed

The Birds

2. Which term(s) above describe the starlings?
3. Give two reasons why it is necessary to regulate the importation of birds.

Alien Plants

4. For what reasons did the early settlers import plants from their native countries?
5. What are the problems created by purple loosestrife and water hyacinth? How are these invasive plants controlled?

The Little (but Mighty) Mollusk

6. Where and how was the zebra mussel introduced into the United States?
7. Give at least two ways that the zebra mussel may affect the fish populations.

Dreaded Diseases

8. Identify two imported tree diseases, and describe how these diseases have changed the American landscape.
9. What steps are scientists taking to save the American elm and chestnut trees?
10. In what way were the Native Americans like the American chestnut and American elm trees?

The Hitchhiker

11. Do you think that the gypsy moth will eventually be found throughout the United States? Support your answer.
12. How did the number of acres affected by the gypsy moth change from 1981 through 1983? What natural factors may have led to this change?
13. What limiting factors are often missing when a population is introduced to a new environment?
14. Describe the changes that you would expect to see in the appearance of a forest after several years with a large gypsy moth population.

The Flight of the Bees

15. Why did a scientist in Brazil import African bees? Describe what happened when the bees escaped the hive.
16. How may the Africanized bees affect the population of European honeybees? Why is this a concern?
17. What other imported pests are affecting the colonies of European honeybees in the United States? Why are scientists importing bees from Russia?

The Medfly Attack

18. Explain why the Medfly is a serious threat to the U.S.?

USDA Animal and Plant Health Inspection Service (APHIS)

19. In what two ways do imported pests cost Americans money?
20. What steps are taken to protect against imported pests?

Know Before You Go

21. Why did England quarantine dogs and cats? Do you think that the new regulations will be as effective as the quarantine requirement?

Environmental Challenge: Preventing Disaster

Research and develop an informational pamphlet that educates the public on a specific introduced species.

- Medfly prevention begins with you!
- Planning to travel with your pet bird?
- What you can do to prevent the purple plague!

Think About It

What are the potential effects of a spacecraft from Earth landing on another planet that has an organically rich "soil"? What, if any, cautions should be taken to minimize the impact of the event?

Will Endangered Species Become Extinct?

OBJECTIVES

- **Identify** factors that cause the extinction of species.
- **Explain** how the Endangered Species Act and Habitat Conservation Plans help endangered species.
- **List** criteria that you would use in approving or rejecting plans to save an endangered species.
- **Defend** a position on the reintroduction of an endangered species into the wild.
- **Evaluate** the roles of sustainable development and saving biodiversity in maintaining a healthy biosphere.

For a list of endangered species, visit www.fws.gov.

Did You Know?

According to the Fish and Wildlife Service, over 70% of endangered species today depend entirely or significantly on private lands.

"The time to save a species is while it is still common."
ROSALIE EDGE,
founder Hawk Mountain Sanctuary

The **Endangered Species Act** of 1973 requires the United States Department of the Interior to identify and protect species that are in danger of extinction. A plant or animal is classified as an **endangered species** if its chances of survival and reproduction are in immediate jeopardy. A species may be listed as **threatened** if it is likely to become endangered. If an endangered species does not get help, it will probably become **extinct**—disappear from planet Earth.

The Act states, "Endangered and threatened species are of esthetic, ecological, educational, historical, recreational and scientific value to the Nation and its people." The Act prohibits killing, harming or in any way "taking" endangered or threatened species. This includes the destruction or "taking" of their habitat. The major goal of the Endangered Species Act is to restore populations of species so that they are self-sustaining members of their ecosystem. To meet this goal, the law requires a "recovery plan" for each endangered or threatened species.

The law requires the U.S. Fish and Wildlife Service to maintain the official list of endangered and threatened species. In 1991 there were more than 639 plant and animal species listed as threatened or endangered. As of 1999, there were 925 endangered species and 258 threatened species on the official list. More than half (703) of the species listed are plants.

In addition to the species on the official list, more than 220 species are waiting to be listed. Studies and procedures for listing a species require both time and money. This limits the number of species added to the list each year. During the 1980s, 34 species became extinct while waiting to be listed.

Extinction—With or Without Humans

Plants and animals have disappeared from planet Earth long before humans existed. There were at least five mass extinctions before modern times. The best known is, of course, the extinction of the dinosaurs. Fossils tell us that dinosaurs once roamed the earth, but they don't tell us why they became extinct. Around 65 million years ago, an unknown event, perhaps an asteroid, caused the extinction of two-thirds of the earth's species; still others were somehow able to survive.

Fossil records suggest that the family trees of frogs and toads can be traced back perhaps 150 million years. Apparently these amphibians were better able to adapt to the conditions that caused the extinction of the dinosaurs. Today there is concern about declining amphibian populations. Harvesting frogs for food and dissection has had an impact on certain

Human activities in deserts have led to an increase in the population of common ravens. The ravens kill young tortoises. It takes 5 to 7 years for their shell to become hard enough to protect them from predators.

Tigers are threatened by illegal hunting and loss of habitat.

Now listed as an endangered species, the Florida panther is getting help. Only time will tell if the help came soon enough to save the panther from extinction.

species. In 1987, India banned the export of frog legs to protect its frog populations. In some cases we cannot explain the declining populations.

Extinction of species is a natural process, but human activities are causing species to disappear at a much faster rate than in the past. Many species are declining in numbers due to human population growth. In Africa, India, Asia and South America, the increasing human population is taking away more and more space from other species.

Habitats are disappearing due to population pressure in North America as well. Rapid residential development in Las Vegas valley and other human activities led to the listing of desert tortoises in the Mojave Desert as a threatened species in 1990. The desert tortoise is an indicator species for the desert ecosystem.

Today there are fewer than 8,000 wild tigers in the world. Tigers are robbed of their habitat and their prey. Conflicts arise as forests disappear and expanding human populations move into the forest. Sometimes humans kill tigers to protect themselves and their livestock. Another threat is illegal hunting or **poaching**. Hunters kill tigers to supply body parts for traditional Chinese medicines. A third threat is the isolation caused by **habitat fragmentation**. When breeding is limited to a small group, the young are born with birth defects and mutations, reducing their rate of survival.

A Little Fish vs. A Big Dam

In 1967, construction began on the Tellico Dam in Tennessee. Construction of the dam had already caused much controversy, when a 3-inch-long (7.6-cm) fish was discovered. The entire population of this small snail darter was thought to live in the Little Tennessee River. Building the dam would change the fast-flowing stream into a lake. The habitat of the snail darter would no longer exist.

Under the Endangered Species Act, no federal projects are permitted that could destroy the habitat of an endangered species. Even though

For more information on the Florida panther, visit www.panther.state.fl.us.

For more information on the suspects in the disappearance of frogs, visit www.aquarium.org/education.
For more information on the desert tortoise and other endangered species, visit www.nwf.org/wildalive.

For more information on tigers, visit The Tiger Information Center at www.5tigers.org.

$100 million had already been spent on the dam, construction was halted. A legal battle began over the dam and the Endangered Species Act.

In 1978, the Supreme Court ruled that the Endangered Species Act was constitutional. Later the same year Congress changed the law. The Act was amended to allow a panel of seven members to examine projects and decide if they should be exempt from the law. If the panel found that the project was more beneficial to the country than the environmental value of the species, the project could continue.

The panel found that the Tellico dam was not necessary. The farmland to be flooded by the dam was more valuable than the money saved by generating low-cost hydroelectric power. The dam seemed to be dead, but Tennessee senators and representatives began a campaign that exempted the dam from the Endangered Species Act. They did this by getting the issue included in another bill. While he disagreed with the building of the dam, President Carter felt other issues included in the bill made it necessary for him to sign the bill.

The completion of the dam did not result in the extinction of the snail darter. The United States Fish and Wildlife Service successfully transplanted the snail darter into a nearby river, and other populations of snail darters were discovered in other streams. The snail darter is no longer listed as an endangered species.

The Kirtland's warbler habitat is protected during the breeding season.

Will the Warblers Be Next?

Populations of passenger pigeons were once so large that they darkened the sky. It was once the most abundant bird species in North America. The species existed nowhere else in the world. Early settlers killed passenger pigeons by the millions, and then there were only a few. When the size of the flocks decreased, the bird's mating instinct was disrupted. The last known passenger pigeon died in captivity in 1914.

The warblers nest only under young pine trees that grow in the soil type known as Grayling sand.

A small (6-inch/15-cm) blue-gray bird with a bright yellow breast, the Kirtland's warbler, would not make such an easy target for a hunter. Its population was never large enough to darken the sky. In fact, the Kirtland's warbler is one of the world's rarest birds. The 1999 Kirtland's warbler census recorded 903 birds. The gun did not threaten the warbler population. The population is threatened by changing habitat and competition from the cowbird.

Kirtland's warblers spend their winters in the Caribbean pine habitat in the Bahamas. The bird's nesting habitat is limited to a few counties in north central Michigan. Ninety percent of the population breeds in the **watershed** of just one stream. They will nest only beneath stands of jack pines that grow in soil known as Grayling sand. They prefer stands of trees that are at least 80 acres (32 ha) and have many small grassy openings.

The US Fish and Wildlife Service attracts birds to seed placed in an enclosed pen. Cowbirds are asphyxiated with carbon monoxide. All other birds are banded and released.

The Kirtland's warbler makes a hole in the sandy soil at the base of a young jack pine tree, and lines the nest with bark and grasses. The sandy soil protects the nest from flooding during heavy rains. As the tree grows, it creates dense shade. This prevents the growth of plants that provide cover for the nest. As a result, the site is abandoned.

Although forest fires are destructive, they are essential to maintain the warbler's habitat. The cones of the jack pine only open when exposed to the heat of a forest fire. As settlers moved in and learned to control forest fires to protect their lives and property, the young jack pine forests matured. With fewer fires, there were fewer areas with young trees and fewer warblers.

Today a part of the Huron National Forest in Michigan is being managed for commercial logging and the Kirtland's warbler. Mature stands of jack pine are cut and the logs are sold. New trees are planted, and the warblers move in when they are about 8 years old. The warblers stop nesting in the area when the trees are about 20 years old, but the trees are allowed to grow until they are 50 years old. Then they are cut and the cycle repeated. This provides a continuous supply of nesting sites and products from the forest.

Providing good nesting sites doesn't protect the warbler from a parasitic bird—the cowbird. The clearing of forests for housing, highways and agriculture fragmented the forest and allowed the cowbirds to expand their range from the Great Plains into the warbler's habitat. In the days where huge herds of bison roamed the plains, the cowbirds (sometimes called buffalo birds) followed the herds and fed on the insects that were disturbed by the large grazing animals.

This wandering lifestyle left no time for nest building or parenting, so the cowbirds laid their eggs in the nests of other birds. The young cowbirds are cared for by other species of birds as if they are their own. Although the cowbirds no longer follow bison herds, they still leave the parenting responsibilities to other birds. This practice is devastating for the young of the warblers and other host species.

The young cowbirds develop more quickly than the smaller Kirtland's warblers and they take most of the food the adult warblers bring to the nest. As they grow, they often push the other birds from the nest. To improve the survival rate of the young warblers, the U.S. Fish and Wildlife Service traps and removes cowbirds from the areas where the warblers are nesting.

The California Condor

The largest North American bird, the California condor, was known as "thunderbird" to the Native Americans. Their range once extended far beyond California; fossils have been found in Texas, Florida, and New York. Ten thousand years ago there may have been a few thousand condors soaring in the sky. By 1800 there were probably only a few hundred and their range was limited to the Pacific Coast.

The gold-miners shot the bird whose wings spread more than 9 feet (3m). Some thought that such big birds must be dangerous; others shot the birds for sport. The quills of the wing feathers were used as containers for gold dust, and collectors sought their eggs. Adult condors do not lay eggs until they are six or seven years old. Normally a sexually mature female lays only one egg every other year. This makes condor eggs valuable; in 1900, at least one condor egg was known to be sold for $300.

As young cowbirds grow, they push smaller birds like these young American Goldfinches from the nest.

Environmental Challenge: Biodiversity

Biodiversity is the variety of plant and animal species and other organisms living in an ecosystem, and the variety of ecosystems in the biosphere.

President Bush did not support efforts to save the earth's biodiversity. The United States was the only leading power that did not sign the biodiversity treaty at the 1992 Earth Summit. Canada, France, Great Britain, Germany, Japan and most other countries signed the treaty. After President Bush lost his bid for reelection, President Clinton signed the biodiversity treaty.

- What do you think about saving the earth's biodiversity?
- How important is it that there be an international commitment to saving biodiversity?
- What criteria would you use to assess the value of an ecosystem?

All condors alive today are descended from only 14 birds.

WWW

For an update on the condors released in Arizona, see "Notes from the Field" at www.peregrinefund.org.

Did You Know?

A single little brown bat can eat up to 1,200 insects in one hour. In Missouri, there are three species of endangered bats that need caves to survive. The Missouri Department of Conservation is using palm-size data loggers to record the temperature and humidity inside caves. Bats store a limited amount of fat, and if disturbed during hibernation they may not have enough energy to survive until spring. The data loggers allow the scientists to monitor the bat's habitat without disturbing the bats during hibernation.

POPULATION LINK

A study in 1972 estimated the condor population to be about 60, and it also confirmed that adult condors were not successfully raising young. Only one or two young were being reared each season. No one knew the reason for the low reproduction rate. Was it loss of habitat? Condors are easily disturbed by human activity. If disturbed, they will desert a nest with an egg or chick.

DDT affected the reproduction of some birds, like the brown pelican. The pelican's eggs had thinner shells and were often broken. And those that didn't break did not hatch. The shells of condor eggs collected between 1964 and 1969 were 30% thinner than the shells of eggs collected before 1943. But the low reproduction rate of condors was not totally due to broken eggs. Most condors were not breeding. In 1985, scientists observed only one breeding pair of condors.

There were no accurate condor population counts until 1982 when scientists began using photographs to identify individual birds. The photographic census revealed that there were only 21 condors remaining in the wild. By 1985 all condors had been tagged and fitted with radio collars. The loss of 5 adult condors during the winter of 1984-85 led to the decision to capture all birds remaining in the wild. In 1987 the last wild condor joined 26 already in captivity. For their own protection, condors were no longer allowed to live free. No one knew if they would ever go home again.

Like their cousin the turkey vulture, condors feed on dead animals. They prefer large mammals such as deer, antelope, and elk. They also clean up the carcasses of dead cattle and sheep. The poison used by ranchers to kill coyotes was a constant threat to the condor. Since condors eat dead animals, they sometimes fed on poisoned carcasses left for the coyote. Poisoned carcasses, intended for coyotes, also kill other large birds. This deadly bait also threatens the bald eagle and the golden eagle.

The law protects condors as an endangered species, but that did not stop the accidental poisoning of these birds. All of the four known condor deaths between 1983 and 1986 were due to poisons. Three died from lead poisoning caused by ingestion of bullets in animals that had been shot, and one died after eating a poisoned carcass set out for predators.

A captive-breeding program, at the San Diego Wild Animal Park and the Los Angeles Zoo, has been very successful. The captive population increased from 27 condors in 1987 to more than 90 birds in 1999. All of the captive-bred condors are descendants of only 14 birds. Because genetic diversity is critical to survival, scientists study the chromosomal make-up of each bird before pairings or releasing the birds to the wild.

The recovery plan called for three populations of condors: the captive population and two wild populations in physically separate habitats. The populations of 10 to 15 breeding pairs had to be self-sustaining. In 1991, two captive-bred, radio-tagged condors were freed in Los Padres National Forest. Now there are more than 50 condors flying free in Southern and Central California and in Arizona, north of the Grand Canyon. To date none have mated to produce eggs.

The free condors are being closely monitored. To ensure a food supply, the U.S. Fish and Wildlife Service provides carcasses, but the birds are discovering carcasses on their own. There are concerns. The birds are curious and show no fear of humans. Problems arise when they identify humans as a source of food. Some birds have been killed by collisions with power lines. Others have been shot, and at least one died from ingesting poison.

It will be many years before we know if the condor populations will be self-sustaining. The condors released are young, and the first nesting is not expected until sometime between 2000 and 2010. The outlook is promising but not certain.

Back from the Brink

When the settlers arrived, the American bison (commonly called the buffalo) and gray wolves were two species that played important roles in maintaining a healthy Great Plains ecosystem. As the pioneers moved west, they slaughtered the bison because they competed with cattle for grassland and because the bison was the key to the survival of the Indians. When the Indians killed a bison, they used nearly all of its parts; even their dung was used for fuel. Professional hunters, including "Buffalo Bill" Cody, slaughtered whole herds taking only the hide and the choicest cuts of meat. The rest of the carcasses were left for the wolves.

By 1900, fewer than 1000 of the perhaps 60 million bison that once roamed North America remained. There were about 550 bison near Great Slave Lake in northern Canada. Twenty-three bison survived in the new national park at Yellowstone, Wyoming. Most bison were in private herds and zoos. In 1894 Congress, realizing that they would soon be extinct, passed a law making it illegal to shoot bison. The U. S. Army was given the task of protecting the bison at Yellowstone, and biologists began a breeding program to increase the size of the herd.

The American bison, once pushed to the brink, is no longer in danger of extinction. Today there are more than 150,000 bison, mostly in private herds. Based on the census taken during the 1999 calving season, there were 2,500 bison in the Yellowstone herd, the largest free-ranging herd of wild bison in the United States. Bison are nomadic grazers and during the winter, when good grass is hard to find, some of the bison wander out of the park.

Some bison and elk in the Yellowstone herd carry the disease **brucellosis** caused by the bacteria *Brucella abortus*. The contagious disease was introduced to North America by European cattle. The disease seems to have little effect on the bison, but it causes pregnant cattle to abort their calves. Local ranchers are concerned that the bison will spread this disease to their cattle. To protect the cattle, bison that leave the park may be shot. The killing is part of a highly controversial bison management plan.

Return of the Wolves

Wolves once existed throughout most of North America. The massive killing of the buffalo and the over-hunting of deer, elk and antelope eliminated much of their prey. The wolves turned to livestock, and

Think About It

In his book, *Sand County Almanac*, Aldo Leopold said: "The last word in ignorance is the man who says of an animal or plant 'what good is it?' If the biota, in the course of eons, have built something we like but do not understand, who but a fool would discard seemingly useless parts? To keep every cog and wheel is the first precaution of intelligent tinkering."

When confined and protected from hunting, populations of bison exceed the carrying capacity of the land.

For more information on bison management in Yellowstone National Park, visit www.nps.gov (search bison) and www.nwf.org/buffalo/.

Think About It

Just outside of Rochester Mills, Pennsylvania, is the land that was deeded to John "The Trapper" Leasure. The original deed was written on a wolf pelt. The 396 acres of prime forest and farmland was deeded to Mr. Leasure in payment for his help in exterminating timber wolves from the frontier. He received one acre for each wolf scalp collected that year.

Can wolves be successfully reintroduced to their former habitat?

www

You can find more information on the status of wolf populations at these Websites: www.fws.gov (search wolves), www.nps.gov (search wolves), www.dnr.state.mn.us and www.wolf.org.

ranchers turned to poisons, traps and guns. Ranchers baited buffalo carcasses with strychnine. The poisoned carcasses were deadly to many animals, including the wolf. More than 100,000 wolves and their pups were killed in Montana between 1883 and 1942.

Today the only large populations of gray wolves are in Alaska (6,000-8,000), Minnesota (2,000) and Canada (50,000). A small population of wolves exists on Isle Royale National Park, an island in Lake Superior. Wolves have moved from Canada into Glacier National Park, in Montana, and into the Selway-Bitterroot Wilderness in Idaho.

The gray wolf was placed on the endangered species list in 1974. It is classified as endangered in every state except Alaska and in Minnesota, where it was listed as "threatened," until recently. The Endangered Species Act requires that the U.S. Fish and Wildlife Service develop recovery plans for endangered species. The Rocky Mountain Wolf Recovery Plan defined recovery as "when at least ten breeding pairs of wolves inhabit each of three specified areas in the northern Rockies for three successive years."

Thousands of red wolves once called the Southeast home, but they too were nearly exterminated. By 1980, biologists had captured the last remaining red wolves from a coastal swamp along the Texas–Louisiana border. Some of the wolves were breeding with coyotes, and genetic studies identified only 14 red wolves. Now there are more than 300. While some remain in captive breeding sanctuaries, about 80 red wolves are once again free to roam their native habitat. The recovery goal is at least 220 in the wild.

The reintroduction of the red wolf was the first attempt to restore an extinct carnivore species to the wild. In 1987, four pairs of red wolves were fitted with radio collars and then released in the 120,000-acre (48,480-ha) Alligator River National Wildlife Refuge, in North Carolina. In 1991, breeding pairs of red wolves were reintroduced to Great Smoky Mountains National Park in Tennessee and North Carolina. Farmers are compensated for any livestock taken by the wolves, and landowners who allow the wolves to den on their property are paid bonuses.

Why Not Let Them Die?

Species have been dying out for generations, so why should we be concerned about losing a few more? Does it really matter whether the Kirtland's warbler or the California condor is extinct? Why should we be concerned about some plant that grows in another country and has yet to be discovered?

Scientists see plants as chemical factories, and some little known plants have produced some very important chemicals used to save lives. Some of these chemical compounds are so complex that they can't be economically synthesized in a laboratory. More than one-fourth of all prescription drugs contain compounds derived from plants. A decorative plant from Madagascar, called rosy periwinkle, is the source of two drugs—vincristine, used to treat childhood leukemia and vinblastine, used in the treatment of Hodgkin's disease.

Each year sales of the drugs derived from the rosy periwinkle plant exceed $100 million.

The most important part of this plant, the May apple, may be its root which produces a chemical used in the treatment of testicular and lung cancer.

Of the 250,000 flowering-plant species in the world, 85% of our food comes from only 20 species. None of the major crops grown for food (rice, wheat, corn, potatoes, beans, soybeans, cane, beets, bananas, and coconuts) are native to the United States. Seeds from plants growing in the wild may contain genetic messages that will improve the yield of these species or make them more resistant to drought, disease or insect damage.

It is important to protect all of the species in our "library of living things." The death of a species is a loss of genetic material. We do not know which of these species we will need in the future. Species not yet discovered may one day be vital to the production of our food, clothing, wood products or medicines.

These species may be vital to the existence of ecosystems that in turn sustain the planet. **Biodiversity** improves the stability of the ecosystem, and the loss of species reduces the diversity of the ecosystem. While every species may not be essential, some species play a vital role that stabilizes the ecosystem. Removal of a **keystone species**—a species that keeps the ecosystem in balance—will cause a chain reaction involving many other species in the ecosystem. There could be a major disruption in the ecosystem. Think of the ecosystem as the framework of a skyscraper. How many beams can be removed before the building collapses?

In the future, even more than in the past, the most critical threat to wildlife will be the destruction of their habitat. Future decisions about saving habitats and using (or not using) chemicals will play a major role in determining which species survive and which do not.

The Future of the Endangered Species Act

Congress passed the Endangered Species Act in 1973. Critics consider it a barrier to development and a threat to the economic growth, and they vow to weaken it. One bill introduced in Congress, the "Human Protection Act,"

Some medicines are made from plant and animal matter.

Think About It

How important is it to maintain butterfly habitats? If we don't save habitats for butterflies, it could have a domino effect on the biodiversity of the ecosystem. Do you agree or disagree with this statement? Explain your position.

WWW

For more information on Habitat Conservation Plans, visit these Websites: www.nwf.org and www.fws.gov.

Environmental Challenge: Sustainable Development

Sustainable development is defined by the United Nations World Commission on Environment & Development as "Development that meets the needs of the present without compromising the ability of future generations to meet their own needs."

In the early 1990s, Merck, the world's largest pharmaceutical company, agreed to pay $1 million to Costa Rica's National Institute of Biodiversity for samples of tropical plants, insects and microorganisms. Local people collected the organisms for the company. The company's chemists analyzed the samples for new chemicals useful in producing drugs. Royalties from any drugs developed by Merck will be used for science and conservation programs in Costa Rica.

- What do you think? Can there be sustainable development of a rain forest? Explain your position.

would make the economic value of a species an important factor in decisions regarding an endangered species. Supporters of the Endangered Species Act say the economy should not be the major issue.

According to the U.S. Fish and Wildlife Service, very few development projects are stopped because of an endangered species. A 1982 amendment to the Act allows an "incidental take" of one or more species listed as threatened or endangered. The amendment is an attempt to balance property rights with the needs of wildlife species. An "incidental take permit" allows a landowner to carry out activities that may harm threatened or endangered species.

"Take" means to harm or kill, and the Supreme Court has ruled that "harm" includes the destruction of the species' habitat. To receive an "incidental take permit," the landowner must prepare a **Habitat Conservation Plan (HCP)**. Specific steps outlined in the HCP must "mitigate" or lessen the impact of the activities allowed in the permit. The "incidental take permit" is issued in exchange for conservation measures that will ensure the survival of the endangered species. The U.S. Fish and Wildlife Service must approve all HCPs.

Development of the Las Vegas Valley came to an immediate halt when the desert tortoise was added to the endangered species list in 1989, until a compromise was negotiated with the Southern Nevada Homebuilders Association. The developers agreed to pay $550 for each acre developed. The money was used to purchase 400,000 acres (161,600 ha) of prime tortoise habitat. In another case, an agreement allowed shrimping to continue but required shrimpers to use "turtle exclusion devices" to save the Ridley sea turtle.

Populations of some species—the bald eagle, peregrine falcon, American alligator, California condor, and red wolf—have benefited from recovery plans developed under the Endangered Species Act, but other species became extinct while waiting to be added to the list. Critics argue that a few "glamorous species" get most of the benefit. *TIME Magazine* once referred to the California condor as the $25 million bird.

Many species are in trouble but they have not been identified as endangered species. Recovery plans have not been developed for many listed species. Many believe that the focus of the Endangered Species Act must be on saving entire ecosystems rather than individual species. Maintaining the stability of the ecosystems may be the key to maintaining the stability of planet Earth.

1.14 Questions for Study and Discussion:

1. Define the following terms: **VOCABULARY**

brucellosis	keystone species
endangered species	poaching
extinct species	sustainable development
Habitat Conservation Plans	threatened species

2. The Florida panther is now listed as an endangered species. According to the Endangered Species Act, why is it important to save the Florida panther and other endangered species?
3. How does the Endangered Species Act provide help for endangered and threatened species?

Extinction—With or Without Humans

4. How is extinction a natural process? Use the dinosaurs to explain.
5. What factors are causing the decline in the populations of large cats, desert tortoises and other species?

A Little Fish vs. a Big Dam

6. Why was the Tellico Dam project stopped?
7. Is the snail darter still listed as an endangered species? Explain.

Will the Warblers Be Next?

8. List the major reasons for the decline in populations of the passenger pigeon and the Kirtland's warbler.
9. The Kirtland's warbler will not be removed from the Endangered Species list until there are at least 1000 nesting pairs. Describe at least three important components of a good management plan for increasing the population of this species.

The California Condor

10. What is the niche of the California condor?
11. List some possible factors to explain the lack of condor breeding noted in the 1972 study.
12. Do you think that the reintroduction of the California condor to the wild will be successful? Justify your position.

Back from the Brink

13. Give two reasons why massive numbers of bison were killed by the pioneers.
14. What actions saved the American bison from extinction? Describe the change in the population of bison between 1900 and 2000.
15. Why do the bison leave Yellowstone National Park? Why does this concern the ranchers?

Return of the Wolves

16. Identify the two areas of the United States where large populations of wolves live.
17. Reintroduction of predators is a highly controversial issue. Do you think that the reintroduction of the wolf to Yellowstone National Park is a good idea?

Why Not Let Them Die?

18. Give possible ways an undiscovered plant might someday affect you.
19. Explain how removal of a species from an ecosystem might cause the ecosystem to collapse. What term describes species that are essential to the balance of an ecosystem?
20. What is the most critical threat to most species of wildlife today?

The Future of the Endangered Species Act

21. Should a species be protected by the Endangered Species Act even though its economic value is low? Defend your position.
22. Should "incidental taking" of a species be allowed?
23. Should the focus of the Endangered Species Act be the preservation of all species regardless of cost or should the focus be the preservation of ecosystems? Defend your position.

Environmental Challenge: Difficult Decisions

Fewer than 20 species have been removed from the endangered species list. Seven species were removed because they became extinct.

In 1993 the median amount spent per species, not including the cost of buying land, was $12,940. Some species received the benefits of very large sums of money: northern spotted owl—$16.8M; Florida panther—nearly $1.6M; grizzly bear—$3.6M; western prairie fringed orchid—$186,000.

Consider these issues:

- Are we doing enough to save endangered species?
- Should we spend more time and money helping endangered species?
- Once all individuals of an endangered species have been removed from an ecosystem, should we reintroduce the species? If so, under what conditions?
- How do you think we should save species—species by species or entire ecosystems?
- Unlike their cousins, the tigers, lions are not endangered in the wild. Why do you think the lion is faring better than the tiger?

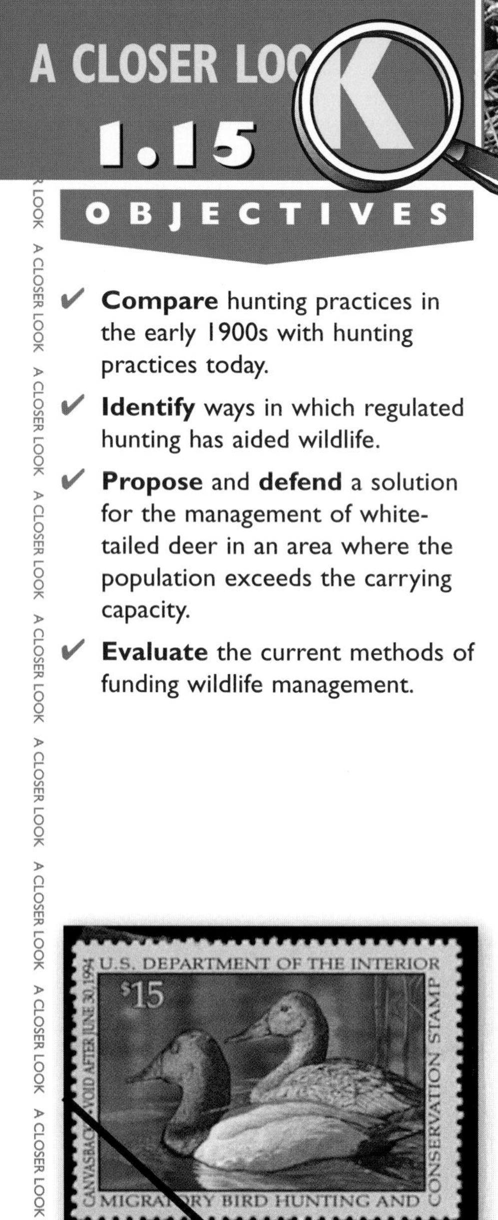

A Question of Hunting

OBJECTIVES

- **Compare** hunting practices in the early 1900s with hunting practices today.
- **Identify** ways in which regulated hunting has aided wildlife.
- **Propose** and **defend** a solution for the management of white-tailed deer in an area where the population exceeds the carrying capacity.
- **Evaluate** the current methods of funding wildlife management.

In the early 1930's, wildlife was in trouble. The activities of the settlers had destroyed much of the habitat. Some species had been nearly wiped out by uncontrolled hunting and trapping to supply furs, feathers, leather and meat for commercial markets. Without changes, many species that are native to North America would soon disappear. To save species from extinction, there must be laws to regulate hunting and money to restore populations of animals.

Money for Wildlife

With the exception of migratory birds, hunting and trapping regulations were left to each state, but the federal government helped finance the restoration of wildlife with federal taxes. Passed in 1937, the Federal Aid in Wildlife Restoration Act, better known as the **Pittman-Robertson Act**, placed a federal tax on hunting licenses, firearms and ammunition, and it required that this money be used for wildlife conservation. The P-R Act was later amended to include taxes on handguns and archery equipment.

In 1950, Congress passed the Federal Aid in Sport Fish Restoration Act or the **Dingell-Johnson Act**. This Act requires that taxes collected on fishing and boating equipment and boat fuel be used for fish habitats. In 1999, the Fish and Wildlife Service received $378 million from the wildlife and fish restoration funds.

The number of hunting licenses sold and the land area of a state determine how much money a game agency receives. The taxes pay for up to 75% of the cost of conservation projects. The state must provide at least 25% of the project's cost. In most states this money comes from the sale of fishing and hunting licenses. The money may be used to:

- Purchase and develop land for wildlife restoration.
- Maintain land in a manner suitable for wildlife.
- Conduct research to solve problems that affect wildlife.

The National Wildlife Refuge System used money from the sale of the "duck stamp" to provide habitat for wildlife.

According to U.S. Common Law, people of the U.S. own the wildlife, and the states have the authority to determine how the wildlife is used. Each state has a conservation department, a department of natural resources, or fish and game agencies that make decisions concerning wildlife. The appropriate state agency decides how to use the state's share of the federal taxes.

A federal requirement for hunting migratory birds is the purchase of a **Migratory Bird Hunting Stamp** (the duck stamp). Money from the sale of the duck stamp has been used to establish the **National Wildlife Refuge System**. More than 90 million acres (36 million ha) have been set aside for wildlife. Habitat loss is the biggest threat to wildlife, and the wildlife refuges provide habitats for many species. Populations of some endangered and threatened species are increasing because the refuges provide essential habitats.

Nearly all of the national wildlife refuges are managed both for wildlife and other public uses. Regulated hunting is allowed in some areas of the refuge, but most visitors are not hunters. Many of the people who visit wildlife refuges (bought with taxes paid by hunters, anglers and boaters) are hikers, bird watchers, wildlife photographers or people who just enjoy being a part of "wild America."

Game vs. Nongame

The Pennsylvania Game Commission is the "trustee" of all wild mammals and birds that breed in the state. The Game Commission's wildlife management programs are almost entirely funded with money from hunting and fishing licenses and money from P-R funds. Pennsylvania has 255 species of breeding birds and mammals, but wildlife management is largely confined to about 20% of these species—the **game species**—those that can be legally hunted.

When hunters pay for wildlife management, and wildlife is managed by game agencies, the management plans often favor game species. When land is managed for game species, the habitat of some non-hunted or **nongame** species may be destroyed. In Pennsylvania, some of the nongame species of birds and mammals have suffered serious declines.

Some people would like to see game agencies replaced by conservation agencies. They feel that nongame species would benefit more if they are managed by conservation agencies that are supported by general taxes instead of taxes and fees paid by hunters. In some states, wildlife is managed by conservation agencies. One of the best in the nation is the Missouri Department of Conservation. In 1937, a voter initiative replaced Missouri's Game and Fish Department with a professionally managed Department of Conservation.

Citizens of the Show-Me State have shown how they care about all natural resources by voting for sales taxes that help fund conservation programs. Missourians (both hunters and non-hunters) support the programs of the conservation department with a 0.125% sales tax. This provides $64 million for conservation. The money improves and maintains habitats for both game and nongame species. An additional 0.1% sales tax supports state parks and soil conservation programs.

One of the most controversial wildlife refuges is the Arctic National Wildlife Refuge in Alaska. To learn about this and other refuges, visit http://refuges.fws.gov.

Citzens of Missouri pay a sales tax for conservation programs.

The Return of the Whitetails

Many game species, including the white-tailed deer, would not be here today without management of their populations by conservation or game agencies. Minnesota, Wisconsin, Iowa, Illinois, Ohio, Pennsylvania and much of New York had no white-tailed deer by the late 1920s. There were less than 400 deer left in Missouri. This was primarily due to unregulated hunting.

After the creation of state conservation or game agencies, refuges bought with money from hunting permits were stocked with deer from other states. Hunting was regulated, and there was strict enforcement of game laws. A high priority was placed on habitat restoration. Now the

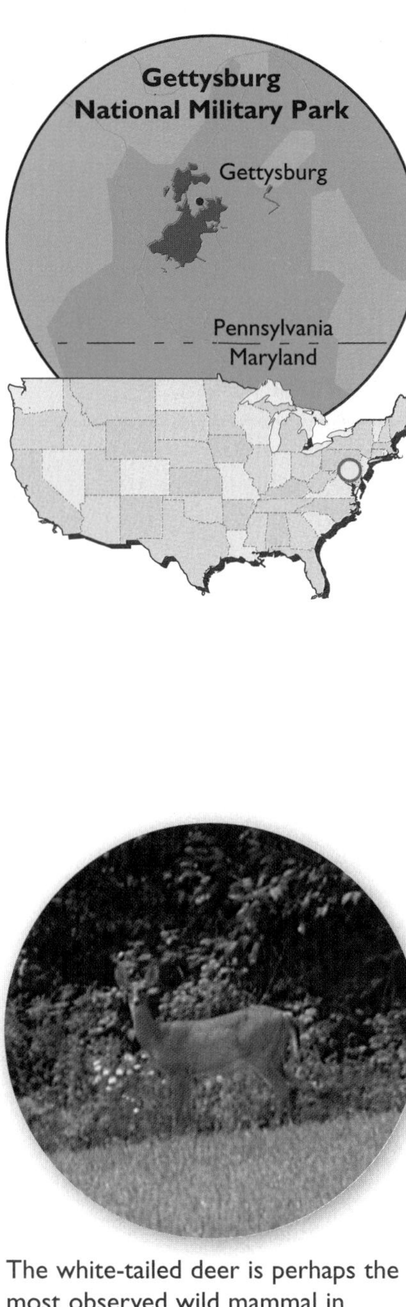

The white-tailed deer is perhaps the most observed wild mammal in North America. State game agencies regard deer as a renewable resource for viewing and hunting.

white-tailed deer is the most abundant big game species in North America with a population of 20 to 25 million. In some areas the population density is too high.

Public hunting is prohibited in Gettysburg National Military Park and the Eisenhower National Historic Site. Population surveys from 1987 to 1992 indicated an increase from 721 to 1,018 deer in the study area. Surveys found deer population densities as high as 447 per square mile of forest. The high amount of browsing prevented tree seedlings from becoming established to regenerate the 13 historic woodlots in the park, and nearby crops were being destroyed before harvest. The park could not meet its goal of maintaining the historic landscapes, which are necessary to aid the visitor's understanding of historic events.

The National Park Service (NPS) conducted 10 years of research and concluded that the number of deer must be drastically reduced. The environmental impact statement examined options for herd management and recommended the use of NPS-authorized personnel to shoot the deer. Between October 1995 and March 1997, 858 deer were removed from the parks. All venison was donated to area food banks.

The goal of the management plan was to reduce and maintain the deer density to 25 deer per square mile. The density had been reduced to 31 deer per square mile, but it increased to 63 deer per square mile when a lawsuit stopped the management plan. A U.S. District Judge ruled in favor of the NPS and 76 deer were removed in 1999. The park superintendent said, "Deer management is an unfortunate necessity of preserving the Gettysburg and Eisenhower parks for future generations."

Nature's Way

The **carrying capacity** of a particular habitat determines the population that can be supported in a given area. In Pennsylvania, the largest deer are found in counties having dairy farms and timber operations. The counties with large areas that are closed to public hunting have smaller deer. Why? When the deer population remains high, there is greater competition for food. Deer in areas with a large population and a limited food supply will be smaller and have smaller antlers.

As the number of deer increases, food becomes scarce, and reproduction decreases. Fewer does produce twins, and fawns with a low birth weight don't survive. Winter is the critical period, and food becomes the limiting factor. Fawns, born the previous spring, are the first to die because they cannot reach the higher buds and twigs. More adults die from diseases and parasites, and are an easy prey for predators.

Game Management

In the absence of other large carnivores, humans have become the deer's major predator. Some people feel that hunting deer, or other species, provides recreation for the hunter. This keeps the populations from building to an unnaturally high level, often followed by a population crash. They feel hunting is necessary to control deer populations in habitats where there are no natural predators. Others feel it is better to let the population regulate itself.

Right or wrong, regulated hunting has become our primary method of wildlife management. The science of **game management** begins with a survey to determine the population density and the carrying capacity of the habitat. Then the managers set limits to allow "harvesting" of the surplus game.

The life expectancy of most small game and many fur-bearers is less than one year. When the population finds good cover, food and weather, the reproduction rate is high, and there is a "surplus" of animals. Unlike wood, the surplus cannot be stored. Eight out of 10 quail hatched this year will not see next spring. If not killed by a hunter, they die of "natural causes." A study of ruffed grouse in Michigan found the same number of grouse in two populations—one with regulated hunting and one that was completely protected.

www

To learn more about the management of deer populations, search "white-tailed deer management" or to learn about Maryland's statewide deer management plan, visit www.dnr.state.md.us.

With 23,500 sightings, the mourning dove was the most frequently reported bird during Cornell University's 1999 winter survey.

Doves in Indiana

On September 1, 1984, Indiana became the thirty-sixth state to allow a hunting season for mourning doves. The doves had been protected for 111 years. There were heated debates prior to the legislative action that created the dove season.

One letter sent by the Committee for Dove Protection began: "They are going to kill mourning doves again. They are going to kill mourning doves during their nesting season. They are, by killing parent birds that are still feeding their young, destroying nesting young as well..." Other arguments of the dove defenders included:

- Doves ought to be protected because they are symbols of peace.
- Doves are closely related to the passenger pigeon, which is extinct.
- Doves are mostly feathers and bone and are not good for eating.
- Doves relieve hay-fever sufferers by cleaning up ragweed seeds.
- Doves are the "prettiest thing I've ever seen."
- Hunters will bag two at a time because the dove always comes to the rescue of his or her mate.

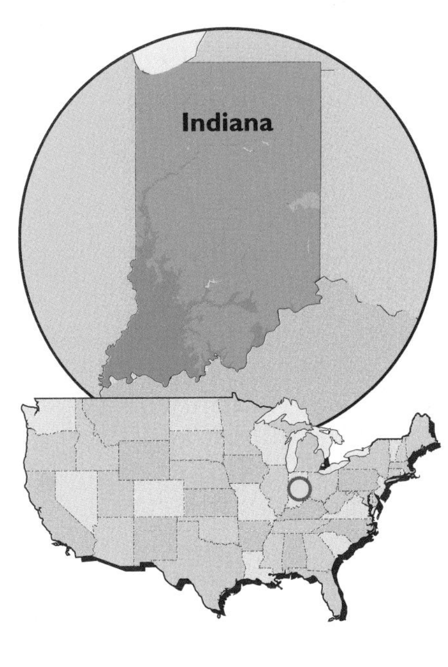

The Indiana Fish and Wildlife Division answered the pro-dove arguments with scientific data. A few doves, no more than 10%, nest during the hunting season. Both parents share the duties of feeding the young, so if one parent is shot, the remaining parent can care for the young. Nesting doves will usually be on the nest, not flying over hunting areas.

Wildlife biologists say that when the shooting begins, doves, like other game animals, think only of themselves. A dove will not fly to the rescue of its mate. Although doves may eat ragweed seeds, they also eat many other types of seeds. They are not a major limiting factor of the ragweed population.

Deer do not always cross at the "cross-walk" and motorists are not always able to stop when they do. The increase in the population of deer and the increase in the number of vehicles creates a serious safety hazard on our highways.

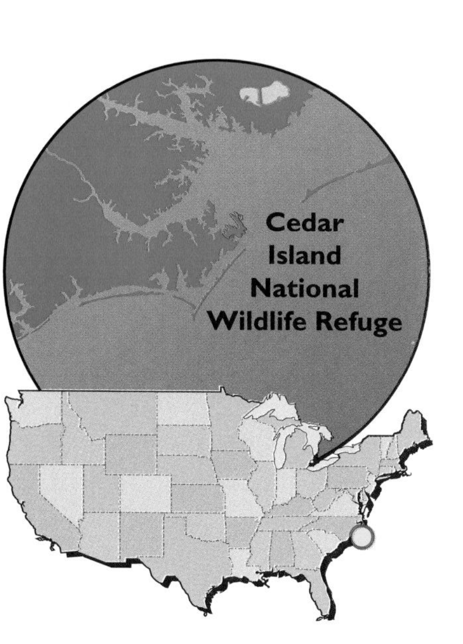

Doves weigh approximately four ounces (110 gm); they are not "mostly bone and feathers," but mostly breast muscle. According to John Madson, in his book *The Mourning Dove*, they are "...rich meat and very special delicacies." Two doves per person provide an ample serving.

Although the mourning dove is related to the passenger pigeon, there are major differences between the two species. Passenger pigeons were not able to adapt to the changing habitat. The passenger pigeon fed only on a few types of forest mast and nested only in mature hardwood forests. The mourning dove eats almost any seed it finds and nests anywhere a site is available—trees, ground or buildings. A pair of passenger pigeons nested once each year and produced a single egg. A pair of mourning doves may nest six times a year and produce two eggs at each nesting. The hunting of mourning doves is regulated; their cousins were victims of unregulated hunting.

To Hunt or Not to Hunt

The days of **market hunting**—killing and selling the game without any restrictions—are long gone. Hunting is regulated, but some hunters ignore the regulations. Studies by wildlife agencies in Missouri, Washington and New Mexico show that more animals are killed illegally than legally. Wildlife **poaching** refers to the taking of wildlife by any method that is illegal.

Although some poaching may provide needed food, most poaching is done for "sport" or profit. Most states have major programs, some with undercover agents, to decrease poaching. It is poaching, not regulated hunting, that threatens certain wildlife populations.

There are many responsible hunters who follow the rules and, although they do take individual animals, fees paid by hunters provide money to buy and improve wildlife habitats. Habitat loss is the biggest cause of the decline in waterfowl populations. Ducks Unlimited bought 3.5 million acres (1.4 million ha) of wetlands, and raises millions of dollars each year to preserve habitat for waterfowl.

Hunters sometimes wound animals without killing them, but nature's way may not be less painful. A "natural" death may be more brutal than a death or even a crippling caused by a bullet. Starvation is not pleasant, but the dead animal does provide food for scavengers. Some people argue that hunters are not a part of the natural ecosystem, but in many cases we have altered the ecosystem and removed the natural predators from it. Humans have become the major predator in many ecosystems.

Everyday some animals must die to allow others to live. Some people still hunt to put food on the table, but most people today are far removed from the process of gathering their own food. Most people are not hunters. They choose to let someone else be the killer of their domesticated prey—cattle, sheep, hogs, and poultry. Some people become vegetarians and choose to go lower on the food chain, but eating fruits and vegetables can have negative impacts on some species of wildlife.

Our technological society allows the choice of hunting, but our technology often causes the accidental death of many kinds of wildlife—we call them road kills. With the exception of the hunting season, more deer are killed on the nation's highways than by any other means. More than 350,000 deer—and 100 motorists—are killed each year on our nation's highways in accidents involving deer.

Like any other controversial issue, there are two sides to the question of hunting. To some people, hunting is wrong—it's a value judgment. To others, hunting is a way of life—a tradition. Both sides have some valid arguments, but decisions regarding management of wildlife—both game and nongame species—must be based on facts, not on emotions. Symbols of peace and beauty are not valid arguments against hunting any more than symbols of evil and ugliness would be valid arguments for hunting.

Developers destroy wildlife habitat.

Wildlife management involves much more than the issue of hunting. It also involves the issue of habitat destruction. Most human activities result in some negative impacts on wildlife habitats. Developers, dam builders, road builders, and swamp drainers destroy more wildlife than hunters. As the human population grows, the choices of land-use will be more and more difficult. Without habitat for wildlife, there will be no wildlife species to hunt.

POPULATION LINK

1.15 Questions for Study and Discussion:

1. Define the following terms: **VOCABULARY**

carrying capacity	National Wildlife Refuge System
Dingell-Johnson Act	nongame species
game species	Pittman-Robertson Act
game management	poaching
market hunting	
Migratory Bird Hunting Stamp	

POPULATION LINK

2. What human activities nearly wiped out much of wildlife by the 1930s?
3. What was needed to restore wildlife to healthy populations?

Money for Wildlife

4. What were the purposes of the Pittman-Robertson and Dingell-Johnson Acts? What was the source of the money?
5. How does the National Wildlife Refuge System benefit endangered species? People? What is the source of money used to finance the NWRS?

Game vs. Nongame

6. What is the difference between a game and a nongame species? Why do wildlife management plans often favor game species?
7. How does wildlife management in Missouri differ from wildlife management in many other states?

The Return of the Whitetails

8. Compare the population of white-tailed deer in the 1920s with the population in the 1990s. What caused this change?
9. Describe the problems associated with the deer population in Gettysburg National Military Park. What steps are being taken to solve this problem?

Nature's Way

10. What is the major limiting factor for a white-tailed deer population?
11. What is the connection between the size of the deer and hunting?

Game Management

12. Which species is the major predator of the white-tailed deer?
13. State arguments for and against hunting as a game management tool.
14. What two facts do game managers need to know in order to determine how many white-tailed deer should be "harvested"?
15. Compare the population of quail or ruffed grouse in the spring when there is a regulated hunting season to the population in an area protected from hunting.

Doves in Indiana

16. List the differences between the mourning dove and the passenger pigeon.

To Hunt or Not to Hunt

17. Does hunting threaten any wildlife populations? If so, explain.
18. What is the biggest cause of the decline in waterfowl populations?
19. How does hunting help wildlife populations?
20. List several human activities that cause declines in wildlife populations.

Environmental Challenge: Too Many Deer

You are the manager of the 185-acre (74-ha) Schlitz Audubon Center in Milwaukee. Here is the problem facing you:

The carrying capacity of the nature center is about 12 deer. During the last 10 years the population of deer at the nature center has increased from 14 to 50. Twenty-seven fawns were born this spring. The deer are damaging the plants at the nature center. A survey of the 60 neighbors who live closest to the center revealed that all but one neighbor had deer visiting their yards. Forty-six of the neighbors (77%) had damage to their plants.

A few of the neighbors like having the deer in their back yards. One person built a feeder for the deer, but most of the neighbors are demanding that something be done.

- As manager of the nature center, you must present the possible solutions to the board of directors for a vote. List at least three possible solutions, and give the advantages and disadvantages of each.

There are too many deer and too few low-growing plants.

UNIT TWO
The Atmosphere

187
183
94
177
150
181
134
120
107
12000+ Ft.
9000-12000 Ft.
7500-9000 Ft.
6000-7500 Ft.
4500-6000 Ft.
3000-4500 Ft.
1800-3000 Ft.
1200-1800 Ft.
600-1200 Ft.
300-600 Ft.
150-300 Ft.
0-150 Ft.
-3000 - 0 Ft.
-6000 - -3000 Ft.
-9000 - -6000 Ft.
-12000 - -9000 Ft.
-15000 - -12000 Ft.
-18000 - -15000 Ft.
-21000 - -18000 Ft.
-24000 - -21000 Ft.
<-24000 Ft.

2.1 The Thin Blue Blanket

OBJECTIVES

- **Compare** the earth's atmosphere to the atmosphere of other planets and **identify** the components of the earth's atmosphere that are essential for life as we know it.
- **Explain** the relationships between CFCs, the ozone layer, and UV radiation.
- **Describe** the biological effects of UV radiation.
- **Evaluate** the actions taken to protect the ozone layer and **predict** the effects of these actions.

First quarter Earth.

Atmosphere is a thin blue line

"For the first time in my life, I saw the horizon as a curved line. It was accentuated by a thin seam of dark blue light — our atmosphere. Obviously, this was not the 'ocean' of air I had been told it was so many times in my life. I was terrified by its fragile appearance."

ULF MERBOLD
German Astronaut

Photographs taken on trips to outer space give us a different view of our world. Looking at the earth's horizon, it appears as if there is a thin blue blanket surrounding the planet. It is this blanket that makes it possible for humans and many other species to call this planet "home." This halo of blue is created when sunlight is scattered by the earth's atmosphere. The **atmosphere** is a mixture of gases—mostly nitrogen (78%) and oxygen (21%). It also contains argon, carbon dioxide, traces of several other gases, water vapor, and dust particles.

The thickness and colors of the blanket surrounding a planet reveal information about its atmosphere and climate. Mercury, closest planet to the Sun, has only a very thin atmosphere. Its atmosphere consists of sodium and potassium atoms blasted from its surface by solar winds. Mercury's horizon is black. Because it is so close to the Sun, daytime temperatures can reach 700°F (370°C), but because it has almost no atmosphere to hold in the heat, nighttime temperatures can drop to 0°F (-18°C).

If astronauts traveled to Venus, they might describe a thick orange blanket beneath a thin blue one. The dense blanket of carbon dioxide (98%) helps create a climate that is far too hot—nearly 900°F (484°C) for astronauts or other earthlings. Far from the sun, Uranus wears an extra-thick, blue-green blanket made mostly of helium and hydrogen with traces of ammonia and methane. You could not breathe on Uranus because of its poisonous atmosphere.

Only Earth, with its atmosphere, provides us with the life-support system we need. Using an apple as a model of the earth, the skin would represent the thickness of the earth's atmosphere. Most of the gases in the atmosphere are held close to the earth's surface. The higher the altitude, the less dense the earth's blanket becomes. This is why airplanes flying at high altitudes must have pressurized cabins, and the climate is cooler in the mountains.

If we could travel back to a time before there was life on this planet, we might find an atmosphere very different from the one that exists today. Some scientists think that the earth's primitive atmosphere contained large amounts of methane, ammonia and water vapor. If this hypothesis is true, our atmosphere has been drastically altered by events that we may never fully understand. One of these events was the formation of the ozone shield.

The Earth's Atmosphere at Sea Level		
Selected Gases (in dry air)	Concentration by percentage (%)	by volume (ppm)
Nitrogen (N_2)	78.08	780,800.00
Oxygen (O_2)	20.95	209,500.00
Argon (Ar)	00.93	9,300.00
Carbon Dioxide (CO_2)	00.0355	355.00
Helium (He)	00.00052	5.2
Methane (CH_4)	00.00017	1.7
Nitrous oxide (N_2O)	00.00003	0.3
Hydrogen (H_2)	00.00005	0.05
Carbon monoxide (CO)	00.00003	0.03
Ozone (O_3)	00.000025	0.025
Nitrogen dioxide (NO_2)	00.00002	0.02
Ammonia (NH_3)	00.000001	0.001
Sulfur dioxide (SO_2)	00.0000002	0.0002

NASA's Nimbus-7 spacecraft, launched in 1978, carried a Total Ozone Mapping Spectrometer (TOMS). A TOMS instrument makes almost 200,000 daily measurements of the total ozone column mapping nearly the entire planet. The Nimbus-7 TOMS fell silent in 1993. TOMS instruments on other satellites have continued measuring ozone levels.

The Ozone Shield—a Natural Sunscreen

Most oxygen in the atmosphere exists in molecules consisting of two oxygen atoms (O_2). When ultraviolet light or bolts of lightning strike an oxygen molecule, it splits the molecule to create free oxygen atoms (O). Some of these atoms join other oxygen molecules to form ozone (O_3).

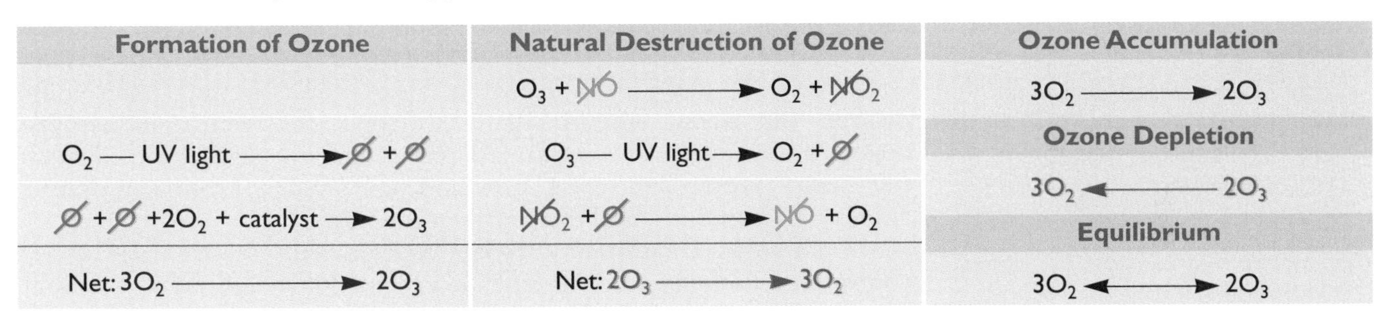

Formation of Ozone	Natural Destruction of Ozone	Ozone Accumulation
	$O_3 + \cancel{NO} \longrightarrow O_2 + \cancel{NO_2}$	$3O_2 \longrightarrow 2O_3$
O_2 — UV light $\longrightarrow \cancel{O} + \cancel{O}$	O_3 — UV light $\longrightarrow O_2 + \cancel{O}$	**Ozone Depletion**
		$3O_2 \longleftarrow 2O_3$
$\cancel{O} + \cancel{O} + 2O_2$ + catalyst $\longrightarrow 2O_3$	$\cancel{NO_2} + \cancel{O} \longrightarrow \cancel{NO} + O_2$	**Equilibrium**
Net: $3O_2 \longrightarrow 2O_3$	Net: $2O_3 \longrightarrow 3O_2$	$3O_2 \longleftrightarrow 2O_3$

Most of the earth's **ozone** (90%) forms a protective shield or filter within the **stratosphere** — a layer about 10–25 miles (15–40 km) above the earth's surface. Here ozone is constantly being produced, but the concentration is never more than a few parts per million (ppm) by volume. Why is there so little ozone? In the presence of certain chemicals, ozone easily breaks down. Nitric oxide (NO) is a naturally occurring gas. By destroying ozone, it counteracts the action of the sun's ultraviolet rays.

Variations in the amount of UV light and the temperature of the upper atmosphere cause natural variations in the concentration of ozone at different altitudes, different geographic locations and at different times of the year. If the system is in balance, the rate of ozone formation is equal to the rate of destruction. This is called equilibrium.

Volcanic ash from Mount Pinatubo.

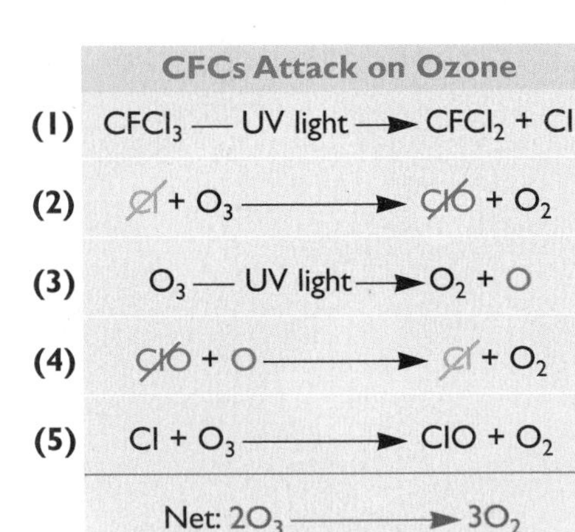

(1) UV light splits chlorofluorocarbon (CFC) molecules, releasing free chlorine (Cl).

(2) The free chlorine atoms (Cl) react with ozone molecules (O_3), forming chlorine monoxide (ClO) and oxygen (O_2).

(3) Oxygen molecules (O_2) and atoms (O) are naturally formed from ozone molecules (O_3) in an equilibrium reaction in the atmosphere.

(4) The oxygen atom (O) in the equilibrium reaction combines with the oxygen atom (O) in a chlorine monoxide molecule (ClO), resulting in a chlorine atom (Cl) and an oxygen molecule (O_2).

(5) The free chlorine atom (Cl) reacts with another ozone (O_3) as shown in step 2 and then repeats the cycle. The result is the continuous destruction of ozone. In this cycle the chlorine may destroy 100,000 ozone molecules.

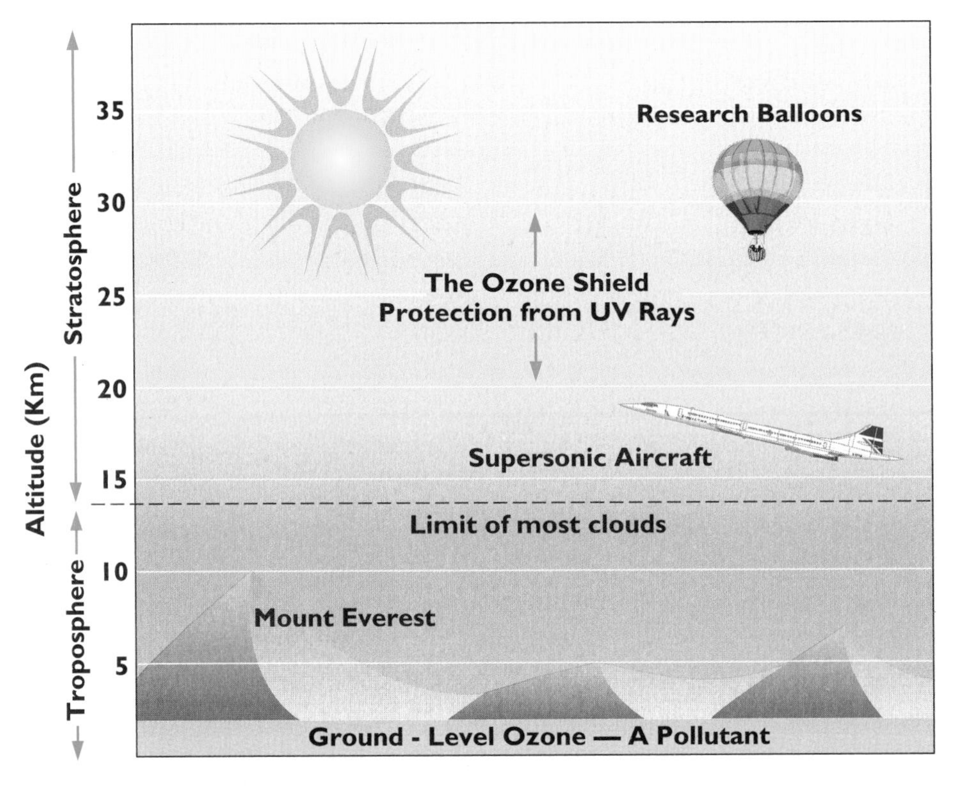

CFCs—The Risks and Benefits of Technology

During the 1970s, three scientists discovered that certain human activities were affecting the chemical reactions that occur in the stratosphere. They were concerned that certain chemicals released into the atmosphere could destroy the **ozone shield**. Paul Crutzen's research demonstrated that nitrogen oxides from supersonic transport jets could damage the ozone layer. Sherwood Rowland and Mario Molina proposed chlorofluorocarbons could destroy the ozone layer.

Compounds containing carbon, fluorine and chlorine are called **chlorofluorocarbons** or CFCs. CFCs are nontoxic and nonflammable. They are also inexpensive to produce. These characteristics made them ideal for several important uses that made life easier, more comfortable and even safer. Methyl chloride—a refrigerator coolant—leaking out of refrigerators caused a series of fatal accidents in the 1920s. This led to the search for less toxic coolants. The first coolant invented was CFC-12. The chart on page 93 shows the history of CFCs.

In the lower atmosphere, CFCs are extremely stable chemicals. Although they are heavier than air, the CFC molecules are distributed in the air by the winds. Slowly they rise into the stratosphere where the sun's UV rays split chlorine from the CFC molecules, and the chlorine attacks the ozone molecules. One chlorine atom may destroy up to 100,000 ozone molecules before it is carried back into the lower atmosphere where it is washed out by the rain.

History of CFCs	
Year	
1930	Thomas Midgeley, a GM chemist, invents CFC-12 known by various trade names including freon.
1945	CFC-12 used in most refrigerators produced in U.S.
1950s	CFCs used as blowing agents to make foam packing and insulation material – known by trade name of Styrofoam.
1960s	CFCs used in air conditioners, as aerosol propellants, and as cleaning solvents.
1974	Rowland and Molina call for immediate ban on CFCs in aerosol sprays.
1976	U.S. government bans CFC propellants to begin 1978.
1978	**NASA launches Total Ozone Mapping Spectrometer.**
1985	"Ozone hole" discovered over Antarctica.
1988	NASA panel reports ozone depletion over heavily populated areas in northern hemisphere.
	Du Pont, the largest manufacturer of CFCs, announces it will halt production as soon as possible.
1996	Amendment to Montreal Protocol orders production of CFCs stopped in developed countries by 1996 and undeveloped countries by 2010.

For their research in atmospheric chemistry, primarily those experiments involving ozone formation and decomposition, Paul Crutzen, Mario Molina, and Sherwood Rowland were awarded the 1995 Nobel Peace Prize in Chemistry. Twenty-one years earlier Mario and Sherwood had called for a ban on CFCs used in aerosol sprays. Since that time we learned a lot about the ozone shield, and what we learned was more than a little disturbing.

Biological Effects

The ozone shield is essential to the existence of life on planet Earth. Ozone in the stratosphere prevents most of the sun's harmful ultraviolet rays from reaching the earth. Wavelengths of light are measured in **nanometers** (nm)—one billionth of a meter. The sun's rays include visible light (400–700 nm) as well as a wide range of ultraviolet wavelengths.

The ultraviolet wavelengths are grouped into bands: UV-A (320–400 nm), UV-B (280-320 nm), and UV-C (<280 nm). UV-C is deadly, but it does not reach the earth's surface because both oxygen and ozone absorb all UV-C wavelengths. UV-B is harmful to most organisms, and it is only absorbed by ozone. UV-A is only mildly irritating to the skin, and it is necessary for the synthesis of vitamin D in humans. It is not significantly absorbed by oxygen or ozone.

UV-B radiation causes photoaging of the skin, certain types of skin cancers and cataracts in humans. The American Academy of Dermatology predicts that 1 in 5 Americans will get skin cancer in their lifetime. The UN Environmental Programme (UNEP) reports that large increases in cataracts and skin cancers are expected in the USA and northwestern Europe if ozone-depleting substances continue to be released into the atmosphere. There is also some evidence that suggests the increase in UV-B will lower the response of the immune system to infectious diseases.

While sunlight is necessary for photosynthesis, ultraviolet light is not. Studies show increasing levels of UV-B radiation can be damaging to

WWW

What is the UV Index? To answer this question and learn more about stratospheric ozone, visit www.epa.gov/docs/ozone and www.noaa.gov.

One in five Americans will get skin cancer in their lifetime.

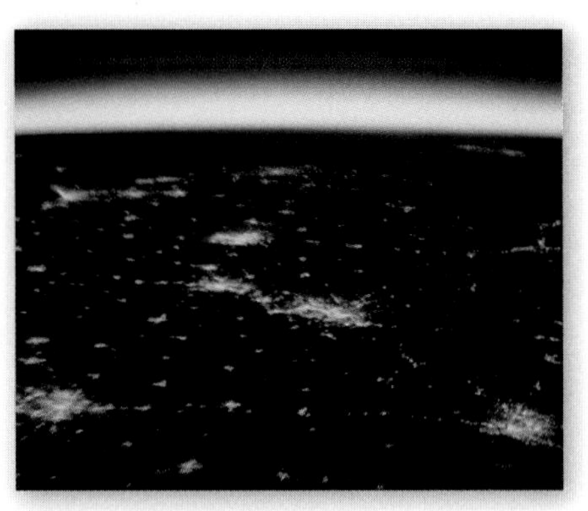

Eastern United States.

The Upper Atmosphere Research Satellite deployed by NASA in 1991 made the first space-based measurements of chlorine monoxide, an important chemical in ozone depletion.

Did You Know?

The major reason, cited by the U.S. government, for shelving a plan to build a fleet of SSTs was the threat to the ozone layer.

Atmospheric model studies predicted that nitrogen oxides in the emissions could lead to "significant reductions" in the ozone layer.

some species of plants and microbes. Some species seem to tolerate increased UV-B, but effects may accumulate from year to year. UV-B may also affect the degree to which plants are attacked by insects and **pathogens** (disease-causing organisms). It is difficult to predict interactions among species. Other environmental factors, such as increasing carbon dioxide levels, lack of water and nutrients, and a warmer climate, may modify how a plant reacts to increased UV-B.

Small aquatic life is very sensitive to ultraviolet radiation. Research shows that UV-A and UV-B decrease photosynthesis, growth and reproduction of phytoplankton (floating algae) that is the basis of the food web in the oceans. Larger algae that are attached to sea grasses are also very sensitive to UV-B. Experiments also show that frog eggs do not develop properly when exposed to increased levels of UV radiation. Current levels of UV-B may be a limiting factor for coral communities. The greatest effects are expected in polar marine ecosystems, which are experiencing the greatest increases in UV-B radiation. Reduced **productivity** of aquatic ecosystems can have serious economic impacts.

Warning Not Heeded

The potential for the destruction of the ozone shield was known as early as 1974. The first action to stop the destruction of the ozone layer was not taken until 1977 when the UN Environmental Programme drew up a **World Plan of Action on the Ozone Layer**. The UN action led the US, Canada, and several European countries to ban the use of CFCs in aerosols.

CFCs were essential industrial chemicals, and alternatives were not readily available. Politicians and scientists wanted more evidence before further restricting the use of such important chemicals. The evidence came in 1985, when a team of scientists reported a 50% decrease in the concentration of ozone over Antarctica—an "ozone hole." Although there is not an actual hole in the ozone layer, there is a significant thinning or reduction in the amount of ozone. Scientists confirmed that the so-called hole was primarily due to the presence of chlorine monoxide (ClO), a by-product of the breakdown of CFCs.

Ozone is being destroyed at a much faster rate than natural processes can replace it. Unique weather patterns during the spring season contribute to the great loss of ozone over Antarctica, but the loss is not limited to the South Pole. Depletion of ozone is now observed over large parts of the globe. Over the highly populated middle latitudes, ozone levels have fallen about 10% in winter and 5% in summer. We can expect to see the effects of the loss of ozone during the next 100 years, but the effects would have been more damaging without the Montreal Protocol.

The Montreal Protocol

If we are to protect life on planet Earth, we must protect the ozone shield. We know that chlorine, from CFCs and other related chemicals, is the major cause of ozone destruction. The best way to limit damage to the ozone shield is to stop the production of these chemicals and prevent their release into the atmosphere.

The thinning of the ozone shield is a global environmental problem, and the solution requires the cooperation of all countries. On September 16, 1987, 35 countries signed the **Montreal Protocol on Substances that Deplete the Ozone Layer**. By 1998, more than 168 parties (most are countries) were working together to protect the ozone shield. The original goal was a 50% reduction in the use of CFCs, but the original agreement reached in Montreal was admended in 1990, 1992, and 1997.

The goal of the Montreal Protocol and its Amendments is the total elimination of production and use of the chemicals that deplete the ozone layer. Millions of tons of ozone-depleting substances (ODS) have been released into the atmosphere and many of them are still on their way up to the stratosphere. As more ODSs reach the ozone layer, more ozone will be destroyed.

Levels of ozone in the stratosphere are now at their lowest point since measurement began in 1978. Thus UV-B radiation is thought to be at its highest level. If all parties comply with the Montreal Protocol as amended, the level of ozone-depleting substances in the stratosphere should begin to decrease after the year 2000. The slow recovery of the ozone shield will occur over the next 50 years.

Finding Alternatives

The recovery of the ozone shield depends upon meeting the targets set by the international regulations. Many experts doubt that this will happen. The high cost of CFC substitutes has encouraged the illegal manufacture and transport of CFCs. The manufacture of CFCs has been banned in developing countries since 1996, but a factory in Russia was still producing CFCs in 1997. Mexico and China are allowed to produce CFCs until 2010, but only for their own use.

In addition to checking for illegal plants and animal shipments, now customs agents look for canisters of CFCs that are being smuggled into the United States. Several people have been sent to prison for breaking laws that regulate ozone-depleting substances. Many other people have been fined.

In place of CFCs, new refrigerators and air conditioning units contain HCFCs, compounds consisting of hydrogen, chlorine, fluorine, and carbon. Although they contain chlorine, HCFCs are less destructive to the ozone layer because they are less stable and fewer molecules reach the stratosphere. The 1990 Clean Air Act mandates that the production of HCFCs be stopped by the year 2030. The chemical industry is searching for replacement chemicals. The chemicals need to be nonflammable, noncorrosive, have low toxicity and be reasonably priced.

Halons are stable chemicals that contain bromine, fluorine and carbon. Bromine is 40 to 100 times more lethal at destroying ozone than chlorine. Halons are primarily used in fire extinguishing systems. The halons in hand-held fire extinguishers are being replaced by carbon dioxide, but carbon dioxide fire extinguishers are not suitable in all situations. In some military situations, carbon dioxide would not effectively reduce the danger of fire and explosions. The additional weight of carbon dioxide tanks creates a problem for airplanes.

Did You Know?

A CFC molecule released into the atmosphere today will rise to the stratosphere in 6–8 years. It may stay there for more than 100 years.

Think About It

You are a molecular scientist and your assignment, should you decide to accept it, is to destroy ozone molecules. You might want to get in your tiny spaceship and take a trip to a place high above the South Pole. What kind of working conditions could you expect? Extremely low temperatures (–80°C) cause condensation of water and nitric acid to form "polar stratospheric clouds." The surface of these tiny particles acts as a laboratory table where chemical reactions occur. Here chlorine and bromine collect and react with ozone. You might want to wait until spring to begin the job because the increasing level of ultraviolet light will provide energy for the chemical reactions. The conditions are perfect for ozone destruction. All you have to do is sit in your tiny spaceship and watch.

Did You Know?

Each 1% decrease in stratospheric ozone results in a 1% increase in UV-B radiation reaching the earth's surface. It can take 20 years or more for some effects of increased UV-B radiation to appear in a population. Skin cancers have a long latent period. The Netherlands Institute of Public Health and the Environment estimates that controls on ozone-depleting substances will prevent 1.5 million cases of skin cancer in the United States by 2100.

The Montreal Protocol and its Amendments required that production of halons cease on January 1, 1994. At present there are no suitable substitutes for halons. As the search for replacements continues, recycled halons and supplies produced before 1994 are the only sources available.

What You Can Do

* Auto air conditioners are a major source of CFCs. Make sure that the repair shop captures and recycles coolant when servicing or repairing your air conditioner.
* Refrigerator service companies are required to recycle coolant when making repairs. Make sure that your service company captures and recycles coolants when repairing your refrigerator.
* Have the coolant drained from a discarded refrigerator or air conditioner.
* Use sunscreen that blocks both UV-A and UV-B rays, and avoid the sun between 10 a.m. and 3 p.m. if possible.
* Wear sunglasses that filter UV radiation.

Ozone measurements, recorded by NASA's Total Ozone Mapping Spectrometer from 1979 to 1994, show an area of severe ozone depletion, 'an ozone hole' over Antarctica. The ozone hole is defined as an area that has less than 220 dobson units of ozone between the ground and space.

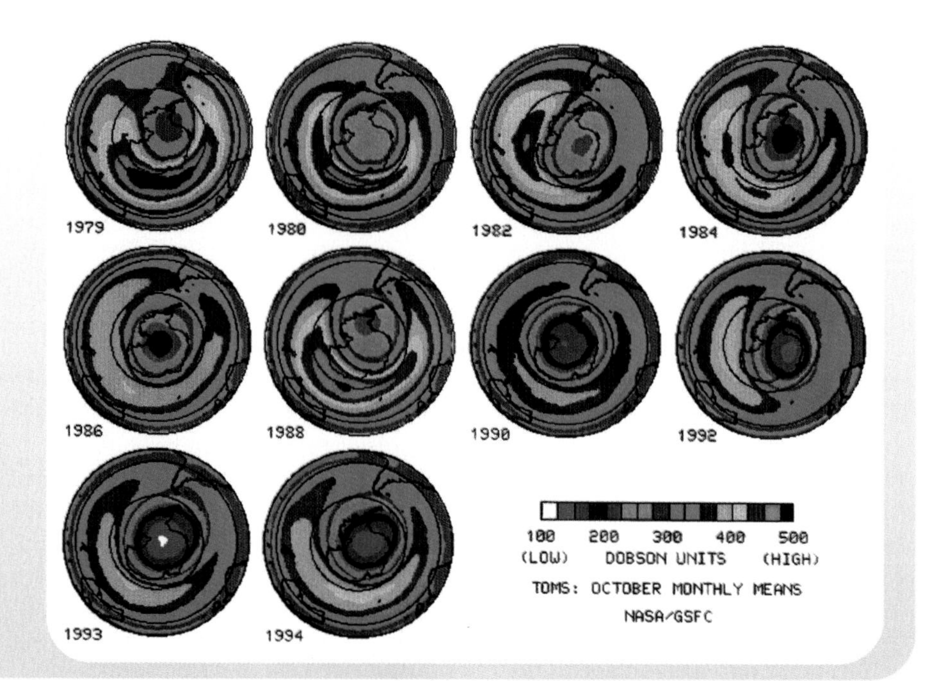

WWW

Check the NASA TOMS homepage to watch the "ozone hole" form and compare the size of the hole on specific dates. Visit http://jwocky.gsfc.nasa.gov.

Did You Know?

If all of the ozone in the stratosphere could be transported down into the lower atmosphere— to the temperature and pressure at sea level — it would form a layer only 3 mm thick.

Think About It

Ozone is a pollutant in the lower atmosphere. A question that is often asked is "Why don't we ship the ozone up to the stratosphere to repair the ozone layer?".

2.1 QUESTIONS FOR STUDY AND DISCUSSION:

1. Define the following terms: VOCABULARY

atmosphere	nanometer
chlorofluorocarbons (CFCs)	stratosphere
halons	World Plan of Action on the Ozone Layer
Montreal Protocol	

2. Identify the two major gases that together form 99% of the earth's atmosphere.
3. Explain why the earth has a thin blue blanket while Mercury doesn't.
4. Identify the environmental conditions that make life, as we know it, impossible on Venus and Uranus.
5. Explain why life is possible at sea level but life support systems are needed only a few miles or kilometers above the earth's surface.

The Ozone Shield—a Natural Sunscreen

6. What are the sources of energy that split oxygen molecules in the atmosphere? What molecule is formed when three oxygen atoms join?
7. Identify the two layers of the atmosphere and describe the position of each layer in relation to the surface of the earth.
8. Where in the atmosphere is the ozone layer found? What prevents the concentration of ozone from increasing?
9. What physical conditions cause a natural variation in the concentration of ozone within the ozone shield?

CFCs—The Risks and Benefits of Technology

10. What human inventions did scientists identify as threatening to the ozone layer?
11. What characteristics made CFCs ideal for use in a number of consumer products?
12. Describe the series of events that occur when CFCs reach the stratosphere. What eventually halts the destructive reactions?

Biological Effects

13. Compare UV-A, UV-B, and UV-C radiation. Explain how oxygen and/or ozone affect each band.
14. What are the effects of UV-B radiation on humans?
15. What are some ways in which UV-B radiation affects plants? Why is it difficult to predict how plants will be affected by increasing ozone levels?
16. In what ways does UV-B radiation affect aquatic ecosystems?

Warning Not Heeded

17. When was the first action taken to stop the destruction of the ozone layer? What action was taken? Why weren't other uses of CFCs banned?
18. What evidence did scientists collect in 1985 that confirmed the connection between the presence of CFCs in the stratosphere and the destruction of ozone?
19. Does the term ozone "hole" accurately describe what is happening to the ozone shield? Explain.

The Montreal Protocol

20. What was the original goal of the Montreal Protocol? How did the amendments change the goal?
21. Why will it take so long for the ozone shield to repair itself?

Finding Alternatives

22. Why do experts doubt that the goal of the Montreal Protocol will be achieved?
23. What chemicals are replacing CFCs in refrigerators and air conditioners? Why is this group of chemicals "safer"?
24. What is the essential use of halons? Why can't all halons be replaced by carbon dioxide?

What You Can Do

25. List one way you can help protect the ozone shield.
26. How can you best protect a small child from UV rays?

2.2 Weather Patterns

OBJECTIVES

- ✔ **Identify** the components of the atmosphere that affect weather.
- ✔ **Identify** technologies used to forecast weather and explain why it is difficult to accurately predict weather.
- ✔ **Explain** how geographic location affects local weather patterns.
- ✔ **Explain** how human activities affect local weather conditions.

Storms along the coast may cause erosion of sand and be dangerous for fishermen.

This sight of migrating snow geese may indicate the coming of cold weather or the approach of spring.

"Achievable improvements in the atmospheric sciences (meteorology) are essential to the better understanding of the most fundamental environmental issues facing the world."
AMERICAN METEOROLOGICAL SOCIETY

Weather Predictions

Meteorology is the study of the physics and chemistry of the atmosphere. **Weather** refers to the atmospheric conditions that result from interactions between temperature, moisture, winds, and clouds. These components of the atmosphere behave according to scientific laws; therefore weather can be predicted.

You may love it or hate it, but every morning when you look out your window there is the weather. One or two extra weeks of cold weather in the mountains may mean additional income for ski resort owners. For the orchard or vineyard owner, it may mean the loss of this season's crop of peaches or grapes.

A rainy day may spoil a picnic or outing for someone who has a day off, but for the farmer, it may mean lost income because a field of hay is spoiled. If high winds come with the rain, it could mean the loss of a boat for a fisherman—and maybe a loss of life. Fishermen and farmers often begin their day by listening to the weather forecast.

People who spend much time out of doors have learned to use signs of nature for short-term weather predictions. Signs that occur because of physical changes in the atmosphere can accurately predict short-range weather forecasts. Some of these signs and their scientific explanations follow. You can probably think of others.

- *A bright, silvery moon in late summer or fall means frost.*

  Explanation: Clouds act as a blanket trapping the heat near the earth's surface. If the sky is clear, the earth will lose more heat, and the chance of frost increases.

- *Swallows fly high; clear blue sky. Swallows fly low; rain we shall know.*

  Explanation: Before a storm, the barometric pressure is low and the birds adjust their flight to compensate for the change in air pressure. When the barometric pressure is low, flying is more difficult. Smoke follows much the same path as the birds. When the barometric pressure is low, smoke from a campfire hugs the ground. When it is high, the smoke rises straight from the fire.

- *When spiders weave their web by noon, fine weather is coming soon.*

  Explanation: Silk shortens and snaps when it absorbs moisture, so the spider must constantly repair the web. In dry weather silk is easier to spin, and the spider will have fewer repairs to make.

Wildlife behavior often provides clues to weather changes. Cats groom their coats more often when a storm is approaching. The increase in static electricity separates the hair and makes the extra grooming necessary. Deer and cattle feed earlier and longer than usual before a storm. If the elk suddenly begin to migrate out of the high country during late fall, it means that heavy snowstorms are on the way. These animals are probably responding to dropping barometric pressure and changing temperatures.

There are many "signs" of a coming bad winter, according to those who practice the folk art of forecasting, but these traditional long-range weather predictions are often wrong. According to folklore, if the woolly bear caterpillar has a wide brown band, the winter will be mild. A narrow band indicates a cold winter. But scientists tell us that the width of the band is determined by the genetic messages the caterpillar inherited, not by future environmental conditions.

At rest areas along interstate highways travelers may find information about weather conditions.

The Weather Forecast

Today, weather forecasting is a complicated science that depends on sophisticated technology. Advances in science and technology make it possible to protect lives, if not property, against the forces of nature. The federal government spends millions of dollars each year to operate the most advanced weather forecast system in the world. Much of this money is spent on environmental satellites, which collect millions of bits of data and images daily, and on super computers that can make up to 16 billion calculations per second.

Only with the use of satellites have scientists been able to see the global view of weather systems. This is a satellite image of a low-pressure system over the Pacific.

Hurricane "Elena" over Florida.

Satellites offer two advantages to weather forecasters. They provide a global view of weather systems and they constantly monitor atmospheric conditions. Two Geostationary Operational Environmental Satellites (**GOES**) orbit the earth at a speed matching the earth's rotation. The information they collect is used to create short-range forecasts. **Sensors** on two Polar-Orbiting Environmental Satellites (**POES**) collect data from remote ocean areas that are needed for long-range forecasting.

Meteorologists still rely on weather balloons and aircraft to collect data because they can provide a more detailed portrait of the atmospheric conditions at low altitudes. Twice each day weather balloons are simultaneously launched at more than 100 sites in the United States and thousands of other weather stations around the world. As the helium-filled balloons rise, a transmitter monitors the height of the balloon, the temperature, pressure, relative humidity and winds. This data along with 25,000 surface observations, data collected by aircraft, and satellite data are sent to super computers in Washington, D.C., which generate models of the atmosphere that are used to create weather forecasts.

Storm Warnings

Since GOES stay above one location on the earth's surface, they can detect changing conditions and monitor the development and movement of storms. Along with information from the GOES, a new Doppler radar system is providing forecasters with better information about developing thunderstorms, hurricanes and tornadoes. By bouncing microwaves off water droplets, Doppler radar can map the velocity of wind currents within a cloud. Using a Doppler radar system (sometimes called Next Generation Radar {**NEXRAD**}), forecasters can see inside a storm cloud, detect tornadoes in their **embryonic** stages, and issue warnings to people in the path of the storm. The NEXRAD has increased tornado-warning time from 5 minutes to 12 minutes.

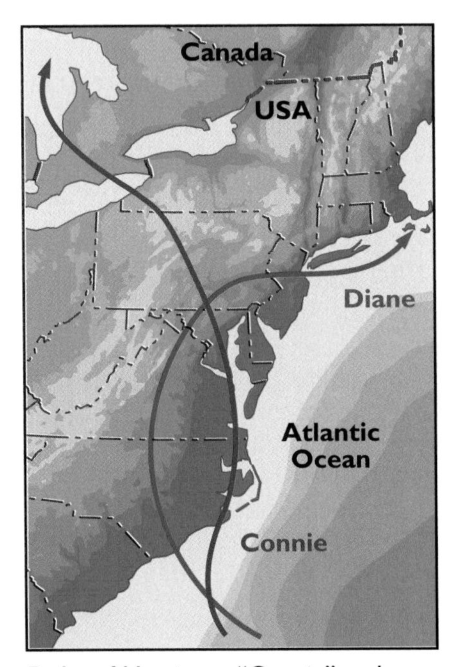

Paths of Hurricane "Connie" and "Diane."

The benefits of Doppler radar and other new technology became clearly evident in Oklahoma and Kansas on May 3, 1999. In a 10-hour period, the Norman, Oklahoma, National Weather Service forecast office issued 116 county warnings. Sixty-six tornadoes hit Oklahoma on that day. One was a category F5 tornado that stayed on the ground for about 90 minutes. Sadly 48 people were killed in Oklahoma, and six people died in Kansas where an F4 tornado traveled 17 miles (27 km) destroying or damaging nearly 10,000 buildings. Historical records show that without these warnings 700 direct fatalities could have occurred.

Hurricane locations were first spotted at sea by passing ships or by "hurricane-hunter" patrol planes. When Hurricanes Connie and Diane hit an unprepared East Coast in 1955, they caused billions of dollars in damage, and 400 lives were lost. The death toll was high because people had little, if any, warning. The destruction caused by these hurricanes led to the formation of the National Hurricane Center at Miami, Florida.

There were no satellite images of hurricanes Connie and Diane. The first weather satellite was not launched until 1960. Today a team of hurricane specialists relies on information from weather satellites, radar

Fujita Tornado Intensity Scale	
Category F0:	gale tornado (40–72 mph {64–115 km/h}): light damage. Chimneys, tree branches, shallow-rooted trees pushed over; sign boards damaged.
Category F1:	moderate tornado (73–112 mph {116–179 km/h}): moderate damage. Lower limit is also lowest hurricane wind speed. Surfaces peeled off roofs; mobile homes pushed off foundations or overturned; moving autos pushed off roads.
Category F2:	significant tornado (113–157 mph {180–251 km/h}): considerable damage. Roofs torn off frame houses; mobile homes demolished; boxcars pushed over; large trees snapped or uprooted; light-object missiles generated.
Category F3:	severe tornado (158–206 mph {252–330 km/h}): severe damage. Roofs and some walls torn off well-constructed houses; trains overturned; most trees in forest uprooted; heavy cars lifted off ground and thrown.
Category F4:	devastating tornado (207–260 mph {331–416 km/h}): devastating damage. Well-constructed houses leveled; structures with weak foundations blown off some distance; cars thrown; large missiles generated.
Category F5:	incredible tornado (261–318 mph {417–510 km/h}): incredible damage. Strong frame houses lifted off foundations, carried considerable distances, and disintegrated; automobile-sized missiles flying through the air in excess of 100 yards; trees debarked; incredible phenomena occur.

and specially equipped aircraft to determine the intensity of a hurricane, project the possible path, and issue public advisories. In 1992, hurricane Andrew hit Florida with a vengeance, causing $26.5 billion worth of property damage, but advanced warning allowed a massive evacuation that saved countless lives.

Advances in science and technology make it possible to protect lives, if not property, from severe storms. This is a satellite image of a cyclone.

Improving the Forecast

With high-tech equipment, we have learned more about weather in the last few decades than in all our previous history. Still there is much to learn. Meteorologists can track the **jet stream**—a 200-mile-an-hour (440 km/hr) river of air that flows 20,000 to 30,000 feet (6000-9000 m) above the earth's surface—but they do not understand why it moves the way it does. A poorly understood phenomenon known as **El Niño**—a dramatic warming of water in the East Pacific—may hold the key to seasonal forecasting.

Using information from hundreds of observation points, computers can predict the probable pattern of the upper atmosphere for the next 24 hours. Still, long-range predictions are very difficult to make because of the many variables that determine the weather. At present, long-range forecasts can only predict trends such as "drier or wetter" and "warmer or colder" than normal for a particular area. Any improvement in the accuracy of long-range weather forecasts will require a better understanding of the connections between ocean water temperatures and weather patterns.

Thunderstorms across the Pacific.

Did You Know?

In March of 1989, two magnetic storms on the Sun's surface collided creating a powerful solar flare. The solar flare warmed the earth's atmosphere causing it to expand, and it lowered the height of low orbiting satellites. It destroyed the electronics on one satellite and disrupted radio communications. A massive surge in Quebec's power grid tripped regulators and shut down a nuclear power plant.

NASA has launched two satellites to monitor activity on the Sun. If scientists could predict solar flares then shutdowns and failures of expensive equipment could be prevented.

Solar energy is the driving force behind all weather.

Solar Radiation — What Happens to It?

The Hydrogen Furnace

All weather is due to the interactions of four elements. The first of these is a giant star, the sun. The relationship between the sun and the earth can be compared by a model in which the earth is the size and weight of a table-tennis ball. The sun in the model would measure more than twelve and one-half feet (4 m) in diameter and would weigh about three tons (2730 kg). It is a gigantic hydrogen furnace. It uses four million tons (3 million metric tonnes) of hydrogen fuel per second. At this rate, the sun has enough fuel to last at least 5 billion years.

Without the sun, there would be no weather. The sun produces energy by a process called **fusion**. The nuclei of two hydrogen atoms are fused to form one atom of helium. The helium atom contains less energy than the two hydrogen molecules. The "extra" energy is released as solar energy. This solar energy is the driving force behind all weather. The atmosphere converts some of the solar energy to wind energy.

The Air Around Us

The second factor that affects our weather is the atmosphere. The transfer of heat or light waves of energy is called **radiation**. As the light energy travels through the atmosphere, some of the waves are deflected by water droplets or dust particles. This is why we often see a rainbow when the sun shines after a rain, and a red sky in the morning or at sunset.

The air, the clouds, and objects on the earth's surface reflect approximately 30% of the incoming solar energy. An additional 20% of the incoming solar radiation is absorbed by clouds, dust particles, water vapor and other gases in the atmosphere. So only half of the solar radiation reaching planet Earth is absorbed by the earth's surface and objects on it.

When solar energy strikes an object, the energy that is absorbed is changed from a short wavelength form (light energy) to a long wavelength form of energy. We cannot see the long wavelengths of energy given off by the object, but we feel the energy as heat. It is the heat energy radiating from the earth's surface that warms the atmosphere.

In a desert, where the air is clear and dry, 90% of the solar radiation reaches the earth and is changed to heat energy. While the daytime temperatures may be extremely high, the nights get cold because as much as 90% of the heat passes back into space. The desert has only a very thin blanket of the atmosphere's major heat-trapping gas—water vapor.

Where the air is humid, the daytime temperatures may be warm, but they do not reach the extreme highs recorded in the desert. The water vapor in the atmosphere acts as a sheer curtain or screen that reflects light energy. The land may receive only 40% of the incoming solar radiation. At night, the water vapor acts as a thick blanket that prevents the heat from escaping, so the nighttime temperatures remain warm.

The earth's atmosphere is like the glass in a greenhouse or car window. While the short wavelengths of light energy pass through the glass, most of the longer wavelength heat energy is trapped. Although the atmosphere does not trap heat in the same way a greenhouse does, this warming of the atmosphere is called the **greenhouse effect**. Planet Earth is a rather pleasant place to live because of the natural greenhouse effect created by its atmosphere.

Another important feature of the atmosphere is the cloud cover. **Clouds** are airborne masses of microscopic water droplets or ice crystals. Meteorologists are spending tremendous amounts of time and money on the study of clouds. They feel that a better knowledge of clouds is necessary to understand the earth's climate and how it changes.

When moist air is pushed upward and is cooled, the water vapor begins to condense around small particles. Smoke, whether from forest fires, chimneys, or automobiles, adds particles to the air. Winds pick up small particles of salt from the ocean or dust from exposed soil. All of these particles or **condensation nuclei** provide surfaces for the condensation of water vapor. Water droplets or ice crystals are formed, depending upon the temperature.

The moisture in clouds is eventually returned to the earth as precipitation. The features of the earth's surface and the movement of its winds determine where the moisture will fall. The amount of moisture that is returned to the earth each year can vary from the average 0.05 inches (1.27 mm) that falls in Iquique, Chile, to the average 38 feet (11.5 m) that falls on Mount Waialeale in Hawaii—the wettest spot on the earth.

Destruction of the tropical rain forest could affect weather over the entire planet. Transpiration from plants in the Amazon rain forest is an important source of water vapor for the formation of clouds. Clouds are an important factor in moderating the earth's temperature. While some clouds are an effective sunscreen reflecting significant amounts of light energy and keeping the earth cool, other clouds act as a blanket trapping heat energy and keeping the earth warm. Still others have a neutral effect. The net effect of the earth's cloud cover is to cool the surface.

How do water vapor and carbon dioxide from stacks like these affect the temperature of the atmosphere?

Short wavelengths of light energy pass through the glass; most of the longer wavelength heat energy is trapped.

Sahara Desert.

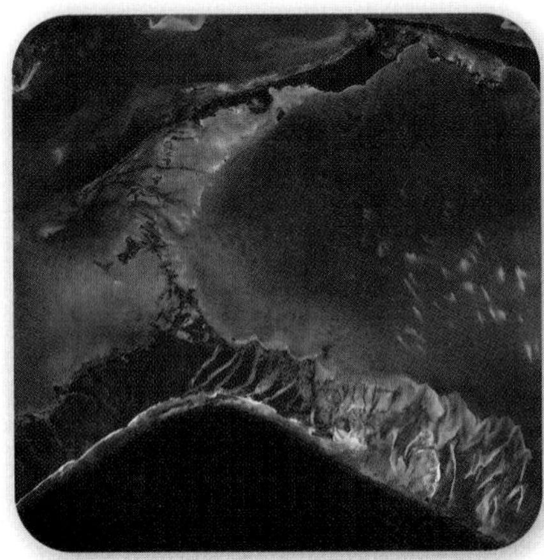

The Bahamas.

Change the chemistry of the atmosphere, and the **climate**—the prevailing weather conditions—may change. The amount of water vapor and other heat-trapping gases in the atmosphere help to regulate the temperature of the planet. The average temperature of planet Earth is 60°F (15°C). This temperature is significant because it allows water to exist in a liquid state, and water is essential for life, as we know it.

Seasonal Weather

The third factor that affects weather is the shape and movement of the planet Earth. The earth is nearly spherical in shape. If you could squeeze a basketball so that both ends were somewhat flattened, then the basketball would be an appropriate model of the earth. If you shine a flashlight on the basketball, the light is brightest where it is at a right angle to the ball. Other regions of the ball are dimmer because the light, striking an object at an oblique angle, spreads out over more of its surface. Areas near the equator are always brighter and warmer than areas near the poles because they receive more direct sunlight (see below).

As the air at the equator is warmed, it rises and is replaced by cooler, denser air flowing in from the north and the south. This flow of air is caused by the difference in temperatures at the poles and the equator. If the earth did not rotate, the movement of air would be from the poles toward the equator; however, the earth rotates on its own axis from west to east. This rotation determines the direction of prevailing winds as well as the ocean currents.

The earth is tilted on its axis. Regions of the earth are tipped toward or away from the sun. It is the tilt of the earth that creates the four seasons.

Prevailing Winds on a Rotating Planet

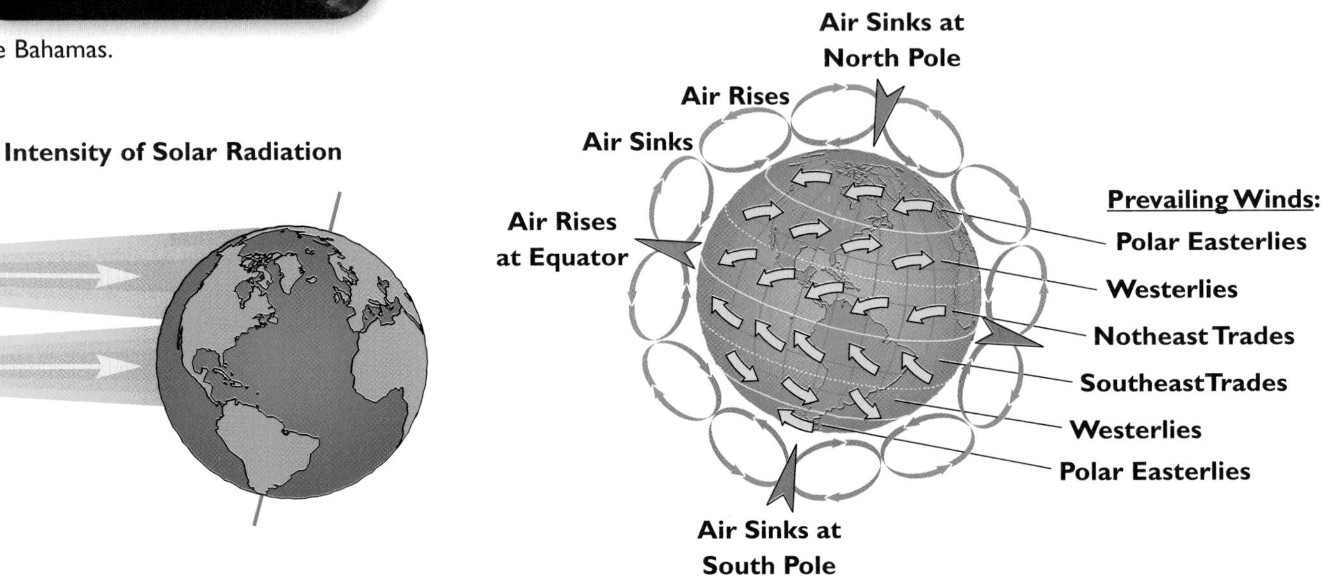

In autumn and winter the Northern Hemisphere is tilted away from the sun. The decreased angle of the sun's rays brings shorter days and colder weather. In spring and summer the Northern Hemisphere is tilted so that the sun's rays strike more directly. The weather becomes warmer.

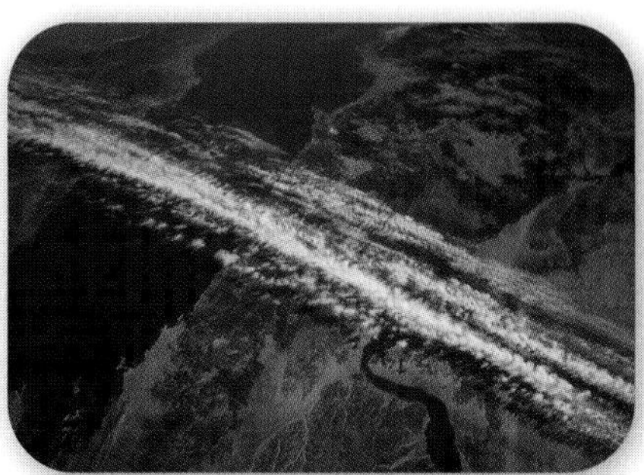

Jet stream over the Middle East.

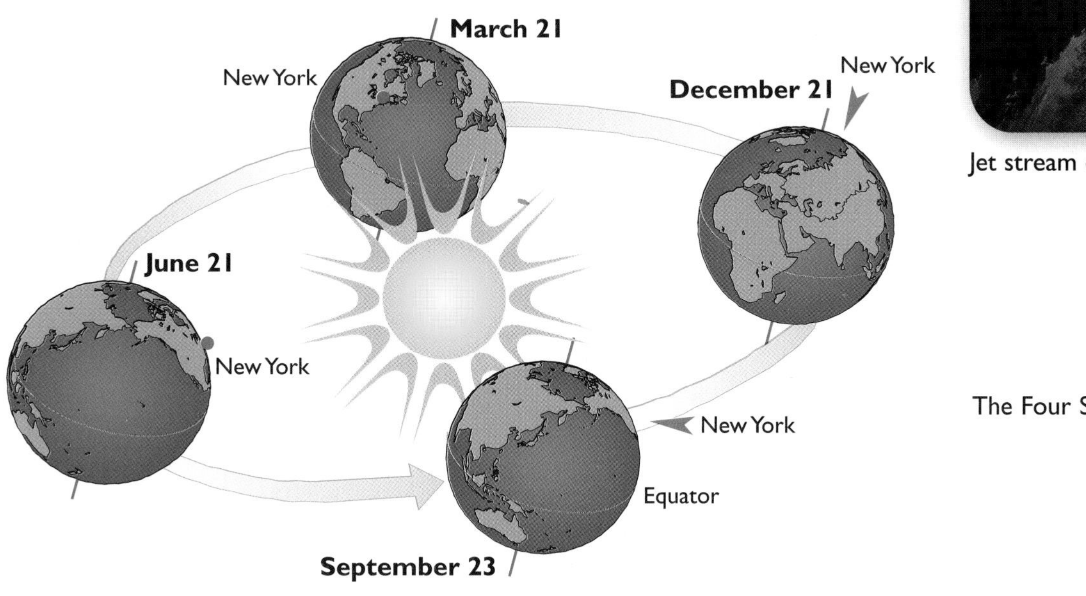

The Four Seasons

Down to Earth

The fourth factor that influences the weather is the shape and make-up of the earth's surface. Due to its molecular structure, water needs a larger amount of heat to change its temperature than most other substances. When the sun is shining, the temperature of the oceans and lakes does not rise as fast as the temperature on the land. At night, when there is no sunshine, water loses its heat more slowly than the land.

Winds blowing over the water drag the surface water along and push the deeper water down, distributing the heat downward 300 feet (91 m) or more. Land is heated only on the surface. The heat cannot easily be transferred to the deeper layers of soil. Thus the water provides a much larger bank for heat storage.

Land gains and loses heat faster than water. The land "bank" loses its heat faster than the "bank" of water. This means that the land will be warmer in the daytime and cooler at night. This difference in the temperatures of the land and the water creates a difference in air pressure that causes the movement of air.

People living near a body of water experience cooler temperatures in the summer and warmer temperatures in the winter than those who live further inland from a body of water. This explains why many people like to spend weekends and vacations at the beach or near a lake.

www

For more information on weather topics, visit these Websites:
The national severe storms laboratory at www.nssl.noaa.gov.
The national hurricane center at www.nhc.noaa.gov.
The interactive weather information network at http://iwin.nws.noaa.gov.
The national weather service at www.nws.noaa.gov.

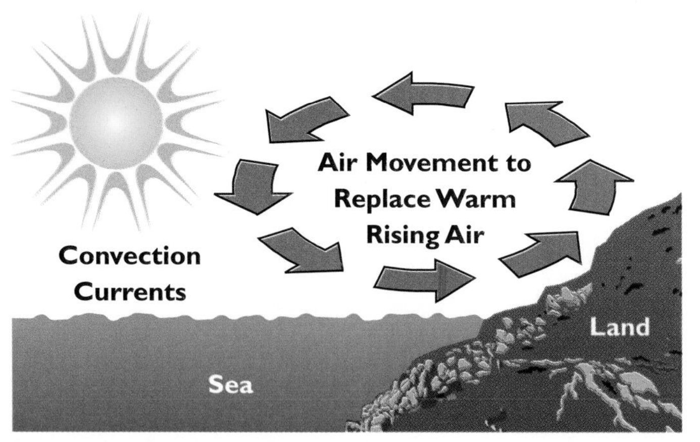

During the day, the land warms faster than the water. As the air above the land is warmed, it expands and rises. The cooler, denser air over the water moves in and pushes the warmer air upward.

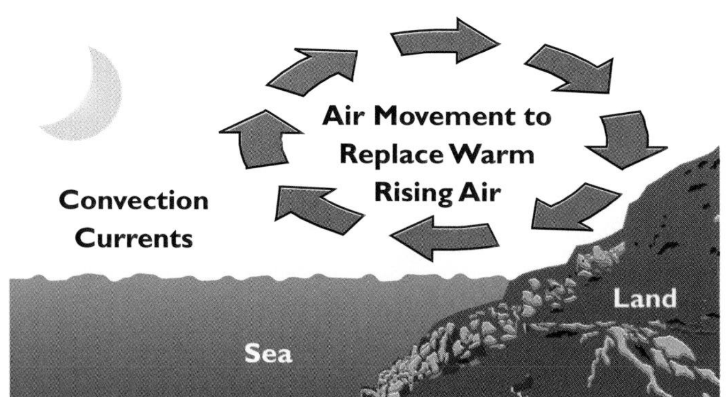

At night the land cools faster than the water. The air above the water is warmed as the water slowly gives up the heat it has stored. As the warm air expands and rises, it is pushed upward by the cooler, denser air from the land.

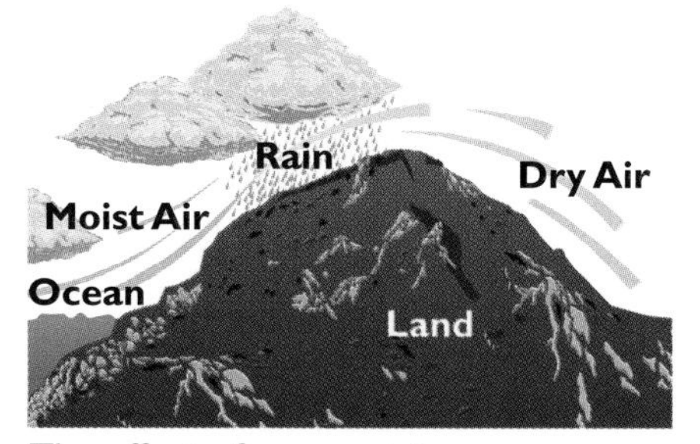

The effect of a mountain range on weather.

Mountain ranges also help determine the weather. The Mississippi River Valley and the Great Plains lie in a depression between the Rocky Mountains in the West and the Appalachians in the East. Cold air masses sweep down from the North. When the cold air clashes with warm, moist air from the Gulf of Mexico, large storms and blizzards occur.

As the storm approaches a mountain range, the air is pushed upward. As the air rises it is cooled, and the water vapor condenses into some form of precipitation. Due to the prevailing wind direction (west to east), larger amounts of precipitation fall on the west side of the mountains in the United States. Our driest regions lie to the east of our tallest mountain ranges.

Humans can change the local weather pattern. Brick, concrete, asphalt, and other building materials absorb and hold heat. The vertical surfaces of buildings collect heat and reflect it to each other rather than back into the atmosphere. Automobiles, air conditioners and industries also give off heat. Another factor altering the climate of cities is the scarcity of trees with their natural cooling effect.

The altered landscape of the city creates the **urban heat island effect**, making the center of the city warmer than the surrounding area. A pronounced urban heat island effect is often observed in Mexico City where some places within the city are as much as 22°F (12°C) warmer than the surrounding suburban and rural areas. Think of the city as an island surrounded with water. If there is no wind, the air moves in a current similar to that of sea breezes. The warm air rises and is replaced by cooler air from the edge of the city.

San Francisco (satellite image).

As the air—filled with tiny suspended particles—moves up over the city, it forms a ceiling. This can easily be seen as a haze. The particles reflect sunlight and the air circulation slows. On windless days, the

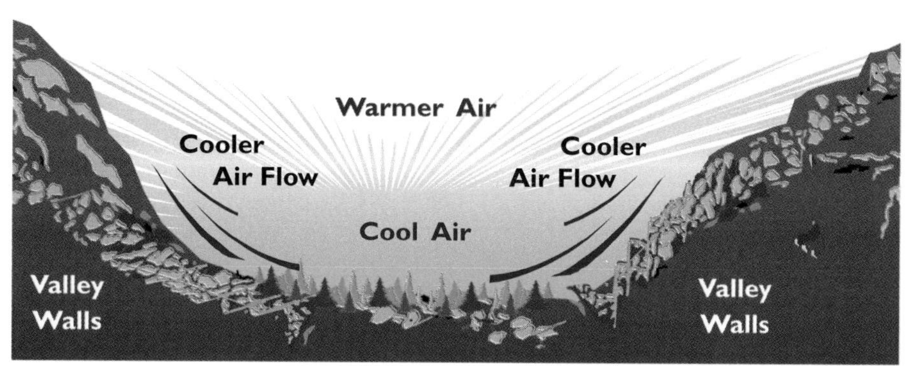

At night: An Inversion Occurs in the Valley.

Early morning finds a valley in the Rocky Mountains covered with a layer of fog. The temperature inversion also traps air pollutants.

city's air becomes filled with pollution. Only a strong prevailing wind will disperse the pollution, moving it away from the city and distributing it elsewhere.

Under normal conditions, the temperature of the atmosphere decreases with altitude. When there is no wind, an inversion may occur. An **inversion** is a condition where a layer of warmer air covers a layer of cooler air beneath it. Inversions frequently occur in valleys after the sun sets, when cooler air flows down the mountain or hillside. A warmer layer of air above the valley traps the cool air.

The inversion disappears when the morning sun heats the earth, and the earth radiates heat to warm the air. This may not happen until the sun is directly over head. During the winter months, Denver, Colorado, often experiences inversions that last all day. A closed ring of mountains also surrounds Mexico City. Mexico City can experience inversions up to 25 days each month between November and May.

Fall and winter generally have the longest lasting and the greatest number of inversions. The major air pollution disasters of our time—Meuse Valley, Belgium (1930); Donora, Pennsylvania (1948); and London, England (1952)—all occurred during the fall or winter months when inversions existed. [See Section 2.6, pages 127 and 132.]

Did You Know?

Light in shorter wavelengths is scattered by molecules in the atmosphere more than light in longer wavelengths. That's why the sky appears blue. Blue light has shorter wavelengths than red light. A sunset appears orange or red because the light is traveling through much more atmosphere, dust and water vapor. The shorter wavelengths are blocked out. If the sunsets are more spectacular than usual, there may have been a dust storm, or a volcano may have erupted.

Think About It

Global Problems

The atmosphere is a vital component of planet Earth's life support system. It is a moving envelope that receives substances from an ecosystem. It transports, transforms, and deposits those substances in another ecosystem. When pollutants enter the atmosphere, an environmental problem may become an international problem.

2.2 Questions for Study and Discussion:

1. Define the following terms: **VOCABULARY**

climate	embryonic	inversion	POES
cloud	fusion	jet stream	radiation
condensation nuclei	GOES	meteorology	urban heat island effect
El Niño	greenhouse effect	NEXRAD	weather

Weather Predictions

2. Identify the four parts of the atmosphere that affect our weather.
3. Give two signs that predict a coming storm.

The Weather Forecast

4. List two advantages of satellites as sources of information for predicting weather.
5. Why do meteorologists still rely on weather balloons and aircraft to provide information for forecasts?

Storm Warnings

6. What type of instrument allows meteorologists to gather information about winds within a developing cloud? What weather event can be identified using this technology?
7. What historic event led to the formation of the National Hurricane Center?

Improving the Forecast

8. Today, because of modern technology, humans can make very accurate long-range forecasts. (True/False)
9. Why is it important to know the temperatures of the oceans?

The Hydrogen Furnace

10. Why is the sun sometimes called a hydrogen furnace? What is the waste product that is produced?
11. How does solar energy create weather systems?

The Air Around Us

12. What two substances in the atmosphere scatter light waves?
13. Why do temperatures in the desert get so cold at night although the daytime temperatures are so hot?
14. How does the atmosphere affect the temperature of the earth? What is this effect on temperature called?
15. If the air at high altitudes is closer to the sun, why isn't it warmer than the air near the surface of the earth?
16. Why do you think that meteorologists are more interested in clouds than in other weather phenomena?

Seasonal Weather

17. Why is the equator always warmer than Canada or Australia?
18. How does the rotation of the earth affect the weather?
19. Explain why the northern states of the U.S. experience a distinct summer and winter season.

Down to Earth

20. On a hot summer day, how will the temperature of land near a lake differ from the temperature of land that is not close to any body of water? Explain the difference.
21. On a cold winter day, how will the temperature of land near an open lake or ocean differ from the temperature of land that is not close to a body of water? Explain the difference in temperature.
22. In many places the air seems to be motionless, but at the shore there is a gentle breeze. What is the cause of this movement of air?
23. Why are cities usually warmer than the surrounding countryside?
24. Describe the flow of air that occurs in a city when the wind is not blowing.
25. What effect does pollution have on air circulation in a city?
26. What physical conditions cause an inversion?

A Changing Climate—What Are the Consequences?

"...the next time you admire the spectacular sunsets created by nature's own volcanic smog, don't forget that this is her fiery reminder that we live and breathe in a thin veil of safety. Its ethereal future is now increasingly in our hands."
STEPHEN H. SCHNEIDER
National Center for Atmospheric Research

OBJECTIVES

- ✔ **Distinguish** between weather and climate.
- ✔ **Identify** greenhouse gases and **explain** how they cause the "greenhouse effect."
- ✔ **Identify** human activities that increase the levels of greenhouse gases.
- ✔ **Predict** possible effects of global warming on habitats, wildlife, and people.
- ✔ **List** actions that individuals can take that will decrease the buildup of greenhouse gases.

Turning the Thermostat Down

Climate refers to the average weather pattern of a location over a period of years including seasonal changes. The earth's climate has had many natural variations. Natural changes in the climate may be the result of interactions between the ocean and the atmosphere, changes in the Sun's energy output, or explosive volcanic eruptions.

During the Little Ice Age (1400-1850 AD), the annual average temperature of the Northern Hemisphere was no more than 2°F (0.6-1.1°C) cooler than it is today. But that was cold enough to freeze rivers in North America and Europe. Cooling the global average temperature by only a few degrees can have a devastating effect.

In 1815, an eruption of an Indonesian volcano, Mount Tambora, sent massive clouds of ash and sulfur dioxide into the air. The year 1816 is known as the "year without a summer." Summer temperatures dropped 1.8° to 4.5°F (1.0° to 2.5°C) below previous years. Killer frosts hit crops in Europe and North America. Snow fell in the New England states in July. The harvest was poor and the following winter was harsh. Scientists think that other factors, such as a change in the normal pattern of the jet stream, may have also contributed to the unusual snow and frost.

Most volcanic eruptions are not powerful enough to affect the upper atmosphere. When Mount Pinatubo, a dormant volcano in the Philippines, erupted in June 1991, the tremendous force of its eruption spewed an estimated 20 million tons (1.8×10^{10} kg) of sulfur dioxide into the stratosphere. Through photochemical reactions, the sulfur dioxide was changed to sulfuric acid or sulfate particles. The particles, also called **sulfate aerosols**, are so tiny that they remain suspended in the atmosphere for several years.

Volcanic aerosols scatter the sun's rays and produce spectacular sunsets. But beautiful sunsets were not the only effect of Mount Pinatubo's outburst. The layer of sulfate aerosols also cooled the Northern Hemisphere by 1°F (0.6°C). The global cooling occurred because the aerosols reflected solar energy back to space, and they also absorbed heat radiated from the earth. The climate change caused by Mount Pinatubo peaked in 1993, about two years after the eruption.

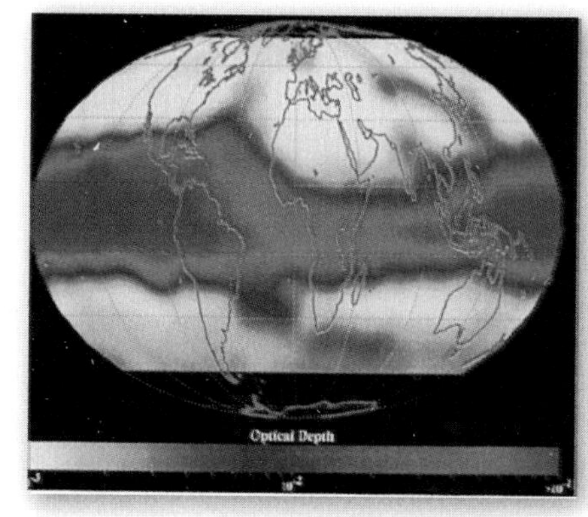

This view of the earth, one month after the eruption of Mt. Pinatubo, shows the global layer of sulfate aerosols that reflected sunlight, causing spectacular sunsets and global cooling.

A CLOSER LOOK A CLOSER LOOK A CLOSER LOOK A CLOSER LOOK A CLOSER LOOK A CLOSER LOOK A CLOSER LOOK A CLOSER LOOK A CLOSER LOOK A CLOSER LOOK A CLOSER LOOK A CLOSER LOOK A CLOSER LOOK A CLOSER LOOK

Do you think the eruption of Mount St. Helens affected the Earth's climate?

Satellite image of Mount Saint Helens.

How might these clouds affect global warming?

Global Warming

While sulfur dioxide reflects sunlight and has a cooling effect, the earth's atmosphere contains other gases called **greenhouse gases** that act as a blanket to trap heat and keep the planet warm. This warming of the earth caused by the greenhouse gases is the natural **greenhouse effect**. Without this blanket of gases, the earth would be 60°F (33°C) cooler than it is today. The ice-coated planet would be unable to support life, as we know it.

For the last 10,000 years, the earth's climate has been relatively stable and the natural "greenhouse effect" has created a comfortable place to live, but what about the future? The earth's climate is changing. Obviously, the earth is warmer now than it was during the Ice Ages. But studies indicate that by the end of the next century the earth will be significantly warmer than it is now. Many scientists think that by 2100 the average global surface temperature could have increased by 1.6–6.3°F (0.9–3.5°C).

The warmest years on record have all occurred since 1990. Over the last century, the average global temperature of the air at the earth's surface has warmed about 1°F (0.6°C). The earth's climate is getting warmer, and most studies conclude that the rate of increase is larger than would be expected if the change was a natural variation in climate. Human activities are contributing to this climate change. By altering the chemical composition of the atmosphere, we are enhancing the "greenhouse effect" and therefore contributing to **global warming**—an increase in the earth's average temperature.

The Greenhouse Gases

Water vapor is the most important atmospheric greenhouse gas. The processes in the water cycle control the amount of water vapor in the atmosphere. It is usually 1–2% of a volume of air. The heat-trapping ability of water vapor is apparent to us when we experience warm nights during a spell of hot, humid weather. The water vapor in the atmosphere traps heat, preventing the nighttime cooling that normally occurs when the air is drier.

While a mass of humid air may trap enough heat to make the weather uncomfortable, the amount of water vapor in the global atmosphere does not appear to be changing. Thus water vapor contributes to the natural greenhouse effect, but it is not responsible for **global warming**. In the future this may change. As the temperature increases, the amount of water vapor in the atmosphere is expected to increase because warm air can hold more water vapor. This increase in water vapor will further enhance the greenhouse effect.

Clouds are an important factor in climate change, but the effect they will have on the climate is unpredictable. If the amount of water vapor in the atmosphere does increase, it could form low sun-blocking stratocumulus clouds that could have a cooling effect. Another possibility is that the water vapor will form high, thin cirrus clouds that will trap heat and contribute to global warming.

Looking somewhat like growth rings in a tree trunk, annual dust layers in ice at the edge of the Quelccaya Ice Cap in Peru provide clues to the history of Earth's climate.

Scientists at the Byrd Polar Research Center drilled into ice caps in Peru and China to collect ice cores that are stored at -30°C.

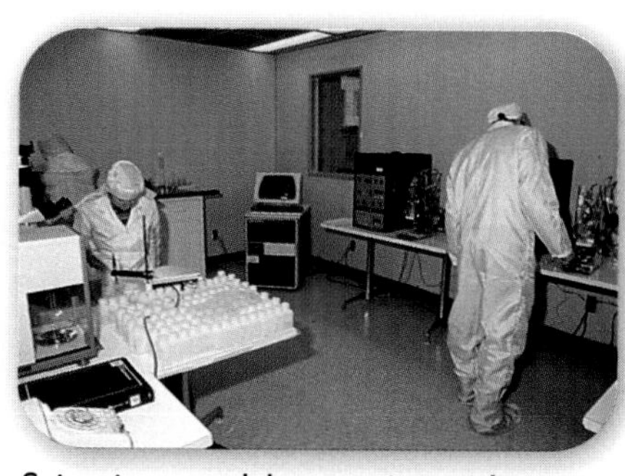
Scientists use laboratories with special clean room conditions to study the ice cores for evidence of climate change.

Of the greenhouse gases that are released to the atmosphere by human activities, **carbon dioxide** is by far the most important. Most carbon dioxide that enters the atmosphere is produced during respiration in plants and the decomposition of organic matter. The quantity of carbon dioxide released by respiration and decomposition is nearly balanced by the quantity of carbon dioxide absorbed by plants during photosynthesis and removed by physical processes such as diffusion in sea water.

POPULATION LINK

Analysis of carbon dioxide trapped in glacial ice indicates that the level of carbon dioxide in the atmosphere changed little during the ten thousand years prior to the industrial revolution. Since the beginning of the industrial revolution, human activities have released massive amounts of carbon dioxide into the air, mainly from the burning of fossil

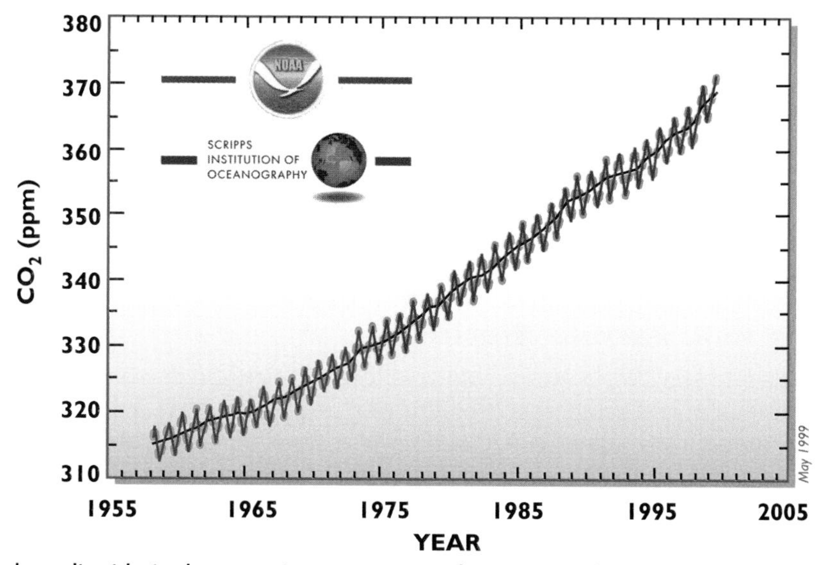

Carbon dioxide is the most important greenhouse gas released to the atmosphere by human activities.

Environmental Challenge: Predicting the Effects

During the past 15 years, biologists have observed a sharp decline and "bleaching" in coral ecosystems.

- Do you think the decline is due to global warming? Support your position.

It has been suggested that the Kirtland's warbler is the "canary in the coal mine" for climate change. [See Section 1.14, pages 74–75, for information on Kirtland's warbler.]

- Explain why the warbler may be an early warning alarm for global warming.

The soil of the Arctic tundra contains a community of microbes.

- How might global warming affect these organisms?
- Could these organisms be a cause of global warming?

What effect does combustion of fossil fuels at power plants and industries have on the earth's climate?

What greenhouse gas does the growing of rice contribute to the atmosphere?

Think About It

Should a nation with less than 5% of the world's population be allowed to continue releasing nearly 25% of the gases that contribute to global warming?

fuels (coal, oil and natural gas). Land-use changes, especially deforestation, also contributed to the increase in carbon dioxide in the atmosphere by reducing the carbon dioxide removed by plants. Together these activities are responsible for adding 7 to 8 billion metric tonnes of carbon to the atmosphere each year.

Analysis of glacial ice cores shows a strong positive correlation between air temperature and the atmospheric concentration of two gases—carbon dioxide and methane—over the past 160,000 years. Prior to the industrial revolution, the level of carbon dioxide in the atmosphere was about 280 ppm. Measurements indicate that the level of carbon dioxide is now in excess of 360 ppm. Without a reduction in fossil fuel combustion and deforestation, the level of carbon dioxide in the atmosphere is expected to be greater than 700 ppm by 2100.

Carbon dioxide is not the only greenhouse gas that is increasing. The level of **methane** (natural gas) in the atmosphere has doubled. Most methane is produced by the decomposition of organic material in wet, oxygen-deficient environments, such as marshes, swamps and rice paddies. Other sources include cattle and sheep ranching, leaking natural gas pipelines and decaying material in landfills.

Chlorofluorocarbons (CFCs) not only destroy the ozone layer, they are also important greenhouse gases. The production of CFCs is being eliminated, but they will continue to be an important factor in global warming. CFC molecules are so stable that they remain in the atmosphere for more than 100 years. Substitutes currently used for CFCs in air conditioning and refrigeration are also greenhouse gases. Their contribution to global warming is small, but it is expected to increase.

Nitrous oxide (N_2O) is a potent greenhouse gas. Although it is present in the atmosphere in very small quantities (300 parts per billion {ppb}), it is 220 times more effective in trapping heat than carbon dioxide. The nitrous oxide concentration has increased about 15% above natural levels. Bacteria in the nitrogen cycle release nitrous oxide into the air from nitrogen fertilizers. It is also a product of burning fossil fuels and vegetation. It is produced during the manufacture of nylon, and tiny amounts are released from dental offices and whipped cream cans.

In the stratosphere (upper atmosphere), **ozone** blocks the sun's harmful ultraviolet rays, but in the troposphere (lower atmosphere), ozone is a harmful pollutant. It is also an important greenhouse gas. As urban air pollution increases, so do ozone levels.

Living in a Warmer World

According to the World Resources Institute, "Greenhouse warming is the most serious and threatening problem of this century." We know that the level of greenhouse gases, especially carbon dioxide, in the atmosphere is increasing and, as the level increases, global temperatures will rise. Most scientists agree that the build-up of carbon dioxide and other greenhouse gases has the potential to produce dramatic changes in the climate. Some of the possible consequences of global warming are described as follows:

Sea Level:

Global warming will cause the expansion of seawater and the melting of polar ice and snow. The greatest increase in sea level is occurring along the U.S. coast. A one-foot (30 cm) rise is predicted along the Gulf and Atlantic coasts by 2050. If carbon dioxide levels double, the rise in sea level could exceed 40 inches (1 m). A one-meter increase in sea level would threaten the homes of more than 200 million people. It will also threaten the homes of aquatic organisms that depend upon coastal wetlands, which will be flooded or damaged by erosion caused by storm surges. Water supplies in coastal regions may be affected by the intrusion of salt water.

Water:

In the United States, both evaporation and precipitation are expected to increase, but in some areas the increase in evaporation will exceed the increase in precipitation. Precipitation is expected to be concentrated in large storms. This will reduce infiltration that is needed to replenish groundwater supplies, and the increase in runoff could cause more flooding. Both flooding and low water levels could affect navigation. Lower water levels in some areas could seriously affect the generation of hydroelectric power.

Habitats and Wildlife:

Climate zones could shift and some plants may not be able to adapt to the changes. Species that depend upon the plants will be affected. Hardwood forests are expected to expand northward or to higher elevations. If the climate warms by 3.6°F (2°C), tree species will have to move 200 miles (300 km) closer to the poles to survive. Unless birds spread the seeds, trees will not be able to migrate at a rate that is necessary to survive. Where soils are drier, forest fires may be more frequent and more severe. Preserves and National Parks may no longer provide the habitat for the wildlife that they normally protect. Roads and development may block migratory routes. Food supplies may not be available when needed by migratory animals.

How might global warming affect Chicago? Will a warmer climate have the same impact on coastal cities?

It's not a pretty flower, but it's food for more than 40 species of wildlife. How will these species be affected if the climate warms and the flowering dogwood cannot adapt to the change?

www

To find out more about the potential impacts of global warming in the state where you live, visit: www.epa.gov/globalwarming/impacts/stateimp/index.html.

Did You Know?

Concern about rising sea levels has led some states to restrict or even prohibit new homes in areas that are likely to erode in the next 30–60 years.

Environmental Challenge: Bangladesh and California

Bangladesh, a country about the size of Wisconsin, has a population greater than 112 million people. In contrast, Wisconsin's population is 4.9 million. The Ganges River flows through Bangladesh and into the Bay of Bengal. Approximately 10 million people—mostly fishermen and farmers—live along the coast.

- Contrast the impact of global warming on the people of Wisconsin and the people of Bangladesh.

California normally has wet winters and dry summers. Water supplies in many areas come from melting snow.

- Predict the impact that global warming will have on California's water supply, assuming that there is no change in the amount of precipitation.

In what ways may global warming affect this Chinese man?

Did You Know?

- For each 10,000 miles that an average new American car is driven, it will release approximately its own weight of carbon as carbon dioxide.
- Each hour that your color television is turned on, 0.64 pounds of carbon dioxide is being pumped into the atmosphere.
- For each gallon of gasoline that your car engine burns, 0.9 pounds of carbon dioxide is being pumped into the atmosphere.
- To meet the energy needs of the average American home, about 10 tons (9 metric tonnes) of carbon dioxide are produced each year.

Exhaust Emissions

Agriculture:

Carbon dioxide is often a limiting factor for plants. In laboratory experiments, a doubling of the carbon dioxide level increased yields of major crops—cotton, wheat, soybeans, and corn—but carbon dioxide is not the only variable. Plants must also adjust to changes in temperatures and moisture levels. Soil moisture is the most important factor during the growing season. Problems with diseases and insect pests are expected to increase.

An international study indicates that crop yields may increase in temperate zones, but the warming may decrease yields in tropical zones. A longer growing season is expected to significantly improve Canadian agriculture. The U.S. Department of Agriculture says that technology available in developed countries will allow agriculture to adapt to climate changes, but the demand for irrigation will probably increase in most areas. In many regions, less water will be available for irrigation.

Weather Predictions:

Scientists do not know what kind of surprises the weather will hold. Warmer temperatures may make the weather prediction more difficult. Storms are nature's way of balancing the energy in the atmosphere. Warmer sea surface temperatures will cause more frequent and more severe storms, particularly in coastal areas. Meteorologists are trying to improve the accuracy of long-term forecasts which may be essential to management of water supplies and advanced preparation for winter storms.

Humans:

Heat waves could become more common in some areas. The warmer temperatures will increase the concentration of ground-level ozone and cause problems for people with asthma and other lung diseases. The elderly are most susceptible to heat stress and would be most affected. Death rates from heat-related health problems will climb, especially in large cities and developing countries. Global warming may also increase the risk of some infectious diseases, especially those spread by insects.

What Can You Do?

To decrease the threat of global warming, we must reduce the production of greenhouse gases. This can be done though increased energy conservation and alternative energy sources. Planting more trees to "soak up" some of the excess carbon dioxide will not, by itself, eliminate global warming, but it will help. See the suggestions below:

Change that light bulb!

A 100-watt light bulb left on for 10 hours uses one kilowatt hour (kwh) of electricity. An average of 1.28 pounds (0.6 kg) of coal must be burned to produce each kwh of electricity. The carbon dioxide released during the combustion of the coal is 1.8 times the weight of the coal or 2.3 pounds (1.0 kg) for each kwh of electricity.

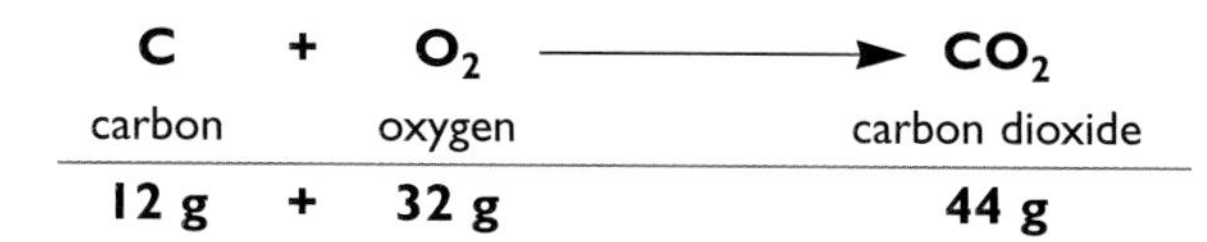

If each household in the United States replaced one 100-watt light bulb with a compact fluorescent bulb that requires only 13 watts, the amount of carbon dioxide released into the atmosphere would be reduced by nearly 27 million metric tonnes. This calculation assumes that the electricity is produced at a coal-burning power plant.

The burning of coal is the main source of carbon dioxide. Switching to oil or natural gas will produce less carbon dioxide than burning coal. Although there may be other significant environmental impacts, nuclear, hydroelectric, solar, and wind energy do not release any carbon dioxide.

Embrace Energy-efficiency:

Buy energy-efficient models of appliances. Use mass transit, car pool, and when you purchase a vehicle make sure that the model you select gets good gas mileage. Recycle. Recycling an aluminum can saves 95% of the energy required to make a new can. Conserving energy reduces greenhouse gases as well as air pollution.

Plant a Tree:

Obviously it will take more than one tree, but one tree will help. A tree is half carbon. Deforestation worldwide adds 1–2 billion metric tonnes of carbon to the atmosphere each year. Finding alternatives to the destruction of tropical forests will slow global warming. Each acre of tropical forest that is not cut will continue to remove carbon from the atmosphere each year.

Planting one million square miles of fast-growing trees in the tropics would remove 2.3 billion metric tonnes of carbon from the air annually. That is nearly half of the carbon that is released by the combustion of fossil fuels. The cost of planting two million km^2 of trees is about $100 billion. Is it worth it? According to the U.S. Environmental Protection Agency, the cost of saving just the U.S. East Coast from the projected sea-level rise caused by global warming could be as much as $111 billion.

International Cooperation

POPULATION LINK

In order to reduce the risks of global warming we must make some difficult choices. The increase in carbon dioxide and methane is directly related to the growth in the size of the human population and the use of technology that has increased the demand for energy from fossil fuels. Although the size of the contribution varies, each person on planet Earth contributes to the build-up of greenhouse gases. Controlling the growth of the human population will slow the build-up of greenhouse gases and slow global warming.

People in industrialized countries contribute far more to global warming than people in developing countries. In 1995 the developed world contributed 73% of the carbon dioxide released to the atmosphere

Think About It

How does population growth affect climate change? How might climate change affect population growth?

New technology can reduce the threat of global warming. Most electricity is produced by burning coal. More energy-efficient light bulbs reduce the production of carbon dioxide.

Using new fluorescent bulbs save energy as shown in this in-store demonstration.

This nuclear power plant near Berwick, PA, doesn't contribute any carbon dioxide to the atmosphere. Is nuclear power a good alternative energy source?

This is a satellite image of the moon setting.

with the United States producing the largest amount (22%). The average person in the United States generates 19 times more carbon dioxide than the average person in India. Changing to technologies that reduce the use of fossil fuels is essential.

Global warming is an international problem, and a solution will require an international commitment. The first step was taken at the Earth Summit in 1992. **The United Nations Framework Convention on Climate Change** (UNFCCC) is an international treaty signed by more than 150 nations. Countries signing the treaty pledged to (1) develop a greenhouse gas inventory, (2) develop programs to slow climate change, and (3) share technology and cooperate to reduce greenhouse gas emissions.

During the summer of 1997 a letter, encouraging the United States to take a leadership role in reducing greenhouse gas emissions, was signed by 2600 scientists and submitted to President Clinton. In December 1997 at a conference in Kyoto, Japan, delegates from countries that signed the UNFCCC treaty met to establish a set of rules for reducing the greenhouse gases. Known as the **Kyoto Protocol on Climate Change**, the rules include a set of binding emissions targets for all greenhouse gases: carbon dioxide, methane, nitrous oxide and synthetic substitutes for ozone-depleting CFCs.

The Kyoto Protocol set target emissions only for industrialized countries. The target for the United States is 7% below the 1990 emissions levels by 2008-2012. To become an international law, 55 countries that signed the UNFCCC must ratify the Protocol, and those countries must account for more than 55% of the greenhouse gas emissions. By 1999 none of the large industrialized countries had ratified the Protocol. Ratification by the U.S. requires approval by the Senate.

The United Nations Environmental Programme reminds us that "We must no longer think of human progress as a matter of imposing ourselves on the natural environment. The world—the climate and all living things—is a closed system; what we do has consequences that eventually will come back to affect us."

2.3 QUESTIONS FOR STUDY AND DISCUSSION:

1. Define the following terms: **VOCABULARY**

carbon dioxide	methane
CFCs	nitrous oxide
climate	ozone
greenhouse effect	sulfate aerosols
greenhouse gases	UNFCCC
global warming	water vapor
Kyoto Protocol on Climate Change	

Turning the Thermostat Down

2. Give an illustration that describes the difference between weather and climate.
3. Compare the annual average temperature of the earth today to the annual average temperature of the earth during the Little Ice Age.
4. What events caused the average surface temperature of the earth to fall in 1816 and 1991? Why was the temperature change temporary?

Global Warming

5. What is the characteristic shared by the "greenhouse gases"?
6. What is the "greenhouse effect"?
7. What is global warming? What evidence is

there that global warming is occurring on planet Earth?

The Greenhouse Gases

8. Identify six "greenhouse gases."
9. Explain how water vapor can sometimes cause warming of the atmosphere and at other times cause cooling.
10. What is the most important greenhouse gas that is being added to the atmosphere by human activity? How do scientists know that the level of this gas is increasing? What is the process that is producing this gas?
11. What human activities are responsible for the increase in methane?

Living in a Warmer World

12. What is the opinion of the World Resources Institute about the impact of global warming? Do most scientists agree with this position?
13. List possible ways in which global warming may affect: wetland species, forests, endangered species, migratory species, humans.

What Can You Do?

14. List actions you could take to help decrease the threat of global warming. For each action, explain how it will reduce the threat.

International Cooperation

15. What is the connection between human population growth and global warming?
16. How does the use of technology affect global warming?
17. Compare the United Nations Framework Convention on Climate Change and the Kyoto Protocol on Climate Change. Do you think that these agreements will prevent global warming?
18. What is the position of the United Nations Environmental Programme on global warming? Do you agree with this position?

Environmental Challenge: Climate Change—What to Do?

The United States is the single largest producer of greenhouse gases, contributing about 22% of the gases released into the atmosphere each year. Countries in Western Europe produce 17% while countries in Eastern Europe and countries of the former Soviet Union produce 27% of greenhouse gases and Asia produces only 4%. In 1995 the developed countries produced nearly three-fourths of the global emissions of greenhouse gases.

The rapid population growth, increasing consumption per person (lifestyle changes) and industrialization in developing countries are causing an increase in the emissions of greenhouse gases. By 2035, the developing countries will be producing 50% of global emissions of greenhouse gases. China will be the single largest emitter at 17%.

- What role should the United States play in addressing the issue of global warming? Justify your position.

Most experts on global warming feel that immediate action should be taken to curb global warming. At the Kyoto Conference, delegates from the United States fought for a 10-year delay before implementing any regulations that would reduce greenhouse gases.

- What is your position on this issue? Defend your position.

Delegates at a conference on global warming recommended a tax on fossil fuels.

- If a so-called Carbon Tax was a question on a ballot, would you vote "for" the tax or "against" the tax?
- If the tax passed, with or without your vote, how could the money be spent to further reduce the threat of global warming?

2.4 The Air Around Us

OBJECTIVES

- ✔ **Identify** the processes through which pollutants enter the atmosphere.
- ✔ **Describe** the conditions that must be present for complete combustion.
- ✔ **List** sources of natural and human-made pollutants and **identify** the processes that produce the pollution.

"Thank God, men cannot as yet fly, and lay waste the sky as well as the earth."
HENRY DAVID THOREAU
1817-1862

The air has never been pure. Sometimes it contains substances that are undesirable or harmful. These substances may be products of natural events such as volcanoes, forest fires or decaying matter. Often the undesirable substances are by-products of modern technology. No matter the source, when a substance is present in an amount that is undesirable or harmful, the substance is a **pollutant**.

Air pollution is not new. King Edward I tried to clear the sky over London in 1272 by banning the use of sea-coal. A man who sold and burned the outlawed coal was tortured and hanged. King Richard III heavily taxed the use of coal, but it did not help. London's skies remained dark and the soot blackened the buildings. The burning of coal continues to be a major source of air pollution.

These photographs show the air pollution problem in Beijing, China. Coal is the major source of energy for electricity and heat, and piles of coal like this one are found outside most buildings. What process produces most of China's air pollution?

Processes that Pollute

Pollutants generally enter the atmosphere by one of three processes:

Attrition:

From a Latin word that means "to rub," **attrition** refers to the wearing or grinding of a substance by friction. Attrition includes sanding, grinding and drilling. It also includes the breaking of a liquid into small droplets—as in spraying. Attrition creates very small particles, sometimes called **particulates**, or fine droplets called **aerosols**.

Vaporization:

Vaporization—the process in which a substance changes from a liquid state to a gaseous state. Vaporization allows us to detect odors. Volatile organic chemicals, such as perfumes and gasoline, vaporize at low temperatures. Other liquids vaporize only under high temperature or pressure.

Combustion:

Combustion—a chemical reaction in which substances combine with oxygen and release light and heat energy. This is the process we often refer to as "burning." One of the major sources of air pollution is the burning of fuels in internal combustion engines.

If combustion of hydrocarbons is complete, the only waste products produced are carbon dioxide and water. For this to happen, three conditions must exist:

- The fuel must be a pure hydrocarbon or an organic compound with only hydrogen, carbon and oxygen. A **hydrocarbon** is a chemical that contains only hydrogen and carbon. Gasoline, fuel oil and coal are all hydrocarbons. However, they often contain other elements in addition to hydrogen and carbon. It is these elements, or impurities, that become pollutants when the hydrocarbon is burned. Alcohol is a clean-burning fuel because it contains hydrogen, carbon and oxygen.

- The fuel must be mixed with the correct amount of oxygen. If there is too much or too little oxygen, the fuel will not completely burn. Unburned hydrocarbon molecules and carbon particles (soot) enter the air as pollutants.
- The fuel must be burned at the correct temperature. At hot temperatures, nitrogen and oxygen in the air combine forming nitrogen oxides. Nitrogen oxides are formed naturally when the energy in lightning heats up the atmosphere to extremely high temperatures. Nitrogen oxides are also formed in the internal combustion engine, furnaces, and in nearly all other situations when fossil fuels are burned.

If these three conditions are met, the only products of combustion are water and carbon dioxide. Except in special situations where conditions are very carefully controlled, one or more of these conditions won't exist, and combustion produces pollution.

Gases from Hawaii's Kilauea volcano can make life unpleasant and perhaps unhealthy for people downwind.

Nature Pollutes

There is no question that, at certain times and in certain places, nature emits devastating amounts of air pollutants. Volcanoes may be the number one source of natural air pollution. On June 15, 1991, Mount Pinatubo, a dormant volcano in the Philippines, erupted emitting enormous plumes of volcanic ash, sulfur dioxide and other chemicals. By the end of June there were 295 people dead and 39 missing. Early evacuation warnings had saved hundreds of thousands of lives.

Hawaii's Kilauea volcano has been active since 1986. There have been no gigantic explosions, just a continuous eruption with a steady flow of lava and gases, mainly carbon dioxide and sulfur dioxide. The volcano is a natural, uncontrollable source of pollution. It is one of the biggest polluters on the island, emitting 1,000 tons (900 metric tonnes) of sulfur dioxide gas each day. The volcanic smog, sometimes called **vog**, is at least unpleasant for the 40,000 people living in and around Kailua-Kona. Evidence from a study at Harvard School of Public Health suggests that sulfate concentrations in the vog could affect human health.

Satellite view of Hawaiian Islands.

Lake Nyos is a volcanic crater lake in the Republic of Cameroon in West Africa. Carbon dioxide from magma dissolves in ground water and is discharged through springs into the lake. It accumulates in the cold deep water at the bottom of the lake. On the night of August 21, 1986, some unknown event, possibly a rockslide, caused a sudden change in pressure within the lake. The lake "burped," releasing an enormous cloud (1 km^3) of carbon dioxide.

Carbon dioxide is twice as heavy as air. The dense blanket of carbon dioxide spread over the valley, killing at least 1,700 people, 3,000 cattle and uncounted numbers of wildlife. The only survivors in one village were women and infants in the hospital's second-floor maternity ward.

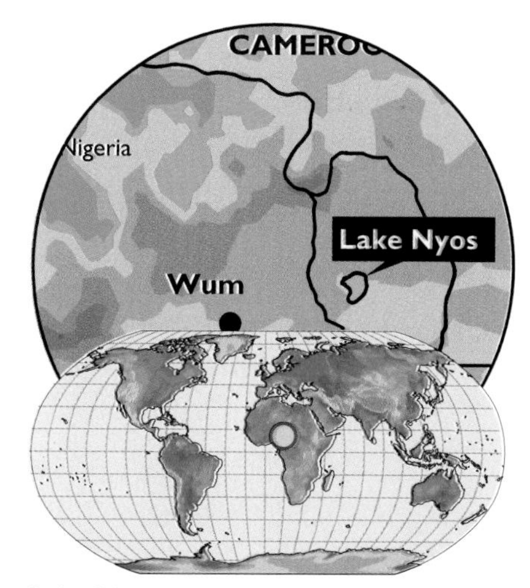

Lake Nyos, a volcanic crater, contains dangerous levels of carbon dioxide.

Herdsmen on hillsides near the lake also survived. (In both cases, the people were elevated above the CO_2.) Two years earlier, 37 people had died when carbon dioxide was released from Lake Monoun. In 1991, scientists warned that the carbon dioxide levels were again building up in the lakes. In 1997, an international committee was established to help coordinate and seek funds for "degassing" projects.

Urban Pollution

Bay Bridge and San Francisco.

Unlike the people who lived near Lake Nyos, most people are not exposed to unhealthy levels of carbon dioxide or other pollutants produced by nature. The major pollutants that affect most people are produced by the combustion of fossil fuels in automobiles, electrical power plants and industries. Although much progress has been made in improving the quality of the air we breathe, there is still work to be done. Consider the following examples:

Mexico City:

Mexico City has very high levels of air pollution. During prolonged episodes, elementary schools are closed to prevent potential damage to children's health. Nearly 26 million people living in the Metropolitan Area of Mexico City breathe a mixture of pollutants including carbon monoxide, sulfur dioxide, nitrogen dioxide, ozone, and small particles. In 1996, levels of at least one, and frequently more than one, of these pollutants exceeded air quality standards on 333 days or 91% of the year.

With more than 2,500,000 registered motor vehicles, the internal combustion engine is the main source of Mexico City's air pollution. Transportation produces 75% of emissions and 12% comes from natural sources, mainly dust from unpaved roads near the city. Mexico City's Comprehensive Program Against Atmospheric Pollution was only begun in 1990. Even though pollution levels have been reduced, approximately 4 million tons (3.6 million metric tonnes) of pollutants entered the air in 1998.

WWW

To view ozone maps, ozone forecasts, and realtime data for the state where you live, visit: www.epa.gov/airnow.

Beijing:

Beijing's air is among the most polluted in China. Each year Beijing burns 28 million tons (25 million metric tonnes) of coal. During the heating season (mid-November to mid-March), the sulfur dioxide levels rise to five times the World Health Organization's (WHO) maximum healthful level and suspended particles increase by 50%. The rapid increase to 1.12 million motor vehicles has increased air pollution. For the year 1996, the average values for the concentrations of suspended particles, sulfur dioxide, and nitrogen oxides all exceeded WHO and Chinese air quality standards.

Los Angeles:

In 1990, the population of Los Angeles was 14 million and there were more than 10 million registered motor vehicles. With almost no public transportation, the area has one of the greatest number of vehicles per person in the world. The increasing number of vehicles leads to traffic congestion and serious air pollution. Strict controls on industrial and vehicle emissions have reduced peak ozone levels from 680 to 300 ppb, between 1955 and 1992. Despite these gains, Los Angeles has the most

serious ozone problem in the USA. The area also fails to meet national standards for particulate matter and carbon monoxide.

The Clean Air Act

The 1970 **Clean Air Act (CAA)** promised that people living in the United States could breathe clean air, and in many places the **ambient air**—the outdoor air—is much cleaner now. The Environmental Protection Agency (EPA) set **National Ambient Air Quality Standards** (NAAQS) for pollutants that endanger public health and the environment. The NAAQS set the maximum amount of specific air pollutants allowed in the outdoor air.

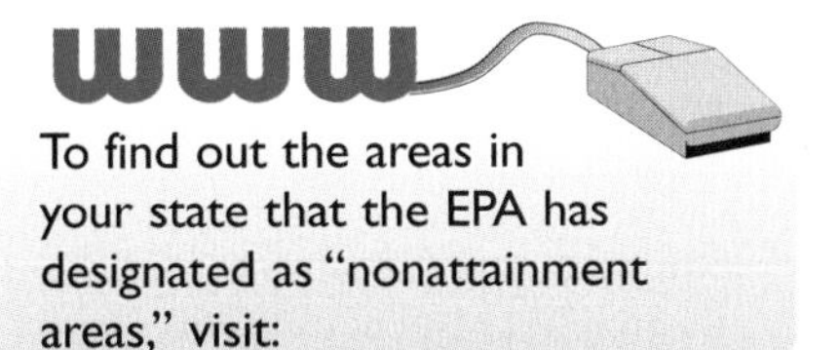

To find out the areas in your state that the EPA has designated as "nonattainment areas," visit: www.epa.gov/airs/nonattn.html.

Since 1970, national total emissions for six major air pollutants: carbon monoxide, lead, nitrogen dioxide, ground-level ozone (smog), particulate matter, and sulfur dioxide declined 31%. The improvement in air quality occurred even though there was a 31% increase in population, a prosperous economy, and a 127% increase in vehicle miles traveled. Although the air in many locations is cleaner, the levels of pollution in some areas are increasing. Ground-level ozone concentrations in some remote locations of the Great Smoky Mountains National Park in Tennessee have increased 20% in the last decade.

POPULATION LINK

The Clean Air Act was amended in 1990. One amendment defines **nonattainment areas** as locations where air pollution levels persistently exceed the National Ambient Air Quality Standards. In December 1998, there were 130 areas that did not meet the NAAQS for one or more pollutants and were designated by the EPA as "nonattainment areas." Approximately 107 million people lived in counties with unhealthy air in 1997. In spite of improvements, the air around many of us is still polluted.

2.4 QUESTIONS FOR STUDY AND DISCUSSION:

1. Define the following terms: **VOCABULARY**

aerosols	NAAQS
ambient air	nonattainment area
attrition	particulates
Clean Air Act	pollutant
combustion	vaporization
hydrocarbon	vog

2. When did air pollution begin?

Processes that Pollute

3. List the three processes that pollute the atmosphere.
4. Which process is responsible for most odors?
5. List the three conditions that must exist in order for the only products of combustion to be carbon dioxide and water.

Nature Pollutes

6. Identify two major air pollutants associated with volcanic eruptions.
7. What chemical caused the deaths of the people in the Lake Nyos valley? This chemical is not often thought of as a pollutant. Why was it so deadly?

Urban Pollution

8. Which process produces most human-made pollution?
9. What are the major sources of pollution in Beijing, Mexico City, and Los Angeles? What are the major pollutants in these urban areas?

The Clean Air Act

10. What evidence is there that the air is getting cleaner? What evidence is there that air pollution is still a problem?

2.5 Chemicals that Pollute the Air

OBJECTIVES

- ✔ **Explain** why birds are sometimes used as environmental monitors.
- ✔ **Identify** and **list** sources of the six major types of air pollutants regulated by the EPA.
- ✔ **Compare** the formation and effects of ozone in the upper atmosphere to its formation and effects in the lower atmosphere.
- ✔ **Describe** the trends in the concentrations of pollutants in ambient air.
- ✔ **Explain** the increased risk from indoor air pollution.

"When the canary dies, it's time to get out of the mine!"

Years ago, miners sent caged canaries down mine shafts to test the air. If the canary kept singing, the miners knew the air was good, and they could enter the mine. But a silent canary meant trouble. Roger Tory Peterson referred to birds as an environmental litmus paper—indicators of the health of the environment. Since birds are smaller and have a higher metabolism rate than humans, pollutants affect them more quickly.

The New York Times reported that employees placed a cage with two brightly colored parakeets near the entrance of a hotel lobby, soon after Iraq invaded Kuwait. Were the employees trying to keep the guests' minds off the war? No. They thought that if there was a gas attack, the death of the birds would be a warning to the people at the hotel.

Nerve gas and mustard gas are both deadly chemicals, and some people were fearful that Saddam Hussein might use these chemicals during the invasion of Kuwait. After a nerve-gas attack in Japan in 1995, police wearing protective clothing and gas masks carried canaries in cages as they searched the property of the group thought to be responsible for the attack. Police officers without protective gear watched the birds closely.

Chemicals used for chemical warfare are not widespread pollutants, but other toxic chemicals have spread around the globe. The connection between agents of chemical warfare and pesticides is not an accidental one. Some of the chemicals developed for warfare were found to be deadly to insects. One of the first uses of dichloro-diphenyl-trichloroethane, more commonly known as DDT, was to protect World War II soldiers against insects that carried disease. DDT was banned in 1972, but we continue to use other forms of pesticides today because they eliminate pests and diseases, and they control crop losses.

The application of pesticides results in an unavoidable pollution of the air, even under the best conditions. Pesticides also enter the air during the manufacturing process and as they vaporize from the treated surfaces. Once in the air, pesticides may travel for thousands of miles before being deposited with rain or snow. DDT has been found in Antarctic penguins even though no DDT was ever sprayed in Antarctica.

Since birds are smaller and have a higher metabolism rate than humans, pollutants affect them more quickly.

Volatile Organic Compounds

Organic compounds refer to chemicals that contain carbon. The EPA identifies organic compounds that readily vaporize and react in the atmosphere to form ozone as **volatile organic compounds (VOCs)**. Some VOCs come from natural sources. The "pine-fresh" scent of the forest and the odor of sweet-smelling flowers are both due to the vaporization of volatile organic compounds.

Volatile organic compounds are used by many industries and found in many consumer products. Refineries, chemical manufacturers, dry cleaners, furniture refinishers and auto body shops regularly release VOCs into the atmosphere. Also, large amounts of VOCs, produced by the action of bacteria on sewage, are released into the air at sewage treatment plants.

Some hydrocarbons are volatile organic compounds. Gasoline is a mixture of hydrocarbons. Its odor is mainly due to benzene (C_6H_6). Hydrocarbons enter the air from the evaporation of fuels from the tank and the escape of vapors during refueling. Polluting hydrocarbons also enter the air during the incomplete combustion of fuels in motor vehicles.

Perfumes, hair sprays, deodorants, glues, inks, paints, charcoal lighter fluid and other consumer products contain VOCs. In 1990, the 30 million people living in California released about 265 tons (238 metric tonnes) of VOCs into the air every day from a variety of consumer products. This was more than all the VOCs released from the gas stations and refineries.

California has set standards to limit the amount of VOCs in consumer products. The goal of California's clean air plan is an 85% reduction in VOCs emitted from consumer products by 2010. Businesses in California must also meet strict emissions standards. The EPA has issued a national VOC regulation for paints and coatings.

California Standards for Volatile Organic Compounds in Consumer Products

Products (1995 Standards)	Percent (by weight)
Aerosol carburetor choke cleaners, fabric protectants, household adhesives	75
Charcoal lighter materials, disinfectants	60
Aerosol automotive brake cleaners	50
Insecticides: foggers, crawling bugs, wasps and hornets	40
Aerosol dusting aids	35
Insecticides: flying bugs	30
Insecticides: flea and tick, lawn and garden, all others	20
Aerosol cooking sprays	18
Nonaerosol household adhesives	10
Nonaerosol dusting aids	7
Hand dishwashing detergents	2

Nitrogen Oxides

The largest sources of nitrogen oxides are high-temperature combustion processes, mainly the burning of fossil fuels (coal, oil, and natural gas) at electric power plants and by vehicles (trucks, buses and automobiles). Space heating is also an important source of nitrogen oxides. Lightning, volcanoes, forest fires and bacterial activity are natural sources of nitrogen oxides.

In the presence of sunlight and VOCs, nitrogen oxide (NO) reacts with oxygen to form **nitrogen dioxide** (NO_2). This brownish-red gas is responsible for the appearance of the smog that is a problem in Los Angeles and other major urban areas. This type of smog occurs only when there is enough sunlight and heat to provide energy for the chemical reactions. Because of this, it is known as **photochemical smog**.

Photochemical smog contains a mixture of up to 100 chemical compounds. One of the most important pollutants in smog is **ozone**. Ozone (O_3) is a form of oxygen molecules containing three atoms instead of the usual two. It is normally found in the atmosphere in very small amounts. Ground-level ozone and nitrogen dioxide are sometimes called **secondary pollutants** because they are usually produced by chemical reactions in the atmosphere.

Ozone in the upper atmosphere is beneficial, but in the lower atmosphere it is a pollutant. Ground-level ozone decreased 16% between 1988 and 1997. The National Ambient Air Quality Standard for ozone is an 8-hour average of 0.08 ppm. In 1998, the EPA designated 38 nonattainment areas for ozone. Included on the list were eight areas in California, four in Texas, three in Pennsylvania, and 10 areas located in the Northeastern region of the U.S.

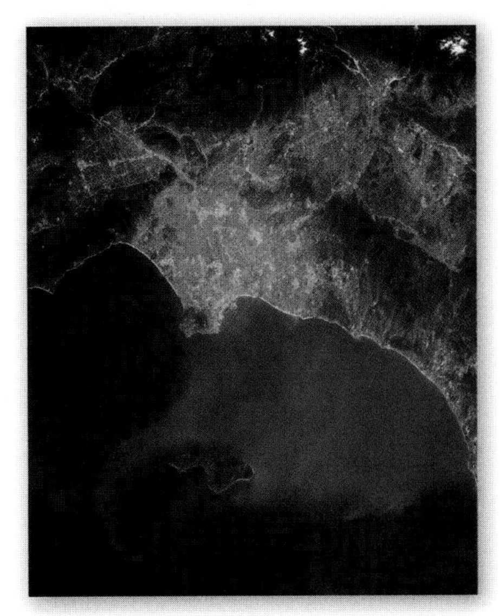

Satellite image of smog over Southern California.

Carbon Oxides

Products of the incomplete combustion of fuels include carbon monoxide (CO) and carbon dioxide (CO_2). Nationally, 60% of carbon monoxide comes from motor vehicle exhaust. Industries and the burning of solid waste produce most of the remainder. Small amounts come from forest fires, burning banks of coal waste, and fires in underground coal mines.

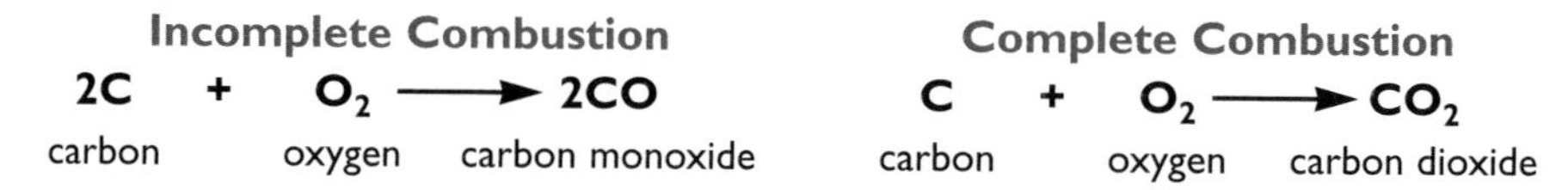

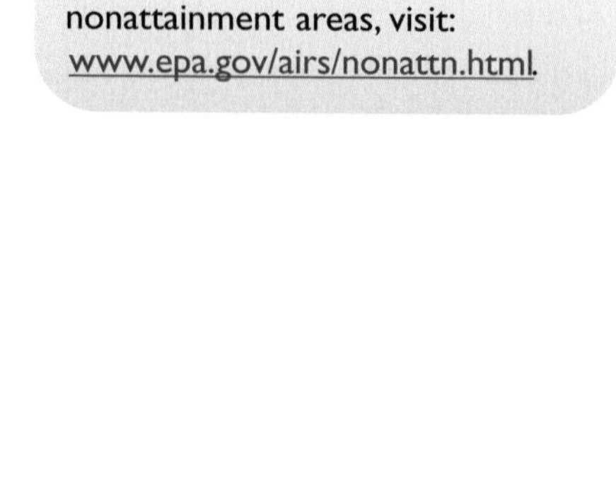

To find out the areas that the EPA has designated as nonattainment areas, visit: www.epa.gov/airs/nonattn.html.

Nationally, the maximum 8-hour average for carbon monoxide concentration in ambient air decreased by 38% between 1988 and 1997 despite a 25% increase in vehicle miles traveled. The highest levels of carbon monoxide occur during the winter months in areas with heavy traffic and frequent temperature inversions. In 1998, the EPA designated twenty nonattainment areas for carbon monoxide.

Carbon dioxide is not usually considered an air pollutant, but it can be deadly in high concentrations. The United States produces 22% of the carbon dioxide emissions created by human activities. Scientists are studying the effects of carbon dioxide on the earth's climate.

POPULATION LINK

Particulate Matter

Particulate matter (PM) is the term used for a mixture of solid particles and liquid droplets that are small enough to remain in the air for long periods of time. Natural sources of particulate matter include sea salt, pollen, volcanic ash and wind-blown dust. Dust also enters the air from mining, quarrying, farming operations, construction projects and traffic on unpaved roads.

The incomplete burning of fuels in motor vehicles, industries, electric power plants, fire places and wood stoves releases small carbon particles known as **soot**. Burning coal and wood also releases small pieces of minerals called **fly ash**. Fly ash may contain toxic chemicals such as lead and cadmium. Other pollutants in the atmosphere may become attached to the surface of the soot and the fly ash. Both solid particles and **aerosols**, small droplets of liquid, are released into the air by industrial processes, agricultural practices, and in diesel exhaust.

The grilling of meat produces organic aerosol emissions. In the Los Angeles area, smoke from grilling meat is a significant source of fine organic carbon particles.

In 1997, the EPA had set national air quality standards for particulate matter based on the size of the particles. One standard set limits on coarse particulates that are less than 10 micrometers in diameter (PM-10). Another standard set limits on fine particulates that are less than 2.5 micrometers in diameter (PM-2.5). For comparison, the diameter of a human hair is about 75 micrometers.

Soot and fly ash are fine particulates. Coarse particulates include particles produced by attrition as well as wind-blown dust and dust from vehicles traveling on unpaved roads. Between 1988 and 1997, the average PM-10 concentrations in ambient air decreased 26%. In 1998, the EPA designated 78 nonattainment areas for PM-10.

Sulfur Dioxides

Sulfur (S) is found in coal and fuel oil. When fuels containing sulfur are burned, the sulfur joins with oxygen from the atmosphere. More than 70%

of sulfur dioxide (SO_2) is produced at coal-burning electric power plants. Sulfur dioxide is also produced during metal smelting and other industrial processes.

Sulfur dioxide is a colorless gas that has a strong and irritating odor. It combines with oxygen to form sulfur trioxide (SO_3). This gas combines with water (H_2O) to form **sulfuric acid** (H_2SO_4). Small droplets of sulfuric acid create a haze that scatters the sunlight and reduces visibility. Between 1988 and 1997, national sulfur dioxide concentrations in ambient air decreased 39%. In 1998, the EPA designated 33 nonattainment areas for sulfur dioxide.

Sulfuric Acid Production in the Atmosphere

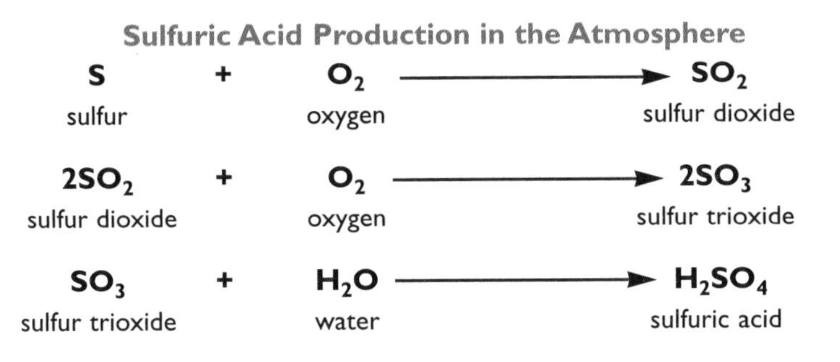

Did You Know?

Although plants absorb air pollutants, the EPA says that there is no evidence that a "reasonable number" of houseplants will remove significant quantities of pollutants from indoor environments. Over-watering indoor houseplants may promote the growth of microorganisms, and that can cause allergic reactions in people who have allergies to molds and mildew.

Lead

In the past most lead entered the atmosphere from motor vehicle exhaust. Now the EPA limits the amount of lead in unleaded gasoline to 0.05 g/gallon (0.01 g/L). Between 1988 and 1997, the concentration of lead in ambient air decreased 67%. Today the highest concentrations of lead are found near metal smelters and battery manufacturers. In 1988, the EPA designated 10 nonattainment areas for lead. Three of these areas are located in Missouri, where the largest lead-producing company in the world is located.

Indoor Air Quality

Most Americans spend 90% of their time indoors. Shutting the windows will shut out some air pollutants, but it may increase the level of others. Indoor levels of many pollutants may be 25 to 100 times higher than outdoor levels. Energy conservation measures have sealed in air pollutants creating **sick building syndrome**. The EPA and its Science Advisory Board rank indoor air pollution among the top five environmental risks to public health.

Long-term and short-term health effects may be caused by high concentrations of indoor air pollutants. Burning eyes, difficult breathing, rashes, dizziness, headaches, nausea, and drowsiness may be symptoms of poor air quality, especially if they occur after a change in the surroundings. Being aware of potential sources of pollutants is an important first step in identifying problems.

Toxic indoor air pollutants are released by construction materials, home furnishings, heating and cooking appliances, tobacco smoke, hobby and craft materials, personal and home care products, and the people and animals that live in the home. Formaldehyde is a colorless, flammable gas

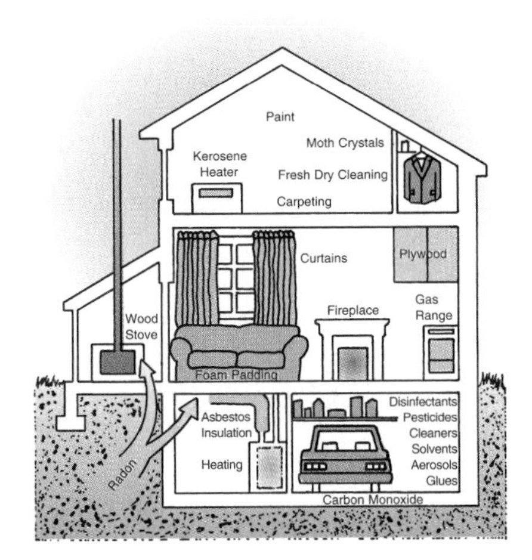

Can you identify any sources of air pollution in the home?

For sources of information on Indoor Air Quality, visit: www.epa.gov/iaq/homes.html.

with a strong odor. Adhesives containing formaldehyde are used in many pressed wood products, such as particleboard and paneling. Formaldehyde is also found in carpeting, upholstery, and draperies.

Gas appliances, unvented kerosene heaters and poorly vented furnaces or stoves are sources of nitrogen oxides and carbon monoxide. Coal or wood stoves and cigarette smoke are major sources of VOCs and particulates. Radon gas, pesticides and tiny airborne fibers of asbestos are air pollutants in some buildings. In the following sections we will investigate the major types of air pollutants and their effects.

2.5 QUESTIONS FOR STUDY AND DISCUSSION:

1. Define the following terms: **VOCABULARY**

aerosol	secondary pollutant
fly ash	sick building syndrome
nitrogen oxide	soot
organic compounds	sulfuric acid
ozone	volatile organic compounds
particulate matter	
photochemical smog	

2. Why did the miners send canaries down the mine shafts?
3. What is the connection between World War II and the war on insects?
4. What is the significance of finding DDT in Antarctic penguins?

Volatile Organic Compounds

5. What are the characteristics of volatile organic compounds?
6. List two natural sources and two human activities that release VOCs into the atmosphere.
7. List three types of consumer products that contain VOCs.

Nitrogen Oxides

8. Identify the human activities that contribute most of the nitrogen oxides to the atmosphere.

9. What physical conditions must exist for the formation of photochemical smog? What chemicals must be present?
10. Identify two secondary pollutants that are in photochemical smog. Why are they called secondary pollutants?

Carbon Oxides

11. Identify the major source of carbon monoxide. What conditions create high levels of carbon monoxide?
12. When is carbon dioxide considered a pollutant?

Particulate Matter

13. Give examples of particulate matter from both natural sources and human activities.

14. Give examples of PM-10 and PM-2.5, and explain the difference between the two types of particulate matter.

Sulfur Dioxides

15. What is the major source of sulfur dioxide?
16. What secondary pollutant results from the release of sulfur dioxide into the atmosphere?
17. Explain how the production of sulfur dioxide, a colorless gas, can reduce visibility.

Lead

18. What was the major source of lead in the atmosphere during the 1970s? What is it today?

Indoor Air Quality

19. What is the “sick building syndrome”? And why are more people suffering from this syndrome?
20. List several sources of chemicals that might be causing poor air quality in your home or school.

The Effects of Air Pollution

2.6

The Disasters

On December 4, 1952, a large mass of cold air began to spread across Britain. Late in the evening and early the next morning, fog began to form. At first it was just another London fog. But when the city awoke, tons of smoke from millions of coal stoves poured into the cold foggy air. Coal-burning power plants added more smoke as people began to use more electricity.

As people went to work, the cars and buses added more pollutants to the cold, morning fog. Smoke poured from the smokestacks of the coal-burning furnaces at the factories and industries. The stagnant air was filled with a mixture of smoke and fog that later became known as **smog**.

It was difficult to see across the street. For several days, it was necessary to use the car's headlights to drive. Even streetlights were needed. Within twelve hours, the first people began to die. By the time the winds came and carried the smog out to sea, many people were ill. The death rate climbed to 4,000 during the next few weeks.

A similar weather pattern occurred again in 1956, and there were 1000 deaths. The British Parliament passed the Clean Air Act and began a program to reduce the pollution from the burning of coal. Stagnant air masses were blamed for 700 deaths again in 1962 and 1963.

The first disaster caused by air pollution was not in London. In December of 1930, the Meuse Valley in Belgium was trapped beneath a blanket of smog. The valley was filled with heavy industry, and the major fuel used by the industries was coal. Pollutants from the burning coal poured into the cold, December fog. During this temperature inversion, more than 1,000 people became ill, and 60 people died.

Donora, a small town on the Monongahela River in Pennsylvania, lies in a valley about 30 miles (48 km) south of Pittsburgh. The town had a steel mill, a plant that made sulfuric acid, and a zinc-reducing plant. The major source of energy for these industries was coal.

In October 1948, after three days of smog-filled air, many people complained of throat irritation, hoarseness, coughs, shortness of breath, and nausea. Six thousand of the 14,000 people living in Donora became ill. Seventeen people died. The death rate was normally two per day.

Stagnant atmospheric conditions caused several hundred additional deaths in New York City in 1953 and again in 1963. Both inversions occurred on weekends. Had they occurred when the traffic was heavy and industries were operating, the death toll would have been higher. In each of these disasters, the people most affected were the young, the elderly, and those who already had heart and lung problems.

Although the air pollution disasters are alarming, most of us are exposed to much lower levels of air pollution every day. We need to know how this pollution affects us. In 1955, the Federal government began research to determine the effects of air pollution. It was not until 1971 that National Ambient Air Quality Standards were established.

OBJECTIVES

- ✔ **Identify** the major source of air pollution and the weather condition responsible for major air pollution disasters.
- ✔ **Compare** studies of the effects of air pollutants on laboratory animals with studies of human populations.
- ✔ **Cite** evidence from human population studies that shows the effects of air pollutants on human health.

- ✔ **Identify** diseases associated with air pollution and describe changes in the respiratory system caused by pollutants.
- ✔ **Explain** why air pollutants cause more damage when other pollutants are present.
- ✔ **Summarize** the concerns about air pollution shared by farmers and the managers of national parks.

Nelson's column, London: before and after cleaning.

Did You Know?

Pollution can be a force for evolution. A particular moth spends much of its time resting on the bark of a certain tree. The moth's coloration was light brown and mottled to camouflage it against the tree's light brown bark. As industries moved into the area, the bark of the tree became encrusted with soot and other industrial emissions. Its bark became dark brown. So the light brown moths resting on the pollution-covered bark were easily spotted by predatory birds and quickly eaten. The moths whose genes gave them a darker coloration were more likely to survive. Over time, light brown moths disappeared, along with their genes, and moths whose genes gave them darker brown coloration survived. Today, all moths of this species are dark, sooty brown. They blend in perfectly with the sooty bark they rest on.

Peppered Moths.

In the Laboratory

In science, a cause-and-effect relationship is usually proven in carefully controlled laboratory experiments. In a **controlled experiment** there is only one difference between two groups of subjects, a control group and an experimental group. The one difference between the two groups is the **variable**.

Mice exposed to nitrogen oxide in concentrations recorded in Los Angeles showed an increased death rate from pneumonia when compared to mice in control groups. Lung infections developed in caged animals that were accidentally exposed to diluted auto exhaust. In the laboratory next door, where there were no fumes, no infections were noted.

The Human Population—What the Studies Show

It is difficult to study the effects of air pollution in the human population because of the number of variables that exist. Yet a number of scientific studies have shown a relationship between long-term exposure to polluted air and diseases of the respiratory system.

- Nashville, Tennessee: A 12-year study showed that more deaths from respiratory disease occurred among people living in the sections of the city where there was the greatest amount of air pollution.
- Seward, PA—New Florence, PA: A study compared Seward to New Florence, both towns with a population of about 1,000. The amount of air pollution was much higher in Seward. Respiratory tests were given to people over 30. Results showed people living in Seward were more often below the normal range for respiratory function.
- Long Beach—Glendora—Lancaster: An 11-year study compared nonsmoking, non-Hispanic residents of three towns in California. Long Beach is a heavily industrialized area. Glendora has some of the highest smog levels in the nation. Lancaster is a desert town with relatively clean air. Tests showed that long-term exposure to industrial air pollution and smog seriously damaged lung tissue. The small airways in the lungs were the most affected.
- Seven U.S. Cities: A study of Medicare data for a period of four years showed that hospital admissions for heart failure increased on days when carbon monoxide levels increased. The effect of carbon monoxide was independent of the levels of other major gaseous pollutants.
- Six-Cities Study: When the Arab Oil Embargo forced electric power plants to switch to coal which is higher in sulfur, the Harvard School of Public Health began a study of respiratory health effects on 8,000 people. It showed children living in communities with higher particulate levels had increased cough, bronchitis, and chest illness, and lower lung function. A follow-up showed that the decreased lung function persisted into adulthood. A follow-up of adults showed that those living in the most polluted cities had a 26% higher mortality (death) rate than those living in the least polluted cities.

- Five-Cities Study: An on-going study is assessing the respiratory health effects of air pollution on inner city minority and/or economically disadvantaged children. Preliminary results indicate that children living in the inner city have an increased sensitivity — a greater response to the same exposure — than children living in the suburbs. Black children are more sensitive than white children; girls are more sensitive than boys; and children with hayfever are more sensitive than children without allergies.

Playground.

What the Surgeon General Says

About 10 million people in the United States have died from smoking-related causes since the first Surgeon General's report on smoking and health in 1964. At least 400,000 deaths are attributed to cigarette smoking each year. Approximately one of every two lifelong smokers will eventually die from causes related to smoking.

Some pollutants cause more damage if they are present with other pollutants than if they are alone. This is called a **synergistic effect**. When present together, cigarette smoke and air pollution have a synergistic effect. The difference in cancer rates between city and rural non-smokers is small. Nevertheless city smokers have a much greater cancer rate than rural smokers. It appears that when city pollution is added to cigarette smoke, the effect of one plus one is greater than two $(1 + 1 > 2)$.

- New York: A study of 1,216 inner-city adults found heavy smokers had a 72% increased risk of an emergency room visit for asthma on the highest ozone day compared with a very low ozone day.
- St. Louis—Winnipeg: Autopsies were performed on the lungs of 300 people from heavily polluted St. Louis, and 300 people from much less polluted Winnipeg, Canada. The group was divided into cigarette smokers and nonsmokers. There was four times as much severe emphysema found in smokers from St. Louis as in smokers from Winnipeg. None of the nonsmokers had severe **emphysema**, but nonsmokers from St. Louis had three times as much mild to moderate emphysema as the nonsmokers from Winnipeg.

Diseases Associated with Air Pollution

The air in many large cities is unhealthy. Less than 1% of the cities in China have clean air, and respiratory disease is the leading cause of death. Each year in the United States, an estimated 50,000 to 120,000 premature deaths are associated with exposure to air pollution. Certain pollutants cause changes in the respiratory system. These changes may result in one of the following diseases:

- **Chronic bronchitis** results when the cilia—short, hair-like projections—in the bronchial tubes are damaged. They normally sweep the mucus, which has trapped small particles and germs, out of the bronchial tubes. The cells lining the bronchial tubes produce more and sometimes

The sleeve around the refueling nozzle recovers gasoline vapors that escape during refueling. This vapor recovery technology is used in areas having high levels of air pollution such as southern California.

thicker mucus. The mucus interferes with the exchange of air, causing a shortness of breath. A chronic cough develops because of the extra mucus.

- **Bronchial asthma** is the result of an allergic reaction of the membranes lining the bronchial tubes. The membranes swell and make the air passages narrow. Extra mucus may also be produced. The smooth muscles in the walls of the bronchial tubes sometimes go into spasms. The spasms close the tubes, causing an asthma attack.
- **Emphysema** results after years of irritation. The air sacs in the lungs lose their elasticity. They are like an old balloon or worn out rubber band. They no longer have the ability to push the air out of the lungs. The air remains in the air sacs. Oxygen and carbon dioxide cannot diffuse across the damaged membranes as easily as they did across healthy ones.
- **Pneumonia** and other infections occur more often when pollutants kill the bacteria-destroying cells, which normally line the respiratory tract. More mucus is produced in response to the pollutants. The excess mucus limits the exchange of air and prevents the cilia from sweeping bacteria and other particles out of the lungs.
- **Lung cancer** results when cell division goes haywire. Cells that wear out are normally replaced by division of the cells below. Inhaled smoke and pollutants cause normal cells to develop into cancerous cells. The cells grow and divide at an unusually fast rate. They may fill the air sacs and bronchial tubes. Air cannot easily diffuse across the cancer cells as it does the normal lung tissue. Some of these cancer cells may break away and move to other sites in the lung or body — a process called **metastasis**.

Did You Know?

Gasoline pumps nozzles have those little rubber collars to minimize escaping fumes. Gasoline contains benzene. Benzene is regulated as a hazardous substance because it causes leukemia. Benzene is also a component of cigarette, cigar and pipe smoke. Smokers inhale it directly and their families inhale it as ETS or secondhand smoke.

Pollutants—How They Affect Humans

Carcinogens:

Carcinogens are substances that cause cancer. Some pollutants, including asbestos, arsenic, benzene, vinyl chloride and radioactive substances are known to be human carcinogens. Environmental tobacco smoke (ETS), also known as **secondhand smoke**, is a mixture of 4,000 substances. More than 40 are known to cause cancer in humans and animals. The EPA classifies ETS as a human carcinogen. ETS is responsible for about 3,000 lung cancer deaths each year in nonsmoking adults.

Respiratory Irritants:

Respiratory irritants irritate the lining of the respiratory system. They include sulfur dioxide, nitrogen dioxide, chlorine, ammonia, formaldehyde, ozone and other chemicals in **photochemical smog** and environmental tobacco smoke.

Short-term exposures of a few hours to levels of ozone existing in Southern California can cause a reduction in breathing capacity, increased susceptibility to infections, and inflammation of lung tissue. There is a correlation between elevated levels of ozone and hospital admission rates. Mortality rates also increase as ozone levels increase.

Animal studies indicate that exposure to ozone in combination with other pollutants is more toxic than exposure to ozone alone.

Sulfur dioxide gas is only mildly irritating. When it combines with oxygen and water in the atmosphere or the respiratory system, it forms sulfuric acid. Sulfuric acid is three or four times more irritating than sulfur dioxide. Even low levels of exposure for a few minutes can cause breathing difficulties for people with asthma.

The EPA has concluded that environmental tobacco smoke (secondhand smoke or ETS) is responsible for 150,000–300,000 cases of bronchitis and pneumonia and other lower respiratory infections in children up to 18 months of age. Cigarette smoke also increases the frequency and severity of symptoms in children with asthma.

Particulates:

Some air pollutants have a greater effect when there are tiny particles suspended in the air. The respiratory system has defenses against large particles. They are trapped by the mucus and swept out of the respiratory tract by the cilia. However, very tiny particles escape these defenses and are carried deep into the lungs. Some of these particles carry other pollutants into the lungs.

It is the fine particles PM-2.5 that are the most dangerous to your health. Studies showed that one in four Americans is believed to be at risk from fine particles. When levels of **particulates** are elevated, there are increases in the number of respiratory infections, number and severity of asthma attacks, and the number of hospital admissions. An American Cancer Society study of 500,000 people in 151 cities showed a 17% increase in mortality risk in areas with higher concentrations of fine particles.

Carbon Monoxide:

Carbon monoxide is absorbed by the blood. It combines with **hemoglobin** in the red blood cells more quickly than oxygen. Unlike oxygen, it is not given up to the body cells. This reduces the ability of hemoglobin to transport oxygen. Moderate concentrations cause fatigue, dizziness, and impaired judgment and impaired fetal development. People with heart disease are the most affected by increases in carbon monoxide. High concentrations from a leaky car exhaust or a malfunctioning furnace are often fatal.

Lead:

Lead is a heavy metal that interferes with the normal activity of the nervous system and the kidneys. Lead compounds may enter your body with the food you eat, the water you drink or through your skin, but the most dangerous route is through the air you breathe. Cigarette smoke is a source of lead, so people who smoke and people who breathe secondhand smoke are exposed to higher levels of lead. Almost all of the lead in the lungs enters the blood.

As many as 1.7 million children under the age of five have elevated levels of lead in their blood. The amount of lead in the blood is measured

Did You Know?

The athletic performance of young healthy men and women is reduced when breathing air with 0.12-0.13 ppm ozone. The NAAQS for ozone is 0.12 ppm (one-hour average) and 0.08 ppm (8-hour average). Repeated exposures to ozone can damage the lung tissue something like repeated sunburns damage the skin.

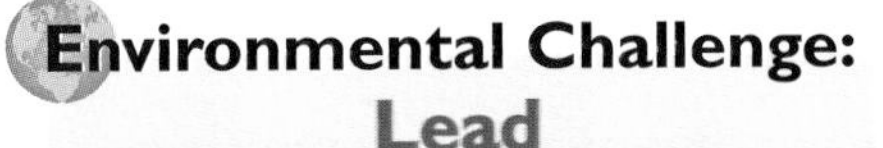

Environmental Challenge: Lead

Create a brochure to educate parents about lead poisoning and how they can protect their children. Visit these Websites for more information: www.epa.gov and www.cdc.gov.

www

Environmental Challenge: Daffodils

"Daffodil Days" is just one of the ways that the American Cancer Society raises money to support its programs. Daffodils in the tight bud stage can be stored for several days. A warning is sometimes included with a bunch of daffodils. It says: "It is important that flowers should not be stored with any fresh fruits and vegetables." Fruits and vegetables emit ethylene as they ripen.

Try this: place a container of cut flowers in a bag with several pieces of fruit and observe the changes in the flowers for several days. Be sure to create a "control" bag without any fruit.

- What differences do you see between the flowers in the control bag and those in the experimental bag?
- If your bunch of flowers had several different kinds, were they all equally affected?

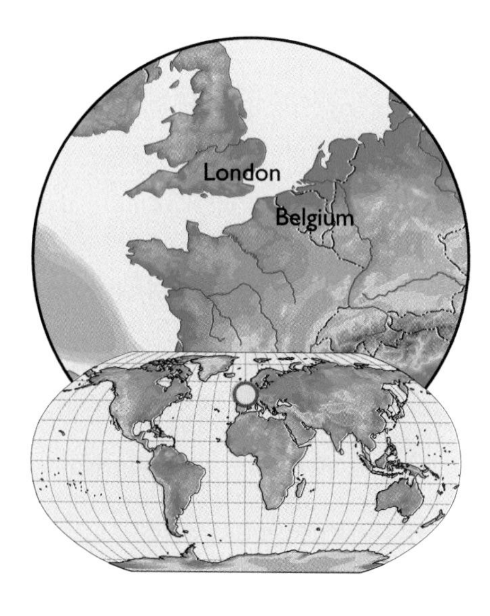

in micrograms per deciliter (μg/dL). The Center for Disease Control (CDC) recommends that testing for lead be a part of health care for children under 72 months of age. The CDC has set 10 μg/dL blood-lead level as a level of concern for children. This is based on the following information:

Harmful Health Effects of Lead in the Blood

Children	Adults	Effects
>125 μg/dL		Death*
80 μg/dL	100 μg/dL	Brain and kidney damage*
60 μg/dL	60 μg/dL	Gastrointestinal symptoms*
40 to 70 μg/dL	50 to 80 μg/dL	Anemia
	40 to 60 μg/dL	Neurological symptoms
	40 μg/dL	Increased blood pressure (men)
	30 to 40 μg/dL	Slow nerve conduction
10 to 50 μg/dL		Decreased IQ scores
10 to 30 μg/dL		Loss of hearing and decreased growth
10 to 15 μg/dL		Premature birth, reduced birth weight

**short-term exposure—less than or equal to 14 days; all others are greater than 14 days.*

Why are children more affected by air pollution than adults?

- Children spend more time outdoors and interact more with the environment.
- They breathe up to three times as much air per pound of body weight as adults.
- They have fewer detoxifying enzymes in their bodies.
- Their bodies are still developing and their cells are dividing rapidly.

Effects on Animals

During the 1952 London disaster [see page 127], a cattle show was in progress. There were 350 cattle being exhibited. Five of them died, 52 became seriously ill, and 9 had to be destroyed. The sheep and swine showed no effects. The horses in London showed no effects. Cases of bronchitis and pneumonia increased among some animals at the zoo. This shows that different species of animals react in different ways to pollution.

Air pollution disasters that harmed animals were usually downwind from an industry. Plants become coated with air pollutants, or the roots absorbed the pollutants which then accumulated in the plants. As the animals fed on the plants, the animals became sick.

1902 Arsenic from a copper smelter at Anaconda, Montana, caused the death of sheep and horses.

1954 Molybdenum from a steel plant in Sweden poisoned cattle.

1955 Lead and zinc from foundries in Germany caused cattle and horses to become so lame that they had to be slaughtered.

1967 Fluoride from a phosphate fertilizer plant in Montana caused fluorosis in cattle and sheep. At first their teeth became discolored. Then they began to lose weight, they gave less milk, and their rate of growth was slower. Eventually their bones became deformed and they had to be slaughtered.

1985 Cadmium, lead and zinc from the New Jersey Zinc Co. at Palmerton, Pennsylvania, accumulated in the soil. Where grass is able to grow, it contains enough zinc to cause lameness in horses. Cattle and horses that graze in the area have high concentrations of lead and cadmium, which can cause illness and fatigue.

Effects on Plants

During the early 1900s the path of sulfur dioxide fumes from copper smelters could be traced by observing the death of plants. Sulfur dioxide enters the pores in the leaf along with the carbon dioxide. As the cells die, damage can be seen as dried, whitened, or discolored areas on the leaf. Sulfur dioxide interferes with growth and decreases the yield of some plants, even when no damage is visible. Not all plants are injured by low concentrations of sulfur dioxide (0.3 ppm). Plants with thin leaves are more sensitive. Plants with fleshy leaves or needles are more resistant.

When there is dew or a light mist, the damage from sulfur dioxide is greater than the damage from sulfur dioxide alone. In the presence of sulfur dioxide, ozone becomes more toxic. This is another example of the **synergistic effect**.

Ozone damages 30 species of plants. The natural level of ozone is 0.025 ppm. Corn, soybeans and winter wheat begin to show damage if the ozone level is 0.05 ppm for three weeks during the growing season. A concentration of 0.25 ppm for 8 months produced broken leaves in orange trees, and 0.5 ppm caused **chlorosis**, the loss of chlorophyll in the leaves.

A seven-year study by the Environmental Protection Agency and the U.S. Department of Agriculture found that ozone is the most damaging of the air pollutants. Ozone is responsible for up to 90% of the reduced crop yield that is caused by air pollution. By weakening sensitive plants, ozone makes the plants more susceptible to diseases, pests, and other environmental stresses. The EPA estimates that the reduced yield of major agricultural crops and commercial forests costs more than $500 million each year.

Another gas that damages plants is **ethylene**, a pollutant in car exhaust. Ethylene leaking from "gas" lamps along city streets caused leaves to drop from trees. It also interferes with the opening of some flower buds in some plants. Other flowers wither or drop off when a few ppb of ethylene are present. Higher concentrations retard the growth of tomatoes.

Property Damage

Air pollution affects both living and nonliving things. Metals corrode faster in industrialized areas. The degree of corrosion is proportional to the amount of pollution. Stone, like metal, is eaten away by pollutants in the atmosphere. **Sulfur oxides** and **carbon dioxide** combine with moisture in

Did You Know?

Have you heard the expression "mad as a hatter"? In 1939, Lewis Carroll wrote about the mad hatter in the story of Alice in Wonderland. Why were most hatters considered "mad"? It was not until many years later that scientists realized the "madness" was a condition caused by their occupation. Fur pelts were treated with mercuric chloride. Anyone who worked with the pelts, especially a hatter, was exposed to the fumes. Mercury is stored in the body and eventually builds up to levels that are toxic. At toxic levels it causes damage to the nervous system and the kidneys.

www

For more information on ozone injury to plants at Shenandoah National Park, visit: http://www.nature.nps.gov/ard/veginj.htm.

Experiments like this one at Penn State test the effects of air pollutants on plants.

The acids dissolve mortar and weaken concrete. In colder regions, chemicals used to keep the roads free of ice may cause some of the damage.

Visibility in the Smoky Mountains is often impaired by air pollution.

the air to form acids. The acids dissolve metals, marble, roofing slate and mortar in our buildings.

Acids weaken the fibers in fabrics and leather. Even your textbook is not safe from pollution. Sulfur is used in the processing of wood into paper. The moisture in the atmosphere reacts with the sulfur compounds to form sulfuric acid. The sulfuric acid reacts with the paper, making it brittle. Historical libraries spend thousands of dollars each year for special air filters to control humidity levels and filter air pollutants.

The **nitrogen oxides** and **ozone** destroy pigments in paint and fabrics. Ozone attacks rubber, making it brittle so that it cracks when stretched. It also damages plastics and paints.

Haze—Spoiling the View

Visibility, the greatest distance that one can see without the aid of technology, is being reduced by air pollution. The major cause of reduced visibility is regional haze. Sulfur dioxide, nitrogen oxides, and fine particle emissions from coal-burning electric power plants, industries, and exhaust from motor vehicles cause the haze. Without these pollutants, the visibility would be approximately 140 miles (224 km) in the West and 90 miles (144 km) in the East. In the West the current visibility range is 33 to 90 miles (53–144 km), while in the East the range is reduced to 14 to 24 miles (22–38 km).

Once particulates enter the atmosphere, they can be transported hundreds or thousands of miles. This makes visibility a regional problem. State governments must work together to reduce or eliminate the sources of pollution that are contributing to the problem. Amendments to the Clean Air Act require the EPA to reduce existing impairment and prevent future impairment of visibility at certain national parks and wilderness areas.

Think About It

Power plants upwind from the Grand Canyon have sometimes made the view more murky than magnificent. Smog and haze from power plants, and even from cities in the region, have often settled in the canyon. Would you favor closing power plants or forcing them to buy expensive pollution control equipment to preserve the view for tourists? What would be the cost to industry and its employees? If nothing is done, what would be the price paid in lost tourist revenue?

2.6 QUESTIONS FOR STUDY AND DISCUSSION:

1. Define the following terms: **VOCABULARY**

bronchial asthma	photochemical smog
carcinogen	pneumonia
chlorosis	secondhand smoke
chronic bronchitis	smog
controlled experiment	synergistic effect
emphysema	variable
lung cancer	visibility
particulates	

The Disasters

2. What was the major source of the air pollution that caused the air pollution disasters?
3. Describe the geographic location of Donora, Pennsylvania. How did this location contribute to the 1948 air pollution disaster? [See Section 2.2, Weather Patterns, page 107.]
4. What groups of people were most affected by the air pollution disasters?

In the Laboratory

5. How many variables exist in a controlled experiment?
6. What happened to mice and other laboratory animals that were exposed to air pollutants? Do you think that these studies can be applied to humans? Why or why not?

The Human Population—What the Studies Show

7. Why is it difficult to study the effects of air pollution on humans?
8. Which of the studies have shown that the city that you live in may affect your health?
9. Identify the variable in each of the studies.

What the Surgeon General Says

10. What diseases are linked to smoking tobacco?
11. Identify the variables that were present in the St. Louis–Winnipeg study. Do you think this was a good study? Why or why not?

Diseases Associated with Air Pollution

12. Identify 5 diseases that are associated with air pollution.
13. For each disease discussed, identify the reasons for decreased amount of air moving through the respiratory system.

Pollutants—How They Affect Humans

14. What are the effects of Environmental Tobacco Smoke (ETS)?
15. List three gases that are irritating to the respiratory system and describe the effects caused by these irritants.
16. Why are small particles more dangerous than large particles?
17. What is the effect of increased levels of carbon monoxide? What group of people is most affected?
18. Compare the effects of lead in children with its effects in adults. Why are children more affected by air pollutants than adults?

Effects on Animals

19. Which animals were most affected by the air pollution disaster in London?
20. Air pollutants may enter the respiratory system of animals with the air that they breathe. Through what other body system may air pollutants enter the bodies of animals?

Effects on Plants

21. Identify two pollutants that damage plants. Which of these is the most damaging to agricultural crops?
22. Identify two conditions that increase the damage caused by sulfur dioxide? Which of these is a synergistic effect?

Property Damage

23. What materials are damaged when certain air pollutants mix with moisture to form acids?
24. Give 3 ways that air pollution costs you money.

Haze—Spoiling the View

25. What is the cause of regional haze? What problem does regional haze cause?
26. Do you think that regional haze is a serious air pollution problem that should be controlled? Why?

Asbestos: Everybody's Problem

OBJECTIVES

- ✔ **Identify** the properties of asbestos that made it an ideal component of many commercial products.
- ✔ **Describe** the health effects caused by asbestos fibers.
- ✔ **Identify** products that may contain asbestos and **describe** the condition that makes a product with asbestos dangerous.
- ✔ **State** the goal of the Asbestos Hazard Emergency Response Act.
- ✔ **Describe** the proper procedure for asbestos removal and disposal.

At one time, asbestos was considered a health risk only for asbestos workers. In 1971, the EPA listed asbestos as a hazardous air pollutant. In 1989, the EPA banned the manufacture of most asbestos products. Because of its widespread use, asbestos is an environmental problem that concerns every community in the nation. Exposure to asbestos may occur at home, at work, or at school. There is a potential danger for anyone who is exposed to asbestos fibers in the air they breathe.

What Is It?

Asbestos is the name given to a group of natural minerals found in certain types of rock formations. Asbestos is mined and processed into fibers that are mixed with a binding material. Asbestos is heat-resistant, very durable, resists corrosion and insulates well. Because of these properties, asbestos became a common material used in construction and by many other industries.

Asbestos has been widely used in many commercial products including sealants, cement pipes, cement sheets, paper products, brake linings, floor tiles, many older plastics and insulation. The qualities that made it suitable for so many uses were its ability to add strength, provide thermal insulation, give fire protection, and deaden sound. EPA's Asbestos Ban and Phaseout Rule prohibits the manufacture, processing and importation of most products containing asbestos.

How Can It Affect Your Health?

The problem is that products made with asbestos may release very tiny fibers that are 1,200 times thinner than a strand of human hair. These microscopic fibers remain in the air for a long period of time. If inhaled, the fibers can enter body tissues where they remain for many years. **Asbestosis** is a disease of the lungs that occurs when asbestos fibers remain in the lungs causing scarring and making breathing difficult. It is a disabling disease and can be fatal.

Asbestos fibers are **carcinogenic**—causing several different forms of cancer, including **lung cancer** and **mesothelomia**, cancer of the thin membrane lining of the chest and abdomen. These diseases take a long time to develop, sometimes 10 to 30 years. Lung cancer causes the largest number of deaths. People who are exposed to asbestos and who smoke are 50 to 90 times more likely to develop lung cancer than people who are not exposed to either of these pollutants.

The presence of asbestos does not always present a danger to health. The product is only dangerous if the fibers escape into the air. The danger of fibers entering the air depends upon whether or not the product is friable. An object is **friable** if it can be crumbled with the hand when it is dry. The products containing asbestos that were sprayed for fireproofing, insulation and decoration are often friable. Other products, such as vinyl flooring, are not likely to lose fibers unless they are sanded or cut.

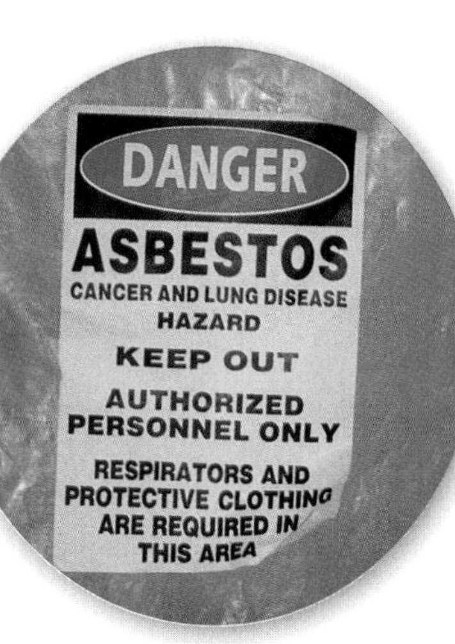

When removing asbestos, workers must be protected from the dangers posed by the tiny asbestos fibers.

Schools and Other Public Buildings

Congress passed the Asbestos Hazard Emergency Response Act in 1986 to protect children and school employees. It required all schools, both public and private, to inspect their buildings for any friable **asbestos-containing materials** (ACMs). The Act also required an analysis of any material of an unknown composition. Schools are required to develop a plan to manage asbestos. Records are required and both parents and workers are to be notified of any activities related to asbestos.

The EPA estimates that there are asbestos-containing materials in most of the nation's schools. Nearly 1/3 of the schools in an EPA study (1984) had potential asbestos problems, but many had already taken steps to correct the problem. Fines are given if the schools do not meet the requirements set by the EPA.

Another EPA survey determined that 733,000 Federal Government buildings, private non-residential buildings and apartment buildings contain friable asbestos. Buildings built during the 1960s are more likely to contain asbestos than other buildings. A survey in 1984 found that 66% of those buildings contained damaged ACMs.

Although asbestos is a hazardous material, the health risk to people who live, work, or go to school in buildings with asbestos-containing materials is low. Removal is often not the best solution and may increase exposure to asbestos if not done properly. Materials that are not friable and are in areas where they will not be disturbed may only need to be sealed or encapsulated. But, before any building is renovated or demolished, the EPA requires removal of the asbestos to prevent "significant public exposure."

Is There Asbestos in Your Home?

Many single-family homes have products made with asbestos. The following products might contain asbestos:

- Vinyl Floor Tiles and Flooring: Asbestos fibers may be released if the tiles are sanded, damaged, cut to fit in place, or severely worn. Do not remove old tiles. Instead, cover them with a new material.
- Patching Compound and Textured Paints: Use of asbestos in these products was banned in 1975. Any old products should be properly discarded. For repair of old materials see the subheading "Safety Guidelines."
- Friable Ceilings: If your home was built or remodeled between 1945 and 1978, the ceilings may be made of friable material that contains asbestos. Trained contractors should be hired to remove it or cover it with a coating.
- Stoves and Furnaces: Cement sheet material around stoves probably will not release asbestos fibers unless scraped. Heat-resistant materials that may be made of asbestos should be handled according to the safety guidelines. Furnace insulation should be replaced if it is in poor condition. See the safety guidelines for the proper procedure.
- Walls and Pipes: If pipes were covered with insulation between 1920 and 1972, it probably contains asbestos. It is better to use wide duct tape to repair a damaged section than to try to remove the insulation. Wall and

Think About It

The city of Aurora, Missouri, agreed to pay a penalty of $57,500 to settle claims alleged in an EPA complaint against the city. The city had received a bid for $12,389 to remove asbestos from the old city hall building, but chose to use city workers instead. The EPA was not notified before workers began to remove ACMs and required procedures were not followed during its removal.

Asbestos fibers can be released from severely worn tiles like these. Special precautions must be taken when removing the old tiles.

The wall of lockers in this school hallway has been covered with plastic as workers prepare to remove asbestos from the ceiling. The floor will also be covered and the classroom doors sealed before removal begins.

Proper disposal of materials containing asbestos is very important.

ceiling insulation installed between 1930 and 1950 may contain asbestos. Trained contractors should remove it before remodeling or destruction.

- Appliances: Appliances with asbestos are safe to use unless broken or misused. Unsafe models have been withdrawn from the market.
- Roofing, Shingles and Siding: In some of these materials, asbestos was used as a binding agent. If they are worn they may be spray-painted to seal the fibers. Follow the safety guidelines when repairing or replacing these materials.

The manufacturer of a product may be able to tell you if the product contains asbestos. People who have worked with products containing asbestos, such as plumbers and building or heating contractors, may be able to make an educated guess about the composition of a product. Positive identification of asbestos requires analysis of samples by a qualified laboratory.

What Should You Do If You Find Asbestos in Your Home?

Any material that contains as little as 1% asbestos is subject to federal asbestos regulations. Most materials containing asbestos do not need to be removed. They should be repaired if there is any damage or deterioration. When maintained in good condition, building materials containing asbestos appear to pose relatively little risk.

When using or working with materials that contain asbestos, keep your exposure to a minimum by following the Safety Guidelines. If you hire a contractor, make sure that the contractor follows the same guidelines. Improper removal can actually increase rather than decrease the risk from asbestos fibers.

Safety Guidelines for Working with Materials that Contain Asbestos:

1. Do not disturb any material that you think contains asbestos unless it is absolutely necessary.
2. Seal off the work area by using plastic and duct tape. Make sure that asbestos dust is not tracked into other areas.
3. Always wear an approved respirator. Also wear protective gloves, hat, and clothing. If possible, dispose of the clothing. If this is not possible, wash it separately.
4. Wet the material with a fine mist. Add a small amount (1 teaspoon per quart of water) of a low-sudsing detergent to help the water penetrate the material.
5. If it is necessary to drill or cut material containing asbestos, do the work outside, if possible. Make sure the material is wet (see number 4).
6. If it's necessary to remove the material, avoid breaking it into small pieces. If possible, remove complete preformed pieces.
7. Place any material removed in plastic trash bags and dispose of it according to EPA regulations [see Disposal, p. 139].
8. After removing the material, clean the area with wet mops, rags or sponges. Repeat the cleaning a second time. Dispose of the cleaning materials in the container with the material removed. **CAUTION**: Do not dust, sweep, or vacuum particles suspected of containing asbestos. The

asbestos fibers are small enough to pass through normal vacuum cleaner filters. Use wet mopping or specially designed vacuum cleaners.

9. If the work is to be done by a contractor, discuss these guidelines to make sure your exposure is minimized.

Disposal of Asbestos Wastes

EPA regulations control the disposal of asbestos wastes. Many states have programs for approving and licensing asbestos disposal sites. A waste hauler must notify a landfill of any load that contains asbestos wastes. The load must be inspected to make sure that the wastes are in leak-proof containers and are properly labeled. If the wastes are not in the proper containers, the landfill operator must keep the wastes wet until they can be covered with a non-asbestos material.

There must be no visible dust during disposal. The EPA must be notified of any accidental releases of asbestos fibers. Within 24 hours a thick covering (at least six inches or 15 cm) of material that does not contain asbestos must be placed over the wastes. Before the final closing of the area where asbestos is buried, 30 inches (76 cm) of non-asbestos material must be added to the six inches of cover already in place. The area must be properly graded and planted so that erosion is prevented.

2.7 Questions for Study and Discussion:

1. Define the following terms: **VOCABULARY**

ACM	carcinogenic
asbestos	friable
asbestosis	mesothelomia

What Is It?

2. What properties of asbestos made it a desirable ingredient in many products?
3. Give three reasons why asbestos might have been sprayed on a surface.

How Can It Affect Your Health?

4. What diseases are caused by asbestos?
5. How do asbestos fibers usually enter the body?
6. Asbestos is dangerous only if it is friable. Why?

Schools and Other Public Buildings

7. Why was the Asbestos Hazard Emergency Response Act passed? What did the Act require?
8. (True/False) Asbestos has been found in government and privately owned buildings as well as multiple and single family homes.
9. In what situations does the EPA require removal of asbestos?

Is There Asbestos in Your Home?

10. Identify three types of materials used in the construction of homes that might contain asbestos.
11. Do you think that there is asbestos in your home? If so, where might the asbestos be located? If not, why do you think that your home does not contain asbestos?

What Should You Do if You Find Asbestos in Your Home?

12. If you or a relative find asbestos in your home, how would you decide whether or not it should be removed?

Safety Guidelines for Working with Materials That Contain Asbestos

13. How should a worker dress when working with material that contains asbestos?
14. What should be done with materials containing asbestos when it is removed?
15. Describe the proper way to clean the area after asbestos has been removed.

Disposal of Asbestos Wastes

16. A truck containing materials with asbestos arrives at the landfill you operate. What procedures should you follow?
17. The landfill has been filled and no more wastes can be accepted. What must be done so that the asbestos will not become a pollutant?

Radiation—as a Pollutant

OBJECTIVES

- ✔ **Compare** and **contrast** alpha, beta, gamma, and cosmic radiation.
- ✔ **Identify** factors that determine the amount of background radiation exposure a person receives.
- ✔ **Contrast** human-made and natural sources of radiation.
- ✔ **List** factors that determine the damage received from exposure to radiation.

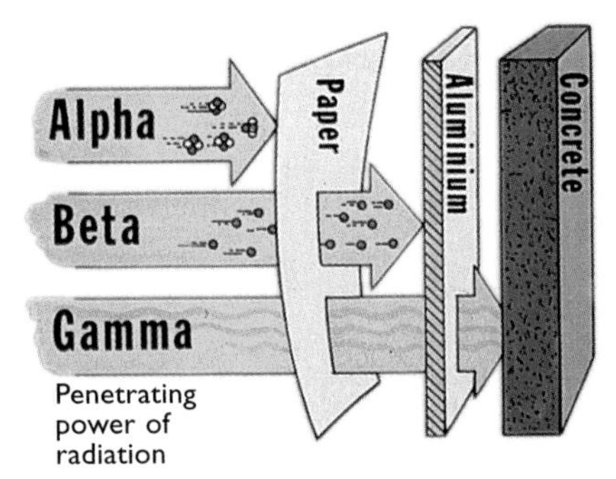

Alpha, Beta and Gamma Radiation.

Where you choose to live is one factor that determines your exposure to radiation.

All matter is made of atoms. An **atom** has a nucleus that is surrounded by particles called electrons. It is the interaction of electrons between atoms that forms compounds. The nucleus contains small particles called neutrons and protons. The neutrons and protons are held together by large amounts of energy. However, the nuclei of some atoms are not stable. The energy and/or particles, released when these nuclei spontaneously disintegrate, is called **radiation**.

Types of Radiation

Three types of radiation result from the breakdown of nuclei. **Alpha radiation** consists of particles that can be stopped by a sheet of paper or the outer dead layer of human skin. **Beta radiation** consists of faster moving particles that may penetrate the skin, but can be stopped by several millimeters of aluminum. **Gamma radiation** consists of energy waves (rays) that travel at the speed of light. They may pass through the human body if not absorbed by tissues. Several feet of concrete or several inches of lead may be required to stop them.

Radiation surrounds us. It is a part of our natural environment. Alpha, Beta or Gamma radiation is **ionizing radiation**—high-energy radiation that can knock electrons from atoms. Some ionizing radiation enters the earth's atmosphere from outer space. We call this **cosmic radiation**. Solar radiation is mostly non-ionizing, low-energy light waves. It includes ultraviolet radiation that is not blocked by the ozone layer.

Radiation From Natural Sources

Radium is a naturally radioactive element. This means that the nuclei of radium atoms are unstable; they spontaneously disintegrate without any outside force. This process is called **radioactive decay**. When the nucleus of a radium atom spontaneously disintegrates or "decays," it changes into a radon atom, and radiation is given off. The new radon atom is not stable. It "decays" and radiation is given off. This process continues until a stable atom is formed.

Radiation is given off by trace amounts of uranium–238 and radium found in soil and rock. Some rocks contain more uranium than other rocks. This means that some parts of the world have higher levels of radiation than other parts. In Kerala, India, the average person receives 1,300 millirems of radiation per year—several times the exposure the average person living in the United States receives from natural sources. A **rem** is a measure of the result of energy deposited in tissue. A **millirem** is one one-thousandth of a rem.

The level of naturally occurring radiation is referred to as the **background level**. The average person in the United States receives approximately 360 millirems of radiation each year. About 80% of that exposure is from natural sources. Where the person lives and the person's lifestyle determines the background level. As we move higher into the atmosphere, we encounter higher levels of cosmic radiation. Airline crews experience higher levels of cosmic radiation than fishing crews.

Natural background radiation differs considerably in different locations, due to differences in elevation and the radioactive elements present in the soil. People living in Denver, Colorado—the mile high city, are exposed to more cosmic radiation than people living in Chicago, which is about 1,000 feet above sea level. And people living in Chicago are exposed to more radiation than people living in Miami.

You will probably be exposed to less radiation in a building made of wood than in a building made of brick. Building materials, such as granite, bricks, wallboard, and concrete, contain small amounts of uranium. In the **uranium decay series**, radon gas (Rn) is released. Solar heated homes that use sand, crushed rock, or concrete slabs for heat storage, may contain more radon gas than homes without these materials. Homes that are built to be energy-efficient may also retain radon gas from the soil and rocks below, especially during the winter months when the house is closed.

All coal contains a small amount of naturally radioactive materials. Most of this radioactive material is contained in the unburned residue and ash, but some is released into the atmosphere. During normal operation the average coal-burning power plant releases more radioactivity into the environment than modern nuclear power plants. While nuclear power plants are closely regulated, there are no regulations regarding radioactivity released by coal-burning power plants.

Uranium Decay Series

Half-Life	Nuclide
4.51×10^9 yr.	U^{238}
	↓ α
24.1 days	$Th^{234}U$
	↓ β
1.18 min.	Pa^{234}
	↓
2.48×10^5 yr.	U^{234}
	↓ α
8.0×10^4 yr.	Th^{230}
	↓ α
1.62×10^3 yr.	Ra^{236}
	↓ α
3.82 days	Rn^{222}
	↓ α
3.05 min.	Po^{218}
	α ↙ ↘ β
Pb = 26.8 min. At = 2 sec.	Pb^{214} At^{218}
	↘ ↙ α
19.4 yr.	Bi^{214}
	↙ ↘
Po = 1.6×10^{-4} sec Tl = 1.32 min.	Po^{214} Tl^{210}
	α ↘ ↙ β
19.4 yr.	Pb^{210}
	↓ α
α β Bi = 5.0 days	Bi^{210}
	α ↙ ↘ β
Tl = 4.20 min. Po = 138.4 days	Tl^{206} Po^{210}
	↓
Stable	Pb^{206}

Radiation from Human-Made Sources

Human-made radiation sources include all of those activities in which humans have concentrated radioactive materials. Nuclear weapons testing resulted in areas where radioactivity levels are higher than natural levels. Nuclear power plants release small amounts of radioactivity into the environment. People living nearest nuclear power plants in the United States are exposed to less than 0.1 millirem of radiation per year, of radiation from the operation of the nuclear power plants.

Medical x-rays are the single largest source of human-made radiation exposure. X-rays are like gamma rays except that they are generally lower in energy and less penetrating than gamma rays. Medical x-rays can be stopped by a few millimeters of lead. X-rays and radioactive substances are used in the diagnosis and treatment of disease. The average American gets about 45 millirems a year from x-rays and radioactive materials that are used for medical diagnosis and therapy.

Biological Effects of Radiation

Radioactive substances enter the body when we eat and breathe. All humans normally have small amounts of radioactive materials inside their body. Most knowledge of the biological effects of radiation is gained through laboratory experiments involving large numbers of plants and

Comparison of Exposure to Radiation from Common Sources

Product	Millirems /Year
Cardiac pacemaker (sealed plutonium)	100
X-ray	40
TV receiver	1
Computer terminal	0.1
LCD watch	0.06
Coal combustion (within 50 miles)	0.03
Nuclear power plant (within 50 miles)	0.009
Smoke detector	0.008

Environmental Challenge: Personal Exposure

Calculate your exposure to radiation. Visit www.epa.gov/radiation/students/calculate.html.

www

Did You Know?

During the 1950s and 1960s, above-ground nuclear tests were conducted northwest of Las Vegas. Everyone living in the continental United States was exposed to radioactive iodine-131 for about two months after each test. The greatest exposure to I-131 was from milk produced by cows that ate plants contaminated with fallout deposited by wind and rain. The National Cancer Institute estimates that the nuclear fallout from the Nevada Test Site may cause a 2–20% increase in cases of thyroid cancer.

animals, but not humans. Humans who have been exposed to radiation because of medical treatments, nuclear accidents, or nuclear weapons testing have also been studied.

The energy of radiation may cause changes in chemicals within the cell. The new chemicals may alter the structure of the cell or interfere with the cell's normal chemical reactions. The cell may no longer be able to carry out its normal functions. If these functions are vital to the life of the organism, the result is death of the organism.

The extent of damage to the organism will depend on several factors:

- **Dose**—the quantity of radiation received at one time. An example of a dose is 45,000 millirems of radiation received by people living near the Chernobyl Nuclear Power Plant at the time of the accident.
- **Dose Rate**—amount of radiation given per unit of time. An example of dose rate is 5,000 millirems/year. The effects are less damaging if the dose is spread out over a longer period of time. This is due to the body's natural repair mechanisms.
- **Type of Radiation**—Alpha particles bombard cells with large amounts of energy and are very damaging if ingested or inhaled. Beta particles, X-rays or gamma rays have less energy, but these forms of radiation are more hazardous due to their greater ability to penetrate into living tissues.
- **Type of Tissue**—Cells that are dividing are more sensitive to the effects of radiation and the result is greater damage. This is why we often see damage in the skin, bone marrow, ovaries and testes.
- **Age**—Younger persons have more rapidly dividing cells, and exposure to radiation results in greater damage.
- **Health**—The cells of a healthy person may be more capable of repairing the damage caused by radiation than the cells of someone who has other health problems.

A large dose of radiation may cause extensive and possibly fatal damage. Smaller doses cause less damage and the damage may not be immediately observable. The period of time that is necessary before the damage can be observed is called the **latent period**. The minimum latent period for leukemia is 2 years from time of exposure. Often 10–40 years passes between the exposure to radiation and the appearance of some forms of cancer. The latent period is shorter for larger doses of radiation and longer for smaller doses.

Clinical effects of doses below 1,000 millirems are not measurable by current technology. These low doses only increase the probability, not the certainty, of any effect. When calculating risks, the assumption is made that any dose of radiation, no matter how small, involves some risk to human health. The risk, however, is very small when compared with other health risks, including diet, alcohol, tobacco, and lack of exercise.

In general we can say that the higher the dose, the greater the chance of damage, and the quicker the effects will appear. The chart above shows the effects of specific doses of whole-body radiation given within a short period of time. All of these health effects may have other causes and do occur in people not exposed to radiation.

Effects of an Acute Whole-Body Exposure to Radiation:

- **10,000,000 millirems**—Person becomes comatose and dies within one or two days from damage to the central nervous system.
- **1,000,000 millirems**—Person immediately experiences nausea, vomiting, and diarrhea. The number of blood cells made in the bone marrow will decrease. Death follows in one or two weeks from blistering of the small intestine.
- **350,000 millirems**—One half of people exposed to this level of radiation will die in the first 60 days from damage to the blood and bone marrow. The people that survive will experience various degrees of nausea, vomiting, diarrhea, reddening of the skin, loss of hair, blisters, decrease in number of blood and bone marrow cells, and a decrease in resistance to infections.
- **100,000 millirems**—Person will not notice any effects although there will be a decreased white cell count. There will be an increased probability of leukemia and a shortened life.
- **10,000 millirems**—There is no scientific evidence that humans are harmed by exposure to radiation below this level. Birth defects may occur if exposure is during early **embryo** stages. Evidence may never be available because, if there are effects, they may be too small and occur too infrequently for detection.
- **1,000 millirems**—No measurable effects. Statistical increase in tumors that occur before the age of ten, but only if exposure occurs during development in uterus.

Radiation is a carcinogen. The EPA estimates that the risk of developing cancer from exposure to natural background radiation is about one in one hundred. While a small percentage of all fatal cancers is caused by background radiation, a smaller percentage is caused by human-made sources of radiation.

The risk of genetic defects in humans is apparently much less than the risk of cancer. Genetic defects have been observed in the offspring of laboratory animals exposed to radiation. Similar damage may occur in humans, but no statistically significant genetic effects were seen even with the high doses of radiation after the bombings at Hiroshima and Nagasaki in 1944.

Scientists have followed the health histories of nearly 76,000 survivors of the Hiroshima and Nagasaki bombings who were exposed to a dose of more than 500 millirems. More than 3,000 of these people died of cancer between 1950 and 1985. The number of cancer deaths was several hundred more than the expected rate. More than 60% of the people exposed were still alive 40 years after the bombing.

In 1987, one year after the accident at the Chernobyl 4 Nuclear Power Plant in the former Soviet Union, the death toll was 31. All of the victims were workers at the power plant, fire fighters, or rescue workers. According to data released by the Soviet Union, experts estimated that about 24,000 people received "fairly serious" radiation doses of about 45

Did You Know?

There are two types of smoke detectors. The most common type contains a small piece of americium (an element) which gives off low-level radiation. The radiation creates a current within the detector. When smoke disrupts the current, the alarm sounds. Very little radiation penetrates the alarm casing, and the alarm may be disposed of with household trash. A second type of smoke alarm, called a photoelectric detector, does not contain any radioactive materials. This type of alarm sounds when smoke particles disturb a beam of light.

Americans receive 200 million X-rays every year. One third of all successful cancer treatments include radiation. When you receive an X-ray, you'll see this symbol with a sign that says, "Caution. Radioactive Material."

Did You Know?

A tiny pellet of plutonium-238 and some advanced technology in a heart pacemaker means that patients do not have to have surgery every few years to replace the battery. The plutonium battery operates for about 10 years. Plutonium is an alpha emitter.

rems (45,000 millirems). Scientists predicted an additional 100–200 cancer deaths among these people.

Radiation is known to cause thyroid cancer, and the release of radioactive iodine was a concern during the accident. In 1992, the World Health Organization reported that childhood thyroid cancers had increased from four cases a year to about 60 in Belarus—a former Soviet republic immediately downwind from Chernobyl. A more recent study reports autoimmune thyroid disease is seven times higher in children who were living immediately downwind of the Chernobyl nuclear plant. Girls who were at least 6 years old at the time of accident were twice as likely to have the disease as boys the same age.

For information about the effects of radiation released during the accident at Three-Mile Island Nuclear Power Plant, [see Section 6.5, page 464].

2.8 Questions for Study and Discussion:

1. Define the following terms: **VOCABULARY**

alpha radiation	gamma radiation
atom	ionizing radiation
background level	latent period
beta radiation	millirem
cosmic radiation	radioactive decay
dose	rem
dose rate	

2. What is the basic building block of all matter?
3. What part of an atom disintegrates, releasing radiation?

Types of Radiation

4. How do Alpha and Beta radiation differ from Gamma rays?
5. Which type of radiation would probably not damage the human body unless swallowed or inhaled?
6. How does ionizing radiation differ from non-ionizing solar radiation?

Radiation from Natural Sources

7. What happens when a radium atom "decays"?
8. What are the sources of background radiation?
9. Why do some people receive more background radiation than others?

Radiation from Human-Made Sources

10. How do human-made radiation sources differ from natural sources of radiation?
11. List 4 human-made sources of radiation.

Biological Effects of Radiation

12. Give two ways that radioactive substances enter the body.
13. Explain how radiation damages the body.
14. Why does radiation more often cause damage in (a) young children and (b) people who have health problems?
15. What are the observed effects of the radiation released by the accident at the Chernobyl 4 Nuclear Power Plant?

Radon—Are You at Risk?

A nuclear power plant was being constructed at Limerick, Pennsylvania. Radiation monitors had just been installed when Stanley Watras reported to work on December 17, 1984. As he walked past the monitors, he set off the radiation alarms. An investigation revealed to officials that the nuclear power plant was not the source of the radiation.

Danger at Home

Scientists went to the home of Mr. Watras to collect air, soil, and water samples. High levels of radon gas were found in all rooms of his home. According to one official, the level was "very high"—165 times higher than the level allowed in uranium mines. The level of radiation was greater than the amount received from 455,000 chest x-rays. Following the advice of health officials, the family moved out of the house, while measures were taken to reduce the levels of radon.

Radon is a naturally occurring radioactive gas. It is produced by the radioactive disintegration or "decay" of radium. Radium is formed in the uranium decay series [see page 141] and is found in certain types of rocks and soils. Houses can be contaminated when the radon gas rises through the soil and enters through cracks in the basement or foundation. In some regions, well water contains high levels of radon. As water is used in washers, sinks, showers, and toilets, it releases much of the dissolved radon into the air.

The Watras' house was built over a layer of granite rock that contains 50 ppm of uranium. In order to conserve energy, the new house had been well insulated. The airtight house trapped radon gas as if it were a huge bowl that had been turned upside down over the soil.

Scientific Studies

A granite rock formation—called the **Reading Prong**—runs from Reading to Easton, Pennsylvania. It continues through northern New Jersey and into southern New York State. In 1979 and 1980, a team of scientists surveyed the Reading Prong looking for commercially valuable deposits of uranium. They mounted an instrument, similar to a Geiger counter, on a Jeep. Then they drove the Jeep along 900 miles (1440 km) of roads within the prong and measured radiation coming from the ground. They marked road maps with colored pencils. Each color showed a specific level of gamma radiation detected on the roads.

The scientists did not locate any deposits that were commercially valuable, but they did find some locations with high levels of radiation. They gave this information to Pennsylvania's Department of Environmental Resources (DER), but it was another source of radiation that received the attention of the DER and the news media. This was the 1979 accident at the Three Mile Island Nuclear Power Plant. Plans to

OBJECTIVES

- **Create** an illustration that shows how people are exposed to radon.
- **Relate** human activities to their level of risk from radon exposure. (POPULATION LINK)
- **State** the EPA's position on testing for radon in homes.
- **Explain** how exposure to radon can be reduced.

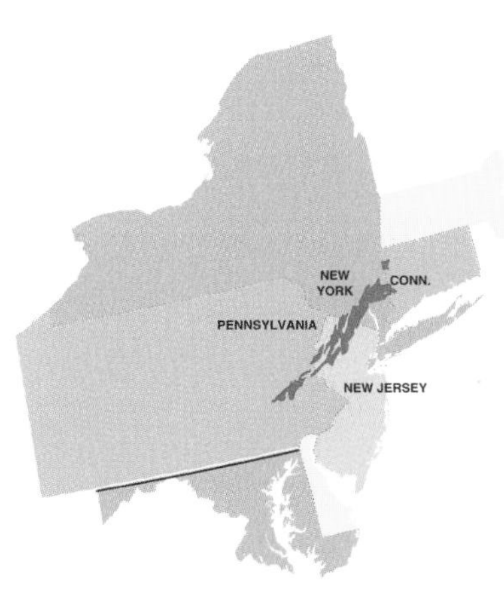

The Reading Prong is a granite rock formation that contains uranium. Some houses built on this rock formation contain high levels of radon gas.

Many homes are built to conserve energy. Sometimes this affects indoor air quality.

check into the problem in the Reading Prong were put on hold, and the information was placed in a filing cabinet.

During 1980 and 1981, Pennsylvania Power and Light (PP&L) Company studied thirty-six homes to see if steps taken to conserve energy were affecting the air quality in the homes. One test measured the level of radon gas. Concerned about the levels of radon found in some homes, they hired scientists to review the results of the tests. Their report was given to the DER and the Environmental Protection Agency (EPA), but the DER officials were still too busy with the TMI accident to give it much thought.

Dr. Harvey Sachs, a geologist who worked on the PP&L study, tried to convince the Department of Environmental Resources that there was a problem. In a letter written in February, 1983, he warned that the radiation from radon was a more serious health problem than the radiation released during the TMI Nuclear Power Plant accident. However, no action was taken until Stanley Watras walked passed the radiation monitors.

Scientists measure radiation in picocuries per liter (pCi/L) of air. A **curie** (named after Marie and Pierre Curie, the discovers of radium) is equal to the decay of 3.7×10^{10} atoms per second or the amount of radiation from one gram of radium. Pico means one-trillionth (1×10^{-12}). A picocurie per liter is 2.2 atoms decaying per minutes in a liter of air.

For more information on radon including a map of radon zones, visit: www.epa.gov/iaq/radon.

After high levels of radon (1,800–4,400 picocuries) were found in the Watras' home, maps were pulled out of filing cabinets and studied. DER officials estimated that there were 20,000 homes in the part of the Reading Prong that lies in Pennsylvania. There were as many as 250,000 homes built over the extension of the prong in New Jersey.

The Invisible Threat

The radioactive decay of radon gas produces solid particles called **radon daughters**. When these particles enter the lungs they give off radiation in the form of alpha rays. The energy bombards the lung cells, and the damage increases the risk of cancer. Radon gas is a known lung **carcinogen** in humans. The danger from high concentrations of radon gas was first detected in uranium miners. Miners are dying of lung cancer at 5 times the expected rate.

Ruins of Keane Wonder Mine.

It is difficult to estimate a person's lifetime exposure to radon. To estimate risks, scientists use information from studies of lung cancer in uranium miners. There are several problems with this risk analysis: miners are generally exposed to higher levels of radon, the majority of miners are male and smokers, and miners inhale dust and other pollutants, too. Scientists also use information from laboratory studies and information about the human population to estimate the risk of radon.

Radon gas is present in outdoor air at very low levels, but indoors it builds up to higher concentrations. A national residential radon survey found that radon is not a problem in most homes, but there are millions of homes and buildings that do contain high levels of radon. Studies of energy-efficient homes show that people living in a few of these homes are exposed to levels of radon similar to levels that have caused lung cancer in uranium miners.

Everyone is exposed to radon, and even low levels may pose some risk. Scientists have not been able to identify a level that has no effect. Experts agree that the risk of developing lung cancer increases linearly as exposure increases. In other words, doubling the level of radon doubles the risk of lung cancer. No one knows the exact number of deaths caused by radon, but the National Academy of Sciences estimates that exposure to radon in homes is responsible for at least 1 in 10 lung cancer deaths, or 15,000 deaths each year.

Radon is the second leading cause of lung cancer; the leading cause is smoking. Smokers who are exposed to excess levels of radon significantly increase their risk of getting lung cancer. This increased risk is due to the **synergistic effect** where the damage caused by one pollutant is intensified if it is present with another pollutant. Most radon-related deaths of smokers could have been avoided if the victim had not smoked.

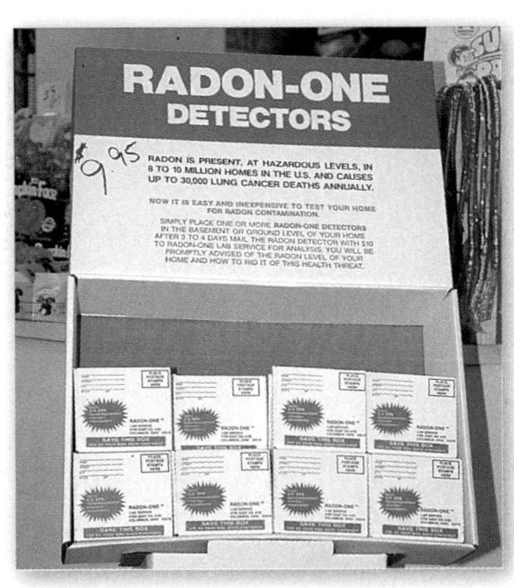

Radon detectors are available and can be used to determine the level of radon in your home.

Are You at Risk?

The EPA recommends that you should take steps to lower the level of radon in your home if it is 4 pCi/L of air or higher. Of the 3,694 homes tested in the Pennsylvania section of the Reading Prong, 66% had levels of radon that exceeded 4 pCi/L of air. The problem is not limited to the Reading Prong; anywhere there is uranium in the earth there is a potential problem. Uranium is usually found in granite rocks. Hot spots with high concentrations of radon have been discovered in several states.

Not all homes built above granite rocks have high levels of radon gas. How the house is built determines whether or not it will trap radon gas. Older homes have fewer indoor pollution problems because they have many cracks that allow air to enter. In many older homes the air is replaced with outside air one or more times each hour. In newer, tighter homes it may take two or more hours for the air inside the home to be replaced by outdoor air.

A charcoal canister is placed in the basement or lower level of a home for several days. The canister is then sealed and sent to a certified laboratory for analysis.

The EPA recommends that all homes should be tested for radon. Check with your state environmental protection agency to find out where to get a reliable test kit. Kits may cost from $15–50. There are two types of passive measurement devices in common use:

- Charcoal canisters contain charcoal that adsorbs radon during a specific period of time, generally 2–7 days.
- Alpha-track detectors—contain a small piece of plastic that is sensitive to the alpha particles released by the radon and radon daughters. Exposure time is usually 2–4 weeks.

The kits provide a quick and inexpensive indication of whether occupants may be exposed to high levels of radiation. The tests are usually placed in the "worst case location"—usually the basement or lowest level of the home, with the doors and windows closed as much as possible.

WWW

For more information on testing and reducing levels of radon in homes, visit: www.Radongas.org and www.nrsb.org.

Radon Risk Evaluation Chart — Environmental Protection Agency		
A	B	C vs D
200	440–770	1000 times average outdoor level
		More than 60 times non-smoker risk
		4-pack-a-day smoker
100	270–630	100 times average indoor level
40	120–380	20,000 chest X-rays per year
20	60–210	100 times average outdoor level
		2-pack-a-day smoker
10	30–120	10 times average indoor level
		1-pack-a-day smoker 5 times non-smoker risk
4	13–50	200 chest X-rays per year
2	7–30	10 times average outdoor level
		Non-smoker risk of dying from lung cancer
1	3–13	Average indoor level
		20 chest X-rays per year
0.2	1–3	Average outdoor level

Legend

- **A** Picocuries per litre
- **B** Estimated number of lung cancer deaths due to radon exposure (out of 1000)
- **C** Comparable exposure levels *versus*
- **D** Comparable risk

Guarding Against Radon

What happened to Mr. Watras and his family? Their home was chosen as the site of a research project because it had the highest levels of radon in the area. After the radon-reduction project was finished, the level of radon was less than 4 pCi/L, the highest level considered acceptable by the EPA. Since the project was completed, the home has been monitored periodically to ensure that the radon remained below the acceptable level. The levels were reduced by:

- Installing a radon barrier and waterproofing the exterior basement walls,
- Sealing the interior basement wall and floor openings, joints and cracks,
- Installing a passive ventilation system.

Since the research project involving the Watras home, engineers have developed efficient methods to lower the radon level in a home. The cost of reducing the radon level in a home may be as low as $300 or as high as $3,000. Putting a radon reduction system into a home while it is being built costs $500–$1,000.

In 1993, the EPA proposed voluntary guidelines for homebuilders to protect a home against radon infiltration. On average, radon trapped in homes accounts for 55% of the radiation exposure (200 millirems every year) for people living in the United States. The EPA encourages state and local governments to include radon protection systems in building codes.

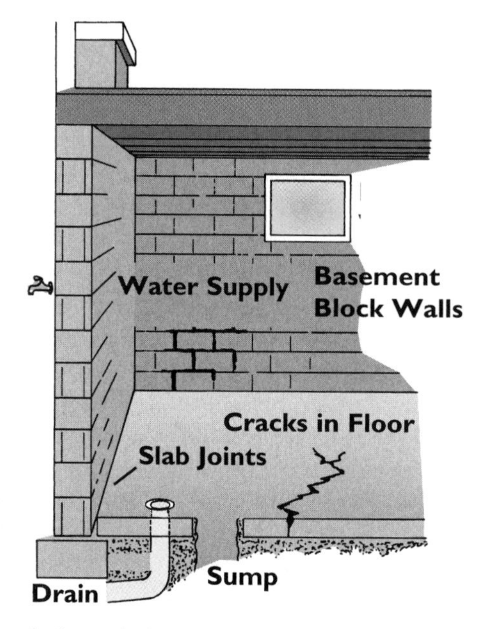

Indicated above are common radon entry points.

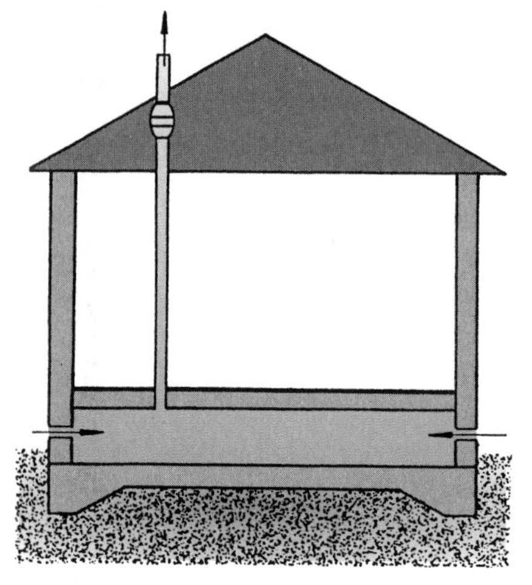

A system of pipes and exhaust fans may be used to reduce the level of radon in a home.

A fan in this active ventilation system draws air from beneath the basement floor and vents it above the roof of the home. Radon test results before installation were near 60 pCi/L, and after the system was operating, test results were less than 0.8 pCi/L.

Think About It

Finland and Canada have set the indoor radon limit at 20 pCi/L. The EPA's limit is 4 pCi/L. Do you think that the EPA limit is too strict? Explain.

2.9 Questions for Study and Discussion:

1. Define the following terms: **VOCABULARY**

curie	radon daughters
picocurie	Reading Prong
radon	synergistic effect

Danger at Home

2. Why did the Watras family leave their home?
3. What was the source of the radon gas?

Scientific Studies

4. What is the Reading Prong and where is it located?
5. Describe the information contained in the two scientific reports that were given to the Pennsylvania Department of Environmental Resources (PA DER).
6. Why did the PA DER postpone investigating the high levels of radiation?

The Invisible Threat

7. What kind of radiation is produced by the radon daughters? What is the effect of this radiation on human health?
8. Why is it difficult to determine the risk caused by exposure to radon?
9. Compare the risk of radon-related lung cancer in a smoker with a nonsmoker living in a house with similar levels of radon.

Are You at Risk?

10. What does the EPA recommend if radon test results are 4 pCi/L or higher?
11. What factors determine the level of radon in a home?
12. Does the EPA recommend that all homes be tested for radon?

Guarding Against Radon

13. Describe three procedures that can reduce the level of radon in a building?
14. Do you think that building codes should require homebuilders to include systems that will protect a home against radon infiltration?

The Blue Mountain—In the Shadow of a Smelter

OBJECTIVES

- ✔ **Identify** the processes necessary to produce metal products.
- ✔ **Relate** the importance of smelting of zinc ores to the development of technology.
- ✔ **Compare** the changes observed in the forest on the Blue Mountain with changes that normally occur in other forest ecosystems.
- ✔ **Identify** the major pollutants produced during the smelting of zinc ore and **describe** their effect on the forest ecosystem.
- ✔ **Relate** the exposure to heavy metals in communities with a smelter to that of other communities.
- ✔ **Evaluate** the risks and benefits of the recycling of metals.

"We know our activities do affect various ecological systems."
RICHARD W. HOGELAND, President
The New Jersey Zinc Company, 1975

The Franklin Ore

A **rock** is a collection of **minerals**—naturally occurring solids with specific chemical and physical structures. A rock that is mined to extract a useful mineral is an **ore**. Scouts, sent out from early settlements in the 1700s, searched for rocks with valuable mineral deposits. In the Franklin-Sterling area in northern New Jersey, they found an unusual ore known as the Franklin ore. It contained zinc, manganese and iron.

Nearby they also found important deposits of copper and iron. The settlers successfully mined the copper and iron ores. They extracted the minerals by a process called smelting. **Smelting** involves heating the ores to high temperatures to separate impurities from **metals**—those minerals that conduct electricity and can be shaped or molded to a specific form.

Zinc Oxide—The First Product

For two hundred years after its discovery, no one mined the Franklin ore because no one knew how to extract the minerals. A small group of dedicated men worked for several years to develop a process to produce zinc oxide from this ore. The first use of zinc oxide was in the manufacture of paint. Paint made with zinc oxide pigment was whiter and brighter than paint made only with white lead. It also covered better. Adding zinc oxide to the white lead pastes also allowed paint manufacturers to produce paints in a thinned, ready-to-use form. This was the beginning of the ready-mixed paint industry.

Today there are many other uses for zinc oxide. Most zinc oxide is used in the enamel finishes on bathroom fixtures, kitchen sinks, refrigerators and other appliances. Large amounts of zinc oxide are used by the rubber industry. In tires and other rubber products, it provides reinforcement against wear and prevents overheating.

Check the labels and you'll find zinc oxide listed as an ingredient in a wide range of products sold in drug stores. A very pure form of zinc oxide is an important ingredient in face powders, adhesive tape, ointments and mineral supplements. It is also an important additive used in the production of plastics and ceramics.

Metal from the Franklin Ore

Eventually a process was developed to make metallic zinc from the New Jersey ore. Metallic zinc has many uses, but its main use is in the process

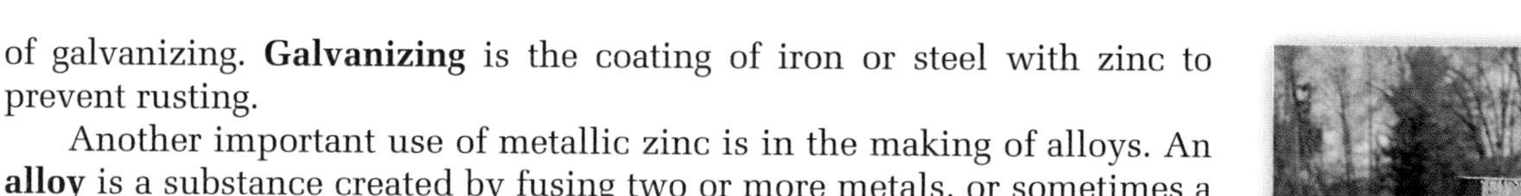

of galvanizing. **Galvanizing** is the coating of iron or steel with zinc to prevent rusting.

Another important use of metallic zinc is in the making of alloys. An **alloy** is a substance created by fusing two or more metals, or sometimes a metal and nonmetal. **Fusion** occurs when the metals are heated to a liquid state. The best known alloy made with zinc is probably **brass**. Brass is made by fusing metallic zinc with copper and other metals including lead.

Another alloy, made mainly of zinc, is important in the die-casting industry. A **die** is the mold or form that determines the shape of the object. **Die casting**—pouring heated metal into a die—produces many parts used in home appliances, office equipment and vehicles. Many modern conveniences including dishwashers, light fixtures, and even automobiles wouldn't work without die-cast parts.

A coating of metallic zinc keeps this guardrail from rusting.

Death on the Blue Mountain

In 1897, The New Jersey Zinc Company decided to build a new smelting plant. They laid out a community and named it Palmerton for Stephen S. Palmer, the company's president. Palmerton, Pennsylvania, was a company town. The first smelter began operating in 1898. The company built a second smelting plant, the East Plant, in 1911. For 82 years the smelters operated. They provided jobs and supplied essential products for other industries.

The Blue Mountain was a picture postcard setting for the town of Palmerton. Dominated by oaks, American chestnuts, and white pines, the dense forest canopy shaded the mountain. In Palmerton, people planted vegetable gardens and grew flowers in their neatly trimmed lawns. They were proud hard-working people, and their life was good.

No one could have predicted that one day the picture on the postcard would show a mountain littered with the skeletons of dead trees and lawns with no grass. Unfortunately, the smelting of metals is not a clean process. Visit Ducktown, Tennessee; Sudbury, Ontario; or other sites where a smelter operated for many years, and the landscape provides evidence of the negative environmental impacts caused by the smelting of metals.

Trees in the original forest were cleared by loggers or destroyed by forest fires. Normally after a fire, the natural process of **succession** eventually produces a new forest ecosystem. On the Blue Mountain, the second growth forest was missing one of the original dominant species. By 1930, the introduction of a fungus—the chestnut blight—had prevented the regrowth of this species, the American chestnut. [See page 65.]

There were signs that the forest ecosystem near the smelters was ailing as early as the 1920s. The smelting operations continued as did the decline of the forest. Aerial photographs of the area taken between the 1950s and 1980s show the gradual loss of the forest on the north-facing slope of the Blue Mountain. By 1970, the forest ecosystem was gone. In some areas there were no signs of life. Other areas supported only scrubby growth—mostly sassafras, and its leaves showed signs of stress. What had caused these changes? This question could only be answered by a detailed scientific study.

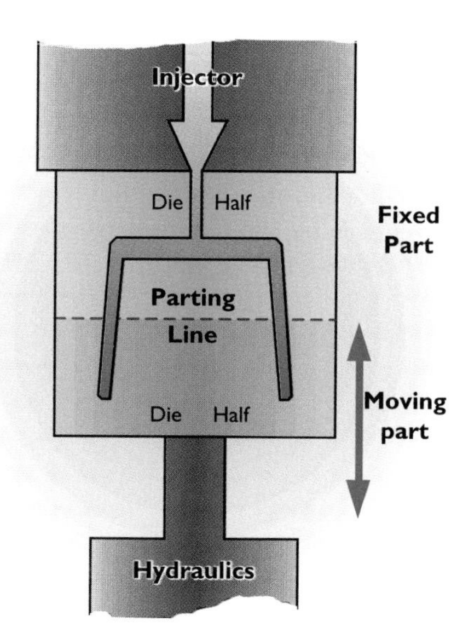

Appliances and automobiles depend upon parts made by injecting a metal or plastic into a mold or die. The die is made of a zinc alloy.

The south-facing slope of the Blue Mountain.

The north-facing slope of the Blue Mountain behind the former Palmerton High School.

A Student Studies the Mountain

Dr. Marilyn Jordan, a graduate student at Rutgers University, conducted an extensive field study of the Blue Mountain's forest ecosystem. She identified the NJZ Company smelters as the probable source of pollutants. The only other industry, a small chemical plant, was located south of the Lehigh Gap. The location and the wind direction made it an unlikely cause of the changes on the mountain.

The prevailing winds blow from the northwest directly toward the Blue Mountain. Because the mountain intercepts the winds, it received a heavy dose of pollutants from the smelter's smokestacks. The major pollutants were zinc, cadmium, copper, lead, and sulfur dioxide gas.

A population census revealed that the density of trees and tree seedlings near the smelters was significantly less than the density at sites farther downwind from the smelters. Plots far from the smelters had twice as many tree species as plots close to the smelters. Could one or more of the pollutants be responsible for the difference in the number and kinds of trees growing near the smelters?

The Blue Mountain — a Study of Trees

Trees	Control	Lehigh Gap
Number per hectare	809	544
Number of Species	13	7
Tree Seedlings	**Control**	**Lehigh Gap**
Number per square meter	4.5	2.4
Number of Species	11	5

The location of the Lehigh Gap plot was 2 km from the smelters.
Control plots were more than 15 kilometers from the smelters.

Adapted from Jordan, Marilyn J. 1975.

Experiments in the Laboratory

Dr. Jordan thought that, "High levels of metals in the soil were preventing germination and/or stunting growth of seedlings." She suspected that the problem was either zinc or cadmium. To find out, she designed a controlled experiment. She grew oak and pine seedlings in soil collected from the top of the mountain. Analysis of soil collected at sites near the smelter (2 km away) showed high levels of zinc and cadmium. Soil samples collected far from the smelter (40 km away) contained much lower levels of the metals.

Analysis of Soil Samples from Blue Mountain

	Zinc (parts per million)		Cadmium (parts per million)	
Distance from Smelter	**Near**	**Far**	**Near**	**Far**
Organic Matter	20,000	300	500	3
Top Soil	2,000	100	10	2

Adapted from Buchauer, M.J. 1973.

The oak seedlings grown in the "near" soil produced less new twig growth and had fewer leaves. The average length of the leaf blades was shorter. The pine seedlings grown in the "near" soil were shorter and showed signs of yellowing. Both oak and pine seedlings grown in "near" soil produced very few new roots.

Were the metals poisoning the plants? Dr. Jordan analyzed oak leaves and pine needles to find out if the plants had absorbed toxic doses of zinc and cadmium. The only metal present at levels known to be toxic was zinc. Although the cadmium levels were not high enough to be considered toxic, cadmium might cause a **synergistic effect**—increasing the toxic effect of the zinc.

Dr. Jordan also collected seeds and acorns from the mountain. She studied the effects of zinc and cadmium on germination and found that zinc inhibits germination and growth of roots. While other environmental factors play some role, Dr. Jordan concluded that the "critical" factor preventing regrowth of the forest was zinc.

Pine seedlings growing in a forest far from a smelter have longer needles and are taller than seedlings grown in soil samples collected near a zinc smelter.

Life and Death on the Forest Floor

Dr. Jordan also studied microorganisms on the Blue Mountain. She found the total number of bacteria and fungi were greatly reduced near the smelters. Another scientist analyzed leaf litter on the forest floor at sites near and far from the smelter. He found thicker layers of leaf litter near the smelter (8.1 kg/m^2) than far from the smelter (3.8 kg/m^2). Other studies also show that there is a slower rate of decomposition in ecosystems polluted with metals.

A population census found the numbers and kinds of small arthropods, especially mites known to feed on leaf litter, were reduced at sites near the smelters. In a laboratory experiment, woodlice were fed samples of leaf litter collected from different sites along the Blue Mountain. The litter that was collected nearest the smelters was toxic to the woodlice. Leaf litter collected at sites further from the smelter was less toxic. A second experiment identified the probable cause of death to the woodlice as zinc poisoning.

In a healthy forest, pine seedlings grow in the clearing created when the old pine tree was blown over during a storm. Near a zinc smelter the zinc in the soil prevents the growth of the seedlings.

Another study compared wildlife in an oak forest 6 miles (10 km) upwind from the zinc smelters with wildlife at a site 1.3 miles (2 km) downwind from the smelters. While earthworms, slugs and snails were common at the upwind site, none could be found at the downwind site. Frogs, toads and salamanders were also very rare or absent.

Much higher concentrations of metals were found in those species that feed on leaf litter. While tests show that some animals contain abnormally high concentrations of metals, it doesn't prove that the metals are killing these animals. A more important factor affecting some species may be the changes in the forest ecosystem.

Effects on Wildlife and Farm Animals

There is evidence that high levels of lead are affecting some species of small mammals and birds, but most of these animals appear healthy. The lead concentrations in two cuckoos were as high as the levels associated

Mature horses in the area near the smelter seemed healthy, but their foals showed symptoms of cadmium poisoning.

with the death of bald eagles, but lower than the levels known to kill some other species of birds. It is important to remember that the level of a pollutant that affects one species may not have the same effect on another species.

Little is known about the effects of heavy metals on wild mammals. Hunters cooperated with scientists from the U.S. Fish and Wildlife Service to collect feces and tissues from white-tailed deer. Analysis of the feces, livers and kidneys showed that zinc and cadmium levels in deer near the site were five times that of a control population. An examination of the hind-leg joints of a deer revealed changes associated with zinc poisoning. Cadmium levels may have been high enough to cause kidney damage in older deer. Further research is necessary to determine the effects of these metals on the white-tailed deer population.

Farmers suspected that the smelters were causing lameness, swollen joints and a decline in the health of horses and cattle. Mature horses seemed healthy, but their foals became stiff-legged and stopped eating. Eventually the foals died, or their owners had them put to sleep. A postmortem examination revealed lesions similar to those found in the joints of animals fed high-zinc diets. One foal had severe osteoporosis and kidney disease. Both of these symptoms are associated with cadmium poisoning. One farmer found that he could raise foals if he bought feed grown outside the area.

Effects on Human Health

Through their play activities, children living near smelters are exposed to higher levels of pollutants.

In 1975, the president of The New Jersey Zinc Company acknowledged that "our activities do affect ecological systems," and he pledged to "improve where possible the quality of life in and around our operations." Scientists have studied the effects of pollution on the mountain, but what about the health of people who were being exposed to high concentrations of metals? No one had studied the risks to human health.

A special team of scientists reviewed the possible health risks at places where high concentrations of heavy metals have been found in the soil. Other communities included in the study were located near smelters in Texas, Arizona, Oklahoma, Montana and Pennsylvania. Randomly selected people donated hair, blood, and urine samples for analysis. They also completed a questionnaire to help identify other possible sources of metals.

The study compared the levels of metals in the environment with the levels found in the body. Scientists concluded that people, especially children, living near smelters are exposed to higher levels of contamination. The study also showed that daily activities, such as smoking and time spent outdoors, affect exposure. It did not attempt to measure the health effects of the exposure to heavy metals.

Below are the effects of heavy metal exposure in populations living near smelters:

- Communities near copper smelters had the highest levels of arsenic.
- Communities near zinc smelters had the highest levels of cadmium and lead.
- Sites nearest the smelters had the highest levels of metals.
- The 1–5 year olds had significantly higher levels of metals found in blood and hair than other age groups.
- In Palmerton, children living nearest the smelter had elevated levels of cadmium in their blood and hair, and elevated lead levels in their hair.
- Males had significantly higher levels of lead in blood and higher levels of all metals (cadmium, lead and arsenic) in hair.
- Many smokers had higher levels of metal in hair and blood than nonsmokers.
- In several cases, individuals who spent more time out of doors had significantly higher levels of metal in hair.

The EPA is concerned about possible health effects from high levels of heavy metals found in the soil near the smelters in Palmerton. The EPA classifies arsenic and cadmium as known human **carcinogens**, and lead as a probable human carcinogen. Prolonged exposure to arsenic may also cause liver or kidney damage. In low doses, cadmium can permanently damage kidneys. Lead also damages kidneys and interferes with the production of red blood cells and sperm. Children with blood levels at or above 10 micrograms per deciliter have significantly lower IQs.

Blood tests show that the levels of lead, cadmium, zinc, and arsenic detected in the Palmerton area may pose a health threat, particularly to young children. The percentage of children in Palmerton with lead levels at or above the CDC "level of concern" is nearly three times the national average. The number of mature adults (aged 40 to 75) residing in Palmerton showing increased levels of cadmium is also a concern.

The Agency for Toxic Substances and Disease Registry (ATSDR) is required by law to conduct public health assessments at all National Priorities List (NPL) hazardous waste sites. After a review of data available at that time, ATSDR concluded no adverse health effect could be linked to exposure to the contaminants in the Palmerton area. But the agency also declared the site a public health hazard because high levels of contaminants and exposure continue. Additional health studies are being conducted.

The zinc company today. The company's efforts to restore the mountain can be seen in this view of the recycling facility.

HRD—Hazardous Dust to Metal Products

The smelters shut down in 1980, and the West Plant of the New Jersey Zinc Company was dismantled. The zinc company, now called Zinc Corporation of America (ZCA), produces zinc products at the site of the east plant. ZCA no longer uses virgin zinc smelted from ores. The company buys recycled zinc—zinc recovered from parts in old cars and appliances—from its sister company HRD.

HRD recycling facility, Palmerton, PA.

Horsehead Resources Development Company, Inc. (HRD) operates a metal recycling facility in Palmerton. Metals are recovered from electric arc furnace (EAF) dust, a hazardous waste product from steel mills. The dust is heated in high-temperature (2,100°F [1,150°C]) kilns to remove zinc, cadmium and lead. In 1991, HRD processed 345,000 tons (310,500 metric tonnes) of EAF dust, and recovered 66,000 tons (59,400 metric tonnes) of metals.

Recycling and the Environment

The EPA lists EAF dust as hazardous waste. Pollution control equipment at steel mills collect EAF dust to prevent the release of zinc, cadmium and lead into the environment. Due to the high zinc content (15%), the EPA prohibits the dumping of EAF dust in landfills where recycling is accessible. According to information provided by the company, HRD is a leader in the recycling of EAF dust. The EPA has designated the High Temperature Metal Recovery (HTMR) process as the Best Available Demonstrated Technology for processing EAF dust.

Recycling of metals provides powerful environmental benefits. Recycling can cut energy required for the production of products from 50–90%. It also reduces pollution associated with mining and smelting the ores, and it eliminates the problems associated with solid waste disposal. To protect the environment we must recycle, but the proper procedures must be followed during the recycling process to minimize air and water pollution.

In 1994, a completed study found the majority of pollution in Palmerton to be industrial in origin. The past smelting operation was identified as the source of 90% of the contamination. The current EAF dust-recycling operation continues to add pollutants to the environment. Lead-based paint was not found to be a significant source of pollution when compared to the industrial contamination of NJZ.

HRD discharged wastewater with high levels of metals into the Aquashicola Creek.

HRD vs. the EPA

According to the company's Annual Report (1991), modernization of the HRD facilities in Palmerton will "assure continued operations in Palmerton with maximum protection for our employees and the environment." But plans to modernize were not enough to satisfy the EPA. The agency is demanding action.

The EPA says that there are serious problems with current operations at the plant. In January 1992, the EPA filed a lawsuit against HRD alleging repeated violations of the Clean Air and Clean Water Acts. According to the lawsuit, HRD:

- Improperly stored hazardous wastes in piles exposed to wind and rain.
- Allowed wastes to escape from storage facilities and open trucks.
- Allowed illegal emissions from smokestacks and bag houses.
- Discharged waste water with high levels of metals into the Aquashicola Creek.
- Operated without necessary permits.

Company officials maintain that the town is a relatively safe place to live. They say that current operations involving the recycling of metals are "an economic necessity" and are "relatively safe." The issue is not the value of recycling metals. The issue is the safety of the recycling operation at HRD in Palmerton.

Some citizens ignore the frequent headlines in the local newspapers that report the on-going negotiations between HRD and the EPA. Other residents follow the stories closely and closely monitor activities at the company. They are suspicious of the company's actions. Yet other people display "NO EPA" signs in their windows.

HRD has a significant economic impact on the community. The company is the largest employer in the area, and it makes large charitable contributions to the community. HRD is "convinced that our technology will enhance the environment and will make us a significant leader in contributing to a cleaner environment." The EPA is taking enforcement actions to ensure that the environment is protected.

2.10 QUESTIONS FOR STUDY AND DISCUSSION:

1. Define the following terms: **VOCABULARY**

alloy	minerals
brass	ore
die casting	rock
fusion	smelting
galvanizing	succession
metals	synergistic effect

The Franklin Ore

2. Some—but not all—rocks are classified as an ore. What kinds of rocks are classified as ores?
3. The ore that became known as the Franklin ore contained a unique collection of minerals. List three minerals found in the Franklin ore.

Zinc Oxide—The First Product

4. Identify 5 industries that use zinc oxide as an additive in their products.
5. List three products that you use that may contain zinc oxide.

Metal from the Franklin Ore

6. Explain how zinc is used in each of the following processes:
galvanizing, fusion, and die casting.
7. Make the connection between the following substances: brass, alloy, and zinc.

Death on the Blue Mountain

8. Compare the Blue Mountain in 1900 with the Blue Mountain in 1970.
9. List positive and negative impacts associated with the smelting of metals.
10. What process usually produces a new forest following a forest fire? Why didn't this happen on the Blue Mountain?

A Student Studies the Mountain

11. Explain why Dr. Jordan suspected that the NJZ smelters were the sources of pollutants affecting the mountain.
12. Identify the major pollutants produced during the smelting of the zinc ores.

Experiments in the Laboratory

13. Soil samples collected near the smelter showed potentially toxic concentrations of two metals.What were these metals?
14. Compare the plants grown in the "near" soil to the plants grown in the "far" soil.
15. According to Dr. Jordan, what pollutant prevented the regrowth of the forest?

Life and Death on the Forest Floor

16. Explain why the dead leaves and dead trees accumulate on the mountain, but in other forest ecosystems they disappear.
17. Identify animal populations in the forest that appear to be suffering from the effects of the pollutants.
18. Zinc is not equally toxic to all species. Explain why a species may be missing from the mountain even though it is not affected by zinc.

Effects on Wildlife and Farm Animals

19. Explain why it is difficult for scientists to predict the effects of the smelting operations on song birds.
20. Identify the heavy metals that may be affecting the white-tailed deer population and describe their effects.
21. How did the pollutants affect farm animals?

Effects on Human Health

22. What group of people is likely to be at the greatest risk from exposure to metals?
23. The EPA is concerned about the presence of two metals in the soil near the smelters. Identify the potential effects of these two metals.

HRD—Hazardous Dust to Metal Products

24. Identify the source of EAF dust.
25. Describe the recycling operation at HRD.

Recycling and the Environment

26. Identify the "positive impacts" associated with the recycling of EAF dust.
27. Identify the "negative impacts" associated with the recycling operation at HRD.

HRD vs. the EPA

28. In Pennsylvania, it is illegal to store hazardous waste without a permit from the Department of Environmental Resources. If HRD applies for a permit to store the EAF dust, and it was your decision to issue or deny the permit, would you grant the company a permit? Justify your position.

The EPA at the "Palmerton Zinc Superfund Site"

"Together, the problems form one of the largest and most complex Superfund sites in the nation."
AMY BARNETT
EPA Community Relations Coordinator

In the 1970s, the United States made dramatic improvements in the quality of water and air. Not until the 1980s did the nation address the issue of hazardous wastes. The **Comprehensive Environmental Response, Compensation, and Liability Act** of 1980 (CERCLA), commonly known as **Superfund**, was enacted to provide a nationwide program to address the most serious threats from hazardous waste, and to make the polluters pay for cleaning up the sites that they contaminated.

The law gave the U.S. Environmental Protection Agency (EPA) the authority to respond to any situation involving a release (or potential release) of hazardous substances into the environment. It also created the **Superfund Trust Fund** financed by taxes on the chemical and petroleum industries. The funds are used by the EPA to "clean up" abandoned or uncontrolled hazardous substances that may threaten public health or the environment.

Anyone who contributed to the release (or potential release) of hazardous substances is liable, and may be sued by the EPA, for the cost of the cleanup. **Potentially responsible parties** (PRPs) include former and current owners of the site, operators of the site, and anyone who disposed of or produced waste found at the site. When no responsible party can be identified, the cost of the cleanup is taken from the $8.5 billion Superfund Trust Fund.

In 1983, the EPA listed approximately 2,000 acres (808 ha) on the north side of the Blue Mountain in Carbon County, Pennsylvania, and a huge **cinder bank** near the NJZ East Plant (smelter) as a National Priority Superfund hazardous waste site. The cinder bank contains 30,000,000 tons of solid waste that was produced during the smelting of zinc. It is contaminated with zinc, copper, lead and cadmium. The EPA identified both current and former owners of the New Jersey Zinc Company (now the Zinc Corporation of America) as being "potentially responsible" for the contamination of the site. Working with the "responsible parties," the EPA is developing and implementing a detailed cleanup plan.

The population of Palmerton is approximately 5,000, with 850 people living within two kilometers of the hazardous waste site. Due to the extremely large size of the "Palmerton Zinc Superfund Site," it is divided into four areas: the mountain, the cinder bank, the valley and the water. Each area addresses one focus of concern.

Area 1: The Blue Mountain

The mountain is covered with 4 million tons (3.6 million metric tonnes) of toxic soil—an amount that cannot easily be sealed in barrels and hauled

OBJECTIVES

- ✔ **State** the goal of the Superfund law and identify the agency authorized to enforce the law.
- ✔ **Identify** the circumstances that make someone a "potentially responsible party" and **explain** their role in the cleanup of a hazardous waste site.
- ✔ **Describe** the actions taken by the EPA to restore the Blue Mountain and protect the people living in Palmerton.
- ✔ **Predict** the success of the restoration project.

Did You Know?

The Agency for Toxic Substances and Disease Registry lists the Top 20 Hazardous Substances. Three of the pollutants at the Palmerton Zinc Site are on the list. The fourth pollutant, zinc, is an essential nutrient in the human diet.

1. Arsenic
2. Lead
3. Mercury, Metallic
4. Vinyl Chloride
5. Benzene
6. Polychlorinated Biphenyls (PCBs)
7. Cadmium

For the complete list, visit: www.atsdr.cdc.gov/cxcx3.html.

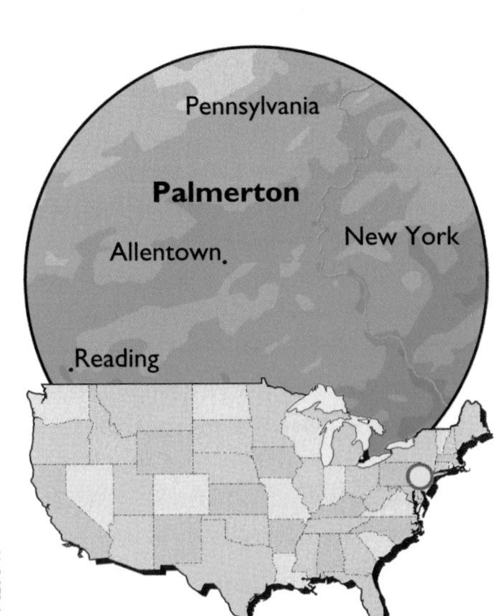

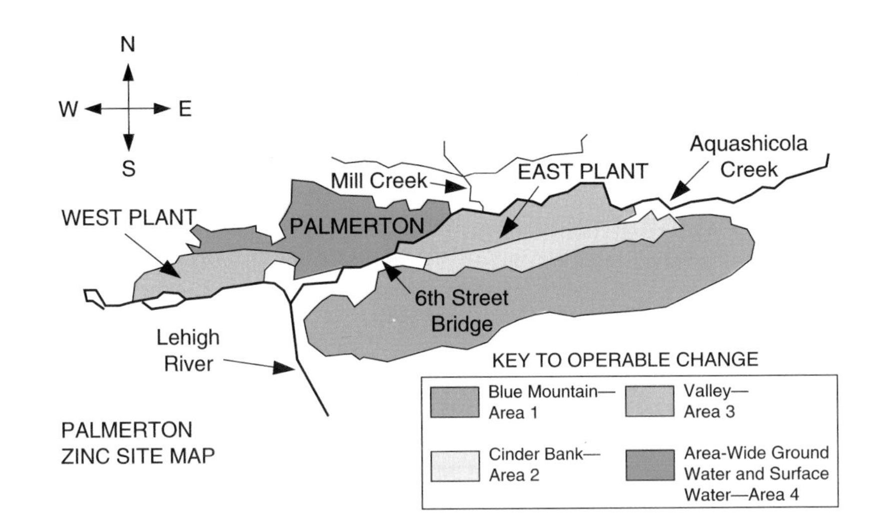

The Aquashicola Creek flows through the zinc company's property. Note the cinder bank on the right.

The revegetation of the Blue Mountain as it appeared during the drought of 1999.

away for safe storage. Even if it was possible to remove the contaminated soil, it is unlikely that plants would grow in the rocky subsoil. Without the roots of plants to hold the soil in place there is massive erosion with each rainfall. The soil, with its load of heavy metals, is carried down the mountainside and into the Aquashicola Creek that flows into the Lehigh River, a tributary of the Delaware River.

To reduce the threat from the hazardous chemicals in the soil, the "cleanup" must: (1) reduce erosion and runoff, and (2) restore the forest ecosystem. The plan, approved by the EPA, requires covering the north side of the mountain with a synthetic soil. The artificial soil is a mixture of sewage sludge and fly ash. **Fly ash** is the collection of particles captured by pollution control equipment at coal-burning power plants. **Sludge** is the solid material that is removed from the wastewater at sewage treatment plants.

The sludge/fly ash mixture was blended with grass and tree seeds and then sprayed on the mountain. Tree seedlings were also planted. After several years of pilot testing, the full-scale revegetation project began in 1991. About 1,000 acres (404 ha) have been revegetated and the process is to continue until the entire area is once again covered with green plants.

Will a healthy forest ecosystem once again shade the mountain? About 1,000 acres (404 ha) have been successfully revegetated with grasses. Fungal disease, competition with plants, and foraging wildlife are limiting the growth of the tree seedlings. Additional efforts will be made to grow trees and other larger plants.

Area 2: The Cinder Bank

The 4 kilometer-long cinder bank, along the base of the mountain beside the Aquashicola Creek, is 200 feet (60 m) high and in places it is 1000 feet (300 m) wide. The EPA estimates that it contains 30 million tons (27 million metric tonnes) of smelter waste including zinc, copper, lead and cadmium that are **leachable**—soluble in water. Runoff from the cinder bank has carried heavy metals into the creek. Rainwater **percolating** through the cinders leached heavy metals that contaminated a shallow **aquifer**.

In 1988, the EPA approved a plan to "clean up" the cinder bank, but then decided that additional studies were needed to investigate significant subsurface fires in the cinder bank. The new "cleanup" plan includes:

- Digging a trench around the pile so that runoff from the Blue Mountain does not come in contact with the cinder pile and become contaminated before entering the creek.
- Covering the cinder bank with a mixture of sewage sludge, fly ash and grass seed.
- Creating a treatment system that collects and treats precipitation that percolates through the cinder bank.

There is still no decision on how to address the 25 acres (10 ha) of the cinder bank where there are subsurface fires.

The cinder bank will be covered with a mixture of sewage sludge, fly ash and grass seed.

Area 3: The Valley

The clean-up plan for a Superfund site must be based on the most current scientific research data. The EPA reviewed the results of extensive soil tests conducted in 1988. At that time the dangers of lead were not fully known, and the EPA ruled that no immediate action was necessary. In 1991, the Federal Government reduced the amount of lead in blood that is "a threshold of concern" from 25 mcg/dL to 10 mcg/dL. Reducing the residents' exposure to lead and cadmium in soil and dust became the EPA's top priority.

In 1991, the Pennsylvania Department of Environmental Resources found high levels of lead, cadmium and zinc in several homes in Palmerton. The EPA tested additional homes and found high levels of lead in the house dust and on porches. Between 1994 and 1997, the agency sampled almost 350 homes, and 200 homes were cleaned (with approval of the occupants).

People in Palmerton take pride in their homes. Some have chosen alternative landscaping because grass is difficult to grow. Others have excavated and replaced the soil around their homes.

Minimum level to qualify for cleanup (ppm)		Maximum level found in sample area (ppm)	
Lead	1,500	Lead	17,700
Cadmium	100	Cadmium	2,501
Zinc	10,000	Zinc	94,200
Arsenic	>0	Arsenic	503

The EPA has not yet issued a decision on the final cleanup. The immediate goal was to reduce very high lead levels in homes with the most vulnerable population—children up to six years old and pregnant women. In some cases cleaning included replacing carpet and excavating and replacing topsoil.

In addition to exposure from dust, people may also accumulate metals through the food chain and tap water. Studies show that people eating vegetables grown in Palmerton's soil would increase their intake of cadmium. An analysis of fish revealed that only those adjacent to and downstream from the cinder pile were contaminated. The EPA recommends that fish from streams in the area be consumed no more than once a week.

To view EPA and ATSDR documents on the Palmerton Zinc Superfund Site, visit: www.epa.gov/reg3hwmd/super/palmertn/menu50.htm;
for a view of the Superfund activities from the perspective of one citizen's group, visit: www.pro-palmertoncoalition.org.

Environmental Challenge: Superfund Sites

About 60 million people live near a hazardous waste site. According to the Agency for Toxic Substances and Disease Registry (ATSDR), one in four American children lives within 4 miles of a hazardous waste site. As of 1999, the EPA had assessed 39,783 uncontrolled hazardous waste sites. Cleanup actions at more than 30,000 of these sites have been completed. Short-term cleanup actions continue at the remaining sites.

The Superfund has supplied more than 300,000 people with alternate water supplies; relocated more than 14,000 people from areas that posed severe immediate threats; and restricted access by fencing, and in some cases by placing guards, at more than 300 sites.

The EPA must identify and rank seriously polluted sites that require long-term cleanup. Seriously polluted sites are placed on the National Priorities List (NPL). Each year the list changes as new sites are evaluated, added to the list, and finally deleted when the cleanup is finished.

In 1999, there were 1,396 sites on the NPL. The EPA had cleaned up 600 of the NPL sites. The largest number of NPL sites are located in New Jersey (116), Pennsylvania (112), California (97), New York (89), Wisconsin (84), and Florida (64).

To find out more about the Superfund sites in your state, visit: www.epa.gov/superfund.

Area 4: The Water

In 1992, the EPA tested Palmerton's public wells for lead, cadmium, arsenic and zinc. One well showed a small amount of lead, but the amount was far below the "level of concern." The EPA suspects that the lead in the drinking water is being leached from the water pipes (plumbing) in the homes. Four home wells nearest the site were tested for lead and cadmium in 1998. The concentrations of both metals were below the Maximum Contaminant Levels for drinking water.

Although a shallow aquifer is contaminated, the EPA considers it unlikely that Palmerton's water supply is in any danger. The aquifer that supplies water to the towns of Palmerton and Aquashicola is 200–400 feet (60–120 m) below the ground. As water percolates through the soil, heavy metals become attached to soil particles. Thus heavy metals will probably be removed from ground water before it reaches the deep aquifer that is the town's water source. More study of the groundwater is needed to ensure that the water supply remains safe.

Life Goes On

The residents of Palmerton deserve a clean, safe place to live. The children certainly deserve a clean and safe place to play. The ballpark, across the street from the East Plant, is owned by the school district and used by the girl's softball team. In addition, 300 children who participate in the Booster Club programs also use it. The Booster Club president described the field as "... like a rock garden when it rains. It has weeds, not grass. There are bare spots ... (and) left field has craters like the moon's surface."

As a goodwill gesture toward the community, the Zinc Corporation of America agreed to landscape the field. The landscaping project included removing the contaminated topsoil and replacing it with soil from outside the contaminated area. The company says that landscaping the field was a "beautification project." The Booster Club president says it is "a step in the right direction." The craters are gone, and the grassy field is far less dusty. The EPA says that a grassy field is safer than a bare field because the children are less likely to inhale dust that contains lead. The field of green is a better and, yes, a safer place to play. Breathing dust—even dust without lead—is not healthy.

Play ball! The home team is now playing on Palmerton soil. The soil was replaced and the field was sodded by the zinc company.

The Cleanup Continues

The cleanup continues at the Palmerton Superfund Site. Amy Barnett, EPA Community Relations Coordinator, says, "Together, the problems form one of the largest and most complex Superfund sites in the nation." To keep citizens informed, the EPA files technical reports and other information at the public library. Interested citizens and public officials may also attend hearings and receive "Superfund Update" fact sheets from the EPA.

Citizen's groups are actively involved. They ask questions and voice their concerns. One group of residents formed the Palmerton Citizens for a Clean Environment. Another group of citizens formed the Pro-Palmerton Coalition to combat negative publicity about Palmerton. Both groups monitor the current operations at the East Plant site and the progress of the cleanup. The U.S. government has sued four companies to recover the $12 million cleanup costs at the Palmerton Superfund Site.

2.11 Questions for Study and Discussion:

1. Define the following terms: **VOCABULARY**

CERCLA	PRP
cinder bank	sludge
fly ash	Superfund
leachable	

2. What environmental problem was the target of the Comprehensive Environmental Response, Compensation, and Liability Act of 1980 (CERCLA)? What is the more common name for this law?
3. Tools are needed to do a job. The Superfund law gave the EPA two important tools that are needed to protect people and the environment from hazardous substances. What were these tools?
4. Identify the "responsible parties" who must clean up or pay for cleanup of the hazardous waste at the "Palmerton Zinc Site."

Area 1: The Blue Mountain

5. What type of hazardous substances threaten the environment?
6. A "cleanup" plan may include removal of the hazardous substances from the site. Explain why removal is not an appropriate cleanup method on the mountain.
7. Describe how fly ash and sludge are being used to restore the forest ecosystem on the Blue Mountain.

Area 2: The Cinder Bank

8. In what ways does the cinder bank threaten the environment?
9. Describe how the "cleanup" plan will further protect the stream and the groundwater.
10. Why was the "cleanup" plan put on hold?

Area 3: The Valley

11. Why did the EPA rule that "no immediate action was necessary," after reviewing the results of the soil tests taken in 1988?
12. What is the EPA's top priority now?
13. What steps is the EPA taking to "clean up" the valley?

Area 4: The Water

14. The EPA concluded that the wells supplying drinking water for Palmerton's residents were (safe/unsafe).
15. A resident is concerned that the town's water supply may become contaminated 5 or 10 years from now. Explain to this resident why the EPA considers contamination of the wells unlikely.

Life Goes On

16. Do you think that the ballpark was dangerous before it was landscaped? Why or why not? Do you think it is safe now?

The Cleanup Continues

17. The "Palmerton Zinc Site" was listed as a Superfund hazardous waste site in 1982. Why is the "cleanup" taking so long?
18. If you were a Palmerton resident, which citizen's group would you most likely support? Why would you choose this group?

Disaster in Bhopal

OBJECTIVES

- ✔ **Identify** the circumstances that contributed to the disaster in Bhopal.
- ✔ **List** reasons why accurate information on long-term health effects of chemicals is not available.
- ✔ **Describe** the proper procedures that should be followed in a controlled experiment that is designed to test the effects of a chemical.
- ✔ **Summarize** the roles of chemical companies, OSHA, Congress and local communities in the protection of workers and the public.

"It came on the evening wind that drifted through the shantytowns.... The lucky ones, alerted by the suffocating odor, escaped. Thousands did not. Some perished in their sleep. Others awoke, dizzy and nauseated, their eyes on fire and their lungs filling with fluid until they could no longer breathe, dying from exposure to a chemical few had heard of in perhaps history's worst industrial accident."

THE NEW YORK TIMES

The site of the world's largest industrial accident was the Union Carbide pesticide plant in Bhopal, India. On December 3, 1984, a large quantity of water was added to a tank containing 41 metric tonnes of methyl isocyanate (MIC), a chemical used in making the **carbamate pesticides** such as SEVIN and Temik. The chemical reaction caused an increase in temperature and pressure in an underground storage tank, and caused a major release of MIC, a gas that is extremely **toxic** to humans.

The Human Cost

Some of the MIC broke down into hydrogen cyanide, a poison that was used in the Nazi gas chambers in World War II. Unfortunately there were no procedures in place for emergency personnel to follow, and a cyanide antidote was not used. The Indian government reported that 1,430 people had died within four months of the incident. In 1991, the count was updated to more than 3,800 deaths. Deaths were most probably due to pulmonary edema, a buildup of fluid in the lungs, and from respiratory infections.

The condition of the survivors depends on how much gas they breathed. There were increases in the number of stillbirths and spontaneous abortions. Other effects included reproductive system disorders and damage to the eyes. At least 11,000 survivors were left with disabilities. Those with lung damage could not get enough oxygen. The EPA reported that 170,000 survivors suffered adverse health effects.

In 1989, the Supreme Court of India approved a $470 million settlement that was paid to the Indian government by Union Carbide. The court ordered the government to purchase medical insurance for 100,000 persons who may develop symptoms later. Criminal charges against Union Carbide plant managers have not been settled. The Bhopal tragedy forced the chemical industry to make some major changes.

Satellite image of India and Sri Lanka.

Safety Tests

According to the EPA, there is no information available on the chronic (long-term) effects of methyl isocyanate in humans or animals. Approximately 100,000 chemicals are used commercially in the United States. A study by the National Academy of Sciences revealed that the federal government does not have enough accurate health studies on most of the chemicals sold in the United States. Why isn't this information available?

The process of testing chemicals to determine their **toxic** or poisonous effects is very expensive. The testing procedure can cost millions of dollars and take several years to complete. The tests usually involve exposing laboratory animals to the chemical compounds. Exact scientific procedures must be followed.

Laws require manufacturers to submit the results of product safety tests to federal scientists. The test data is used to determine if a product is safe enough to market. The data is also used to determine safe levels of chemical residues on food, and in drinking water, air, and the workplace. While testing has shown that the majority of chemicals on the market are not dangerous, some chemicals are known to cause health and environmental problems.

Senate hearings in 1974 revealed that test data is not always the result of good scientific work. Officials have testified that some of the nation's major drug manufacturers submitted inaccurate test results. Scientists at the Federal Food and Drug Administration used these results to register seven new drugs. Why would a company submit inaccurate test results?

The Controlled Experiment

In every scientific study there is the potential for a serious mistake. Consider the problem of feeding a group of rats exact amounts of a chemical every day for two years. During this time another group of rats must be treated in the same way, except these rats do not receive the chemical. The group of rats that does not receive the chemical being tested is the **control group**. The group of rats that receives the chemical is the **experimental group**.

Each animal's condition must be recorded daily. The weight of each animal must be recorded at least twice each week. If a rat dies, its death must be recorded and samples of its body tissues preserved. At the end of the study, the remaining rats are killed. Slides of various body organs are prepared and analyzed. A two-year study will produce some 250,000 slides.

Consider some of the possible problems that might occur during this study. Over the weekend a technician fails to check the laboratory. In one cage the automatic watering system fails to work, and some rats in that cage die of dehydration while others become weak and listless. Another lab assistant fails to clean the cages, and some rats die of bacterial infection. Still another assistant does not read carefully, so one group of rats is fed the wrong substance.

Mistakes like this should be recorded and reported with the results of the study. Any mistakes in procedure must be evaluated with the data from the study. Some labs have found it easier to fake results. They know that repeating the study will cost the company time and money, and the people responsible may fear being fired.

Another problem is the fact that **toxicology**—the study of the effects of poisonous compounds—is a biological science. In physical science,

Did You Know?

The EPA reports that methyl isocyanate has been detected in cigarette smoke. Occupational exposure can occur for workers who use insecticides and herbicides produced from methyl isocyanate.

Think About It

When reviewing data from a controlled study, a pathologist from the Federal Food and Drug Administration suspected that data had been fabricated. What was the clue? None of the rats had developed cancer. Pathologists know that some rats and mice will develop cancer and die during long-term studies. When the data indicated that none of the rats developed cancer, the pathologist knew something was wrong. After an investigation, three top company officials were convicted of fraud.

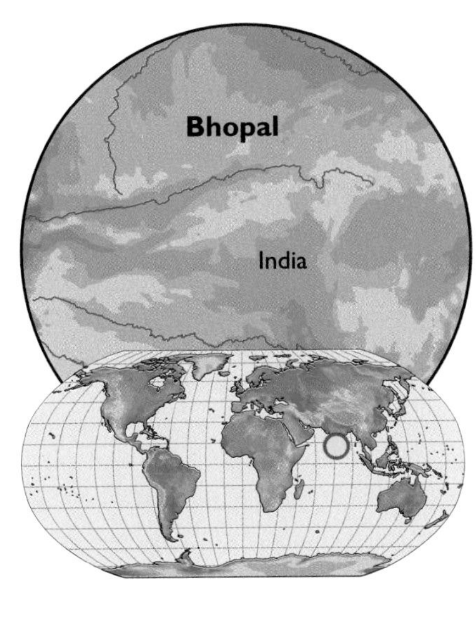

objects act according to certain physical laws, such as gravity. Using these laws, scientists can predict the action of the objects. In biological sciences, this is not always the case.

The fact that rats develop cancer when exposed to a chemical does not necessarily mean that, when exposed to the same conditions, humans will develop cancer. Different species of animals have different reactions to the same chemical. Even members of the same species may react differently to the same substance. These are the gray areas that lead scientists to have different opinions about the results of a scientific study.

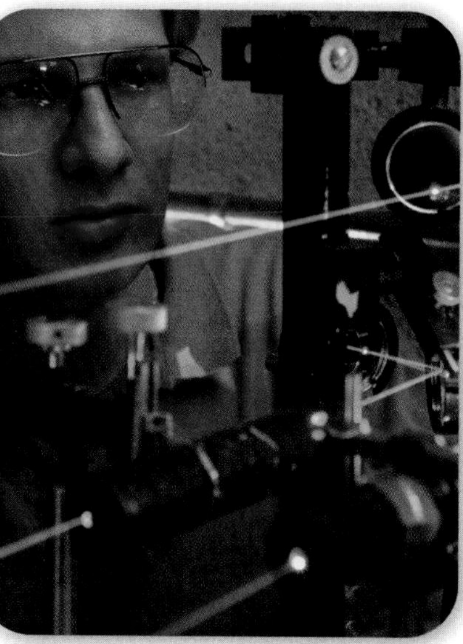

Everyday we take for granted the benefits of technology. Only when accidents happen, do we realize the risks involved with technology.

Manufacturers can accurately predict how much money a new chemical can make for the company, how many jobs it can create, and how useful it will be to society. These are the benefits. It is not as easy for scientists to predict the dangers or the risks of using the chemical.

A new technique is being developed so that the toxic effects of a chemical can be studied by using cells that are grown in laboratory dishes—a method called **tissue culture**. This will make testing much easier. It will also mean that testing can be done faster and with less cost. At the present time, testing animals is the only way we can predict the long-term effects of chemicals.

Union Carbide manufactured nearly 20 million pounds (9 million kg) of MIC in the United States, but the company had not performed toxicity tests on the chemical. The Federal Insecticide, Fungicide, and Rodenticide Act requires toxicity tests for pesticides, but MIC is an intermediate chemical used in the manufacture of a group of insecticides, not an end product. The EPA considers methyl isocyanate to be a "high concern" pollutant because of its acute toxicity. The agency could have used the Toxic Substances Control Act to require Union Carbide to test MIC, but the company was never asked to provide toxicity test results.

A study conducted after the accident by the National Institute of Environmental Health Studies revealed that rats exposed to large doses of MIC develop scar tissue in the small air passageways of the lungs. Researchers think that these scars are permanent. They will make rats or humans more susceptible to respiratory disease and less able to do physical labor. On the other hand, MIC did not affect the reproductive and immune systems of the rats.

The Question of Safety

Could such a tragic event occur in the United States? Since many chemical industries are located in areas with a high population density, a major chemical accident could affect thousands of people. Although most chemical companies have good safety records, the potential for a major chemical accident in a densely populated area of the United States does exist.

An EPA study completed after the Bhopal disaster uncovered 11,048 accidents or "Acute Hazardous Events" that occurred in the United States between 1982 and 1988. The events caused 309 deaths and 11,341 injuries. There were 464,677 people evacuated from their homes and jobs.

The EPA found that 17 of these events could have been more damaging than the Bhopal accident.

In the past, federal inspectors did not seriously consider the possibility of major accidents, but that has changed. Interviewed after the Bhopal accident, a chemical engineer who helped create a list of hazardous chemicals, said: "This country (the U.S.) has been very lucky that it has not had a major chemical accident killing a lot of people. There have been many warnings. Those who try to minimize the hazards are totally wrong."

Preventing Accidents

Plant managers determine what safety precautions are taken. Prevention is better than any emergency plan. Managers have the responsibility to determine whether chemical processes are safe. They are responsible for installing proper equipment, such as temperature gauges and alarm systems, which will monitor reactions and warn of dangerous situations.

The federal **Occupational Safety and Health Administration** (OSHA) regulates hundreds of toxic chemicals in the workplace. Chemical plants are required to have safety equipment and limit exposure to toxic chemicals for workers in chemical plants. The massive number of chemical plants creates problems. Only one out of five chemical plants is inspected each year.

Plant managers are responsible for the installation of safety equipment to warn of dangerous situations.

Safety during transport of chemicals is also a concern. Good safety measures cannot guarantee that an accident will not occur, but they can reduce the risk. A trailer carrying 3,000 gallons (1.1x104 L) of methyl isocyanate nearly separated from the truck as it was being hauled from the plant in West Virginia to a pesticide plant in New York. Fortunately, an emergency crew accompanies all shipments of MIC. The accident was prevented because the crew following the truck noticed sparks beneath the trailer and notified the truck driver. The driver was able to pull off the road. Another truck was sent to return the cargo to the plant because Pennsylvania law prohibits shipments of hazardous chemicals, such as MIC, at night.

After the Bhopal tragedy, Congress took steps to make sure communities are better informed and ready to respond to an emergency situation. Experts agreed that better information about the location of hazardous chemicals was essential to reducing risks. If communities are to be properly prepared for a possible accident, they have to know this information. In 1986, Congress passed the **Emergency Planning and Community Right-to-Know Act**. The Act requires these actions by communities and companies:

- Chemical manufacturers must inform state and local authorities and make available to the public information on the quantities of hazardous materials they handle.

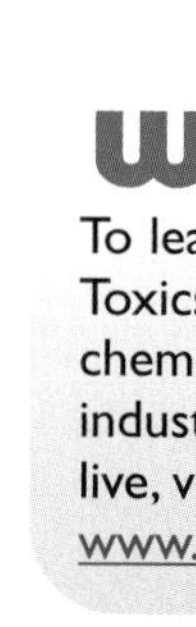

To learn more about the Toxics Release Inventory and chemicals that are released from industries in the state where you live, visit: www.epa.gov/opptintr/tri.

- Larger companies that make or use certain chemicals must report amounts released to the environment. The EPA reports the total releases of more than 600 hazardous chemicals in the **Toxics Release Inventory**.
- Companies must immediately notify national, state, and local officials when there is an unexpected release of certain hazardous substances.
- Local communities must develop an emergency response plan for chemical accidents.

The best way to reduce the chance of an accident is to avoid the use of toxic chemicals. Manufacturers are redesigning processes and improving procedures to minimize the risk of accidental releases of toxic chemicals. Companies are devising procedures that eliminate the need for toxic chemicals. Where toxics can't be replaced, a good emergency plan can reduce injuries and save lives.

2.12 QUESTIONS FOR STUDY AND DISCUSSION:

1. Define the following terms: **VOCABULARY**

carbamate pesticides	Right-to-Know Act
control group	tissue culture
controlled experiment	toxic
experimental group	toxicology
OSHA	toxics release inventory
plant manager	

2. Describe the events that occurred in Bhopal, India, on the night of December 3, 1984.

The Human Cost

3. How did the poisonous compound, methyl isocyanate, affect people?

Safety Tests

4. What was the conclusion of the study done by the National Academy of Sciences?
5. Give two reasons why companies like to avoid testing new chemicals.
6. How are the test results used?

The Controlled Experiment

7. List some reasons why test data is sometimes faked.
8. What is the difference between the control group and the experimental group? Why is a control group needed?
9. Explain why the science of toxicology is more controversial than the science of physics?
10. What new technique is being developed that may some day allow us to study the effects of chemical compounds cheaper and faster?

The Question of Safety

11. Do you think that an accident like the one that happened in Bhopal, India, could happen in the United States? Justify your position.

Preventing Accidents

12. What is the role of the plant manager in the prevention of accidents at a chemical plant? What is the role of OSHA in the prevention of accidents?
13. How does Union Carbide try to ensure the safety of people when methyl isocyanate is being transported in the United States?
14. What law, passed after the Bhopal accident, requires communities and companies to work together to reduce the risk from chemical releases?
15. List the 4 requirements of the Act passed by Congress in 1986.

Forecast: Acid Deposition (Acid Rain)

"The clams go first, then the snails, then the crayfish ... then out go the fish. ...the lakes look like they have Astroturf on the bottom."

HAROLD HARVEY
University of Toronto

OBJECTIVES

- ✔ **Explain** why acid rain is both an environmental and political problem.
- ✔ **Describe** natural processes and that create acid deposition.
- ✔ **Contrast** a healthy aquatic ecosystem and one that is affected by acid deposition.
- ✔ **Evaluate** the risk of acid deposition in watersheds with different types of rocks.
- ✔ **Summarize** the current understanding of the impacts of acid deposition on field crops and forests.
- ✔ **List** ways in which acid deposition affects humans.
- ✔ **Identify** steps that the government and individuals can take to reduce the acidity of precipitation.

Acid Rain: A Political Issue

A British chemist coined the term "acid rain" in 1872. It was not until one hundred years later that acid rain became an important scientific and political issue. At the 1972 United Nations Conference on the Human Environment, a Swedish scientist told the world about acid rain and acid snow in Sweden and Norway. He thought that the source of the acid rain was industry in Western Europe, and he suggested that acid rain was a kind of "chemical war."

Acid rain became a major environmental issue during the 1970s and 1980s. It has been a source of political disputes between Great Britain and Scandinavian countries, between the U.S. and Canada, and between Midwestern and Northeastern regions of the U.S.

When President Reagan visited Canada in 1981, a crowd confronted him outside of Parliament. They nearly drowned out the President's speech with chants of "Go home, acid rain." A demonstrator held up a stuffed fish with the words "save me." It was the largest demonstration ever held in Canada for a foreign leader.

In 1982, the Canadian Film Board distributed a film concerning the issue of acid rain. The film's narrator says, "Winds do not respect political boundaries." The film describes pollution carried by winds from the United States to Canada. President Reagan's administration banned the film. Anyone showing the film in the United States was required by law to read a statement that said: "The Reagan administration has determined this film to be propaganda." Scientists, attending a conference sponsored by the National Wildlife Federation, declared the film to be "scientifically sound."

The controversy surrounding acid rain continued. Prime Minister Mulroney and President Reagan appointed Special Envoys to explore the issue of acid rain. In a speech at the New England Governors' Conference, Drew Lewis, President Reagan's special envoy, said: "Saying [sulfur oxide] doesn't cause acid rain seems to me the same as saying smoking doesn't cause cancer. ...I will recommend the Administration acknowledge there is a problem."

The Special Envoy's joint report concluded that acid rain is a serious environmental and diplomatic problem requiring a U.S.—Canada agreement. On March 19, 1986, President Reagan endorsed the report. This was the first time that the U.S. Administration acknowledged that acid rain was an international problem that required a joint action by both countries.

Acid Rain: Defined

The acidity of a substance is measured on a **pH scale.** The range of numbers on the pH scale is from 0 (very acidic) to 14 (very basic or alkaline). The pH value of 7, in the middle of the scale, is neutral. A change of one whole number on the scale represents a 10-fold change in acidity. A pH of 5 is ten times more acidic than a pH of 6. A pH of 3 is one thousand times more acidic than a pH of 6.

The pH Scale: The color distribution of the chart represents the indicator colors of pHydrion paper that is used to determine the pH of liquids.

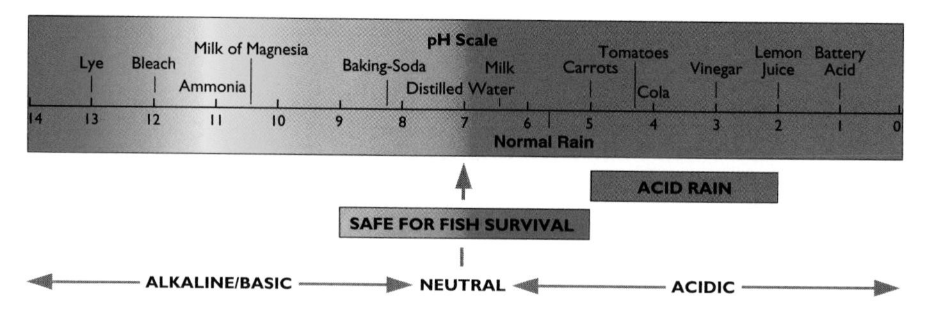

If no pollutants entered the atmosphere, rain and snow would be naturally acidic. Carbon dioxide produced by natural processes combines with water vapor in the atmosphere, forming **carbonic acid**. Although it is somewhat variable, the pH of natural rainfall is generally between 5.0 and 5.6.

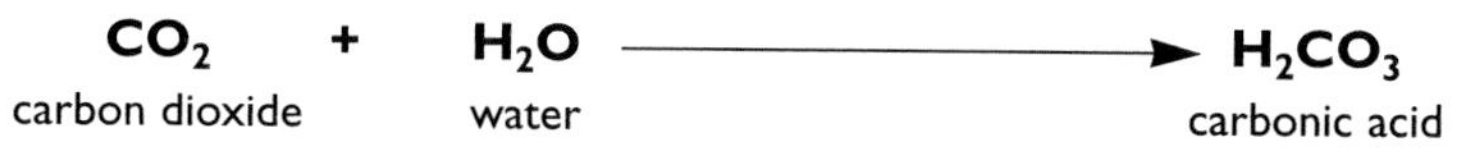

$$CO_2 + H_2O \rightarrow H_2CO_3$$

carbon dioxide + water → carbonic acid

The term **acid rain** is commonly used to describe any substance in the atmosphere that produces a pH lower than natural rainfall. Since these substances come in both wet and dry forms, scientists prefer the more accurate term **acid deposition**. Wet substances include rain, snow, sleet, hail, clouds, fog, dew, and frost. Dry substances are either gases or small particles that behave like acid rain when they come in contact with any form of moisture. Any precipitation with a pH value less than 5.0 is considered to be acid rain. Frequently it is ten times more acidic than natural rain.

Natural pollutants change the pH of precipitation. Wind-blown dust from alkaline soils in prairie or desert regions can raise the pH above 5.6. During thunderstorms, lightning changes nitrogen oxides into nitric acid. Sulfur from hot springs, volcanoes or decaying matter is changed into sulfuric acid. These acids can lower the pH below 5.0. The pH of rain falling after one volcanic eruption was 2.8.

Human Activities and Acid Rain

The major sources of chemicals that produce acid rain are human activities. Since the industrial revolution, humans have been creating vast amounts of pollutants that cause acid rain. In the eastern region of North America, human activities produce 90% of the sulfur emissions and 95% of the nitrogen emissions. Over 20 million tons (18 million metric tonnes) of these gases enter the atmosphere each year.

Fossil fuel combustion is the biggest single source of chemicals that form acids when released into the atmosphere. Fossil fuels—coal, oil, and gas—contain large amounts of sulfur and nitrogen. When these fuels are burned, sulfur dioxide (SO_2) and nitrogen oxides (NO_2) are released into the atmosphere. Chemical reactions, between oxygen, water and other chemicals in the atmosphere, convert these gases to sulfuric acid, nitrous acid, and nitric acid.

Production of Acid Rain in the Atmosphere

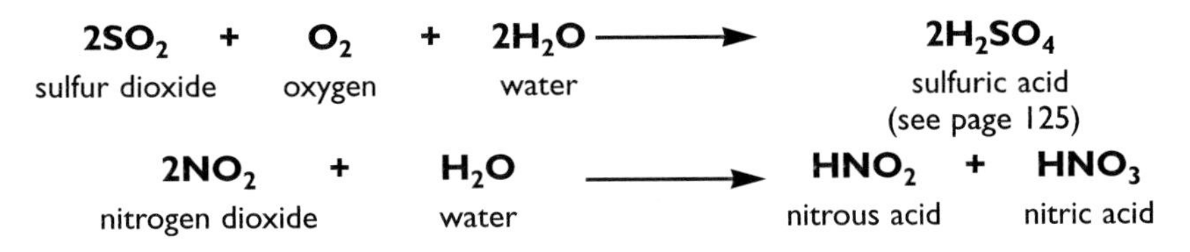

Metal smelters are the largest single source of sulfur dioxide emissions in Canada. In the United States, thermoelectric generating stations (power plants) produce most of the sulfur dioxide. The highest concentration of power plants and industries producing sulfur dioxide is in the Ohio River Valley.

In both the U.S. and Canada, motor vehicle exhaust is the major source of nitrogen oxide emissions. On the West Coast of the U.S., nitrogen oxides from vehicle exhaust seem to be the major cause of acid rain. In December 1982, the pH of a Los Angeles fog was 1.7. The pH of rain in the mid-continental states averages 4.4–5.0, while rain in the Northeast frequently has a pH of 4.0–4.5. Individual storms are sometimes much worse. In Wheeling, West Virginia, one rainstorm had a pH of 1.5.

The state of Pennsylvania holds the record for the most acidic average annual rainfall in the nation (4.08-4.26). Pennsylvania is directly downwind from fossil fuel-burning industries and electric power plants in the Ohio River Valley and Midwest. Pennsylvania is also one of the largest producers of chemicals that cause acid rain.

WWW

For more information, visit www.epa.gov/oar and btdqs.usgs.gov/acidrain/. Also conduct search for "National Atmospheric Deposition Program."

The Midwest-Northeast Controversy

For many years, scientists have believed acid rain comes from pollutants that pour out of the tall smokestacks in the Midwest, but this has been difficult to prove. The solution to pollution during the 1960s and 1970s was taller smokestacks. Smokestacks were built higher to carry pollutants farther away from their sources. It was thought that the pollutants would be diluted and destroyed if they were released high into the atmosphere.

Until now there was little scientific evidence to prove what really happens to the gases after they leave the stack. Now we know that the gases can react with water, oxygen, and other chemicals in the atmosphere. As the gases are carried by winds and weather systems, they are changed into sulfuric and nitric acids. These pollutants fall back to earth as "acid rain" hundreds of miles away from their sources.

The world's tallest smokestack is at the International Nickel Co. in Sudbury, Ontario, Canada.

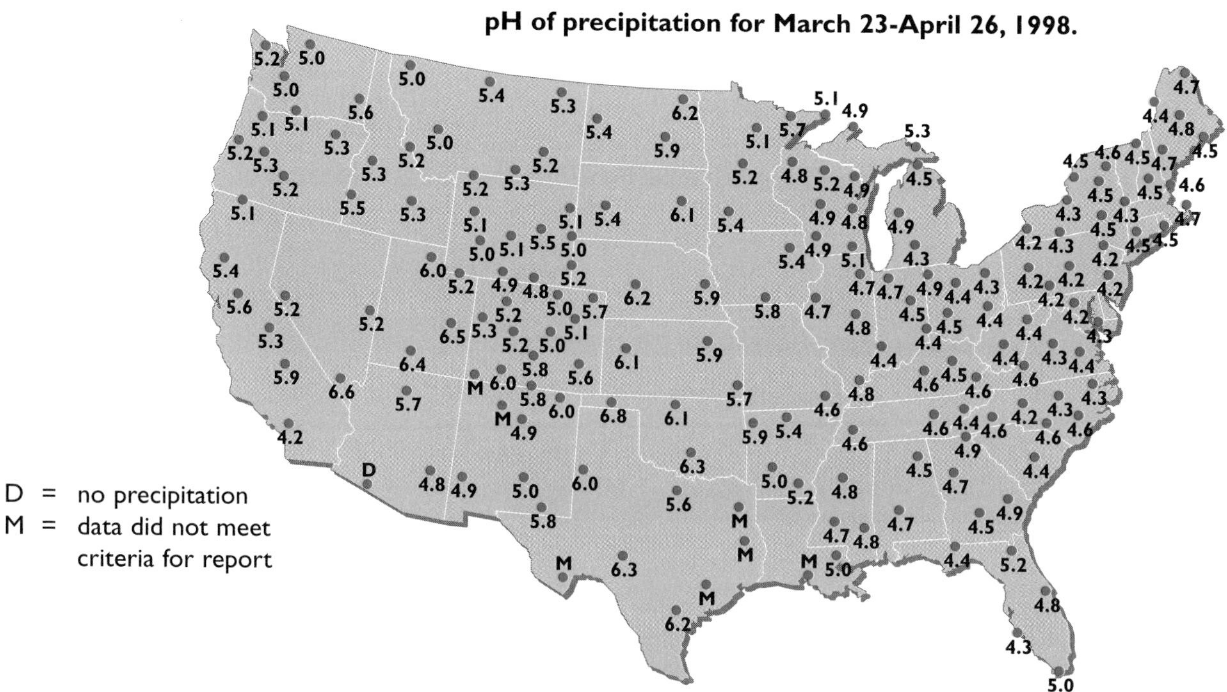

It has been estimated that 50% of the sulfate emissions deposited in Canada come from the United States. How do you prove a chemical that lands in Toronto or even Philadelphia came from a certain smokestack in the Ohio River Valley? Experiments using tracer chemicals may identify the exact sources of pollution.

Tracers are chemicals that are not normally found in the atmosphere or chemicals that are found in only very small amounts. Some tracers are radioactive substances that can be detected by sensitive instruments. Others are unique chemicals that do not react with other chemicals in the atmosphere.

In 1983 scientists began an experiment that released a tracer substance from two different sites. One site was in the United States (Dayton, Ohio) and the other was in Canada (Sudbury, Ontario). The experiment was named **Captex** for Cross Appalachian Tracer Experiment.

The tracer substance was a compound containing carbon and fluorine. This gas—perfluoromonomethylcyclohexane—is normally found in the atmosphere in very small concentrations. For two weeks after the tracer substance was released, weather balloon stations monitored the air currents. Air samples were taken at ground level and at different levels in the atmosphere. Scientists, flying in airplanes, collected air samples from clouds and from air masses. Computers plotted the path of the tracer chemicals and pollutants.

The experiment was originally designed to determine the path of pollution from a dangerous chemical explosion or a nuclear accident, but it also helped us learn more about the path of pollutants that cause acid rain. The experiment, Captex, cost about $2 million, and the data took more than a year to analyze.

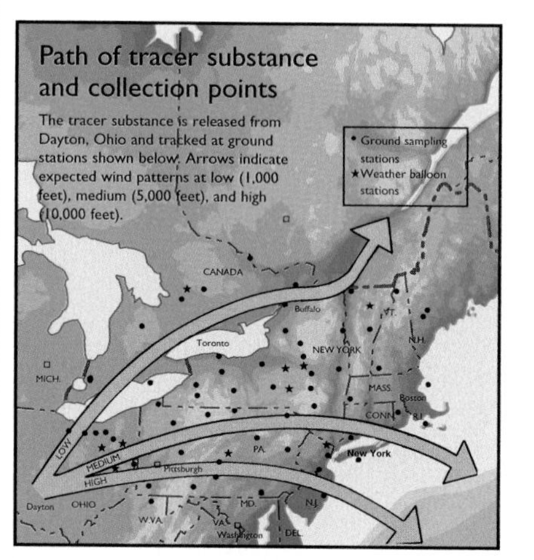

Paths of tracer substance from Coptex.

Acid Rain: Is It Deadly?

Living organisms cannot survive if the pH is too low or too high. The normal pH of human blood is 7.35–7.45. If the pH does not remain within this narrow range, the person becomes ill. Likewise, aquatic organisms become ill or die if the pH of their environment does not stay within their acceptable pH range.

The main concern about acid rain is the damage it is causing in aquatic ecosystems—especially lakes and streams. The Canadian government has estimated that 14,000 lakes are acidic. In the Adirondack Mountains of New York, many lakes are so acidic that fish cannot live. Trout and other aquatic life in many streams in the Appalachian Mountain region have been killed by acid rain.

Like the canary in the coal mine, fish can tell us when something is wrong with the aquatic ecosystem in which they live. Some species of fish are more sensitive to pH than others. Brook trout can live in water with a pH of 5.0 or lower; brown trout need a pH of 5.5 or higher; and rainbow trout need a pH of 6.0 or higher. Water with a pH below 4.3 is generally fishless.

When the pH falls below 6, many species of fish can't reproduce. Fewer eggs are released, and frequently they do not hatch. Even if the eggs hatch, the young fish cannot develop properly. It matters little that the adults can live at this pH; without a new generation, the species won't survive.

Most fish and amphibians breed in spring. Unfortunately this is also the time when lakes and streams receive all of the acid that has been stored in snow during the winter. The sudden increase in acid, caused by snow melting or heavy downpours, causes a condition called **acid shock**. Acid shock sometimes kills entire populations of fish. Because of the heavier snow cover, acid shock is a greater problem in Canada and in the higher elevations in the United States.

The salamander breeds in temporary ponds that are formed by melted snow or spring rains. A scientist at Cornell University hatched spotted salamander eggs in artificial pools. Ninety-nine percent of those eggs in pools with a pH near neutral (7.0) hatched normally. Most eggs in pools with a pH less than 6.0 did not develop properly. Sixty percent of these salamanders died.

Many minerals are dissolved in the water of lakes and streams. These minerals are usually found in very small amounts. Researchers found that water with a low pH contains higher levels of some minerals. The acidic water dissolves aluminum and other minerals such as cadmium, copper, lead, nickel, manganese, and mercury from the surrounding rocks and soil. This process in which minerals are dissolved from rock and carried away by water is known as **leaching**.

The aluminum compounds dissolved in the water collect in the gills of the fish. In response to the increased levels of aluminum, the gills become coated with mucus. The mucus prevents the exchange of oxygen and carbon dioxide across the gill membrane, and the fish suffocates.

Acid rain and a lack of natural buffers in some regions threaten the survival of trout and other species.

Effect of Acid Shock on Fish.

Salamander.

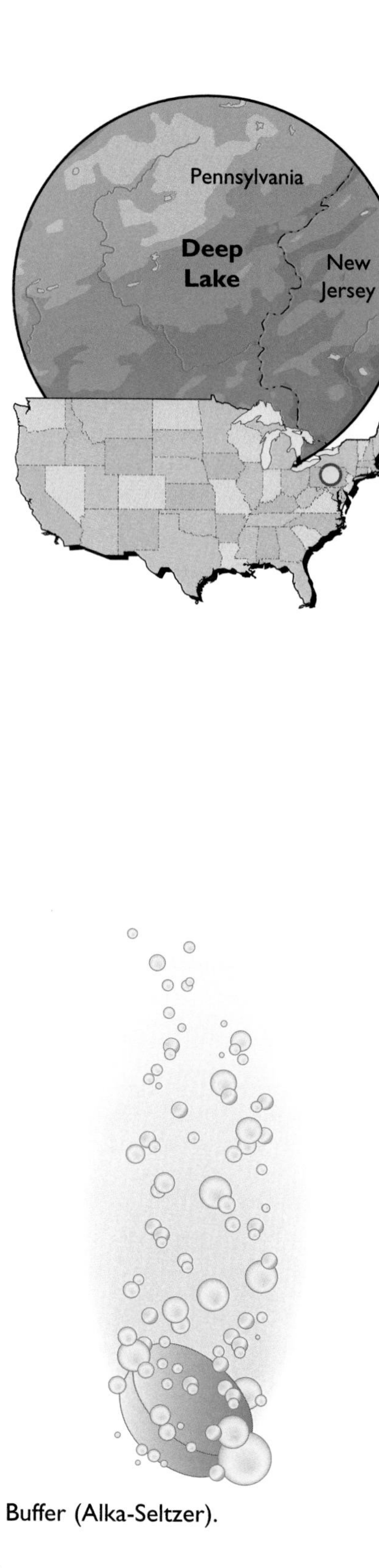

Buffer (Alka-Seltzer).

The high level of aluminum also interferes with the absorption of calcium and sodium. Fish become deformed when they can't absorb enough calcium for a strong skeleton. A lack of sodium causes spastic muscle contractions that lead to death. Fish and amphibians are not the only organisms affected.

Certain species of plants and animals begin to disappear when the pH of an aquatic ecosystem approaches 6.0. Mayflies, stoneflies, mussels, snails, and other organisms disappear at pH 5.0. A few species, such as the whirligig beetle and the water boatman, will survive and reproduce in water with a very low pH (3.5). These species are said to be **acid tolerant**.

As the lake becomes more acidic, many kinds of aquatic plants and algae disappear. Only a few kinds of mosses and algae survive, but the populations of these acid-tolerant species increase. The loss of certain species affects the stability of the food web within the aquatic ecosystem. The acid-tolerant species are less desirable as food sources. Ducks and other waterfowl that depend upon aquatic organisms for food are also affected.

Many people visiting Deep Lake, in Pennsylvania's Pocono Mountains, would not notice that the lake is sick and dying. The crystal clear water is misleading. Clear water is a sign that the many tiny organisms that normally cloud the water are missing. The many lively schools of Pumpkinseed sunfish seem healthy enough. It is not the presence of sunfish but the absence of other fish that indicates the lake is in trouble. A closer look at the sunfish indicates that their growth is stunted.

Deep Lake is an example of an acid lake. Its average pH is 4.0. Where many different kinds of organisms once lived, scientists now find only a few types of organisms. The few kinds of organisms that do survive are present in great numbers. An acid lake is not a dead lake, but it is not the healthy complex ecosystem that it once was.

Certain species of mayflies and stoneflies and many bacteria feed on dead leaves that have fallen or blown into the water. There are few, if any, scavengers or decomposers in acid lakes. Leaves may lie on the bottom of the lake for years. The dead organisms do not decay. The nutrients in the lake or stream ecosystem remain trapped in the bodies of the dead organisms. They are no longer a part of the normal nutrient cycle.

The Buffer Factor

Some lakes become acidic; others don't. Lakes that receive rainfall with the same pH may have very different pH readings. For example, the Great Lakes receive rainfall that is almost as acidic as the rainfall in the Adirondack Mountains, but the Great Lakes are not acidic. Within the Adirondacks, lakes that are only a few miles apart show different pH readings. What causes this difference? Some lakes contain buffers; others do not. A **buffer** is a substance that, when placed in water, prevents large changes in the pH. The buffers are a natural Alka-Seltzer. They neutralize the acids that enter the lakes. The drainage area, or **watershed**, around a lake contains rocks. The type of buffers that are found in a lake depends upon the kind of rocks and soil in the watershed.

The watershed around the Great Lakes contains a lot of limestone. Limestone (a buffer) is mainly calcium carbonate. The minerals in limestone are easily dissolved in water. Water containing low concentrations of calcium and magnesium is called **soft water**. If the concentration of these minerals is high, the water is said to be **hard water**. Hard water lakes are not readily affected by acid rain because they contain many more minerals, some of which act as buffers.

Lakes and streams in a watershed that contains hard rocks—like granite—contain few minerals. Watersheds with hard rocks have soft water and are sensitive to acidic deposition because they do not have minerals that neutralize the acids. During storm events the pH drops. Eventually the lakes and streams lose the ability to support reproducing populations of trout and other fishes.

The Appalachian Mountains are made mostly of sandstone and shale. Sandstone and shale do not contain many buffers. They contain few minerals that can neutralize acids. Still, sandstone and shale have more buffers than the granite of the Adirondack Mountains.

The watersheds of some lakes in the Adirondack Mountains contain limestone that was deposited by glaciers. These lakes are not sensitive to acid rain. The water in these lakes has a pH of 7 even though the pH of the rainfall is near 4.0. Other lakes, without these limestone deposits, are very sensitive to acid rain. Hundreds of these lakes are too acidic for the survival of sensitive species of fish.

Think About It

A study at the Netherlands Institute of Ecology reports that great tits (a species of bird) lay weaker eggs when snail populations decline. Snails, it seems, are the source of calcium for the birds, and the snail populations decline when soils become acidified. Studies in Britain suggest that eggshell thinning began before the introduction of DDT and may be associated with industrial pollution. No research on the effect of acidification on eggshells has been done in the United States.

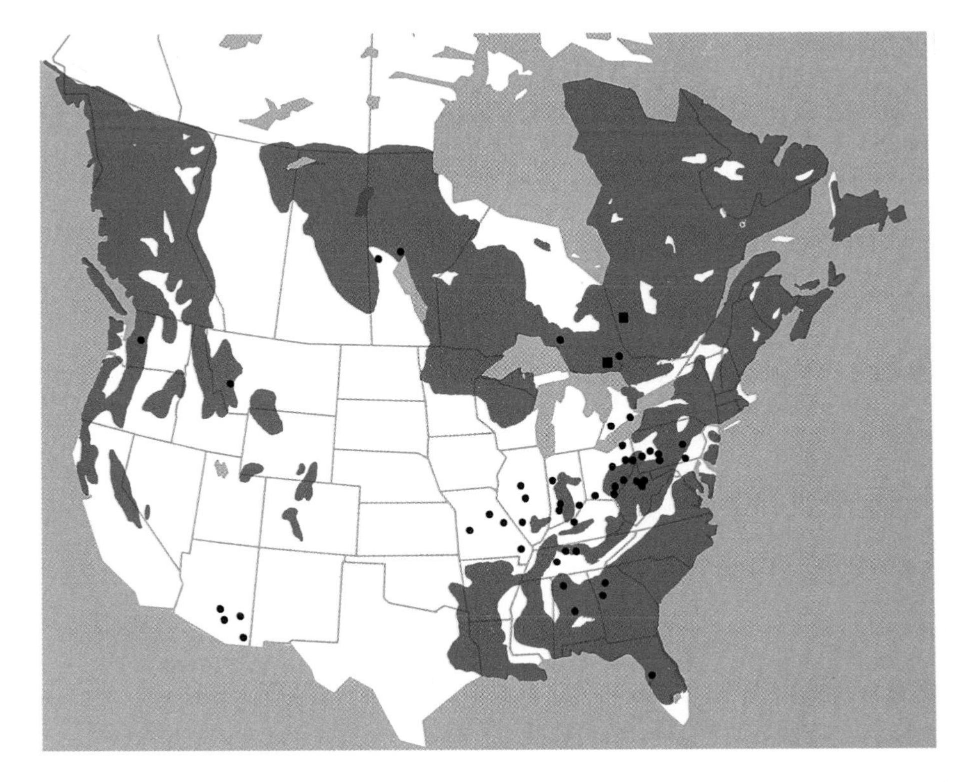

Areas Most Sensitive To Acid Rain

The sections marked in red are low in natural buffers and are susceptible to acidification. The black dots indicate sources with heavy concentrations of SO_2 emissions. The squares indicate sources having SO_2 emissions of more than 500 kilotonnes per year. Smaller sources form a significant proportion of total emissions.

The aquatic ecosystems at greatest risk are located along the Appalachian Mountain chain from the Adirondacks to the Southern Blue Ridge. The Pennsylvania Fish and Boat Commission no longer stocks some species of trout in streams that are acidic. Some pre-season stocking has been stopped because of acid shock. The commission considers acid rain the "greatest threat to future fishing."

In controlled experiments, some plants benefited from acid rain. This may have been due to the fertilizing effects of the nitrogen.

Can the Ecosystem be Saved?

To save their lakes, New York and Sweden have dumped tons of limestone into them. Limestoning is an expensive and temporary measure—a band-aid approach. More than 4,000 of Sweden's lakes have been limed. The Swedes are trying to buy some time until pollution controls reduce acid rain.

Limestoning of lakes is an experiment. Will the organisms that once lived in the lakes be able to live there again? No one really knows what the long-term effects of this experiment will be. Sweden has found that, in some lakes, the lime causes a population explosion of certain species of algae. The clear blue water of Sweden's Lake Gardsjon changed to green—an algal soup.

Impacts on Field Crops

Artificial acid rain has been sprayed on field crops grown in plastic cages. Most of the plants did not seem to be affected. Some plants did not grow as well as usual, while others seemed to benefit from the acid rain. This may be because sulfur and nitrogen are both plant nutrients (fertilizers).

Fertilizers are normally acidic. The fertilizers necessary to grow the crops add far more acid to the soil than is added by acid rain. Farmers regularly add limestone to the soils to neutralize this acid. At the present time, scientists conclude that the nation's agriculture is not being damaged by acid rain.

What You Can Do

- Reduce the amount of energy used in your home.
- Reduce the amount of pollution created by your driving.

Impacts on Forests

Forest decline describes a forest where many trees show signs of stress: a thinning of the foliage, premature yellowing or loss of foliage, and an increase in the number of dying trees. What is causing the decline in growth of the red spruce at high altitudes in the Appalachian Mountains and the sugar maples in the northeastern United States and Canada? Is acid rain killing our forests?

Trees (mostly conifers) seem to be dying at unusually rapid rates in certain locations. Many of the red spruce trees on Camel's Hump, a mountain near Burlington, Vermont, are more than 300 years old. About half of them are either dead or dying. Such a large loss of trees in such a short time period indicates that something is wrong. The damage is slowly spreading down the mountainside. Other species of trees are showing signs of damage. The tips of the branches of fir trees are brown. The maple and beech trees are not growing at their normal rate. Young seedlings are not replacing the dying trees.

Scientists have studied the forest on Camel's Hump for more than 25 years. One study showed that, at several sites, the level of lead in the forest soil had doubled during a 10-year period. The amount of organic matter—dead plant material—in the soil had also doubled.

At first, it may seem that this increase in organic matter is good. After all, gardeners want to increase the organic matter in their soil. Instead of being a good sign, the increase in organic matter shows that something is wrong with the decomposers in the forest ecosystem. The level of organic matter is increasing because the decomposers are not breaking it down and returning the nutrients to the soil. Mountain soils are only a few inches deep and hold very few nutrients.

Calcium is an essential nutrient for tree growth. Concentrations of available calcium in northeastern red spruce forests have decreased. Scientists think that acid rain is probably leaching the calcium from the soil. It may also release toxic metals, such as aluminum, from the soil. Aluminum can enter the root hairs and inhibit the uptake of calcium by the plant roots. Other toxic metals, such as lead and cadmium, may damage fine root hairs and kill decomposers.

Special stainless-steel augers (borers) are used to take core samples from trees. The growth rings provide a permanent record of how the tree grew in each year since the tree sprouted. The growth rings show that the growth rate of red spruce is declining. They also show that the amount of aluminum in the wood has tripled since 1950.

Scientists have found that acidic cloud water, in combination with other factors, increases winter damage in red spruce growing at high elevations. They also found that exposure to acid fog and sulfur dioxide affects root growth in ponderosa pine and Douglas fir.

While current research does not show a direct link between acid rain and widespread forest damage, it does show that soil chemistry is changing. The U.S. Forest Service concludes that these changes in soil chemistry will have negative impacts upon forest productivity in the future.

Scientists agree that ozone is a more important factor in causing forest damage than acid rain. Studies show that high levels of ozone, from the Los Angeles basin, caused the decline of some species of trees in the San Bernadino Mountains of Southern California. Studies also show that ozone has damaged white pine trees in parts of the eastern United States.

The Forest Service suggests that forest declines are caused by a combination of factors. In addition to air pollution, climate, insects and diseases also stress the trees. The combination of factors varies for different species and different locations. Research on the decline of forests continues for there is still much to learn.

Deciduous forest shows decline due to a combination of factors including insects, climate and air pollution.

The Statue of Liberty

Steel bridges, tombstones, and statues—including the Statue of Liberty—show signs of damage. Many factors, including acid rain, are responsible for this damage. Dry deposition destroys buildings and structures made of marble and limestone (both forms of calcium carbonate). Sulfur dioxide

Did You Know?

Both marble and limestone are forms of calcium carbonate. Marble is a metamorphic rock that can be formed from limestone.

Did You Know?

Before the restoration was completed in 1986, the Statue of Liberty was leaking like a sieve. When moisture came in contact with the iron superstructure that supports the thin copper skin, a weak current of electricity was created. Over time this caused severe corrosion of the iron supports and threatened the stability of the statue. During restoration, openings in the copper skin were closed to prevent leaks, and new stainless steel ribs replaced the corroded iron ones. New insulation between the supportive ribs and the copper skin stopped the flow of electricity.

In addition, the outside of the statue was cleaned with mild detergent. When copper is exposed to the weather, it oxidizes forming a bluish-green patina that resists further corrosion including acid rain. The lady's copper skin shows few effects of acid rain.

dissolves in moisture that condenses on the stone. It reacts with the calcium carbonate in marble and limestone to form gypsum—a white powdery mineral.

The National Academy of Sciences estimates that acid rain causes $5 billion in damages each year in the eastern United States. In Gettysburg, Pennsylvania, war memorials are being destroyed by acid rain. It is damaging the paint on houses and cars. Acid rain is everybody's problem. It is not just a question of a few mountain lakes.

Can Acid Rain Harm People?

The recommended pH for water that is used in homes is between 7 and 8. Acidic water causes plumbing to corrode, and the metals give an unpleasant taste to the water. The water contains levels of both lead and copper that are higher than normal. Babies living on a farm in Sweden had spells of diarrhea caused by high levels of copper in the drinking water. Blondes don't always have more fun. After washing their hair in water with high levels of copper, their hair may be tinted green.

In Vermont, where pipes are frequently made of lead, people have higher than average levels of lead in their blood. High levels of lead (0.8 ppm) in the blood can cause brain damage, especially in children. The first five years of a child's life are extremely important to the proper growth and development of the brain.

Environmental scientists from New York's Department of Health give the following advice to people using water that is acidic. When using the water for drinking or cooking, let faucets run a few minutes if they have not been used for several hours or overnight. This will flush water that contains high concentrations of metals leached from the pipes.

Sulfur gases form sulfate aerosols when combined with moisture in the lungs. Studies at Harvard and New York Universities show that higher levels of sulfate aerosols are linked to increased sickness and death from certain respiratory diseases such as chronic bronchitis and asthma. The EPA estimates that reductions in SO_2 emissions will reduce hospital admissions, emergency room visits and deaths. Annual health benefits could be worth more than $12 billion.

The True Cost

We enjoy the benefits of burning fossil fuels. They provide energy for comforts like air conditioning, heating, lighting, appliances, transportation and many forms of recreation. We need these forms of energy to maintain our present lifestyle, and we want the cost to be low. The fact is that we have not been paying the true cost.

The **true cost** of a product must include technology that will prevent pollution of our environment. How will we pay this cost? We can pay more for our utility bills to prevent acidic pollution, or we can pay even more for structural repairs and additional health care.

Some industries say the cost to prevent acid rain is too high. They say the damage caused by acid rain cannot justify spending billions of dollars to prevent it. Not all industries are against controlling smokestack emissions. One official for an electric utility, speaking at a conference on acid rain, said: "I think we have dragged our feet...and we ought to get on with it."

Getting On With It

In 1980, Congress authorized a 10-year, $536 million study of acid rain. The **National Acid Precipitation Assessment Program** (NAPAP) study involved more than 1000 university and government scientists. While the study did not find acid rain to be the disaster that some had predicted, it did find some serious problems.

The 1990 Clean Air Act Amendments (CAAA-90), signed into law by President Bush, officially recognized acid rain as a serious environmental problem and set up an ambitious program to control air pollutants that cause it. A major reduction in sulfur dioxide and nitrogen oxide emissions is now a goal of clean air regulations in both the U.S. and Canada.

The U.S. regulations require a 10-million-ton (9-million-metric-ton) reduction in annual emissions of SO_2 by the year 2010. Phase I of the CAAA-90 focused on electric power plants that are located east of the Mississippi River. In 1995 sulfur dioxide emissions from 445 power plants were reduced by 3 million tons (2.7 million metric tonnes). Reductions in sulfur dioxide emissions have resulted in rainfall being less acidic in the Ohio River Valley and the Mid-Atlantic States.

Nitrogen oxide pollution is expected to increase in the next 20 years. The Canada–U.S. Air Quality Accord, signed in 1991, addresses the need to reduce nitrogen oxides. This agreement requires each country to reduce nitrogen oxide emissions from stationary sources (power plants and industries). While this agreement is a step in the right direction, it does not address the major source of this pollutant. Transportation is the major source of nitrogen oxides in both countries. Each country must address the problem created by the growing number of vehicles contributing to the formation of acid rain and smog.

Did You Know?

Some manufacturers use acid-resistant automotive paints to reduce the damage caused by acid deposition. The average cost is $5 for each new vehicle or $61 million per year for all new cars and trucks sold in the U.S.

Reducing SO_2 and NO_2 will require adding wet scrubbers to older powerplants.

2.13 Questions for Study and Discussion:

1. Define the following terms: **VOCABULARY**

acid deposition	buffer	hard water	tracer
acid rain	Captex	leaching	true cost
acid shock	carbonic acid	pH scale	watershed
acid tolerant	forest decline	soft water	

Acid Rain: A Political Issue

2. Why is acid rain a source of political dispute between countries?
3. What was the conclusion of the Special Envoys?

Acid Rain: Defined

4. Identify the term that describes substances with the following pH numbers: 3, 8, 6, 7, 4, and 12.

5. What is the pH of a substance that is 10 times more acidic than a substance with a pH of 4? What is the pH if the substance is 100 times more alkaline than a substance with a pH of 4?
6. What causes natural rainfall—without any pollutants—to be acidic?
7. Give examples of wet and dry forms of acid deposition.

Human Activities and Acid Rain

8. What two gases form the major pollutants in acid rain?
9. What is the biggest single human activity that is a source of chemicals that form acids when they are released into the atmosphere?

10. How can you prove that a chemical, which lands in Toronto or Philadelphia, actually came from a certain smokestack in Ohio? Give two types of chemicals that are used as tracers.

Acid Rain: Is It Deadly?

11. Why are many fish populations reduced if the pH is below 6?
12. Why are lakes and streams often more acidic in spring than summer?
13. Researchers have found that water with a low pH usually contains (lower/higher) levels of minerals than water with a high pH. Why is this true?
14. What mineral prevents the normal exchange of oxygen and carbon dioxide across the gills of fish?
15. Name two species of water insects that are acid-tolerant.
16. Which species of trout is the most acid-tolerant? Which species of trout is the most sensitive to acid waters?
17. Layers of leaves are often found lying on the bottom of an acid lake. The same situation occurs in bogs. What is the cause of this?

The Buffer Factor

18. Why do some lakes become acidic while others do not?
19. Which lake will contain more buffers—one with hard water or one with soft water?
20. According to the Pennsylvania Game Commission, what is the greatest threat to future fishing?

Can the Ecosystem be Saved?

21. Do you think that the best solution to the acid rain problem is treating the lakes with limestone? Support your position.

Impacts on Field Crops

22. Give a possible reason why some plants grow better when sprayed with acid rain.
23. How do farmers prevent the soil in their fields from becoming acidic?
24. At the present time, do scientists feel that our food supply is threatened by acid rain?

Impacts on Forests

25. What evidence is there of forest decline on Camel's Hump?
26. The amount of organic matter is increasing on Camel's Hump. Is this good or bad? Why?
27. According to the Forest Service, what is causing the forest decline?

The Statue of Liberty

28. Acid rain is everyone's problem. Explain this statement by describing how acid rain can cost you money.

Can Acid Rain Harm People?

29. Explain how acid rain sometimes causes high levels of metals, like copper and lead, in drinking water.
30. What steps can people take to lower the level of lead in their drinking water?
31. What air pollutant forms "acid rain" within the lungs? What are the effects of this "acid rain" on the respiratory system?

True Cost

32. What is the true cost of a product?
33. Explain how you could justify the additional expense to someone who is against the cost of pollution prevention?

Getting On With It

34. What steps are being taken to address the problems caused by acid rain?

Clearing the Air—Stationary Sources

2.14

At one time people thought smoke pouring from factory chimneys, and city streets lined with cars were both signs of a better life. Today we know that emissions from both factories and vehicles contain pollutants that damage the environment and affect human health. For humans and other species too, a better life depends upon cleaner air.

Thousands of industries and millions of vehicles add pollutants to the air. Scientists believe that air pollution is the source of nearly 90% of the DDT, PCBs and lead in Lake Superior. There is evidence that up to 25% of the nitrogen polluting the Chesapeake Bay comes from air pollution. Snowflakes deposit toxic chemicals in the Arctic ecosystem. Cleaning the air is a big job, but raindrops and snowflakes are efficient scrubbers. The only way to prevent the pollution of rain and snow is to reduce the load of pollutants entering the air.

Air Quality Standards

In 1970, the Nixon Administration established the **United States Environmental Protection Agency (EPA)**. Among other tasks, the Agency is required to set and enforce air quality standards. An **air quality standard** is the maximum amount of pollutant allowed. There are two kinds of air quality standards. Standards are set for emissions and for ambient air.

Emissions include gases and particles entering the air from smokestacks, chimneys and exhaust pipes. An **emission standard** is the maximum amount of an emission allowed to enter the atmosphere. Standards are set for the exhaust from certain stationary sources, such as electrical power plants and other industries, as well as from new motor vehicles and from aircraft.

Ambient air is the scientific term that refers to the air outdoors. It includes the air from ground level to about ten miles (16 km) above the earth's surface. It is the air we breathe. The 1970 Clean Air Act required the EPA to establish **National Ambient Air Quality Standards (NAAQS)** for six principal air pollutants. These are:

sulfur dioxide	ground-level ozone	particulate matter
nitrogen dioxide	carbon monoxide	lead

Since Congress passed the 1970 Clean Air Act, emissions of five of the six principal air pollutants have decreased. Between 1970 and 1997, emissions of nitrogen oxides increased 11%. Nitrogen oxides contribute to the formation of two major pollutants: ground-level ozone and acid rain. Most ozone is formed in the atmosphere.

OBJECTIVES

- ✔ **Describe** the role of the EPA in controlling air pollution.
- ✔ **Distinguish** between emission standards and ambient air quality standards.
- ✔ **Identify** the types of information considered in setting standards.
- ✔ **Explain** how allowance trading reduces air pollution from power plants.
- ✔ **Evaluate** various methods of pollution control.

Did You Know?

Developing countries and countries in Eastern Europe and countries of the former Soviet Union have air pollution with high levels of particulates. Countries with higher per capita income have lower levels of particulate pollution because they have more money available for pollution controls.

Space Shuttle Endeavor.

Setting Air Quality Standards

The EPA must set standards based on:

- The best available scientific evidence of the effects caused by the pollutant.
- Information gathered from citizens at public hearings—public opinion.

The standards must protect human health and prevent damage to the environment. They must also reflect the opinions and needs of the public. How willing are we to pay for the technology needed to control the pollution? What changes in our daily life will be required to meet the standard? What inconveniences must we endure? Will we enjoy the warmth of a fire in the fireplace on a cold winter night or cooking a steak over coals on the grill in our backyard?

It is the job of the EPA to weigh the **risks** of pollution against the **benefits** of the product. Consider these two sources of energy:

How clean do we want the air? Do the benefits of grilled foods outweigh the risks?

Electricity

Benefits: Electricity for lighting, heating, cooling, and appliances.

Risks: Increased levels of sulfur dioxide and **particulates** from electrical power plants that burn fossil fuels OR the release of radiation from nuclear power plants OR the loss of wildlife habitat for a hydroelectric dam, and the possible loss of life if the dam fails.

Wood

Benefits: Wood is the only source of energy for cooking food in many parts of the world. In some areas it is less expensive than other sources of energy for home heating. Burned in a fireplace or campfire, it provides a desirable setting for a relaxing evening.

Risks: Burning wood produces carbon monoxide, soot and other particles, and cancer-causing chemicals. In some valleys, carbon monoxide and particulates exceed the National Ambient Air Quality Standards.

Controlling Air Pollution—Tall Stacks

The first attempt to control pollution was to send the pollutants up, up, up and away. In the 1970s, to improve the local air quality, industries and coal-fired electrical power plants increased the height of the smokestacks. "Tall stacks" do not remove the sulfate particles or sulfur dioxide gas from the emissions. They simply send the pollution higher and spread it out farther. The pollutants come back to earth, perhaps in another city, many miles from the power plant's "tall stack."

A nickel and copper smelting plant in Sudbury, Ontario, is the site of the world's tallest smokestack. The smokestack rises almost 1,300 feet (380 m)—higher than the length of 4 football fields. In 1970 the smelter released nearly 5 tons (4.5 metric tonnes) of sulfur dioxide for each ton of metal the plant produced. As a part of the Canadian sulfur dioxide control strategy, the company installed additional pollution controls. By 1987, the smelter released only 2 tons (1.8 metric tonnes) of sulfur dioxide per ton of metal produced.

The **Clean Air Act of 1970** made "tall stacks" illegal, but this part of the law was not enforced. Citizens may take industries or government agencies to civil court if they allow pollutants to exceed EPA standards. Certain environmental groups, such as the **National Clean Air Coalition** and the **Natural Resources Defense Council** hire lawyers to argue cases in court.

In 1983, an environmental group filed a lawsuit against the EPA. As a result of the court's decision, the EPA was required to enforce the Clean Air Act. Industries and electrical power plants could no longer install "tall stacks" to avoid the cost of more expensive pollution controls.

The world's tallest smokestack is in Sudbury, Ontario.

The 1990 Clean Air Act Amendments

A "grandfather clause" in the 1977 amendments to the Clean Air Act (CAA) protected existing electrical power plants from the expense of costly pollution controls. Only new or "substantially renovated" power plants were required to install pollution controls. The 1990 CAA amendments required nitrogen oxides to be reduced below 1980 levels by two million tons (1.8 million metric tonnes) and sulfur dioxide to be reduced by 10 million tons (9 million metric tonnes). To meet this goal, older power plants had to clean up their emissions.

While the EPA sets the standards, it allows the electrical power companies to choose the most cost-effective way to meet the standard. Phase I, which began in 1995, required more than one hundred coal-fired power plants that produced the most sulfur dioxide to reduce their emissions. Five years later, phase II tightened emissions limits for phase I power plants, and also required smaller, cleaner power plants to reduce their emissions. To reduce emissions, companies may use energy conservation or renewable energy, switch to lower sulfur fuels, or use pollution control technology.

The 1990 CAA amendments established an **emissions cap**—a maximum amount of sulfur dioxide that can be released into the atmosphere from all electrical power plants. Some power plants are allowed to pollute more than others do, but the total amount of pollution is limited to 8.9 million tons (8 million metric tonnes). One **allowance** permits a power plant to emit 1 ton (0.9 metric tonnes) of sulfur dioxide. An electrical power company may buy, sell, trade or hold allowances. Fines are imposed for emissions that exceed the allowances held by a company.

The 1990 amendments to the Clean Air Act will not be fully implemented until 2005. When the controls are in place, air pollutants entering the air each year will be reduced by 56 billion pounds—that's 224 pounds (102 kg) per person. The anticipated cost of air pollution controls is $25 billion per year. According to the EPA, that is 24 cents per person per day. Annual health benefits are estimated to be between $12 and $40 billion.

Environmental Challenge: Pollution Allowances

Create a board game or card game in which the players are electrical power companies and the goal is to reduce the sulfur dioxide emissions. For more information on the sulfur dioxide allowance trading system, visit www.epa.gov/acidrain.

Did You Know?

When coal is burned, 8% turns into fly ash. It is used to make a lightweight and strong concrete product, which is used in areas prone to earthquakes. It is also being used to reclaim land at abandoned coal mines and as a sub-base for roads and airport runways. Only about 25% of fly ash is reused.

Why Burn Coal?

When **fossil fuels** (coal, oil, natural gas) are burned, the sulfur combines with oxygen forming sulfur dioxide ($S + O_2 \longrightarrow SO_2$). **Soft coal** (bituminous) contains 0.5–4.5% sulfur (by weight). A large electrical power plant may burn 10,000 tons (9,000 metric tonnes) of coal each day. If a power plant burns coal that contains 3.0% sulfur, a smoke stack without pollution controls will send out approximately 600 tons (540 metric tonnes) of sulfur dioxide each day.

Why don't electrical power plants use fuels that contain less sulfur, if sulfur is causing a problem? **Hard coal** (anthracite) contains only 0.4–0.8% sulfur, but deposits of hard coal are very small compared to the deposits of soft coal. About 85% of soft coal that is low in sulfur is in the western U.S., but most coal is used in the eastern U.S. Transporting the large amounts needed is expensive.

Oil contains much less sulfur than coal, and natural gas contains even less sulfur than oil. While some industries and power plants use these cleaner fuels, many choose to burn coal. Why? Soft coal is widely available and less expensive than other fuels. Depending upon the location of an electrical power plant and the cost of alternative fuels, soft coal may be the only affordable fuel. While there is enough coal in the earth to last perhaps 150 years, most of it contains large amounts of sulfur.

High sulfur coal can be burned without releasing large amounts of sulfur dioxide in emissions. Proven, reliable and cost-effective technologies are available to remove sulfur. It may be removed before, during or after combustion. The development and use of **clean coal technology** can create new jobs and preserve jobs in the coal mining industry.

Clean Coal Technology—Cleaning Coal

Sulfur and other impurities may be removed from coal prior to combustion. Washing the coal can remove 33% of the ash and 25% of the sulfur. In addition to reducing air pollution, coal washing decreases maintenance and increases the efficiency of combustion.

Other methods of cleaning coal are being investigated. Washing coal removes the inorganic sulfur but not the organic form. Scientists are investigating ways to break the chemical bonds. Other scientists, using biotechnology techniques, are trying to develop bacteria that will eat the sulfur compounds in pulverized coal.

Wet Scrubber

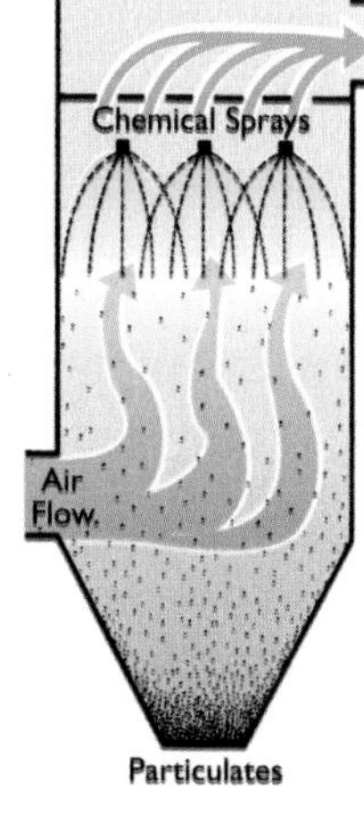

Clean Coal Technology—Wet Scrubbers

In a **wet scrubber**, the emissions pass through a spray of water, which has been mixed with finely pulverized limestone. The sulfur dioxide mixes with the limestone (calcium carbonate) to form gypsum (calcium sulfate) sludge. Wet scrubbers can remove about 90% of the sulfur dioxide from the emissions, but they are costly to install and operate.

The cost of operating a scrubber can increase the cost of electricity by one or two cents per kilowatt-hour. Scrubbers require huge amounts of

This building houses the wet scrubber that cleans the emissions. Compare the emissions from the smokestacks in these photos and identify the one which does not have a scrubber.

energy, making the power plant less efficient. At large power plants, scrubbers may use as much as 1,000 gallons (3785 L) of water per minute. This can be a problem in areas where the supply of water is limited. Another problem is the disposal of the vast amounts of **scrubber sludge** or wastewater produced.

Clean Coal Technology—PFBC

A new way to burn coal is **pressurized fluidized bed combustion—PFBC.** A PFBC boiler can burn low-grade fuels, including high sulfur coal, without producing large amounts of sulfur dioxide and nitrogen oxides. Other fuels that can be burned in PFBC boilers include wood waste, sewage sludge, municipal waste and tires.

Pellets of limestone **(calcium carbonate)** and fuels are injected into the boiler along with air. The velocity of the air is controlled so that the force of the air lifts and mixes the small pellets forming a "fluidized bed" of burning coal or other fuel. During combustion the calcium reacts with the sulfur to form gypsum. Some of the gypsum is removed as bottom ash. Smaller particles entering the stack are called fly ash. **Fly ash** is removed from the emissions by **electrostatic precipitators** or **fabric filters**.

PFBC offers several advantages. The fuel is burned at lower temperatures, reducing the amount of nitrogen oxides formed. Since levels of both sulfur dioxide and nitrogen oxides in the emissions are low, scrubbers are not required. The crushed limestone used in PFBC is less expensive than the powdered limestone needed for scrubbers. PFBC also produces less solid waste than other coal-fired boilers. Another advantage is that the boilers are more compact and require much less space.

Did You Know?

One large 1000-megawatt power plant, which burns coal with 3% sulfur and uses wet scrubbers, produces enough gypsum sludge to cover one square mile (2.6 km^2) of land to a depth of one foot (0.31 m) over a one-year period. The alternative to disposal is recycling. At a factory built next to a power plant in Chicago, scrubber sludge is being made into gypsum for wallboard. An artificial reef made of sludge floats in the Delaware Bay and has created habitat for oysters and shellfish.

Removing Particles

Cyclones:

Cyclone

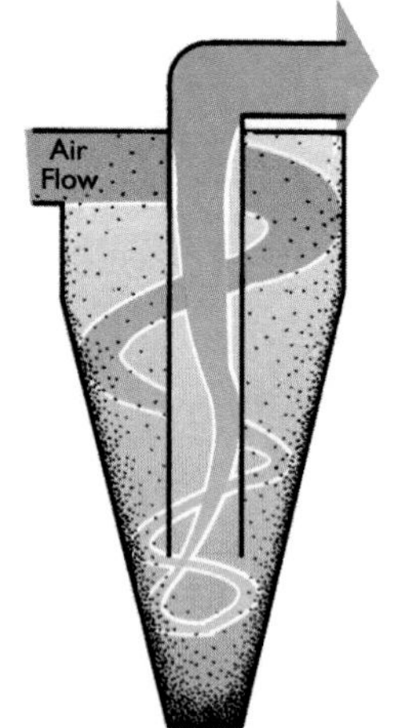

In a **cyclone**, flue gases are forced through a vertical tube in which a whirlwind throws the larger particles against the sides of the tube. The particles fall to the bottom where they are collected, and the cleaner air passes upward through the center of the tube. Cyclones are less expensive and require less maintenance than other methods, but they only remove the larger particles.

Wet scrubbers can be used with a cyclone to collect the smaller particles. The flue gases are passed through a chamber where water is sprayed to simulate rainfall. The artificial "rain" cleans the gases before they leave the stack.

Electrostatic Precipitators:

Electrostatic Precipitator

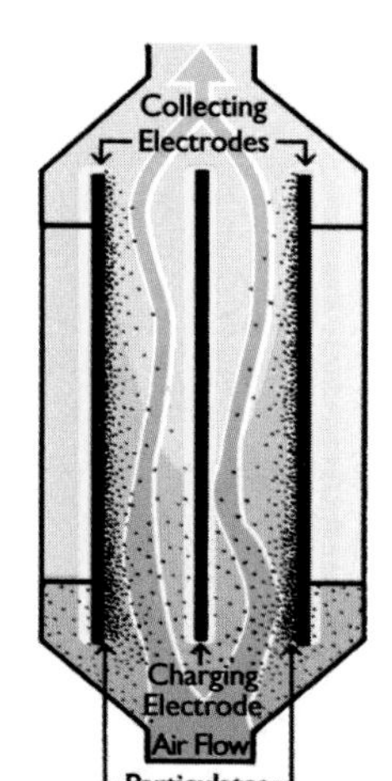

The electrostatic precipitator gives particles a strong electrical charge. The charged particles are attracted to metal plates with an opposite electrical charge. Periodically the plates are vibrated to remove the particles. This method can remove 99.9% of the particles. The precipitators are expensive to install, but they are much cheaper to operate than wet scrubbers.

Fabric Filters:

Fabric Filter

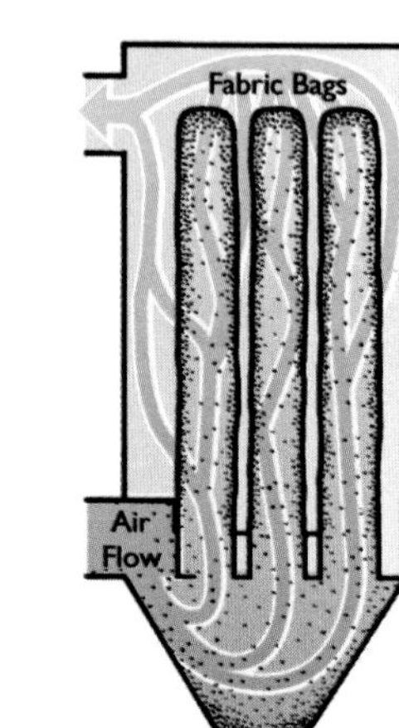

The process of filtering is used in coffee makers, furnaces, and vacuum cleaners. A **fabric filter** must be designed for each specific use. At some electrical power plants, baghouses hold a series of fabric bags that filter emissions. Filtering is comparable to precipitators in cost and efficiency.

Wood Stoves:

Smoke from combustion of wood in fireplaces, stoves and furnaces contains more particulates and hazardous air pollutants, including cancer-causing chemicals, than smoke from gas or oil-fired furnaces. Newer wood stoves are much less polluting than older models. By using EPA-certified stoves, performing routine maintenance and burning dry wood, particulates can be reduced by about 70%. In many areas it may be necessary to prohibit the use of stoves and fireplaces when there is a stagnant weather pattern.

Removing Other Gases

Sulfur is only part of the air pollution problem. Nitrogen oxides (NOx) contribute to the formation of ground-level ozone and acid rain. Nitrogen and oxygen in the air combine at high temperatures during combustion. Newer electrical power plants are designed to reduce nitrogen oxide emissions.

Pollution controls must be installed at older electrical power plants and other major stationary sources of nitrogen oxides. Controlling the flow of air and lowering the temperature of combustion reduces nitrogen oxides by up to 50%. Recirculation of flue gases also reduces nitrogen oxides and hydrocarbons in the emissions.

Space heating is another source of nitrogen oxides. Homes and buildings with newer models of oil-fired furnaces produce fewer nitrogen oxides. Because there are a large number of homes with older furnaces, it will be many years before there is a significant reduction in nitrogen oxides from this source.

Reduction in nitrogen oxides and **volatile organic compounds** (VOCs) will reduce ozone levels. The EPA now limits the VOC emissions from industries that use painting and coating processes as well as industries that use organic solvents in cleaning processes. Controlling pollution from stationary sources is only part of the battle. Motor vehicles are a major source of nitrogen oxides found in urban air pollution.

> **Did You Know?**
> During prolonged temperature inversions that trap pollution, local governments issue red advisories. Mandatory woodburning restrictions apply to nearly everyone who lives below 7,000 feet in the six-county metropolitan area of Denver, Colorado. Exceptions include those who use Phase II EPA-certified woodburning stoves and those whose stoves or fireplaces are their primary source of heat.

Environmental Planning

As a result of controls placed on stationary sources of pollution, our air quality is improving. There still are problems that remain, and the fight for clean air goes on. If we are to enjoy the benefits of electricity and the products of industry, we must pay a price. The price will either be the effects of air pollution or the cost of preventing pollution.

Environmental planning can play an important role in the design of new buildings and the remodeling of old ones. The EPA is encouraging corporations as well as state and local governments to install energy-efficient lighting. Denver International Airport's Teflon-coated fiberglass roof takes advantage of natural lighting and energy-efficient lights, reducing the demand for electricity. Increasing energy efficiency reduces pollution and saves natural resources.

As the number of chimneys and the number of vehicles increase, it becomes more and more difficult for urban areas to meet the ambient air quality standards. Changing to cleaner energy sources can reduce pollution. Alternative fuels for vehicles are discussed on page 194. Other alternative energy sources are discussed in Section 6.3.

Canada Pavilion Expo '86 Vancouver, Canada. The roof material allows natural light into the pavillion while keeping the rain outside.

2.14 QUESTIONS FOR STUDY AND DISCUSSION:

1. Define the following terms: **VOCABULARY**

air quality standard	electrostatic precipitator	fabric filter	pressurized fluidized bed combustion
allowance	emission standard	fly ash	scrubber sludge
ambient air	emissions	fossil fuels	soft coal
clean coal technology	emissions cap	hard coal	wet scrubber
cyclone	EPA	NAAQS	
		particulates	

2. Explain how air pollution is contributing to water pollution.

Air Quality Standards

3. What federal agency was created to control pollution? When was this agency established?
4. Compare an emission standard to an ambient air quality standard.
5. What are the 6 major air pollutants that have National Ambient Air Quality Standards?

Setting Air Quality Standards

6. Standards set by the EPA must be based on two types of information. What are the two sources of information?
7. Why does the EPA set ambient air standards for ozone and other pollutants?

Controlling Air Pollution—Tall Stacks

8. What was the first solution to air pollution from electrical power plants and industries? Why wasn't this a good way to control air pollution?
9. EPA sets and enforces standards. What is done if these standards are not met?

The 1990 Clean Air Act Amendments

10. What was the "grandfather clause" in the 1977 amendments to the Clean Air Act? What changes were made in the 1990 amendments?
11. What is an emissions cap? How does the "cap" affect the building of a new electrical power plant?

Why Burn Coal?

12. Which type of coal contains more sulfur, soft or hard coal?
13. If sulfur is a dangerous pollutant, why can't we simply use fuels that are low in sulfur?
14. What are the benefits of clean coal technology?

Clean Coal Technology—Cleaning Coal

15. What are the advantages of washing coal prior to combustion?
16. Why doesn't washing remove the entire sulfur content from the coal? What technology may increase the amount of sulfur removed?

Clean Coal Technology—Wet Scrubbers

17. Describe how wet scrubbers remove the sulfur dioxide before it reaches the atmosphere.
18. What are the disadvantages of using wet scrubbers to control air pollution?

Clean Coal Technology—PFBC

19. What additional pollution control must be used with PFBC boilers?
20. What are the advantages of PFBC technology?

Removing Particles

21. List four ways of removing particles from flue gases. For each method, describe how the particles are removed.
22. Give one advantage and one disadvantage of each method listed above.

Removing Other Gases

23. Under what conditions are nitrogen oxides formed? How can the amount of nitrogen oxides be reduced?
24. What environmental problems are caused by nitrogen oxides and VOCs?

Environmental Planning

25. What changes in the design of buildings can help to clean the air?

Clearing the Air—Automobiles and Other Vehicles

"Consumers have little incentive to demand more energy-efficient autos, as fuel accounts for only 15% of the cost of car ownership. Still, costs are not the only reason to develop alternatives to gasoline-powered vehicles."
NATIONAL INSTITUTE OF HEALTH

OBJECTIVES

- ✔ **Describe** the conditions that create pollution during the process of combustion.
- ✔ **Compare** the pollution produced by a 4-stroke internal combustion engine with pollution produced by other types of engines.
- ✔ **Relate** vehicle use to the production of photochemical smog.
- ✔ **Evaluate** various methods of reducing pollution caused by vehicle use.

Where It All Begins

Most of the poisonous gases in automobile exhausts are waste products of incomplete combustion. **Combustion** is the burning of a mixture of fuel and oxygen. If conditions were perfect, the waste products would be carbon dioxide and water, but engines are not perfect. When there is not enough oxygen, combustion is incomplete and carbon monoxide and unburned hydrocarbons are formed. The high temperature in the car's engine causes nitrogen to combine with oxygen to produce nitrogen oxides.

In the **internal combustion engine** the fuel burns or explodes inside a **closed cylinder**. A movable plunger called a **piston** is tightly fitted into the cylinder. Gasoline is fed to the engine along with air by either a carburetor or fuel injectors. Most internal combustion engines work on a 4-stroke cycle. Power is delivered to the crankshaft once in each cycle.

Think About It

If you are part of the problem, you can be part of the solution!

The 2-stroke engine powers small equipment such as lawnmowers, leaf blowers, string trimmers, chain saws, boats and personal watercraft. As the air-fuel mixture is drawn into the 2-stroke engine, some of the unburned fuel exits the engine with the exhaust (increasing pollution). What can you do to reduce air pollution?

- Replace equipment with newer, cleaner engines. There are 12 million marine engines in the U.S. In many areas of the country they are a major source of hydrocarbons and nitrogen oxides. The marine industry is working to develop low-emission, high-performance engines.
- If buying new outdoor tools, look for models with 4-stroke engines. Four-stroke engines are heavier but cleaner.
- Look for 2-stroke engines with Compressed Air-Assisted Injection. Air is drawn in first, separating the incoming fuel from the exhaust. This may cut emissions by 75% and reduce fuel consumption by 30%.
- Avoid spilling gasoline during refueling. The EPA estimates that 17 million gallons (64 million L) of fuel are spilled each year during refueling—more than the Exxon Valdez spilled in the Gulf of Alaska.
- Maintain equipment properly.
- Eliminate unnecessary idling of engines.
- Buy electric equipment which is cleaner than gasoline-powered engines. A 3.5-hp gas mower can produce as many hydrocarbons in one hour as a new car driven 340 miles (544 km).
- Buy a human-powered reel mower which generates no emissions.
- Decrease lawn size and mowing frequency.
- Replace grass with low-growing ground covers that require no mowing.

Offroad engines (snowmobiles, ATVs, lawnmowers, tractors, etc.) were not regulated by the EPA until the mid-1990s.

* **First Stroke**: As the piston moves down, the gas-air mixture is drawn into the cylinder.
* **Second Stroke**: The intake valve closes. The piston moves up, compressing the air and gas mixture.
* **Third Stroke**: The compressed mixture of gases is ignited by a spark plug. The burning fuel gives off hot gases that expand. The expanding gases push against the piston that is connected to a rod. The motion of the piston is transferred through the rod to the crankshaft and finally to the wheels of the vehicle.
* **Fourth Stroke**: After the explosion, the cylinder is full of waste products including: carbon monoxide, nitrogen oxides and unburned hydrocarbons. The exhaust valve opens, and the piston moves up to eject the waste products.

Four stroke cycle

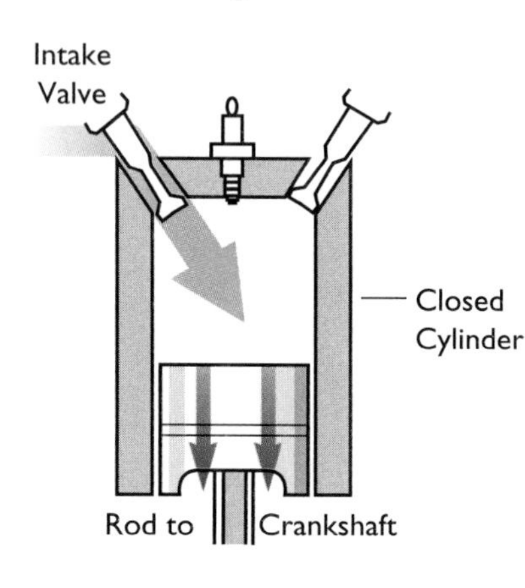

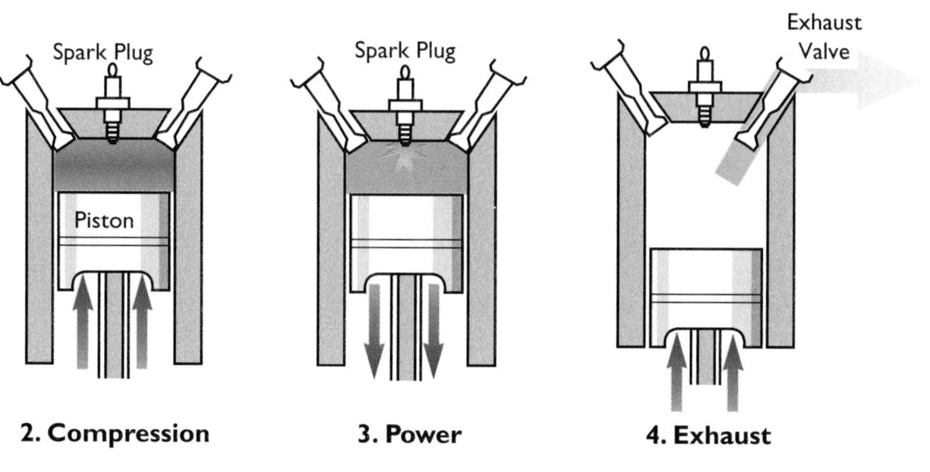

Environmental Challenge: Hoy No Circula

Mexico City's pollution control efforts include a program called Hoy No Circula [Don't Drive Today]. The system is based on the last digit of a car's license plate. The program includes taxis. The program reduces the number of private cars on the road each day by 20%.

- Should everyone who can afford a car be able to buy one?
- Should the price of cars be based on their emissions?
- Should cars with less than three passengers be prohibited from entering the major thoroughfares of big cities?

Too Many Cars, Too Many Miles

In 1970, the vehicles in the United States traveled 1 trillion (1,000,000,000,000) miles. By 1990, the total vehicle miles traveled had doubled, from 1 trillion to 2 trillion. Between 1983 and 1990, the average U.S. commute grew by more than 30%. Nearly 90% of the total miles traveled are by automobile. If the total number of miles traveled continues to increase, the total amount of pollutants produced will also increase.

The United States has strict regulations for emissions from vehicles. Today's cars produce fewer pollutants compared to cars made in the 1960s. But controlling air pollution is difficult when more people are driving more vehicles more miles. The U.S. car population, at 200 million, has grown faster than the human population. Cars produce 90% or more of the carbon monoxide in urban areas. They also contribute 35–70% of ozone-forming pollutants and several known or probable human carcinogens.

The Government Steps In

California was the first state to require pollution controls on cars. All cars sold in California since 1963 have had some type of pollution control. The Federal Government adopted the original California standards starting with 1968 models. In 1970, the Clean Air Act set strict standards for the three major air pollutants in car exhaust—hydrocarbons, carbon monoxide, and nitrogen oxides. Amendments to the Clean Air Act required manufacturers to design newer models that pollute less than older vehicles.

While the EPA sets the standards, the manufacturers must decide what technology can best be used to meet the standards. Several methods can be used to reduce pollution from vehicle exhaust:

- Combustion can be improved by recycling the vapors and gases back into the engine.
- Additional air may be injected into the manifold to make combustion more complete.
- Catalysts may be used to assist in the complete burning of fuels.

The Catalytic Converter

Pollution can be reduced by chemically changing the pollutants before they leave the car's exhaust pipe. **Catalytic converters** are stainless steel containers, about the size of a liter of soda, that contain a platinum catalyst. Beginning in 1975, they were installed on exhaust systems to reduce hydrocarbons and carbon monoxide in the emissions. The platinum allows oxygen to react with more carbon monoxide and unburned hydrocarbons before the exhaust leaves the tailpipe. The Clean Air Act prohibits the removal or disabling of catalytic converters.

Introduced in 1980, the second-generation catalytic converters are monitored by on-board computers and oxygen sensors. The newer catalytic converters include a "three-way" catalyst, which splits nitrogen from the nitrogen oxides to form nitrogen and oxygen. The oxygen reacts with carbon monoxide and hydrocarbons to form carbon dioxide and water. Newer cars with these efficient exhaust systems produce about 70% less nitrogen oxides and 90% less carbon monoxide and hydrocarbons than cars without pollution controls.

Get the Lead Out

Why was lead added to gasoline? Gasoline refineries did not have the ability to produce the amount of high-octane gasoline needed for the more powerful engines. By adding tetraethyl lead, the refineries could produce high-octane fuel from low quality crude oil. Adding lead was the cheapest way to make low-grade gasoline burn efficiently and prevent small explosions (engine knocking). The lead also lubricated the valves.

The phase-out of leaded gasoline did not occur because of known health effects, but because it ruined the catalytic converter. Lead in gasoline coats the platinum in catalytic converters. In addition to changing

Did You Know?

There are over 200 million passenger cars and light trucks on roads and highways in the United States. Since 1970, government regulations have required automotive manufacturers to reduce emissions from vehicles. Manufacturers produced vehicles that polluted less by changing engine design, adding pollution controls, and reducing the size and weight of vehicles.

Vehicles that are lighter weight and more aerodynamic use less fuel, and vehicles that use less fuel produce less air pollution. But today more and more people are buying bigger vehicles. The demand for light trucks, including full-sized pick-up trucks, minivans and sport utility vehicles is increasing. The shift to larger vehicles for general transportation is increasing fuel consumption.

In addition to using more fuel, light trucks are allowed to emit up to three times as much pollution per mile as cars. California has become the first state to require "light trucks" to meet the same emissions standards as passenger cars. The new regulations will go into effect on 2004 models. The EPA is developing new standards for light trucks that will go into effect the same year. The new standards will be based on the California standard.

In 1997, the corporate average fuel economy (CAFE) for passenger cars was 28.6 mpg and 20.4 mpg for light trucks. Unless manufacturers can improve the fuel economy for vehicles classified as light trucks, they will still produce more pollution than passenger cars. In this case bigger and heavier is not better; at least it is not better for the quality of our air.

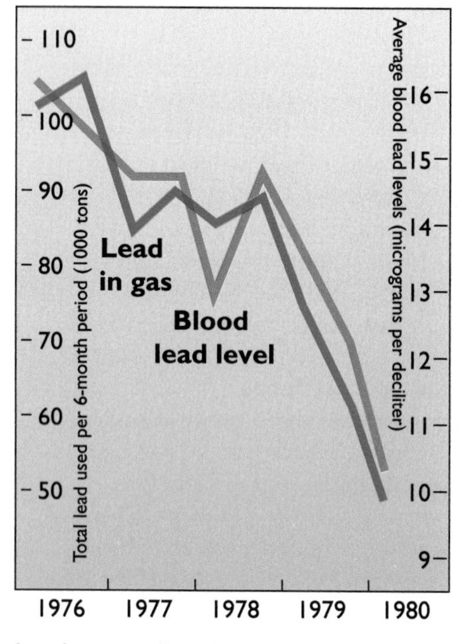

Lead use in Gasoline and Average Blood Lead Levels

the catalyst so that it cannot reduce the carbon monoxide and hydrocarbons in the exhaust, lead itself became a pollutant. Studies linked the amount of lead used in gasoline to levels of lead found in the blood.

EPA regulations make it illegal for someone who sells gasoline or operates a fleet of motor vehicles to put, or allow someone to put, leaded gasoline in a vehicle that is designed for unleaded fuel. The EPA gradually lowered the amount of lead allowed in leaded gasoline. An immediate ban on lead would have forced older refineries to shut down. Lead levels in gasoline averaged 2.0 grams per gallon (0.52 g/L) in 1975. The limit was 0.10 grams per gallon (0.02 g/L) in 1988. In the United States, the EPA limits the amount of lead in unleaded gasoline to 0.05 g/gallon (0.01 g/L). Leaded gasoline is still available today in England, western Europe and in many developing countries.

Redesigning the Engine

Another way to reduce the amount of pollutants is to change the design of the engine. **The stratified internal combustion engine**, introduced by a Japanese auto manufacturer (Honda), has two combustion chambers in each cylinder. The temperature of the burning gases in the main chamber is lower than the temperature in the conventional internal combustion engine. The result is fewer nitrogen oxides. The temperature in the second chamber is high enough, and enough time is allowed, for more of the fuel to burn completely. This prevents the formation of large amounts of carbon monoxide and hydrocarbons.

The diesel engine provides two advantages over the gasoline engine: less carbon monoxide and hydrocarbon emissions, and better fuel economy. In a **diesel engine**, only air enters the chamber during the intake stroke. An exact quantity of fuel is injected into the cylinder during the compression stroke. Compression is greater in the diesel engine. The crowded molecules collide more often, and the heat created by the collisions ignites the fuel.

The major problems with diesel engines are the excessive amounts of nitrogen oxides and particulates in the exhaust. Diesel trucks account for up to 90% of vehicular particulate emissions. New York passed the Heavy-Duty Vehicle Emissions Reduction Act, which requires all trucks in areas with serious air pollution to pass annual emissions inspections. Roadside inspections and heavy penalties help reduce emissions from trucks passing through the state.

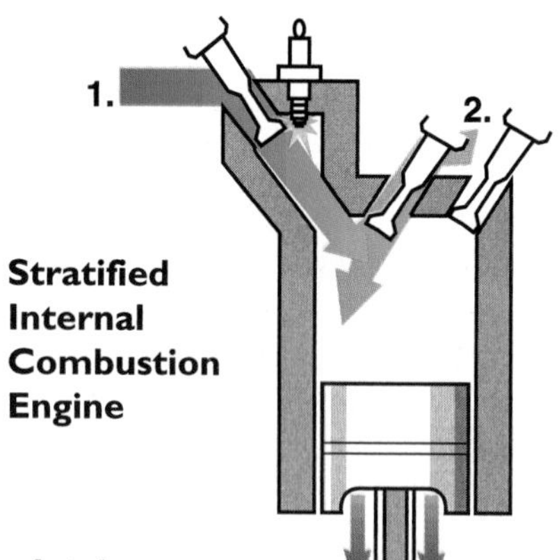

Stratified Internal Combustion Engine

Intake:

1. A rich fuel-air mixture (more fuel/ less air) enters the intake valve of the first chamber. It is ignited by a spark plug.
2. A lean fuel-air mixture (less fuel/ more air) enters the intake valve of the second chamber. It is ignited by the flame of the fuel burning in the first chamber.

Is It Time for a Tune-up?

Most of the air pollution produced by automobiles on the road today comes from cars that are poorly maintained. A good engine tune-up is required to keep emission levels low. Colorado has a hotline and e-mail address to report excessively smoking vehicles. It is designed to provide owners with information that they can use to make needed repairs.

More than 85% of the cars tested at a University of Michigan clinic showed a significant decrease in pollutant levels after a tune-up. The

Structure	Condition	Result
Air Filter — cleans air entering carburetor.	Clogged with dust and grime; not enough air gets through.	Increased hydrocarbon and carbon monoxide levels.
Carburetor — mixes air and gasoline.	Too much air; not enough gasoline. Too much fuel; not enough air.	Increased levels of hydrocarbons. Increased hydrocarbon and carbon monoxide levels.
PCV (positive crankcase ventilation) System — recirculates the vapors that squeeze past the pistons.	Clogged system.	Increased hydrocarbon and carbon monoxide levels.
Ignition System — sends an electric charge to the spark plugs.	Improper firing of spark plugs.	Increased hydrocarbons.
Spark Plugs — ignite the air-fuel mixture in the cylinder.	Worn or dirty plugs.	Increased hydrocarbons.

This chart identifies the normal function of structures associated with the internal combustion engine, and describes conditions that can lead to increased air pollution.

tune-ups included replacing spark plugs and ignition points, and adjusting timing and the carburetor. Before the tune-up, some cars produced 7–10% carbon monoxide. After the tune-up, they produced less than 1% carbon monoxide.

Can We Meet the Standards?

Today there are more vehicles traveling more miles. Cars and trucks together are the greatest source of carbon monoxide and ozone-forming pollutants. Although vehicles built today emit fewer pollutants than older models, the average car on the road emits 3–4 times more pollution than the standards allow for new cars. About 30% of cars that are 5 years old and 55% of cars that are 7 years old emit high levels of pollution.

In December 1998, the EPA designated 20 nonattainment areas because they did not meet the carbon monoxide standard, and 38 major urban areas were designated nonattainment areas for ozone. The 1990 amendments to the Clean Air Act required states with areas that exceeded the federal standards to set up "enhanced" vehicle I/M (inspection/maintenance) programs. The goal of these programs was to make sure that emission controls on inspected vehicles were working properly.

The high-tech tests closely simulate actual driving conditions. They also check for leaks in the car's **evaporative emission system**. Since 1971, cars have been built with a closed system that collects vapors from the gas

Did You Know?

Because cold engines don't burn gasoline as efficiently as warmer engines, they produce more emissions. Catalytic converters work properly only when they warm up. Thus most air pollution is produced when the car is first started. When starting your car on a cold day, don't allow it to idle for more than 1 or 2 minutes. This will warm the catalytic converter, and idling any longer will only waste gas.

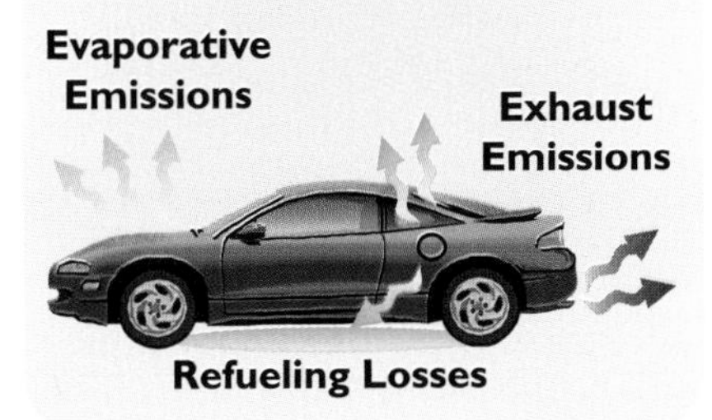

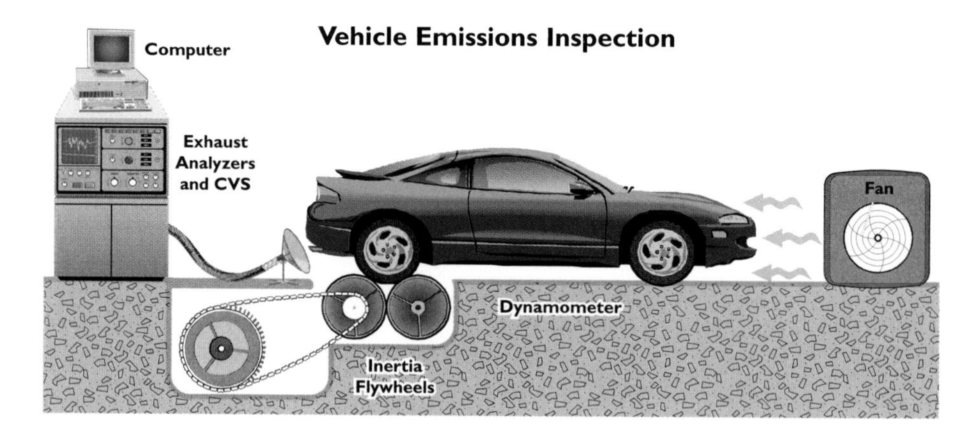

Enhanced vehicle inspection and maintenance programs can ensure that systems which control emissions in exhaust and from evaporating fuel are working properly.

tank. This prevents hydrocarbons from entering the atmosphere, but only if the system doesn't leak. In hot weather, evaporative emissions can be a much bigger source of hydrocarbons than exhaust emissions. Hydrocarbons entering the atmosphere contribute to ozone formation.

Hydrocarbons also enter the atmosphere as gasoline vapors when fuel is pumped into the fuel tank. **Stage II vapor recovery** systems, found at some gas stations, collect the vapor and send it back to the underground storage tank. When the truck delivers fuel to the storage tank, the vapors are transferred to the tank truck by a Stage I system. The tank truck returns the vapors to the terminal where they are destroyed or recovered. The stage II vapor recovery system is required in areas that are "moderate to extreme" nonattainment areas for ozone.

In order for the nation's most polluted cities to meet the ambient air quality standard for ozone, many vehicles must switch to **reformulated gasoline** (RFG) and other cleaner burning fuels. Reformulated gasoline has fewer highly volatile organic compounds and toxic chemicals, including benzene—a known human **carcinogen**. RFG also has at least 2% oxygen by weight. RFG may produce 25% fewer emissions than conventional gasoline.

States with areas that do not meet the carbon monoxide standard must provide **oxygenated fuels** during the winter months. The oxygen comes from additives, called oxygenates, that reduce the amount of carbon monoxide produced during combustion. The two most common additives are ethanol and methyl tertiary butyl ether (MTBE). MTBE has been found in some water supplies.

The 1990 Clean Air Act Amendments required fleets of vehicles operating in cities with high ozone and/or carbon monoxide levels to meet lower emissions standards. These fleets of vehicles could use RFG or one of the clean fuels. **Clean fuels** include compressed natural gas, methanol (from natural gas), ethanol (from corn) and electricity. They are called clean fuels because they produce 90% less pollution than conventional gasoline.

Did You Know?

Two rental car companies created the nation's first fleet of electric vehicles (EVs) at Los Angeles International Airport. To encourage the use of electric vehicles, their introductory rates for several different makes were cheaper than rates for gas-powered vehicles.

It is unlikely that Southern California will meet federal standards before 2010. California has adopted vehicle emission regulations that are stricter than the federal regulations. In addition to strict pollution controls, improved fuel efficiency of new cars helps reduce pollution. With improved designs, use of lightweight materials and modification of engines, fuel efficiency can be improved. Ten percent of all cars sold in California by 2003 must be ZEVs—zero emissions vehicles (electric cars).

With so many cars in large cities, traffic congestion is a problem that is only expected to worsen. Each year, drivers stuck in traffic in Boston waste an estimated 300 million gallons (1.136×10^9 L) of gasoline and add to the city's air pollution. Will the traffic congestion be reduced when construction of the expanded Central Artery—a $5 billion highway project—is complete? Some experts predict that the new highway will only attract more vehicles.

Well-designed cities and mass transit systems can reduce pollution. Portland, Oregon, violated federal standards for carbon monoxide 100 days per year. But since the 70s, the city has revitalized the downtown area, replaced a roadway with a park, limited parking spaces, built new transit lines instead of roads, and changed zoning to encourage high residential density along transit corridors. Now there are 30,000 more jobs in downtown Portland, and 40% of commuters are using public transportation. And the number of days per year that Portland exceeds carbon monoxide standards is zero.

Mass transit must clean up its act, too. Seventy-eight areas did not meet the standard for particulate matter in 1998. Black clouds of diesel exhaust from trucks and buses are major sources of particulates. One diesel-powered bus can emit as much particulate matter as 40–60 cars. The EPA reduced the amount of sulfur allowed in diesel fuel in 1993. This will reduce the emissions of particulate matter and toxics.

Diesel exhaust is by far the largest source of fine particulate matter in New York City. New York is converting 15% of its fleet of more than 4,000 diesel buses to compressed natural gas (CNG). Natural gas buses emit 90% less particulate soot than the cleanest diesel buses. Sacramento Rapid Transit District has a fleet of buses that run on CNG. Not only are they cleaner than diesel buses, but they cost 20 to 40% less per mile to operate than diesel buses.

The Clean Air Act Amendment in 1995 challenged companies to look for alternatives for commuting workers. In 1990, 4 million workers used telecommuting over traditional commuting to work. The number of stay-at-home employees increased to 11 million by 1997. The number of telecommuters is expected to increase. Telecommuters produce even less environmental impact than those driving a zero emission vehicle.

Did You Know?

California's Santa Barbara County does not meet National Ambient Air Quality Standards. Since motor vehicles are a major source of air pollution, the county's Air Pollution Control District is buying cars and trucks manufactured before 1973. The owner of an eligible vehicle is given $500 and the vehicle is "retired" from the road.

Environmental Challenge: Emissions Standards

Discuss the following questions and make a decision that reflects the majority of the group. Support your position.

- Should the EPA issue emissions standards for lawn mowers?
- Should people in areas that don't meet the ozone standard be required to use electric or battery-operated lawn mowers?
- Should emissions standards be issued for dune buggies and off-road vehicles?
- Should emissions standards be issued for construction equipment? Farm tractors?

2.15 QUESTIONS FOR STUDY AND DISCUSSION:

1. Define the following terms: **VOCABULARY**

catalytic converter Clean Air Act Amendment clean fuels	closed cylinder combustion diesel engine	evaporative emission system oxygenated fuels piston	reformulated gasoline stage II vapor recovery stratified internal combustion engine

Where It All Begins

2. How do complete and incomplete combustion differ?
3. In your own words briefly describe what happens in the cylinder during each stage of the 4-stroke cycle in an internal combustion engine.

Too Many Cars, Too Many Miles

4. How have the total vehicle miles traveled changed since 1970?
5. How do emissions from cars today compare to emissions from cars in the 1960s?

The Government Steps In

6. Identify the state that first required pollution controls on automobiles. What effect did this have on automobiles in other states?
7. What is the role of the EPA and the automobile manufacturers in reducing emissions in auto exhaust?
8. Give three changes in engine design that will improve combustion.

The Catalytic Converter

9. How does the platinum catalyst reduce pollution?
10. How do second-generation catalytic converters differ from the first generation?

Get the Lead Out

11. Why did refineries add lead to gasoline?
12. Why were refineries forced to eliminate the use of lead?

Redesigning the Engine

13. Describe the conditions in the stratified internal combustion engine that prevent the formation of large amounts of carbon monoxide, hydrocarbons, and nitrogen oxides?
14. What are the advantages and disadvantages of using diesel engines?

Is It Time for a Tune-Up?

15. What can car owners do to assure that their cars are not big polluters?
16. Describe two ways that an auto mechanic might "tune" your car engine so that it pollutes less.

Can We Meet the Standards?

17. Since newer vehicles pollute less, why are urban areas unable to meet the National Air Quality Standards?
18. What steps has California taken to reduce the level of ozone? What additional steps should be taken?
19. Compare Boston's and Portland's solutions to traffic congestion and air pollution. How do you think the air pollution levels will change in these two cities during the next decade?
20. What steps are being taken to decrease pollution from mass transit?

UNIT THREE
Food for the Table
230
256
198
219
213
238
250
271
12000+ Ft.
9000-12000 Ft.
7500-9000 Ft.
6000-7500 Ft.
4500-6000 Ft.
3000-4500 Ft.
1800-3000 Ft.
1200-1800 Ft.
600-1200 Ft.
300-600 Ft.
150-300 Ft.
0-150 Ft.
-3000 - 0 Ft.
-6000 - -3000 Ft.
-9000 - -6000 Ft.
-12000 - -9000 Ft.
-15000 - -12000 Ft.
-18000 - -15000 Ft.
-21000 - -18000 Ft.
-24000 - -21000 Ft.
<-24000 Ft.
Food for the Table
3

3.1 Food — Before the Big Mac

OBJECTIVES

- **Identify** the two lifestyles that provide food for the table and **compare** the length of time that each has been practiced.
- **Describe** the methods used by archaeologists that provide information about the types of food and technology used by early humans.
- **Compare** the traditional methods of growing and harvesting wild rice with the growing and harvesting of corn.

"Humans have always needed plants for food, for shelter, and for fire. Even when other materials are available for shelter and fire, plants are still needed for food."

The Hunters and Gatherers

Early humans did not raise plants and animals. They were **hunters and gatherers**, who depended upon the wild plants and animals for food. It is said that the Shoshone Indians used 100 different kinds of wild plants. Women did most of the gathering. The young girls soon learned from their mothers the plants that could be eaten and the kinds that were poisonous. Most of their time was spent finding and preparing food. They had little leisure time.

During most of the time that humans have lived on Earth, hunting and gathering supplied their food. If the time since humans first appeared on Earth was represented by 50 years, humans were hunters and gatherers for the first 49 of these years. **Agriculture**, the planting and harvesting of crops for food, did not appear until the very last year.

How Do We Know?

Archaeologists are scientists who study the things that early humans left behind. By studying the "dumps" of early humans, scientists can determine which kinds of plants and animals were important as well as how they were used. The dumps must be carefully excavated. Each remaining piece of the people's trash is carefully removed, and its discovery is recorded. Later the pieces are examined more carefully.

The items that once belonged to these early people are called artifacts. **Artifacts** are objects that were modified in some way by humans. Also found in the trash are bones, shells and seeds. These things tell us something about the life of the people that lived at that time. One of the things that archaeologists want to know is the age of the items found. This tells them how long ago these people lived.

A process known as **radiocarbon dating** can tell us the age of a once-living object, such as a bone or a shell. All living things contain two types of carbon: carbon-12 and carbon-14. Carbon-12, the most abundant form of carbon, is not radioactive. Carbon-14 is a radioactive form of carbon that is made by the action of cosmic rays on nitrogen in the air.

The age of the dead organism can be determined by comparing the amount of carbon-14 in the dead organism and the amount of carbon-14 in a living organism today. As long as the organism is alive, the amount of carbon-14 remains the same. When the organism dies and no longer takes in carbon, the amount of carbon-14 decreases due to radioactive decay.

This McDonald's in Chicago was the beginning of the fast food industry. Though your generation doesn't remember life before the Big Mac, most generations were "hunters and gatherers."

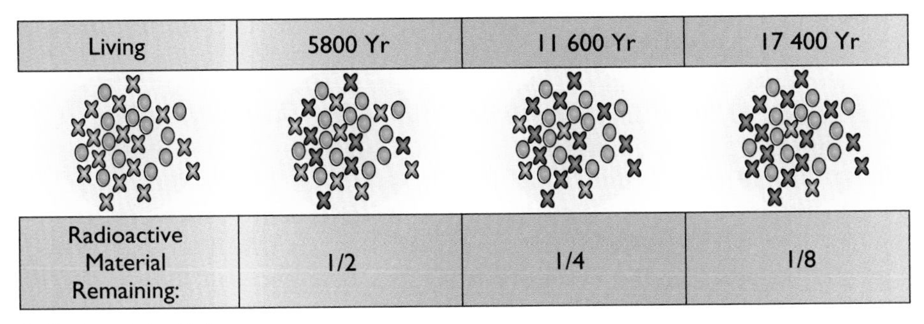

Carbon-14 Still Present
Carbon-14 Decayed
Other Atoms

The decay of carbon-14 tells us the age of an object that was once living. If the object has 1/8 of the carbon-14 found in a living object, it is 17,400 years old.

Objects found by archaeologists tell us how people lived and sometimes what they ate.

The amount of time it takes for 1/2 of a radioactive element to break down is known as its **half-life**. Carbon-14 has a half-life of about 5,800 years. A dead organism is about 5,800 years old, if it has 1/2 of the carbon-14 found in a living organism. It will take an additional 5,800 years for 1/2 of the remaining carbon-14 to break down. If a dead organism has 1/4 of the carbon-14 found in a living organism, it is 11,600 years old. If a dead organism has 1/8 of the carbon-14 found in a living organism, it is 17,400 years old. This method can be used to date organisms that are between 1,000 and 50,000 years old

The Beginning of Technology

Early humans used the knowledge they had gained and the natural resources that were available to make products or develop processes that would improve their lives. This is applied science. Today we call it **technology**. The technology used by early humans may seem very primitive, but sometimes it was as effective as our modern technology.

To improve the chance of a successful hunt, weapons were made from stone and bones. One type of stone that was used to make arrows was obsidian. **Obsidian** is a type of rock formed when hot volcanic lava cools very quickly. The quick cooling prevents the formation of crystals and the rock appears to be made of glass. The broken edges of this volcanic glass are very sharp. When scientists tested obsidian arrowheads, they found that the obsidian penetrated flesh better than arrows made with modern steel tips.

The making of arrowheads was an important skill. A well-made arrow improved the chances of a successful hunt.

Before Wheat and Corn

Before there was wheat, flour was made from acorns. After the nuts were picked and shelled, they were put into a bowl-shaped container called a **mortar** and pounded into a coarse powder. The mortar was sometimes a "pot hole" in a ledge of granite rock. A smooth rock from the creek was used to pound the nuts against the sides of the mortar.

The Indians called it mahnomen, a word meaning "good berry." The botanist calls it *Zizania aquatica*; some call it wild rice.

Acorns contain a bitter chemical called **tannin**. The tannin must be removed from the flour before it can be used to make bread or mush. A hole was made in the ground and lined with sand or cedar bark. The hole was then filled with the acorn flour, and water was added. The water dissolved the tannins, and they were carried away with the water as it slowly drained from the hole. This process in which chemicals are dissolved and gradually carried away by water is known as **leaching**.

Hot water was used for the final leaching. To heat the water, rocks were first heated in the campfire and then dropped into baskets filled with water. Baskets, made to hold water and cook mush, were woven very tightly. The design and weave of the basket depended on how the basket was to be used.

A Waterweed: Wild Rice

Most of the plants we use for food today have been changed in some way. The science of **genetics** has provided us with bigger plants and fruits, fruits that ripen at nearly the same time, and plants that give us larger yields. There is one plant, however, that resisted change. The Indians called it mahnomen, a word meaning "good berry." The botanist calls it *Zizania aquatica*; some call it wild rice.

If you want to eat as the Indians sometimes ate, you could buy some wild rice at the grocery store and cook it with a few quail, doves or a rabbit. The flavors will taste the same as they did to the Indian. If you want to cook it as the Indian did, you will need a tightly woven basket, a campfire, some stones, and a specially bent twig to get the stones out of the campfire. You may want to substitute a little modern technology, perhaps a stainless steel pan and an electric stove.

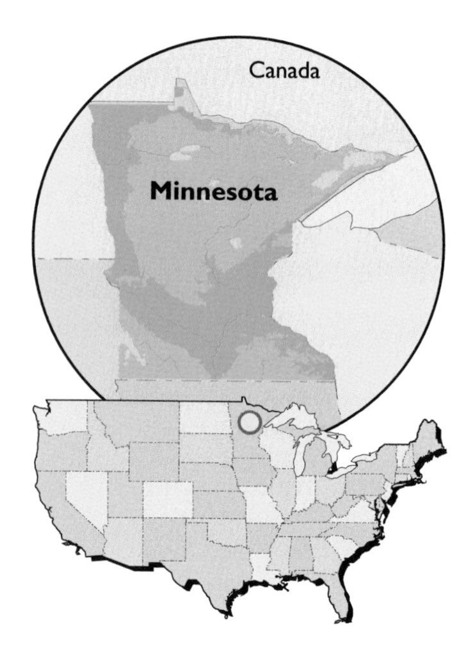

Most wild rice that is sold in markets is not native wild rice. It is a **shatter-resistant** variety produced in fields where the water level is controlled by **dikes**. A cultivator tool attached to an airboat thins the plants, and a machine harvests the rice. Native wild rice grows in cold rivers and lakes in Minnesota and Canada. Another kind of *Zizania* grows in Japan and China. The Japanese call it the "fruit-of-the-waterweed." Wild rice growing in Minnesota State waters is regulated and must be gathered by traditional methods using canoes.

Wild rice is a member of the grass family; a cousin of oats and rice. The stalks are rooted in water and stand ten to twelve feet tall. Near the top of these stalks are male and female flowers. The wind blows the pollen from the male flowers to the female flowers on another plant. When the seeds are ripe, they drop into the water and are buried in the mud. In spring they begin to grow.

Harvest time is in the early fall. The gatherers set up camp beside the lake. The rice stalks grow so close together that it is impossible to paddle a canoe, so the canoe is pushed with a pole. The person in the front of the canoe uses one stick to bend the stalks into the canoe and a second stick to beat the stalks, knocking the grains of rice into the canoe.

Since all of the rice does not mature at the same time, some of the rice is still green and remains on the stalks. Other grains will have already fallen into the water. This uneven ripening ensures the planting of next year's crop.

Immediately after harvest, the rice grains are **parched** (cured and dried). Some Indians set the rice in the sun or built platforms of bark and kept a small fire underneath. Others stirred the rice in baskets with hot coals. Later, they traded with the settlers for metal kettles. Today, at modern mills, this parching is done in large drums that rotate over slow gas fires.

The drying cracks the hulls of the rice. The Indians put the rice on clean skins and beat it with sticks to loosen the hulls from the grain. Some preferred to dig a shallow hole, line it with a clean skin, and then dance on the rice with moccasined feet. These may have been the first unofficial aerobics classes.

When the hulls were loosened they had to be separated from the kernels. This process was known as **winnowing**. The seeds were placed on wide shallow baskets or trays of birch bark. With a gentle bouncing of the seed, the wind lifted the hulls from the grain. In today's modern mills, big machines that have mechanical shakers and power fans take off the hulls.

Today the native wild rice sold at markets comes from the same rice lakes that it has for centuries. Much of it is still harvested by the Indians who make yearly trips to the rice lakes. Wild rice is a primary source of income for roughly 300 Indian families in Saskatchewan. One company hires gatherers and transports them in planes that land on the water. The gatherers camp at the lake during the harvest and the plane returns when the harvest is completed. This allows for the harvesting of rice at some lakes that cannot easily be reached by land.

Corn: Tamed by Humans

Today corn is a major source of food grown in most of North and South America. Scientists classify it as a kind of grass, but it is very different from other grasses. Most grasses have seeds that are light and easily scattered by wind. Some, with heavier seeds, have brittle stems that fall to the ground. Still others have seeds that are caught in the fur of animals.

The corn plant has several hundred seeds that are tightly held on a cob. The cob is wrapped in several layers of "leaves" and attached to a strong stalk that does not break easily. The protective wrapping prevents the seeds from being scattered. Even if the wrapping is removed, the seeds are too heavy to be carried by the wind and there are no projections that will catch in the fur of animals.

Corn is pollinated by wind. Directions in seed catalogs suggest that corn be planted in blocks of at least four rows, rather than in a single long row. This improves the chances of pollination and the development of cobs that are completely filled with kernels.

When corn is not harvested, the cob often remains securely attached to the standing stalk. If the stalk is knocked to the ground, several hundred seeds must compete with one another for space, minerals and water. Few of them will survive to produce a mature corn plant. Few of the plants that reach maturity will be pollinated and few seeds will be

The world's only corn palace, in Mitchell, South Dakota. Each year scenes are created on the outside of the building using thousands of bushels of corn and other grasses. Early settlers displayed the results of their harvest to encourage immigrants to move to SD.

To see the current scenes, visit: www.cornpalace.org.

If this corn is not harvested it will remain attached to the stalk. The heavy seeds are firmly attached to the cob which prevents their dispersal.

If the stalk falls to the ground, many seeds must compete for space, water and minerals.

Few of these plants will reach maturity. They are not properly spaced for good pollination, so few seeds will be produced.

produced. Without humans to plant the seeds of corn, this kind of grass plant would not survive.

Scientists have found other wild grasses from which humans have developed wheat, barley and oats. They have not found any corn that has grown without the aid of humans. According to written records, corn did not grow in Africa, Asia, Europe, or in England. The Spaniards who traveled with Christopher Columbus were probably the first Europeans to see corn. They were given corn that was planted and tended by the native Indians.

Decorated pumpkin.

Archaeologists have concluded that corn was the main cereal crop that sustained the civilizations in the Americas. Many archaeological digs have given us evidence of the importance of corn. It decorated pottery and was carved in the stone of sculptures. Golden stalks of corn decorated temples. Vessels thought to be corn poppers were made of pottery. Cobs of corn, made from pottery, were possibly used as toys. Real cobs of corn have been found in graves.

The search for the wild corn plants has so far been unsuccessful. On the bottom layer of a trash heap in Bat Cave (New Mexico) were tiny cobs of corn about the size of a penny. Radiocarbon dating showed their age to be 5,600 years. The kernels from the tiny cobs were small and hard like unpopped popcorn. Upper layers of the trash heap yielded larger kernels of corn.

Scientists think that each of the kernels was enclosed in a separate leafy wrapping. Corn that has each kernel wrapped separately is called **pod corn**. It sometimes appears as a freak in fields of corn today. The Indians considered it a sign of good luck. Scientists have experimented with crossing pod corn and a primitive kind of popcorn. They have managed to produce tiny cobs of corn similar to those found in Bat Cave. This proves that some of the traits of the corn found in Bat Cave are still found in corn today.

The corn in Bat Cave had probably lost the ability to scatter its seeds. No one knows what the wild corn plants looked like, but the pollen of corn plants has been found in dirt taken from a 200-foot (60 m) hole drilled for the foundation of a skyscraper. Corn pollen is the largest pollen of any grass plant and can be easily identified. The pollen is 80,000 years old. How the wild corn seed was scattered remains a mystery. But the growing of corn appears to mark the beginning of farming as a way of life.

3.1 Questions for Study and Discussion:

1. Define the following words: **VOCABULARY**

agriculture	half-life	parched	technology
archaeologist	hunters and gatherers	pod corn	winnowing
artifact	leaching	radiocarbon dating	
dikes	mortar	shatter-resistant	
genetics	obsidian	tannin	

2. List three ways in which humans use plants.

The Hunters and Gatherers

3. During most of the time that humans have been on Earth, how had food been provided?

How Do We Know?

4. Early humans left no written records. How do we know what kinds of food were eaten by these early people?
5. How can we tell the age of a tool made from bone? Is a tool made from a bone an artifact?
6. If a dead organism has one-half of the C-14 found in a living organism, how old is it? If a dead organism has one-sixteenth of the C-14 found in a living organism, how old is it?

The Beginning of Technology

7. List examples of technology used by early humans, and give the natural resources used.

Before Wheat and Corn

8. What type of seed was used to make flour before wheat?
9. Describe the process that the Indians used to make flour.

A Waterweed: Wild Rice

10. Describe how native wild rice grows and is harvested.
11. Why is there no danger that all of the wild rice will be taken at harvest and none will be left as seed for next year's crop?
12. Compare the methods that the Indians used to process the rice to the methods used today.

Corn: Tamed by Humans

13. Give two reasons why corn cannot survive without the help of humans.
14. Describe the corn found in Bat Cave. How do we know that it is more than 5,000 years old?
15. Why do scientists think that corn marks the beginning of agriculture?

3.2 Agriculture — The Development of Technology

OBJECTIVES

- **Compare** early methods of providing food for the table with modern methods of food production.
- **Trace** the development of technology used for preparing the soil, planting seeds, and harvesting the crops.
- **Explain** how the development of technology has changed natural ecosystems and the impact it has had on the lives of humans.
- **Compare** agriculture in the developed countries with agriculture in less developed countries.

"Where there are increases in population without advances in agricultural technology, the standard of living declines, starvation appears, and famine threatens."
WORLD RESOURCES INSTITUTE

Agriculture, the growing of crops for food, began with a very primitive technology. Hunting was still important to provide meat, but the crops that were planted promised a greater supply of food. Berries and wild seeds were still an important part of the diet and were necessary to provide certain vitamins and minerals. The practice of agriculture allowed the land to support a larger population.

Early Tools

The first farm tool was probably the **digging stick** that had been used for digging roots and bulbs. It was a strong, straight stick that had been sharpened at one end. Today in isolated parts of the world primitive farmers use only two farming tools, the digging stick and the **machete**, or big knife. Their method of farming today is probably very much like that of the first farmers.

Trees and brush are cleared with the machete, allowed to dry, and then burned. The stick is used to poke holes through the ashes and into the soil so that the seeds can be planted. The seeds are planted around the stumps and logs that still remain in the field. With each passing harvested crop, the soil is less fertile, so after two or three years, a new plot of ground is cleared.

The American Indians used the same kinds of tools and methods used by the Stone Age people who had lived thousands of years before them. They had stone axes, fire-hardened sticks, and clam shells. Hoes were also used to prepare the ground for planting. Some hoes were L-shaped tree limbs with blades of stone or shell, while others had blades made of the shoulder bone of a deer or buffalo.

Tools used by Native Americans were often made of sticks and bones.

Bigger Machines to Prepare the Ground

After humans tamed animals, the hoe could be pulled through the fields. Egyptians used two oxen to pull this new invention that was called a **plow**. The first plows were made entirely of wood. They were little more than big digging sticks that had been attached to a beam that was pulled by the oxen. Then in 1797, a New Jersey farmer named Charles Newbold invented a cast-iron plow.

Newbold's plow was not practical because the entire bottom had to be replaced when one surface was worn out. Using mathematical computations, Thomas Jefferson designed a **moldboard plow**. He was trying to design a plow that would work in all soils. The **moldboard** is a

This cast-iron plow was replaced by a plow made of hardened steel.

The newer plows have replaceable shins, plowshares and a coulter to cut through the sod.

Today farmers use gang plows. This 3-bottomed gang plow is pulled by a 50-horsepower tractor.

curved metal plate. At the bottom of the moldboard is the **plowshare** that cuts through the soil. A **shin** on the front edge of the moldboard also cuts through the soil. The plow rests on a **landslide**—a straight piece of metal that guides the plow.

An improved plow had the plow share, moldboard and landslide in separate pieces, so that only the worn parts would have to be replaced. At first people were afraid the cast iron plow would poison the soil and cause weeds to grow. It would be 25 years before the plow was accepted.

A few years later in 1837 John Deere, a blacksmith in Illinois, invented the steel plow. The cast-iron plow could not turn over the heavy, sticky soils of the prairie. Every so often the moldboard would have to be cleaned with a paddle. Some people thought the prairie was not fit for farming, but the new steel plow could cut through the heavy, sticky soil.

Modern plows have a circular steel blade, or **coulter**, which cuts through the sod or debris on the surface as a circular saw cuts through wood. The sod is then turned completely over by the moldboard. Thousands of these plows were made in factories and sent out West to the "sod busters."

Pulled by teams of horses, the first moldboard plows had one coulter and one moldboard. Today **gang plows** have several coulters and moldboards. Pulled by tractors, gang plows turn over the soil as if two to fourteen plows were being used at once. Today's tractors do the work of many horses.

The development of our nation followed the development of the plow. It was the plow that allowed humans to change the earth. It brought some good changes as well as bad. The plow made it possible for fewer people to produce more food, but the plow has also caused the loss of much of our topsoil.

Before a field can be planted, the clods left by the plow must be broken up and the soil made level. Dragging a **harrow** back and forth across the field breaks the clods and levels the soil. The first harrows were logs or tree branches. These were replaced with long boards that had wooden prongs along the bottom. Later iron spikes were pounded through the boards, and today the iron spikes are attached to iron frames. Iron or steel discs are sometimes used to cut through the clods before the harrow is used to smooth out the seedbed.

Machines for Planting

Grain drills pulled by horses made planting easier.

Wheat and barley were scattered by hand before the invention of the hand-cranked **broadcast seeder**. The broadcast seeder hangs by a strap over the shoulder. The seed sifts down on top of a small fan that scatters the seed over an area a few meters wide. How fast the person walks and how fast the seeder is cranked determine the amount of seed planted. Hand-cranked seeders are still used by people for lawns and gardens, and people only wanting to plant just a few acres.

Grain drills are used on larger farms. The drill is a long box with planting tubes that carry seed to the ground. At the bottom of the tubes are discs that make a shallow trench for the seeds. Most drills also have boxes where fertilizer can be added. The first drills planted a strip of ground two meters wide. Modern drills can plant and fertilize a strip of ground six to eight meters wide. Some drills can cut through the sod and plant the seed without plowing and making a seed bed. These drills are called **no-till drills**. For more information, see pages 222 and 223.

Today farmers use no-till drills to plant corn and grains such as wheat and barley. No-till planting eliminates the need to prepare the soil, but it requires the use of herbicides to control the growth of weeds.

Corn was planted by making a hole with a hoe, dropping in seeds, and covering the hole. This procedure was repeated every few steps until the field was planted. The first mechanical device used to plant corn was the **jab planter**. A steel blade was jabbed into the ground to make an opening. Then by moving the handles of the planter, three or four seeds were dropped through a tube into the hole. When the planter was pulled out of the ground the dirt fell in and covered the seed. Jab planters are still useful to the gardener and the research scientist.

Machines for Reaping

The first tool used for reaping was the **sickle**. A sickle is a curved blade on a short handle. The first sickle blades were made of sharpened stone; later blades were made of metal. The **scythe** was simply a larger blade with a longer curved handle.

Sometimes a **cradle** was attached to the scythe to catch the grain. It was made of pieces of wood fastened to the scythe. After each sweep of the blade, the stalks of grain were dumped to the ground. A few stalks were used to tie the grain into bundles, or **sheaves**, which were then placed in groups called **shocks**, and left in the field to dry.

A mechanical **reaper**, or binder, was perfected, manufactured and marketed by a man named McCormick (1831). It was a heavy machine made of wood and metal, and it took several horses to pull it. The inventor had studied the movement of the arms and legs as the wheat was cut with a scythe. A large reel, with wooden blades, pulled the grain toward the cutting blade. The cut grain was then carried on a canvas conveyer to a binding mechanism that tied the bundles of grain with a type of string called **binder twine**. Men followed the reaper and stood the bundles together to form shocks.

Most farmers thought that they couldn't afford such a machine, even though it could cut six acres (2.4 ha) in a day. This was six times as fast as a man could work with a scythe. McCormick persuaded the farmers to buy the machine by allowing them to pay with several installments. This may have been the first installment-buying plan.

Now it took only a few men to reap the miles and miles of wheat that could be grown on the plains. During the Civil War, when many men were fighting instead of farming, more wheat was grown than ever before. The invention of the reaper helped provide the money, food and men necessary for the North to win the war.

Now that grain could be reaped quickly, there was a greater demand for the threshing machine. Until the threshing machine had been invented, the grain had been separated from the straw by beating it with flails on the floor of the barn. This particular floor of the barn became known as the **threshing floor**. A **flail** is a long stick with a heavy beater-stick fastened to the end. With ten hours of hard work, a man could beat out seven or eight bushels of wheat.

The first threshing machines were pulled and powered by horses; later ones would be powered by steam engines that burned coal. The **threshing machine** separated the grain from the straw and the **chaff**, the protective sheaths that covered the individual grains. It took several men to operate the threshing machine, but 300 bushels (10.6 m^3) of wheat could be threshed in one day, unless the machine broke down.

Today self-propelled **combine harvesters** are used to harvest all types of grain, including wheat, rice, soybeans and corn. The machine got this name because it is a combination reaper and harvester. Some combines can harvest a strip of grain more than 24 feet (8 m) wide. These huge machines are moved from farm to farm as the grain ripens on the Great Plains. More than a million combines are in use today.

Of course the Indians and pilgrims used their bare hands to husk the cobs of corn from the stalks. Farmers invented a variety of **corn pegs** to make the husking easier. The first peg was a thin piece of wood or bone that had been sharpened to a point at one end. A piece of string or leather bound it to the middle joint of the fingers on the right hand.

The peg was used to slash open the husk that was then pulled back from the ear of corn. The best corn peg developed was a kind of fingerless leather glove with a steel hook that ripped the husk open. A good husker could husk a bushel of corn in less than one minute.

Corn was often harvested with a binder, and the bundles of corn stalks were placed in shocks until they were needed. Binders were later replaced with a mechanical corn harvester, commonly called a **corn picker**. A **header** on the corn picker guides the stalks toward rows of revolving, snapping rollers. The rollers pinch and snap the cob from the stalk. As the picker moves down the row, the ear of corn is husked and tossed into a wagon. On large farms the combine harvester that picks, husks and shells the corn has replaced the corn picker.

Shocks of corn and grains are left in the field to dry.

Two combine harvesters make harvesting this wheat an easy task. After changing the header, the combine harvester will be used to pick and shell the corn.

Using this header, a farmer can harvest six rows of corn at once.

Corn that is picked by hand, or by a corn picker, must be shelled. Small farmers in Africa, who grow only a few hectares of corn, still shell the corn by hand. Shelling is done by one of the following methods:

- The cob is held in the palm of the hand and the kernels of corn are removed with the movement of the thumb.
- A shelled cob is rubbed on another cob to remove the kernels of corn. This method is faster than using the bare hands, but it requires more energy and skill.
- The husked cobs are put in a bag and beat with a stick while the bag is turned. The cobs are removed and any kernels of corn left on the cob are removed by one of the first two methods.
- The cobs are spread on a raised platform made of sticks and bamboo poles. The cobs are beaten with a stick, and the kernels of corn fall through spaces in the platform. Any kernels left on the cob are removed by one of the first two methods.

A **shelling board** made with U-nails (fence staples) is three times more efficient than any of the methods listed above. Two rows of nails are placed 0.8 inches (2 cm) apart on a wooden board, and a space of 1 inch (2.5 cm) is left between nails within each row. The cob of corn is rubbed against the nails to remove the kernels of corn.

Amish farmers still use horses to pull equipment that is powered with gasoline engines. Here a field of hay is being cut and crimped (crushed) in preparation for baling. The hay will be stored to feed the dairy cows and the horses during the winter.

Several hand-cranked **corn shellers** have been invented and are still used by small-scale farmers. Some models have a large flywheel that makes the sheller more powerful, and reduces the amount of human energy needed to turn the handle of the sheller. The handle is turned to start the rotation of the flywheel. Once the flywheel is turning, the hand crank can easily keep the gears in the sheller moving, and corn can be shelled as fast as it can be fed into the opening.

A spring adjustment allows the sheller to adapt to cobs of different sizes. The cobs pass between toothed, cast-iron shelling plates. As one of the plates rotates, the cobs are forced against the teeth that remove the grains of corn. The cob is ejected out of an opening, and the kernels of corn fall through another opening into a container.

Some hand-cranked corn shellers have been adapted with motors that turn the flywheel. One type of sheller used a treadle and flywheel to move the gears. It could shell 300 to 350 bushels (10.6–12 m^3) of corn per hour. New models of corn shellers are adapted to the power take-off shaft of a tractor. They can shell 350-500 bushels (12–17.6 m^3) of husked corn per hour.

A number of machines have been developed to harvest root crops. The simplest and oldest machine for harvesting potatoes is still in use by small-scale farmers. The **potato digger** has a modified moldboard that digs and raises the potatoes onto prongs. The potatoes are carried along a conveyor made of metal chains. The soil is shaken from the potatoes and falls through the links of chain as the potatoes are moved toward the back of the machine. They either fall to the ground or are placed on a cart. Stones and other debris must be removed before the potatoes are placed in bags.

Harvesters have been invented for many different crops. A celery harvester moves through a field at a rate of five or six feet (1.5–1.8 m) a minute. Twenty-four rows of celery are cut, trimmed, washed, sorted and packed in crates as the harvester moves across the field.

Did You Know?

George Washington used his Mount Vernon plantation as an experimental farm. He worked to develop better strains of wheat, but his greatest success may have been the introduction of the mule to America.

More Food with Less Labor

Gasoline and diesel tractors are used with many different machines. Bigger and better machines meant that fewer people could farm more land, and provide food for more people. Machine power replaced the power of millions of workhorses. The horsepower of the internal combustion engine has replaced the 27 million head of mules and horses used in the early 1900s. The millions of acres needed to grow food for the animals can now be used to grow food for humans.

In 1880, it took 180 man-hours of labor to produce 100 bushels of corn. In 1978 it required only four man-hours. Wheat production required 373 man-hours in 1880 compared to 10 man-hours in 1978. The labor needed to produce a bale of cotton was reduced from 300 to 11 man-hours by 1978.

In 1880, 22 million people, or 44% of the U.S. population lived and worked on farms. By 1979 there were only 6.2 million, or less than 3% of the total population living and working on farms. Today one person produces food for an additional 35 people.

This reduction in farm labor is not totally due to the use of bigger and better machines. The development of better varieties of seeds, chemical fertilizers, and chemicals to control diseases, weeds, and insects, allow farmers to produce more food. Although fewer people actually work on the farm, agricultural technology provides nearly 25% of all available employment in the United States. This includes the technology needed to transport, process and sell the products of agriculture.

In most of the world planting and harvesting is still done with animals and human labor. Cows are used in the rice field in China to prepare the soil for planting.

In Other Parts of the World

Farming in the U.S. is not like farming in many other countries. In most countries farming methods have not changed much for hundreds of years. Wooden plows are still used, and seeds are still scattered by hand. On the farms in many countries, more than 90% of the power is still produced by humans and other animals. Bigger and better machines are not always the answer to food shortages in these countries. The production of food is also dependent upon good soil and moisture.

3.2 QUESTIONS FOR STUDY AND DISCUSSION:

1. Define agriculture and describe the way in which each of these technologies is used in agriculture:

VOCABULARY

binder twine	discs	moldboard	shelling board
broadcast seeder	flail	moldboard plow	shin
combine harvester	gang plows	no-till drill	shocks
corn peg	grain drill	plow	sickle
corn picker	harrow	plowshare	threshing floor
corn sheller	header	potato digger	threshing machine
coulter	jab planter	reaper	
cradle	landslide	scythe	
digging stick	machete	sheaves	

Early Tools

2. What are the tools that are used by primitive farmers living in isolated parts of the world today?
3. What materials did the Indians use for the blades of their hoes?

Bigger Machines to Prepare the Ground

4. List the types of material used to make plowshares.
5. Compare the plows invented by these men: Charles Newbold, Thomas Jefferson, and John Deere.
6. Describe the "good" and "bad" changes that occurred because of the plow.
7. Identify the two types of farm equipment that are used to prepare the seedbed after the field has been plowed.

Machines for Planting

8. How does the planting of seed with a broadcast seeder differ from the way seed is planted with a grain drill?
9. What was the first invention that made corn planting easier?
10. What is the advantage of the no-till drill?

Machines for Reaping

11. Discuss the importance of McCormick's invention.
12. What piece of equipment was replaced by the threshing machine?
13. What machine replaced the reaper and threshing machine?
14. How did a corn peg differ from a corn picker?
15. How do combine harvesters differ from mechanical corn pickers?
16. Compare the harvesting of corn on a small farm in Africa with the harvesting on a large farm in the United States.
17. How does a potato digger differ from a plow?

More Food with Less Labor

18. What developments have made it possible to produce more food even though fewer people are farming?
19. What percent of the total population lives and works on farms today? How many people can one farmer feed?
20. What percent of jobs in the U.S. are provided by "off-the-farm" agricultural technology?

In Other Parts of the World

21. What provides the power for most farming that occurs outside the U.S. today?
22. If you were given the money from a large benefit concert, and you were asked to spend it to benefit the people in countries that do not have enough food, how would you spend it?

The Good Earth

3.3

"Scientists in early times gave little attention to the soil. Like other things of everyday life, it was not thought to be a fit subject for study ... Agriculture was for slaves."
CHARLES E. KELLOGG

Better seeds and human-made chemicals have made it possible for us to produce more food than this country can use. Advances in agricultural technology allow us to produce this food with less effort. Some food is produced in greenhouses with the plant roots suspended in a solution of nutrients (fertilizers)—a method called **hydroponics**. However most plants are still dependent upon the soil for their nutrients.

The Formation of Soil

Soil is sometimes called "black gold" because it is so valuable, but soil is not always black. **Soil** refers to that thin layer on the surface of the earth that is made by the interaction of five factors: rocks, sunlight, water, air, and living organisms.

The formation of a meter of soil may take as little as 100 or as many as 100,000 years. In some locations, soil may be only one or two centimeters deep, but it may be several meters deep in other places. On mountain slopes some rocks are not covered by any soil at all. The soil that might have formed there has been blown away by the wind or carried away by water.

The climate determines the rate of soil formation. Soil formation occurs faster in a climate with higher temperatures and more rainfall than it does in colder and drier climates. The rainfall provides water needed for chemical reactions and the warmer temperature increases the speed of the reactions.

The material available and the amount of rainfall determine the type of soil that is formed. The same type of rocks in New York and Montana will produce different types of soil. The greater amount of rain in New York causes leaching of certain minerals. The Montana soils will have higher concentrations of these minerals because the climate is drier and there is less leaching.

The Parent Material

Rocks are the parents of the soil. The rocks are broken apart by the physical and chemical forces in nature. These smaller pieces of rock become a part of the soil. Rocks contain certain compounds called **minerals**. The minerals in the soil are those that were present in the rocks. The color of some soils is partly due to the minerals they contain.

OBJECTIVES

- ✓ **Describe** the physical and biological processes that are responsible for the formation of soil.
- ✓ **Explain** how the size of the mineral particles and the amount of humus present in the soil affect the characteristics of the soil.
- ✓ **Describe** a typical soil profile and compare the composition of the different layers.

Lichens and mosses growing on rocks produce acids that dissolve minerals in the rocks. The pressure created by the roots of larger plants and the expansion of freezing water break rocks apart, creating mineral particles. The process of soil formation has begun.

Did You Know?

Soil Survey parties began to inventory and map the Nation's soils in 1899. Over the next 100 years, scientists identified 18,000 different soils in the United States. A classification system places similar soils into groups much like similar plants and animals are grouped together. Farmers, engineers, builders and homeowners use soil maps in land-use planning.

Weathering

The process of breaking rocks apart or removing minerals from them is called **weathering**. The **weathering agents** are the chemical and physical forces that break rocks apart and/or remove minerals from them. They include water, ice, wind, temperature changes, sand, glaciers and the roots of plants. The weathering agents work in the following ways:

- Temperature changes cause rocks to expand and contract. These changes may cause the rocks to crack producing small particles containing minerals.
- Freezing water (ice) expands within the cracks and, like a wedge, splits the rock apart.
- Tree roots act as a wedge as they grow into the cracks in the rock splitting it apart.
- Plant roots produce chemicals that dissolve minerals from the rocks.
- Sand and rocks carried along by moving water scour the soil and rocks beneath.
- Glaciers can carry much bigger rocks that file and scrape the rocks below.
- Wind-blown sand acts like a sandblaster on the surfaces of rocks.

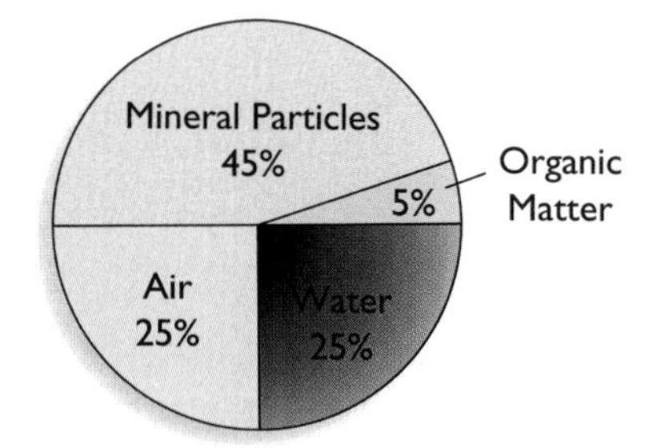

Although the percentages vary depending upon the soil type, the average soil is mainly composed of mineral particles that come from rocks. The organic matter was once living tissue or animal waste.

Chemical Changes in Rocks

The minerals in many rocks contain a compound called ferrous oxide (FeO). When these rocks are first broken the new surfaces have a bluish-gray color. Once the new surfaces are exposed to the air, chemical weathering occurs. The chemical produced in this reaction is ferric oxide (Fe_2O_3). We recognize it by the rusty color of the rock's surface. It is the same chemical that is formed when a piece of metal containing iron is changed to rust.

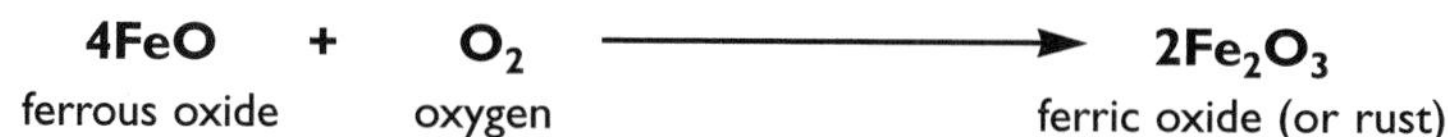

Soil that has poor drainage and lacks air may contain ferrous oxide and appear bluish-gray. This is typical of soil in many swamps and bogs. A red color indicates that the soil is well drained and contains pores filled with air.

Another type of chemical weathering occurs when acids react with certain types of rocks. The roots of plants produce carbon dioxide. When the carbon dioxide combines with water in the soil, it forms carbonic acid.

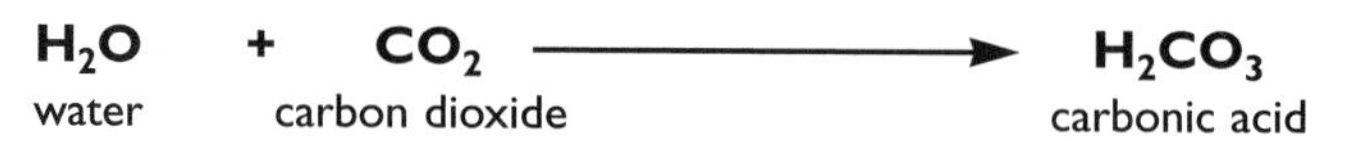

The carbonic acid dissolves the **calcite** in limestone and marble. The calcium and bicarbonate ions are soluble in water. Plant roots absorb the calcium ions. Similar reactions are also caused by acid rain. Other minerals are also dissolved from rocks by carbonic acid. A mineral that is common in soils is aluminum. If too much aluminum is released from the rocks, it can be toxic to the plant roots.

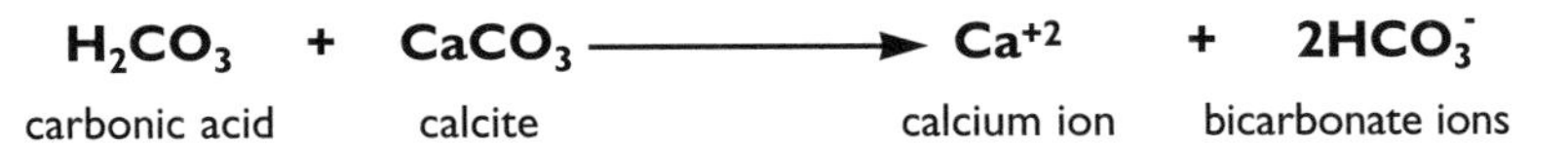

Virginia, Kentucky and Missouri are states that have many caves. The caves are formed when carbonic acid dissolves the calcite from the limestone rocks. **Stalactites** hang, like icicles, from the cave ceilings. Stalactites are formed as the dripping water evaporates and leaves behind the calcite that it had been carrying. Sometimes they join the **stalagmites** that have built up from the cave's floor. Other minerals in the water may color these formations.

Stalactites hang, like icicles, from the ceiling of Crystal Cave in southern Missouri.

Texture of the Soil

The mineral particles that are a part of soil may be classified by their size. The size of the particles determines the **texture** of the soil. Particles larger than a grain of wheat or corn are not generally considered a part of the soil, even though they are found within the soil and on its surface.

Size of Mineral Particles in Soil

Size	Diameter (mm)	Can be seen with
Gravel	greater than 2.0	naked eye
Coarse Sand	2.0–0.2	naked eye
Fine Sand	0.2–0.05	naked eye
Silt	0.05–0.002	light microscope
Clay	less than 0.002	electron microscope

Different soil textures are produced by the combination of sand, silt and clay in different proportions. **Loam** is a term used to describe soils that are made of a mixture of sand, silt, and clay. Often other terms are also used with loam to give a better description of the soil's composition. Some of the common soil textures are listed below:

- Sand: contains 85% or more sand; 15% or less silt and clay particles.
- Sandy loam: may contain 60% sand; 30% silt and 10% clay.
- Loam: may contain 40% sand; 40% silt and 20% or less clay.
- Silt loam: may contain 30% sand; 60% silt and 10% clay.
- Clay: contains 60% or less silt and sand particles; 40% or more clay.
- Clay loam: may contain 30% sand; 40% silt and 30% clay.

As the dripping water evaporates, the mineral deposits form stalagmites that seem to grow from the cave's floor.

The pie charts shown on page 214 represent different soil samples. The correct texture of any soil sample can be easily determined by the use of a "Soil Triangle" that is published by the U.S. Department of Agriculture. First you must find the amount of each particle size present in the sample. This can be done by a simple laboratory procedure.

Too many clay particles in soil can make it difficult to work, but they are an important part of the soil. Clay particles increase the soil's ability to hold both water and nutrients. Nutrients enter the soil from the processes of weathering and decay. The nutrients are dissolved in water and may be carried away as the water drains through the soil. This process is known as **leaching**.

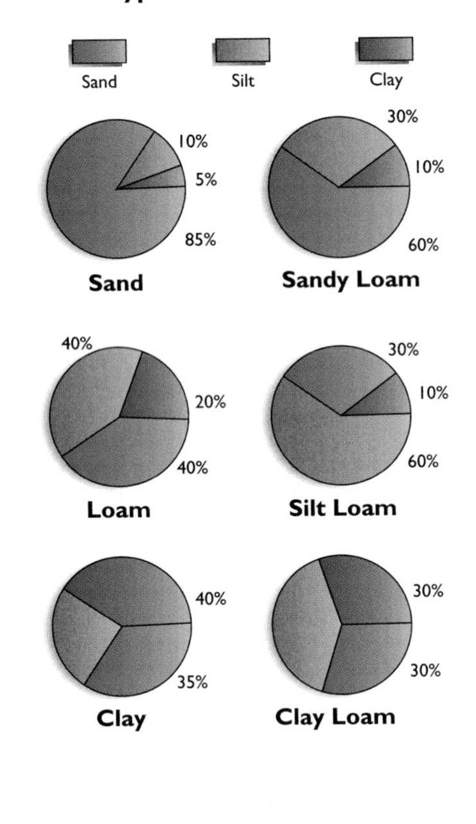

Cracks form in clay soil as it dries and the small particles shrink. When it rains, the particles will swell and the cracks will disappear.

Clay particles attract and hold nutrients. The clay particles have a negative charge. Essential plant nutrients like calcium, magnesium and potassium have a positive charge. They are attracted to the negative charge of the clay particles where they are stored until the plants need them.

Humus

The "moon dust" brought back by the astronauts contains some of the same minerals found in the soil on Earth. The dust consists of particles from rocks like those found on Earth. Soil on the planet Earth contains more than broken pieces of rock. It contains another very important substance called humus. Since there is no life on the moon, moon dust does not contain any humus. The absence of humus means that there is no soil on the moon, for there can be no soil without life.

Humus is the partly decomposed organic matter that was once living, or was produced by a living thing. The more plants and animals that lived and died in the soil, the more humus the soil contains. Dead leaves and stems of plants on top of the soil, and dead roots within the soil become humus. Waste products and dead bodies of animals also become humus.

Many species of bacteria, fungi, protozoa, insects, spiders, centipedes, millipedes, snails, slugs, earthworms and other animals feed on the dead plant and animal matter. These organisms help to change the dead matter into humus. The activities of the animals in the soil also help to mix the humus with the mineral particles.

Like clay, humus also has the ability to attract and hold both water and nutrients. We can increase the water-holding capacity of soil by increasing its humus content. Through the process of decay the humus releases its nutrients, which then become available to the plants growing in the soil.

Can There Be Too Much Humus?

Most soils contain between 1 and 5% humus by weight. Desert soils have very little humus, often less than 1%. Peat or bog soils may contain close to 100% humus. **Muck soils** have been formed by the decay of peat moss that lies above the water level. They contain 20% or more of humus and are black in color.

Muck soils are easily worked and have a good structure. Because of the large amount of organic matter, muck soils usually contain high levels of nitrogen and phosphorus. In Wisconsin they have produced a record yield of 600 bushels of onions per acre and up to 800 bushels of potatoes per acre—four times the national average.

There are some disadvantages of muck soils. They often lack the minerals that are normally supplied by the usual parent material—rocks. Because they are formed in swampy areas, the water level must be lowered through a series of ditches or drainage pipes with holes that collect water. Laws protecting wetlands may make it illegal to drain muck soils. Another disadvantage is that once the muck is allowed to dry, it is easily carried away by the wind.

Structure of the Soil

Many organisms in the soil produce chemicals that act as a "glue." As the animals feed on the dead material, they also take in sand, silt and clay particles. Bacteria and fungi produce a slimy substance that contains enzymes that break down part of the dead material. The mineral particles and the partly digested organic matter (humus) are glued together forming small clumps. The result is a loose crumbly soil.

When individual particles are glued together to form larger pieces, they give the soil a physical characteristic called **structure**. If the particles are glued together into rounded clumps, with a diameter of less than 1.5 cm, the structure is called **granular**. If the clumps are irregular instead of rounded, it is called a **crumb structure**.

A crumb structure is created when making pie dough or biscuits. Flour and salt are mixed together and then a kind of fat is cut into the mixture with a blender or two knives. The fat glues the flour and salt mixture into small clumps or crumbs the size of peas. When the baker sees this structure she or he knows it is time for the next step in the dough-making process.

If soil particles are glued into thin horizontal plates, the structure is **platy**. Other arrangements give structures called prismatic, columnar, and blocky. Some types of soil do not have any structure. Desert sand consists of individual grains that do not stick together. Soil with large amounts of clay may stick together in large masses. Structure can be developed in both types of soil by adding humus.

Did You Know?

The darker the soil, the higher the soil quality. Darker soils have more organic matter and are more fertile.

The particles in this soil are glued together to form thin horizontal plates. The name given to the soil structure is based on the shape of the particles. This type is called platy.

Spaces in the Soil

Plant roots are made of living cells. The soil must supply these cells with both water and air. Between the particles or clumps of soil are spaces. Normally 40–60% of a volume of soil is pore space.

These spaces allow water and air to travel through the soil. If there are no spaces, the roots cannot get the air and water they need. If the spaces are too big, the water will quickly drain through the soil. Soil with big spaces cannot hold water that will be needed by plants during dry periods.

The pore space determines the amount of rain that will run off and the amount of rain that will enter the soil (**infiltration**) and move downward through the soil (**percolation**). The ability of air and water to move downward through the soil is measured in inches per hour.

The size of the spaces in the soil depends upon the soil's texture. Smaller spaces are found in soils with smaller particles. Larger spaces are found in soils with larger particles. The chart on the next page shows the relationship between soil characteristics (infiltration, water-holding capacity, aeration).

Since spaces in sandy soils are large, water and air move through the soil very quickly. Sandy soils dry out rapidly after a rain. The spaces in soils with a large amount of clay are small, too small for water to move through. If the land is level, water will stand on the surface and prevent air from entering the soil. The roots will die because they can't get oxygen.

Description of Percolation Rate

	Downward movement of water (per hour)
very slow	< 0.06 inches (0.15 cm)
slow	0.06 to 0.20 inches (0.15-0.5 cm)
moderately slow	0.2 to 0.6 inches (0.5-1.5 cm)
moderate	0.6 to 2.0 inches (1.5-5 cm)
moderately rapid	2.0 to 6.0 inches (5-15 cm)
rapid	6.0 to 20 inches (15-50 cm)
very rapid	> 20 inches (50 cm)

Soil texture: size of mineral particles.

Infiltration: the ability of water to soak into the soil.

Water-holding capacity: the ability of the soil to store water.

Aeration: the ability of air to move through the soil.

Soil Texture	Soil Characteristics		
	Infiltration	**Water-Holding Capacity**	**Aeration**
SAND	Good	Poor	Good
SILT	Medium	Medium	Medium
CLAY	Poor	Good	Poor
LOAM	Medium	Medium	Medium

Erosion at the beach has revealed the soil profile. Beneath the thin layer of topsoil is a thick layer of sand (subsoil) that has been deposited over a thick layer of organic matter (dark).

The amount of humus and the structure of the soil also affect the pore space. By adding humus and creating a crumbly soil structure, we can increase the amount of water that will enter clay soils. Adding humus to sandy soils will also increase their water-holding capacity.

A Soil Profile

Since most of the plant and animal materials that form humus are located near the surface of the soil, the top layer is normally darker than the soil below. This top layer of humus-rich soil is called **topsoil**. The layer of soil beneath the topsoil does not contain humus. It is called the **subsoil**.

Subsoil has a higher clay content than the soil near the surface. Water moving through the soil picks up clay particles from the topsoil and carries them down into the subsoil layer. The minerals it contains determine the color of the subsoil. Beneath the subsoil is the weathered **parent material**—the pieces of rock that lie on top of solid rock. The solid rock is called **bedrock**.

When a hole is dug for the foundation of a building or for a septic system, the soil profile can easily be observed. The thickness of each layer varies. Not all soils have a well-developed profile.

Environmental Challenge:

Missouri has designated the eastern bluebird as the state bird. Pennsylvania has designated the eastern hemlock as the state tree. Many states have designated a specific type of soil as the state soil. Does your state have a designated state soil? To find out the answer and to see photos of a variety of soil profiles, visit: www.nrcs.usda.gov, click "go now," and choose "soils."

To learn more, visit: www.florence.ars.usda.gov/kidsonly/high/hsdrt.htm.

Montauk soil has a dark topsoil and a yellowish brown subsoil. Beneath the subsoil, at a depth of 24 inches the parent material is glacial till — rocks and mineral particles deposited by a glacier. Note the arrow pointing to a boulder in the glacial till.

Ryder soil has a deep topsoil with a reddish subsoil. The red color is due to the presence of iron oxide. The parent material at 40 inches is shale.

3.3 QUESTIONS FOR STUDY AND DISCUSSION:

1. Define the following terms: **VOCABULARY**

aeration	infiltration	percolation	subsoil
bedrock	leaching	platy	texture
crumb	loam	soil	topsoil
granular	mineral	stalactites	weathering
humus	muck soil	stalagmites	weathering agent
hydroponics	parent material	structure	

2. Which term refers to the process of growing plants without soil? If plants can be grown without soil, why is it so important that we study and protect our soils?

The Formation of the Soil

3. List the five things that are needed to make soil.
4. Explain why the same type of rocks may produce different soils in two different climates.

The Parent Material

5. Why are rocks sometimes referred to as the "parents of the soil?"

Weathering

6. Identify 5 factors that interact to create soil.
7. Which of these factors are most important in soil formation in a desert ecosystem?

Chemical Changes in Rocks

8. Why does the blue-gray color of some rocks change to a red color when the rocks are broken?
9. How do plants increase chemical weathering?
10. What mineral is released by the action of carbonic acid? What type of rock is weathered by the action of this acid?

Texture of the Soil

11. What determines the texture of the soil?
12. How does sandy loam differ from sand?
13. Give one disadvantage and one advantage of clay particles.

Humus

14. We know that plants depend on the soil for their life, but the soil is also dependent upon plants. Explain this statement.
15. Explain how earthworms, bacteria and fungi are important to the soil.
16. How is humus like clay?

Can There Be Too Much Humus?

17. Which do you think would be the best use for land with muck soil—housing development or a farm specializing in fresh vegetables? Explain.

Structure of the Soil

18. Explain how structure is developed in soils.
19. What do the names of various soil structures describe?
20. How can structure be developed in clay or sandy soil?

Spaces in the Soil

21. Why is it important to have pore space in the soil?
22. Which soil texture has the best infiltration rate?
23. Often plants do not grow well in sand or in clay. What is the cause of the problem in each soil type?

A Soil Profile

24. Describe the differences between topsoil and subsoil.
25. In a soil profile, what lies beneath the subsoil?

OBJECTIVES

- **Identify** four types of soil erosion and **describe** situations where each type of erosion would occur.
- **Describe** conservation practices that reduce soil erosion.
- **Compare** the effects of erosion with the effects of erosion control practices.

What You Can Do

(1) Using an apple as a model of the earth, cut it in quarters.

(2) Put three of the quarters of the apple aside. They represent the water.

(3) Cut the remaining quarter through the center. One part represents the regions that are mountains, deserts, or covered with ice. Push it to the side.

(4) Cut the remaining part into four equal pieces. Push three of them to the side. They represent the cities, roads, shopping malls, swamps, and other areas that aren't suitable for farming.

(5) Peel the small piece of apple that is in front of you. The peeling represents the topsoil that grows the food that feeds the 6 billion people living on planet Earth.

"The nation that destroys its soil destroys itself."
FRANKLIN ROOSEVELT

The Land Provides

The Indians thought of the earth as their Great Mother who provided for their needs. Some Indian tribes cleared small areas of land to grow maize (corn). If the land was not productive, they moved on to other areas. The type of farming practiced by the Indians had little effect on the land. There were few Indians, and there was plenty of land.

The Indians did not like the farming methods used by the colonists. They felt that plowing the earth was like wounding their Great Mother Earth with a knife. Neither the settlers nor the Indians realized how much the plow would change the land.

In Europe there was little land, and there were many people. When they came to America, the colonists saw miles and miles of land that they could own and use as they wanted. It seemed that there would always be plenty of good land for everyone.

Erosion occurs when wind or water moves the soil to some new location. Before the colonists came, erosion was a slow and natural process. After 300 years, much of the good soil was gone. The colonists did not intend to destroy the land. They did not realize that the soil was lighter than the soil they had farmed in Europe, or that the rains were sometimes heavier and the winds stronger.

The Debts Must Be Paid

There had been so much land that the colonists did not see the need to care for it. They did not know that more and more colonists would come to America to live off the land. Many were able to come because trading companies paid their transportation costs. In return they were expected to provide the trading companies with goods that could be sold in Europe. People living in the New England colonies provided fish, furs and lumber. Those living in the southern colonies paid their debt with tobacco.

Tobacco grows well only if the soil is rich in nutrients. As soon as they were settled, the colonists cut and cleared the forests to grow tobacco. The humus in the new fields provided the nutrients the tobacco needed. Each year the colonists planted the same crop on the same land. This practice of growing only one type of plant on a large area is called **monoculture**. After only three or four years, the soil was light in color because the humus was gone. When no profit could be made, the land was abandoned.

By the end of the seventeenth century, it became obvious that the land was wearing out and washing away. After the trees had been cut, the heavy rains made gullies (deep ditches) in the slopes. Farming practices also created gullies. The gullies got bigger and bigger.

Westward Ho!

The colonists moved west in search of better land. The western movement finally brought people to the area called the Great Plains. The grassy plains that had belonged to the Indians and buffalo became the property of the settlers and their cattle. Soon there were too many cattle, and there was too little rain. The little grass that remained could no longer support large herds of cattle, so the cattlemen sold out or moved further west.

The native prairie grasses that grew on the plains were tough and could tolerate long dry periods; they were **drought-resistant**. The grass had developed thick root systems that soaked up the rain and held the soil in place. The thick sod prevented evaporation of water from the soil. Below the sod was some of the richest soil in the world. The "sodbusters" used steel plows to cut through the soil and turn over the sod. The Indians looked at the sod and muttered "wrong side up," but the settlers were pleased with how well their plows cut and turned the sod.

Did You Know?

Five tons of topsoil spread over an acre is only as thick as a dime. The National Resources Inventory reports that the United States loses about 6.4 tons of soil per acre each year from land that is planted in row crops such as corn and cotton. Erosion by water removes 3.5 tons (3.1 metric tonnes) and 2.9 tons (2.6 metric tonnes) is carried away by the wind.

The Dirty Thirties

Europe was at war and needed wheat. More of the Great Plains was turned "wrong side up." For several years there was enough rain, and the plow continued to cut and turn more and more sod. Sometimes the rains did not come when needed, and the winds always blew. The early 1930s brought several years of extremely dry weather. The corn and wheat that the farmers planted were not drought-resistant like the native grasses that had grown in the dry prairie soil. The crops failed.

With no roots to hold it in place, the dry soil was easily picked up by the wind. The **black blizzards** began as strong winds and carried the topsoil east. In the nation's capital, the sky grew dark. Dust settled on desks in New York City and engulfed ships at sea. On the Great Plains, the topsoil drifted like snow along fencerows, buried farm machinery, gravestones, and sometimes buildings.

The southern part of the Great Plains, where Kansas, Oklahoma, Texas, New Mexico and Colorado meet, had become known as the **Dust Bowl**. Hugh Hammond Bennett, from the U.S. Bureau of Soils, spoke to Congress about the need for a national program to save the soil. As he spoke, a large cloud of dust from a storm in Oklahoma darkened the sky. He pointed to the window and said, "There, gentlemen, goes Oklahoma."

This field of soybeans growing on a farm in the Midwest is an example of a monoculture.

A National Plan to "Save the Soil"

It was 1935, and finally there was a new concern about saving the land. Although the Dust Bowl had not been the first or the only major loss of soil, it led to the first national program to "save the soil." Congress created the **Soil Conservation Service (SCS)** within the U.S. Department of Agriculture. Hugh Hammond Bennett became its first Chief. Conservation specialists were employed by the SCS to help people better understand and protect their land. Another federal agency, the Agricultural Stabilization and Conservation Service (ASCS), now called the **Farm Service Agency (FSA)**, was established to provide money to help pay for the cost of the conservation work.

These fields of wheat and cotton are evidence that erosion is still destroying our farmland.

Today the **Natural Resources Conservation Service (NRCS)**, which replaced the SCS, and the FSA help individuals, organizations, cities, counties and states to protect their land and water resources. States have been divided into soil **conservation districts** that usually follow county lines. A group of locally appointed or elected individuals is responsible for planning, approving and implementing the conservation projects within the district.

The major goal of the NRCS is to protect our soil and water. Conserving soil and water is not a simple task. There are 18,000 different types of soil in the United States. Since 1935 the SCS (now NRCS) has surveyed and mapped the soil types found throughout most of the United States. Information from these **soil survey maps** is used to plan the methods of conservation that will be used.

Types of Erosion

Conservation of soil and water cannot be achieved without reducing the rate of erosion. Although erosion is a natural process, human activities increase the rate at which it occurs. Most erosion is caused by rain. There are three types of soil erosion that are caused by the force of moving water:

- **Gully erosion** is the most obvious form of erosion. It occurs on steep slopes where there is little or no plant growth. The fast-moving water collects in channels and cuts away the soil, forming small ditches. With each rain the ditches become wider and deeper, and big ditches or gullies are formed. Gullies eventually become too wide for animals or vehicles to cross.
- **Rill erosion** occurs on gentle slopes with little or no plant growth. Water collects and runs off in small channels. The rills or small ditches are only a few inches or centimeters deep.
- **Sheet erosion** occurs on land that has a very gentle slope with enough plant growth to prevent rill erosion, but not enough to completely prevent erosion. Sheet erosion is the very gradual removal of a thin layer, or sheet, of topsoil. It can often be seen as muddy runoff water.

What type of erosion is this?

When water is absent, wind often causes sheet erosion. Soil particles become air-borne when the soil is dry, the wind speed is high, and the land surface is not covered with plants. The largest area of land subject to strong prevailing winds and a lack of moisture is the Great Plains, although these conditions may occur in nearly any location.

Although gully erosion is the most obvious, most topsoil is removed by rill and sheet erosion. Many farmers that have fields without gullies may not realize that their fields are losing topsoil. Traditional farming methods can easily cause a loss of 5 or more tons (4.5 metric tonnes) of topsoil per acre, each year. If this amount of topsoil is evenly spread on an acre of land, the depth of the layer would be 1 mm or about the thickness of a dime.

Another type of erosion occurs when certain types of soil become saturated with water and move down a slope due to the force of gravity. This movement of soil is known as **mass erosion** or **slumping**. Mass erosion is seen as a landslide on a steep slope or a cave-in of a bank that overhangs a stream. Although this mass erosion occurs in many places, the most famous examples are the mudslides of Southern California which damage homes and close roads.

Storms frequently cause severe erosion and threaten houses on the beach.

Slowing the Rate of Erosion

Soil scientists think that natural weathering processes can replace topsoil, on most farmland in the United States, at a rate of five tons (4.5 metric tonnes) per acre per year. The rate at which topsoil can be replaced is called the **tolerance value**. The rate of erosion during the dirty thirties far exceeded the tolerance value.

Scientists from the NRCS help landowners reduce the rate of erosion on their land. A conservation plan, designed by a soil scientist, might include several of the following conservation practices:

Contour Planting:

Contour planting refers to plowing and/or planting across the slope rather than up and down the slope. Thomas Jefferson called it "horizontal plowing." The plow furrows and rows follow the curves of the hills on a level. The rate of erosion is slowed because the furrows and rows slow the speed of water as it flows down the slope.

Strip-Cropping:

Strip-cropping also slows the speed of moving water. Strips or bands of close-growing plants (clover, alfalfa, grasses, wheat, oats) are planted next to crops that are planted in rows (corn, soybeans). Strip-cropping works best when the strips are planted on the contour.

Diversion Terraces:

Diversion terraces are needed on steep slopes. **Diversion terraces** are ridges of soil that are constructed along the contours. This creates a series of stair steps that make the slopes shorter and slow the speed of the flowing water. The terraces are planted with permanent grasses or with crops that will be harvested.

Contour planting slows the rate of erosion.

Waterways:

Waterways are used to prevent gullies on steep slopes. A **waterway** is a wide ditch that is planted with a permanent grass cover. It allows surplus water to run off without creating gullies.

Crop Rotation:

Crop rotation refers to the practice of planting a series of different crops in the same field. For example, wheat may be planted in a field after the corn is harvested. Then clover is grown before corn is planted again.

Runoff from this field would create a gully without this permanently grassed area called a waterway.

Conventional planting practices in this field leave soil bare and vulnerable to erosion.

Soil conservation practices in this field include crop rotation and no-till planting. The corn has been planted in the residue remaining after rye was harvested.

Data gathered during a fourteen-year experiment at the Missouri Agricultural Experiment Station showed that land planted with a corn–wheat–clover rotation lost an average of 2.7 tons (2.4 metric tonnes) of topsoil per acre each year. Similar land where corn was planted year after year lost 19.7 tons (17.7 metric tonnes) of topsoil per acre (0.4 ha) each year.

By reducing the speed of the wind, windbreaks like this one help reduce soil removed by wind erosion.

Windbreaks:

Windbreaks are strips of trees, shrubs or tall grasses that are planted in rows that are perpendicular to the direction of the prevailing wind. They reduce the speed of the wind, and help to reduce wind erosion. Other benefits of windbreaks include trapping blowing snow, reducing moisture loss, and protection of plants and animals. The disadvantage of windbreaks is that one acre of land is removed from production for each quarter mile of windbreak.

Conservation Tillage:

Conservation tillage includes several methods that reduce the amount of tilling and avoid the use of the moldboard plow. The soil is not "turned upside down." This allows the root structure to remain in the soil and the stems of plants to remain as a mulch, or covering, on the soil surface. Some kind of conservation tillage is used on more than one-third of the nation's farms. Farmers in the lower Rio Grande valley in Texas use conservation tillage on more than 100,000 acres (40,000 ha).

One method of conservation tillage uses a **chisel plow** instead of the moldboard plow. The chisels loosen the soil without turning under the sod or other plant material. Another method is called no-till planting. A **no-till planter** (drill; page 206) prepares the soil and plants the seed in one operation. A no-till planter has a **cutting coulter** that cuts a slit in the soil. A **double-disc opener** pushes the slit open, and a **planter** drops the seed in the soil. Then the **press wheel** closes the soil over the seeds. There are several benefits of no-till planting:

Contour planting in this field helps prevent erosion of a sloping field.

- The cost of growing the crop is reduced since:
  - Fewer trips across a field reduces labor.
  - Fewer pieces of machinery are required.
  - Less fuel is needed to plant and cultivate the crop.
  - Less soil is lost to wind and water erosion.
- In some circumstances it increases yield and income:
  - Better retention of fertilizers on well-drained soil.
  - Less water is lost to evaporation and thus more is available to plants.
  - More water is absorbed and available to plants.
- There is less water and air pollution:
  - Less compaction of the soil by heavy equipment increases infiltration.
  - Plant residue that remains after the harvest creates small dams that store water, reducing runoff.
  - Plant residue protects the soil from wind erosion.
- Improves habitat for fish and wildlife:
  - Plant residue provides cover and food for wildlife.
  - Improved water quality due to less sediment and chemicals in runoff.

No-till planting also has its disadvantages:

- Before the plants begin to grow, they look "trashy." To farmers who consider straight rows and clean bare fields signs of a good farm, no-till planting is not acceptable.
- Planting must be delayed in the northern part of the United States because the soil temperature is cooler when the soil has not been plowed. This may be a problem for some plants that require a longer growing season. Planting requires greater management and planning.
- No-till planting requires greater use of herbicides and pesticides. It is estimated that no-till planting of corn requires 50% more pesticides. However, chemicals are much more likely to remain in the soil instead of being carried away with runoff.
- No-till planting does not work in all soil types. It works well in sandy soils, but not in heavy clay soils and compacted soils.

This farmer is using a no-till planter to plant soybeans. Can you identify the parts of the no-till planter in the picture above?

Cover Crops:

Cover crops are grasses or **legumes** that are planted to hold the soil in place. Field corn is planted in rows that are about 30 inches apart. In many regions it is picked late in fall when the temperatures are too cool for another crop to grow. Even if the cornfield is not plowed, much of the soil is left exposed to the wind and the rain during the winter months. Some farmers hire a helicopter to seed rye in the field before the corn is picked.

Dense residue from no-till farming provides a winter food source for many wildlife species such as Canadian geese.

The rye grows during the cool fall weather and its root system helps hold the soil in place until the spring planting.

After Harvest:

If traditional plowing is necessary, there will be less erosion if the crop residue is left on the field during the winter. The major problem with this is that the plant residue becomes a nursery for pests. In Texas, a "plowdown law" requires growers to shred and destroy all standing residue after cotton harvest, but this requirement can be met without plowing. Farmers can now use a new conservation tillage tool called a **stalk puller**, which plucks the cotton stalks from the ground.

We've Learned Our Lesson—Or Have We?

In 1972 the United States sold wheat and other grains to the Soviet Union. Farmers were encouraged to plant more grain. Any extra grain produced would be sold to other countries. The Secretary of Agriculture, Earl Butz, advised farmers to "plant fencerow to fencerow." Grasslands and hillsides that should never have been plowed were planted in wheat, corn, and soybeans to "feed the world."

Many of the soil conservation practices that had been developed after the Dust Bowl were ignored. Crops planted in rows replaced hay and pastureland. Farmers tore out windbreaks and fencerows so that they could use bigger machinery. Some farmers abandoned the practice of farming on the contour. With such big machinery it is much easier to go in a straight line.

Cotton farmers use the stalk-puller to pluck out the cotton plants.

It was December 1977, and for the second year in a row there was a drought in Bakersfield, California. Fields were plowed and ready for spring planting. The cattle had stripped the rangeland of any grass that they could find. It was a cold day in the San Joaquin Valley when a windstorm approached. One hundred mile-per-hour winds lifted topsoil, sand, and rocks the size of nickels.

The two feet (0.6 m) of topsoil, removed from freshly plowed fields, fell as red rain hundreds of miles away. Geologists estimate that the winds removed 25 million tons (22.5 million metric tonnes) of soil from the freshly plowed fields in the valley and an additional 25 million tons (22.5 million metric tonnes) from overgrazed rangeland. When rain finally came, it washed soil onto highways and into lakes and streams. Pesticides and herbicides attached to particles of clay were carried into drinking water supplies.

In 1977, wheat fields in eastern New Mexico lost three feet of topsoil to strong windstorms. Although 1977 was a year with less rain and stronger winds than normal, much of the erosion would not have occurred without the changes that had been made by humans. For example, overgrazed lands lost far more topsoil than land that was properly managed. The market and climate determined which crops were grown. The benefits of crop rotation had been ignored.

On 60% of all farmland the same crop is planted in the same field year after year. Just as Kansas is a part of the nation's "breadbasket," Iowa is a part of the nation's "corn belt." In many parts of Iowa the deep black topsoil that was once fourteen inches (35.6 cm) deep now measures only six to eight inches (15-20 cm). The tops of some hills are gray and their slopes are much darker. The dark topsoil has moved down the slope leaving the subsoil exposed on the top of the hill.

Some farms are losing more topsoil today than they lost during the Dust Bowl. The NRCS has determined that about 1/4 of U.S. cropland is eroding at a faster rate than its **tolerance value**. James Smart, a scientist who studies crop production and soil management in Texas, says "If farmers don't use conservation tillage, parts of south Texas and Mexico could become a dust bowl."

Loss of topsoil is not a problem only for the American farmer. Scientists in California can tell when spring plowing begins in northern China. Soil particles removed from fields in China by wind erosion travel across the Pacific to North America. During the summer months, winds carry African dust across the Atlantic to the East Coast. Farming practices in all of the major food-producing countries cause billions of tons of topsoil to be lost each year.

Crown vetch planted on a roadside bank prevents erosion, but gullies will form where tracks from off-road vehicles disturb the groundcover.

It's Not Just the Farmers

Studies show that many other activities also increase the rate of erosion. Some examples follow:

Rate of Erosion	
Human Activity	**Compared to Natural Rate**
Highway construction in Virginia	200 times faster
Building a shopping center in Maryland	100 times faster
Surface mining in Wyoming	11 times faster
Logging in Oregon	4 times faster

Off-road vehicles removed more soil in some areas than nature will make in the next 1,000 years. A hillside near Salt Lake City, Utah, slid into a residential subdivision after off-road vehicles had destroyed the plant cover. The U.S. Geological Survey estimates that landslides cost Americans a billion dollars a year.

No, it's not just the farmer, but the steel plow has caused more erosion than any other single piece of modern technology. The rain or the wind is carrying away soil that should never have been plowed. Sometimes government policies have allowed, and even encouraged, big business interests to become "sodbusters." Changing highly erodible land from grasslands or forests to cropland increases the rate of erosion.

More money can be made from an acre of cropland than from an acre of grassland. The short-term cost of reducing erosion is three times greater than the short-term benefits the farmers will realize. Because of these economic factors, big businesses and poor farmers often do not practice soil conservation.

Did You Know?

Wes Jackson, recipient of a MacArthur "genius" award, is a plant scientist who is trying to save the soil and the people of the Great Plains. His research involves cross-breeding native prairie grasses with agricultural crops to produce a high-yield grain that enriches and holds the prairie soil. His task is not easy.

All plants get energy from sunlight. Native prairie grasses use most of this energy to produce roots that enrich and maintain the fertile soil of the plains. Native grasses are perennials; their roots live in the ground all year. Their genes make them drought-resistant. Native grasses produce some seeds, but not many. Agricultural grains, on the other hand, use most of their energy to produce lots of seeds that we eat as grain. Their roots are shallow because they have little energy left over to put into root growth. The roots die during the winter, and the ground must be plowed and the annual crops replanted each spring. Wes Jackson is trying to develop a seed-rich perennial that is drought-resistant and whose roots hold and enrich the soil. It's a tall order!

The Effects of Erosion

Though humans may gain short-term benefits, fish and other aquatic life suffer from the effects of erosion. Studies have shown that four to five billion tons of sediment are deposited in streams each year. Soil is out of place in a body of water—it is a pollutant. It smothers the eggs of fish and other aquatic organisms. It clogs storm sewers and irrigation canals, clouds our drinking water, and increases the chance of flooding and the need for dredging our navigable waterways.

Most plants get nutrients from the top few inches of soil where most of the organic matter and microorganisms are found. As the topsoil gets thinner, the **productivity**—the amount of food produced per acre—declines. American farmers use technology, such as hybrid seed, chemical fertilizers, pesticides and herbicides to make up for any loss of productivity caused by erosion.

It is estimated that, for each inch of topsoil lost, the yield declines by three bushels per acre. Agricultural technology has continued to increase the yield per acre and have hidden the effects of erosion. In the 1980s, farmers produced more food than was needed. The surplus was due to the increased use of technology as well as an increase in the number of acres farmed.

The production of our food and the quality of our environment depend upon the wise use of the soil. Soil erosion is decreasing the productivity of land on every continent. As the natural fertility declines, greater amounts of crude oil must be used to manufacture the fertilizers needed. We must remember that oil is not a renewable natural resource—its supply is limited. Soil is a renewable resource only if we use it wisely.

The Effects of Erosion Control

One tenth of the wheat-growing area of eastern Washington has lost all of its topsoil. But monitoring shows that erosion control practices begun since the late 1970s have reduced erosion from cropland in the Palouse River Basin by about 1.7 million tons annually. Reduced or no-till farming methods are helping protect the light silty volcanic soils from wind erosion. Reducing runoff is also helping to keep the fertile soil in place and improve water quality.

Missouri has a very serious soil erosion problem. The state has the fourth highest rate of erosion in the United States. In the last 100 years, half of the state's topsoil has been lost. In 1984, Missouri voters approved a 0.1% sales tax which is divided equally between the state parks and soil conservation. Since the tax was first approved, soil erosion has been reduced by half, but there is still much to do.

The USDA has calculated that the environmental damage caused by erosion is between $2 and $8 billion annually. To reduce the amount of damage, the USDA provides incentives to farmers and ranchers through the **Conservation Reserve Program**. The program pays farmers to take highly erodible and environmentally sensitive cropland out of production for 10 to 15 years. In addition to rental payments, the government pays up to 50% of the cost of establishing permanent cover—grasses, trees, or other protective plants. Payments average $49 per acre.

According to the USDA, the erosion controls on 36.4 million acres (14.7 million ha), about 15% of the nation's cropland, has reduced soil erosion in the United States by more than 600 million tons (540 million metric tonnes) annually. In addition to preserving the soil, the changes in land use improve water quality and reduce damage from wind-blown dust. The planting of trees and growing of native grasses have provided habitat needed by many wildlife species. The benefits far exceed the cost to the government of $1.6 billion annually.

Big bluestem, a native grass, was planted in this field as a permanent cover. It reduces erosion and provides habitat for wildlife.

3.4 Questions for Study and Discussion:

1. Define the following terms: **VOCABULARY**

black blizzards	diversion terrace	monoculture	slumping
chisel plow	double-disc opener	Natural Resources Conservation Service (NRCS)	Soil Conservation Service (SCS)
conservation district	drought-resistant	no-till planter	soil survey maps
Conservation Reserve Program	Dust Bowl	planter	stalk-puller
conservation tillage	erosion	press wheel	strip-cropping
contour planting	Farm Service Agency (FSA)	productivity	tolerance value
cover crops	gully erosion	rill erosion	waterway
crop rotation	legumes	sheet erosion	windbreak
cutting coulter	mass erosion		

The Land Provides

2. Describe the Indian's method of farming.
3. What is the difference between the land the Colonists found in North America and the land they farmed in Europe?

The Debts Must Be Paid

4. Describe how the farming practices used by the colonists were destructive to the land.

Westward Ho

5. Why did the cattle but not the buffalo destroy the grass on the Great Plains?
6. Explain why the native prairie grasses could withstand long dry periods.

The Dirty Thirties

7. The early settlers could not use all of the wheat they grew. Why did they plant it?
8. What was Hugh Hammond Bennett referring to when he said, "There, gentlemen, goes Oklahoma"?

A National Plan to "Save the Soil"

9. There are two USDA agencies that work to save the soil. List the agencies and explain their role in soil conservation.
10. What is the purpose of a soil conservation district?

Types of Erosion

11. Compare the three types of soil erosion caused by water and describe the slope where each would occur.
12. What type of erosion damages houses, roads, and the banks of streams and is caused by soil saturated with water?

Slowing the Rate of Erosion

13. What is the tolerance value for most farmland in the United States?
14. Describe five conservation practices used on farms, and explain how they reduce soil erosion.
15. Explain how a chisel plow prepares the ground for planting.
16. List the 4 parts of a no-till planter and describe their role in planting.
17. Evaluate the pros and cons of no-till planting.

We've Learned our Lesson—Or Have We?

18. How did the soil erosion that occurred in the 1970s compare with the 1930s Dust Bowl?
19. Explain why some farmers do not hesitate to use the conservation practices that will reduce the loss of topsoil.
20. It is said that some of the soil in the Midwest is silt from Asia. Do you think this could be true? If so, how did it get there?

It's Not Just the Farmers

21. List 5 human activities, other than farming, that increase the rate of erosion.
22. What single piece of equipment has caused the most erosion?
23. Why do farmers plant crops on hillsides and dry grasslands even though they know it will increase the rate of erosion?

The Effects of Erosion

24. Describe the ways in which eroded soil affects bodies of water.
25. How does erosion affect productivity?
26. How does the loss of topsoil make us more dependent upon oil from the Middle East?

The Effects of Erosion Control

27. Why is wind erosion a problem in the Palouse River Basin, and what is being done to reduce it?
28. How have Missourians shown that they are committed to reducing soil erosion?
29. Explain how the Conservation Reserve Program (CRP) reduces soil erosion.
30. In addition to reducing soil erosion, what are other benefits of the CRP?

Environmental Challenge: Farm Service Agency

The Farm Service Agency (FSA) is the branch of the USDA that works with farmers and ranchers in the Conservation Reserve Program (CRP). Contact your local FSA office or visit the FSA website at www.fsa.usda.gov to answer the following questions:

- How many acres in your state are enrolled in the CRP?
- What is the Environmental Benefits Index and how is it used?
- Give examples of special conservation practices that farmers may use to reduce soil erosion and provide other environmental benefits on their land.
- Give examples of wildlife species that benefit from the CRP.
- What are the economic benefits of the program?
- After examining the program's costs and benefits, do you think that the CRP is a good way to use taxpayer dollars?

www

A National Monument Created by Erosion

"The Indians called it mako (land) sica (bad); we know it as the Badlands."

OBJECTIVES

- ✔ **Describe** the relationship between the formation of the Rocky Mountains, the Black Hills and the Badlands.
- ✔ **Explain** why the rate of erosion in the Badlands is greater than many other areas which receive more rainfall.
- ✔ **Compare** the Badlands National Monument to other National Monuments.

The region of South Dakota known as the Badlands lies between the Black Hills—with its famous Mount Rushmore—to the west and the Missouri River to the east. The Indians thought this wilderness of rock and grass had been created by a big bad storm. Now we know that the natural forces that cause erosion had carved it. Today erosion continues to change the shape of the Badlands.

Millions of years ago, when the earth's climate was warmer than it is now, the sea covered this part of the United States. Mud and organic matter from the bodies of dead organisms were deposited on the sea floor. Year after year new layers were added, and the old layers were pressed into a kind of soft black rock, called **shale**.

The earth began to push gently upward; the movement was very slow. As the internal forces continued to push, the sea gradually drained into the Gulf of Mexico. Just as it had taken millions of years for the muddy material to collect on the bottom of the sea, it took millions of years for the sea to be drained. For a long time, a subtropical forest covered the land around the retreating sea, but the climate became cooler and drier, and the forests disappeared.

The movements within the earth pushed a big mass of granite rock upward. The granite rock began as molten magma deep within the earth. The magma cooled slowly forming a very hard rock beneath the black shale on the floor of the ancient sea. Eventually this mass of granite rock with its covering of shale became the Black Hills of South Dakota. The soft shale rock was exposed to the agents of weathering. As the shale weathered, bits and pieces of the rock were carried down the mountainsides.

The deposits of eroded rocky material, at the base of the Black Hills, began a building process that would eventually form the Great Plains. Silt and clay particles were carried and deposited by streams. Sometimes eruptions of volcanoes, forming the Rocky Mountains, sent ash high into the air and the winds spread it over large areas. The ash was deposited in layers, as if it were icing on a cake. As the Rocky Mountains became higher, layer after layer of sand, clay, silt and volcanic ash was added.

The building of the plains finally came to an end. Once erosion had removed the shale from the Black Hills, the harder granite was exposed. Now erosion was much slower. The volcanoes that had built the Rocky Mountains quit belching out a supply of ash. Seeds, carried by the wind, were deposited in the newly formed soil. Gradually grasses began to grow on these new plains that stretched from Canada to Texas, and from the Rocky Mountains to the Mississippi Valley.

The famous sculpture on Mount Rushmore is carved in granite which is resistant to weathering.

The clay bluffs that form the Badlands are soft and erode easily.

In some places, ridges of rock that are more resistant to erosion form dikes.

At some places the Great Plains were 5,000 feet (1.5 km) above sea level. Erosion began to wear them down, just as it had the Black Hills. Streams of water with their load of eroded material moved toward the lower elevations. The rock that had built the plains was very soft. As the water cut through the soft rock below, gullies were formed and sometimes the gullies became deep ravines. Today one of the highest elevations on the Great Plains is Sheep Mountain Table in South Dakota that stands nearly 3,300 feet (1 km) above sea level.

Erosion caused drastic changes in the appearance of the Great Plains. They began to look like a miniature mountain range. Geologists now call any area with this appearance a "badland." In some places there are **dikes**—ridges of harder rock that are resistant to erosion. In other places there are **pedestals**—odd mushroom shapes that are formed when rocks that are more resistant to erosion protect a column of softer material below.

Two hundred feet below Sheep Mountain Table is the White River. Sometimes it carries only a small stream of water; often the riverbed is dry. The river's name refers to the chalky white clay particles that are carried by its water. The annual rainfall average is only 16 inches (40.6 cm). It doesn't rain often, but violent summer rainstorms cause the river to flood, and the floodwaters eat away at the land.

The climate is extremely hot and dry in summer, cold and dry in winter. It is not unusual for the temperature to be 110°F (43°C) in the afternoon and 50°F (10°C) at midnight. It is this quick change in temperature that causes the local thunderstorms. The heavy cloudbursts and strong winds send walls of water against the clay bluffs. The water tears the shallow roots of the grasses from the thin topsoil.

Once the grass is removed, the water cuts through the layers of soft rock. The size of Sheep Mountain Table and other grasslands continues to decrease each year as streams eat away its soft sides. Some areas of the Badlands are being cut away at the rate of one half inch (1.3 cm) each year. This is a very fast rate of erosion. In some other parts of the country it may take 500 or even 1,000 years for this amount of erosion to occur.

Almost always a strong wind blows from the west across the Badlands. It is always a dry wind. Any moisture it holds is lost as it is forced up and over the mountains on the west. The wind is a strong weathering agent. With the force of a baseball pitcher, it hurls the particles of sand that it carries against the soft rocks of the Badlands. This giant sandblaster produces new sand, silt, and clay particles that will be carried away by the wind or the water. Many of these particles were once a part of the Badlands, and are now a part of the fine silty soils in Iowa, Illinois, Minnesota and Wisconsin.

Some people tried to farm the Badlands. Having no success, most of them moved on. Finally after the Dust Bowl years, homesteads were abandoned or were sold to the government. Some talked of making the threatened wilderness into a national park or monument. Others thought the idea was ridiculous.

Finally in 1939 the Badlands National Monument was established, and in 1978 it was redesignated as the Badlands National Park. It was not intended to be a lasting monument that should be polished and repaired. The park includes 64,000 acres (25,856 ha) that are officially designated as a wilderness area—an area that is designed, created, and changed by natural processes. It also includes the largest protected mixed grass prairie in the United States. For those who take the time to observe and study, it is a place that helps us understand and appreciate the natural processes at work on planet Earth.

www

More than 1 million people visit Badlands National Park each year. To learn more about the role of fire, the management of bison, and the reintroduction of the black-footed ferret, see these websites: www.nps.gov/badl and www.badlands.national-park.com.

3.5 Questions for Study and Discussion:

1. Define the following terms: **VOCABULARY**

dikes	shale
pedestals	

2. Where are the Badlands located?
3. Describe how the Black Hills were formed.
4. What was the soft rock that was eroded from the Black Hills?
5. Since much of the Black Hills has eroded, why is it that the famous carvings of the Presidents still remain?
6. Describe the two events that built the Great Plains.
7. Once the Great Plains were formed, what began to happen?
8. Explain what causes dikes and pedestals to form.
9. Why is erosion so severe in the Badlands when the annual rainfall there is only 16 inches?
10. What types of erosion occur in the Badlands? Where does the soil from the Badlands go?

Lighted interior of Carlsbad Caverns National Park, New Mexico.

Double arch, Arches National Park, Utah.

3.6 Providing Food for an Expanding Population

OBJECTIVES

- **Graph** the growth of the human population.
- **Compare** the growth rate of the United States' population to the growth rate of other countries.
- **Explain** how human population growth affects natural resources.
- **Identify** factors that determine the ability to provide food for the human population.
- **Explain** the relationship between the affluence of humans and the food chain.
- **List** changes that are necessary to ensure the earth can feed the human population in the future.

Most children living in Beijing, China, don't have brothers or sisters. Since 1979, the Chinese government has imposed stiff penalties on families having more than one child.

"The earth cannot support a larger population of any species than it can supply food for."
ISAAC ASIMOV

The Population Connection

Around 1800, about a billion people were living on planet Earth. The world population doubled by 1930. In 1960 it reached three billion; in 1974, four billion. In 1987, the population reached five billion; in 1999, six billion, and it continues to climb. The United Nations expects the world population to reach eight billion by 2025, and it could increase to nearly ten billion by the year 2050.

The growth rate of the world's population was 2.2% in 1963. By 1998 the growth rate had dropped to 1.4%. The **population growth rate** is the percentage change in the population over time. Ninety-seven percent of the world's population growth occurs in less developed countries where 80% of the world's population lives.

There are three major factors that determine the population growth rate:

- Fertility rates—the average number of children per woman. The **fertility rate** in as many as 75 countries has reached the replacement level of 2.1 children or less. In at least 58 countries in Africa and Asia, the fertility rate is 5 or more children per woman. In Ethiopia, the fertility rate is 7 children per woman.
- Death rates—improvements in health care and sanitation cause death rates to drop. Child mortality rates declined from 21 million in 1955 to 11 million in 1990. The spread of AIDS in Africa and the return of several parasitic and infectious diseases are currently slowing the world's population growth rate.
- The number of women of childbearing age. Even though each woman may have fewer children, more women give birth. In 78 countries, more than 40% of the populations are under 15 years of age. In the next generation there could be more than 3 billion people in the active reproductive age group.

The **natural increase** in a country's population is due to a greater number of births than deaths. The rate of natural increase in the United States' population is 0.6%, one of the highest rates among the more developed countries. The population growth rate of a country is also affected by migration. Net immigration adds about 800,000 people to the United States' population each year, bringing the population growth rate to 0.9%.

Why People Go to Bed Hungry

The number of humans continues to increase with 78 million people added to the world's population each year. That means there are 78 million more people to feed. The increasing population puts greater pressure on our forest, grassland, soil and water resources. There is a severe lack of fuel in some areas. One-third of the world's population still uses firewood as the major source of fuel for cooking.

More than 800 million people do not have enough to eat even though there is sufficient food produced to feed the world population today. The 1959–61 famine and deaths of 30 million Chinese led China's government to promote a "one-child family" policy. The government's efforts to reduce the population growth rate and to increase food production have reduced the problem of hunger in China.

Poverty is the major cause of hunger. Many less developed countries cannot grow enough food and cannot afford to import the food they need. The UN has designated 86 countries as low-income food-deficit countries. Forty-five of these countries may double their populations in 30 years or less. During the 1990s, 1/3 of the world's children were underweight. Millions of people, mostly in Africa and Asia, do not get the protein and essential vitamins and minerals needed for good health.

In August 1999, the United Nations reported that there were nearly 10 million people in sub-Saharan Africa who needed emergency food assistance. A combination of drought and civil conflicts in 16 African countries displaced people and disrupted food production. Political fighting in Somalia disrupted the distribution of food by relief workers and placed 400,000 people at risk of starvation. Political stability is essential if efforts to feed the world's hungry are to be successful.

For more population information, visit these websites: www.populationinstitute.org and www.prb.org.

Think About It

Sit quietly for 30 seconds. That's how long it takes for 51 people to die and 133 babies to be born. That's a net increase of 82 people. According to the Population Reference Bureau, this adds up to an additional 86 million people—the increase in the world's population in 1997.

The World's Tillable Land

India, China, the United States, Canada and the countries of the former Soviet Union, have more than 1/2 of the world's cropland and produce more than 1/2 of its food. In spite of this India, China and the countries in the former Soviet Union do not have the ability to produce all of the food they need. Only the United States and Canada produce a surplus of food.

The regions of the world with the largest populations do not have equally large areas of tillable land. For example, China has 21% of the world's population, but it has only 5% of the world's tillable land. The United States and Canada have only 5% of the world's population, but they have 4% of the world's tillable land.

Each acre of tillable land is not equally productive. The **productivity** of about two-thirds of the cropland in India has declined due to erosion and loss of nutrients. Climate and soil types determine what kinds and how much food can be grown on the tillable land. Some areas have little rainfall and without irrigation this land is not very productive. In other areas the cold means that fewer crops can be planted and short-season varieties of seeds are needed.

A billboard in Xiamen, China, promotes the government's "one-child family" policy.

Small farms like this one in Japan produce the highest yields per acre because of intensive farming methods.

With 22 percent of the world's population, China has only 5 percent of the world's tillable land. Much of the land is too steep and rocky for farming. In some places bench terraces held in place by rock walls create small plots for growing crops.

Misuse of land is also an important factor causing food shortages. Throughout history there are many cases where increases in population have led to the cutting of forests and the farming of land that is not suited for farming. The farming methods increase the rate of erosion and remove the humus from the soil. Soil lacking humus lacks the ability to hold water, and rain quickly percolates through the soil or runs off the land. The land that was once covered by forest or grassland becomes a desert.

Japan

Japanese farms are usually no larger than 5 acres (2 ha), yet Japanese farmers have the highest **yield**—amount produced per unit area of land—in the world. The high yield is due to three factors:

- The development of seed varieties that produce high yields,
- The use of large quantities of fertilizer, and
- Labor that does not depend on the use of large equipment.

Bigger is not always better. Very few Japanese farmers own a tractor or any other piece of large equipment that is essential to the American farmer. The largest piece of equipment used by most Japanese farmers is a two-wheeled rototiller.

Large equipment does not increase the yield per acre. Mechanical planters waste seed. Since the ground is not completely level, mechanical planters often drop seeds that are not planted at the proper depth. Mechanical pickers cannot distinguish between green and ripe produce. Although varieties of fruit have been developed which ripen at nearly the same time, the ripening is not perfect and some fruit is lost. Mechanical harvesting also increases the amount of fruit that is bruised and will spoil during storage.

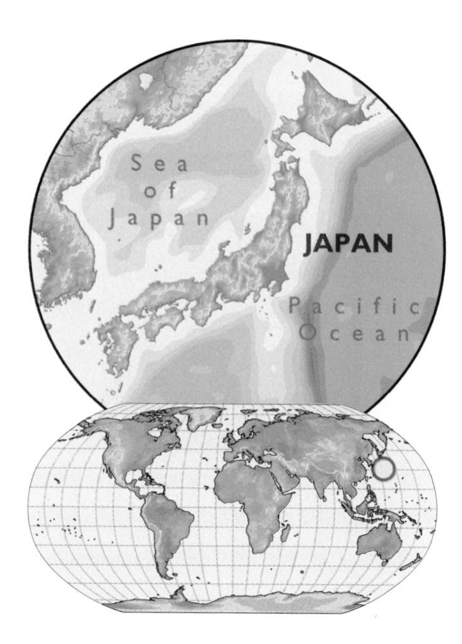

The Green Revolution

To prevent hunger, farmers in developing nations must increase the amount and quality of food they grow. Scientists from developed nations serve as advisors to farmers in developing countries. They help the farmers improve their methods of farming so that they can improve their yields.

Better farming methods do not depend on importing expensive farm equipment. The lack of available fuel and spare parts in many developing countries would make the equipment useless. The production of high-yielding seed varieties is the technological development that has done the most to help the hungry.

During the 1960s, new varieties of wheat and rice were developed to produce higher yields. This was called the **Green Revolution**. An American scientist, Dr. Norman Borlaug, was awarded the 1970 Nobel Peace Prize for his role in the development of the high-yielding, disease-resistant varieties of wheat. Many countries have improved their production of grain by using new seed varieties.

Scientists continue to develop improved varieties of seeds. Dr. Borlaug did not believe that the development of new varieties of wheat and rice was the solution to world hunger. He said the Green Revolution is simply "buying 20 to 30 years of time ... in which to bring population into balance with food production." About population growth, he said: "Unless tamed, it will one day wipe us from the Earth's surface."

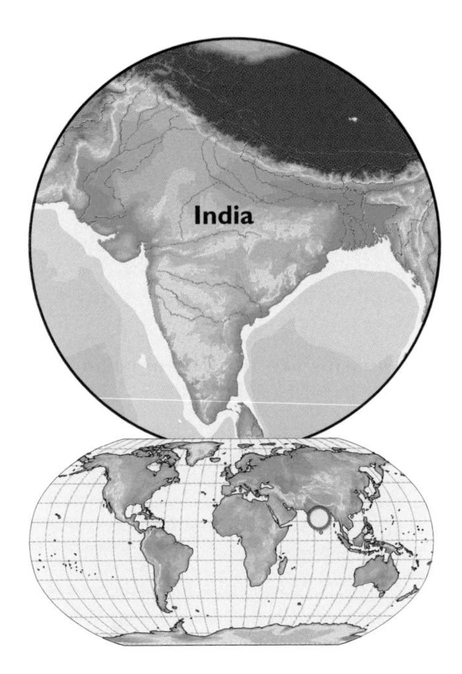

India

The United Nations estimated that the population of India reached 1 billion in 1999. Each year India adds another 18 million people. By 2050 the population may swell to 1.5 billion people. One third of the people in India live in poverty. More than 1/2 of India's children are malnourished and underweight even though early-maturing, high-yield varieties of rice and wheat have tripled the food production since the 70s.

Although scientists continue their efforts to develop seeds that produce higher yields, India may lack the ability to produce the food needed by its exploding population. Without good soil and plenty of moisture, seeds cannot produce the maximum yield. In 1999 the amount of land per person available to grow grain was 1/2 the amount available in 1960. If the population continues to grow at the current rate, by 2050 there will be less than 1 acre or 0.4 hectares (about the size of a football field) to grow grain for a family of five.

One reason that food production has increased is the use of irrigation. More than half of the grain (55%) is grown on irrigated land. Water is pumped from **aquifers** at a rate that is twice the **recharge rate**. The International Water Management Institute estimates that lack of water may reduce India's grain production by 1/4.

Many people live in parts of India that lack trees. They cannot afford to buy coal or oil for cooking. They sometimes travel for miles up the sides of mountains to the nearest wood supply. The destruction of the forests increases soil erosion and decreases the fertility of the soil.

Did You Know?

In 1947, Indian women averaged 6.0 children each. In 1997, women in India averaged 3.5 children each. In the 50 years between 1947 and 1997, India's population grew from about 350 million to 970 million, an increase of 270%. India's population growth rate is almost twice as high as China's. By 2035 the population of India will be greater than that of China.

Did You Know?

Just three crops—rice, wheat, and corn—provide 49% of the calories that people consume.

Environmental Challenge: Irradiation of Food

One way to reduce the spoilage of food is to treat it with radiation. Food safety is also an issue even in the more developed countries. While eating is essential for life, eating food contaminated with bacteria such as Escherichia coli 0157:H7 can be life threatening. In the United States, a single E coli outbreak made more than 700 people sick and caused four deaths.

Find out:

- How are foods treated with radiation?
- What are the benefits of irradiating food?
- What risks are associated with the process of irradiating foods?
- Does irradiation increase or decrease the cost of food?
- Do you think that radiation should be used to reduce losses and increase the safety of food?

Visit these websites to find out more about irradiation of food: www.foodsafety.org, www.cast-science.org and www.exnet.iastate.edu.

Some Indian women follow the cows and collect the dung. After it is dried, the dung is burned to supply the heat for cooking. This natural source of valuable nutrients is used for today's fuel instead of next season's fertilizer. The demand for some resources already exceeds the supply. Some doubt that India's resources can support 1.5 billion people.

More Protein Needed

Although the Green Revolution increased the amount of food available and decreased the amount of hunger, it reduced the amount of protein available. Fish raised in the irrigation canals of the rice fields were poisoned by the fertilizers and pesticides used to grow the new rice varieties.

The best way to provide low-cost protein is through foods that are already familiar to the people. In Tanzania, farmers raise fish in hand-dug ponds. The ponds are dug and filled with water from springs. They are stocked with Tilapia fingerlings. The fish are fed garbage, cornmeal and bran. Rotting fruit and other plant material thrown into the pond provides nutrients for algae and food for small organisms that the fish eat. Six months later the fish have grown to eight inches and may provide much of the protein in the family's diet.

Plants are the main source of protein for most of the world's hungry. The soybean is the world's leading source of high-quality protein. Two-thirds of the soybeans harvested in China are consumed as tofu, soy sauce or other soy products. China also imports soybean meal, a high-protein feed supplement for livestock and poultry feed.

The United States—Always A Land of Plenty?

The new varieties of wheat have increased the yield in the United States as well as in other countries. The world grain harvest increased by 182% between 1950 and 1990, but the increase between 1990 and 1996 was only 3%. More recently the growth in yield has been near 1%. The production per person has declined 6% since 1984.

Most of the wheat imported by many countries comes from the surplus produced by the United States and Canada. People in other countries drink milk and eat foods produced by animals that are fed corn and soybeans grown in the United States. Soybeans are also used to make high-protein foods. Seven ounces (12 mL) of a soy mixture that is similar to milk can provide the daily nutritional requirements of a child.

Will the United States always be able to produce more food than its population needs? In 1999 the population of the United States was 272 million. The projected population for the U.S. in 2025 is 335 million. Each year it takes more of the food produced in the United States to feed people living in the United States. Neither the United States nor Mexico has seen any improvement in wheat yields for 13 years.

Farmers have increased food production by increasing yield, expanding the land area planted, and increasing irrigation. While some additional land might be converted to cropland, it would mean a loss of wood production, wildlife habitat, and grazing land, and possibly increased soil erosion. Unfortunately prime farmland is also prime property for development. Developments, office buildings and parking lots now stand where wheat and corn once grew. Many of today's most productive farms are being lost to development.

Prime farmland is being developed at an alarming rate. Farmland preservation programs in Pennsylvania and other states protect farmland from development.

Preserving Farmland

Can technology make up for the acreage lost to development? We cannot guarantee advances in future technology. But we can guarantee that future generations will have productive farmland if we protect our tillable land. Protecting farmland requires the cooperation of politicians and landowners, and possibly a change in our way of life.

Two methods are currently used to protect agricultural lands. Property is taxed on the basis of its development value. Land used for farming and grazing is taxed at a low rate. Residential and commercial lands are taxed at higher rates. Some states require penalties if land that has been taxed at an agricultural rate is developed. In some states, inheritance taxes are also lower if the land continues to be used for agriculture. These laws can delay the development of land, but they cannot prevent it.

The second method prevents development and ensures the land will remain as agricultural land. The state, county, or a conservation group buys **development rights** to the land. Selling of "rights" is not a new idea. Timber, mineral, oil, hunting and fishing rights have been sold for many years.

After selling the development rights, the owner still owns the land, can live on it and farm it. A restriction is placed on the deed to ensure that the land will always be used for agricultural purposes. The land can be sold, but cannot be developed. The development rights are usually sold for the difference between the agricultural and development values of the land. This compensates the owner for taking away the owner's development rights.

Before this field was developed, it was part of a large farm that produced potatoes and other crops.

Increasing Yields with Irrigation

Fertilizers and higher yielding varieties of seeds are useless without water. The ability to triple the world grain harvest was dependent upon expanding irrigation. While only 16% of the world's cropland is irrigated, it provides 35% of the world's food supply. Developing countries are especially dependent upon irrigation to meet their needs.

Farmers in northern Bangladesh need low-cost irrigation technology. An example of this type of technology is the bamboo tube-well with a twin-cylinder bamboo treadle pump. The treadle pump is run by human power. Farmers that are using bamboo pumps are now harvesting three crops a year instead of the one or sometimes two that can be harvested without irrigation.

Take an airplane flight over the Dust Bowl today and you will see green circles that look like checkers on a huge game board. Irrigation

Did You Know?

By using computer-controlled irrigation systems that supply water to plants only when it is needed, Israel reduced the amount of irrigation water used per hectare by 36% between 1951 and 1990 without any loss in productivity.

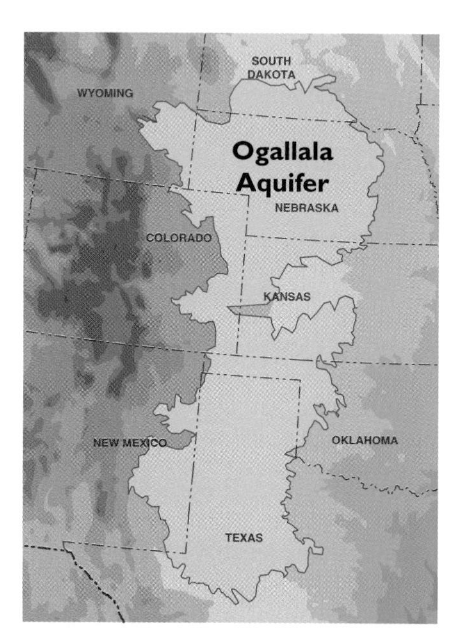

Will the sea provide? Fishermen from a small fishing village in China cast their nets upon the water. Their methods are primitive compared to the high-tech fishing vessels from developed countries.

technology allows farmers and ranchers to farm the dry land of the Great Plains. Today corn, which requires vast quantities of water, is grown on land that was once only good for grazing cattle.

Turbine pumps pull water from deep wells and feed it to "walking water" or center-pivot irrigation systems. Center-pivot irrigation systems have self-propelled sprinklers which "walk" in a huge circle and spray water on land that normally gets less than 20 inches (500 mm) of rain each year. The source of water is the Ogallala Aquifer that runs deep beneath the soil, from South Dakota to Texas.

Today the Ogallala supplies water to irrigate two million acres (0.8 million hectare) of land in Kansas. Corn grown on this land is fed to cattle in large feed lots. Not far away, in Garden City, Kansas, is the world's largest beef-packing plant. The automated plant can convert a 500-pound (227-kg) steer into "boxed-beef" in less than one hour. The plant slaughters 5,000 cattle a day—1.5 million each year. Forty percent of the beef produced in the United States depends upon water from the Ogallala Aquifer.

The Ogallala Aquifer is a fossil aquifer. Like oil deposits, the Ogallala water deposit is a nonrenewable resource. The water is being "mined." In some areas, farmers have had to return to less productive dryland farming. The USDA reports that underground aquifers are being mined to supply water for 21% of U.S. irrigated cropland.

Overpumping of aquifers is occurring in other areas of the world as well. In India, the level of groundwater is falling as water is pumped from more than 6 million tube wells. In parts of northern China, the groundwater level is dropping more than one meter per year.

Long before the mining of the Ogallala Aquifer began, irrigation had produced large yields of grains in other regions of the world, but in some areas it also destroyed the soil. The area between the Tigris and Euphrates Rivers was once known as the Fertile Crescent. Six thousand years ago farmers irrigated the land, and crops grew abundantly. Eventually salinization ruined the land. **Salinization** occurs in dry climates when the irrigation water evaporates and leaves its minerals in the soil. Today, 6,000 years later, farmers struggle to grow crops there.

More efficient use of irrigation water could increase yields or provide water for more irrigated land. In many irrigation systems, the plants use less than 50% of the water applied to the crops. The rest of the water is lost through seepage, evaporation and runoff. Computers can control the distribution of water and reduce the amount of water used. Technology is available for irrigation processes that use water more efficiently and do not ruin the soil, but such technology is very expensive.

The Sea as a Source of Food

Seventy-one percent of the earth is covered with oceans. Will the oceans be the solution to the world's increased need for food? Fishing vessels equipped with modern technology have the ability to take more fish from the oceans than the oceans can produce. Technology increased the harvest of fish from

19 million tons (17 million metric tonnes) in 1950 to 93 million tons (83.7 million metric tonnes) in 1996, but the fish catch is no longer growing.

The capacity of the ocean to produce fish is limited, so as the human population grows, the amount of fish that the ocean has produced per person has declined since 1988. Many species of edible fish—salmon, tuna, sardines, flatfish and others—are already being threatened by intense fishing practices. Countries are restricting fishing rights to stop over-fishing and maintain a sustainable yield. There were more than 100 disputes among nations over fishing rights in 1997.

Land development along the coasts also threatens fish populations. Marshlands were cheaper than other land, so developers bought, filled and built on thousands of acres of marshlands. The food chain of many deep-water fish begins in the marshlands. The **estuaries** are the nurseries for many species of fish. The small fish produced in one acre (0.4 hectare) of estuary produces 240 pounds (108 kg) of edible fish. Protecting the marshlands and estuaries is essential to our food supply.

Pollution of the ocean is another threat to our food supply. Fish, oysters, crabs and other organisms that live near the coast accumulate poisons in their body fat. This is the area of the ocean that produces the most food. This is also the area that is the most likely to be polluted.

Can the Earth Feed 10 Billion People?

In 2000, farmers were producing enough food to feed 6 billion people. Using the middle range of the UN population projections, farmers will need to produce enough food to feed another 3 or 4 billion people in 50 years. Some experts think that Earth can feed 10 billion people; others believe that a population that large exceeds Earth's carrying capacity.

Of the world's 6 billion people, 3.1 billion live in Asia. As Asians become more affluent, they are moving up the food chain. China is the world leader in pork production and will soon overtake the United States in producing poultry. As more people increase their consumption of meat in their diet, more grain is needed to feed the animals.

The number of people that farmers can feed depends partly upon what the people eat. The grain and other foods produced in 1990 can support 10.9 billion people if they eat the diet common in Bangladesh. The same food production can only support 2.3 billion people if they eat a typical North American diet that is high in fats, sugars, and animal products.

Cutting losses of food during production, storage, and shipping can provide more food for people. Between 10 and 20% of all food produced is lost after harvest to insects, bacteria, and rodents. Latin America has twice as many cattle as the United States, but produces only half the beef because of losses to pests and disease. According to the USDA, reducing losses due to animal disease by 6% would provide food for 250 million additional people.

The world's ability to feed the population in the future is in question. No one knows what breakthroughs in technology will occur, but it is clear

Environmental Challenge: Antibiotics

About 1/4 of the antibiotics dispensed in the United States aren't for treating infections. Instead, they are feed additives used to promote weight gain in apparently healthy livestock. In 1986 Sweden banned the use of antibiotics to promote livestock growth.

- Is the practice of administering subtherapeutic doses of antibiotics to farm animals necessary to produce food for a growing human population?
- Does this use of antibiotics pose a risk for human health?
- Should this use of subtherapeutic doses of antibiotics and of other closely related drugs that are also prescribed for people be banned in the United States?

that we will not be able to provide for our increasing population unless we use our cropland wisely and protect our oceans and coastal wetlands. To prevent starvation we must share our knowledge and resources with other countries and transport food to areas where it is most needed.

Unfortunately, social and economic differences may always ensure that some people will go hungry. While 75% of the fish caught in the world belong to developing countries, the catch may do little to reduce the hunger of the needy people who live there. Nearly half of the fish go to other countries with the majority going to wealthy nations.

3.6 Questions for Study and Discussion:

1. Define the following terms: **VOCABULARY**

aquifer	population growth rate
development rights	recharge rate
fertility rate	salinization
green revolution	yield
natural increase	

The Population Connection

2. How has the world's population growth rate changed? Create a graph showing the information from the first paragraph.
3. What two factors determine the growth rate of a country?
4. How does the growth rate of the United States compare to the growth rate of the world?
5. What regions of the world have the highest growth rate?

Why People Go to Bed Hungry

6. How has the population growth affected our natural resources?
7. What is the Chinese government doing to try to reduce the number of hungry people? What event led to this action?
8. What is the major cause of hunger? What other factors contribute to hunger?

The World's Tillable Land

9. List the 5 regions that have most of the world's cropland and produce most of the world's food. Which of these countries have a surplus of food?
10. How does the amount of tillable land in China compare to the amount in the United States and Canada? How does the population of China compare to the population of the United States and Canada?
11. The U.S. and Canada both have 4% of the world's tillable land. Which country grows the most food? Why?

Japan

12. What is the typical size of Japanese farms? What type of equipment do they use?
13. How does the yield per acre on Japanese farms compare to other farms? Give three factors that increase their yield.
14. Give two ways in which equipment reduces the yield per acre.

The Green Revolution

15. The term Green Revolution refers to what technological development?
16. What did Dr. Borlaug believe were the essential parts to the solution of the problem of world hunger?

India

17. What two technologies have increased the production of food in India?
18. What factors limit India's ability to produce food?
19. In what two ways does the lack of fuel in India hurt the soil?

More Protein Needed

20. How did the Green Revolution decrease the amount of protein in the diets of people who grew rice?
21. What is the best way to increase the protein in the diet of people in other countries? How is this being accomplished in Tanzania?

22. What plant is a good source of protein? List ways in which this plant is used.

The United States—Always a Land of Plenty?

23. How did the wheat yield change between 1950 and 1990? Predict the change in yield between 1990 and 2030?
24. Give two ways that farmers in the United States have increased food production.
25. Do you think that the United States will always be able to produce enough food to meet the needs of people in this country and have excess to export? Explain.

Preserving Farmland

26. How can tax laws encourage people to use land as farmland instead of developing it?
27. How can we guarantee that farmland will not be developed?

Increasing Yields with Irrigation

28. Describe the technology that is increasing the production of food in Bangladesh. What is the energy source?
29. What development of modern technology allows corn to be grown on the Great Plains today?
30. Is the Ogallala Aquifer a renewable resource? Explain.
31. The Fertile Crescent was once one of the most productive areas of irrigated farmland in the world. Now few crops will grow there. Why?

The Sea as a Source of Food

32. Explain the role of technology in the harvest of fish, and what is necessary to produce a sustainable yield.
33. Why is it important to protect the marshland along the coasts?

Can the Earth Feed 10 Billion People?

34. What do you think—can the earth feed 10 billion people? Explain.
35. What steps can be taken to increase the number of people that the earth can feed?

Environmental Challenge: Aquaculture

The greatest change in the diet during the last 50 years has been the increase in portions of animal protein consumed. Since we have reached the limits of the ocean to supply fish, there has been an increase in aquaculture or fish farming.

Chickens require 2 kilograms of grain concentrate to produce 1 kilogram of live weight. Poultry and pork producers supplement grain with soybean meal. Soybeans are the world's leading source of high-quality protein. Another high-quality source of protein is fish.

Research aquaculture and find out:

- How does fish farming compare to poultry and pork production?
- What are the advantages of fish farming?
- What are the environmental consequences?
- Will fish farming help India feed 1 billion people? Defend your answer.
- Are fish farms a form of sustainable agriculture? Explain.

3.7 Fertilizers: Organic vs. Inorganic

OBJECTIVES

- **Identify** the primary nutrients present in fertile soils.
- **Describe** the effect of farming on natural soil fertility.
- **Compare** the advantages and disadvantages of using synthetic fertilizers with the use of "organic" or natural fertilizers.

Long before scientists understood the nutrient cycles, people observed that plants grew well in some soils and poorly in others. The soils in which plants grew well were said to be **fertile**. After plants had been grown in the same soil for a few years, they no longer grew as big or looked as healthy. The soil was "worn-out."

By trial-and-error people learned how to make the soil grow better crops. Ancient writings referred to the practice of applying manure when crops were planted. The American Indians taught the colonists to put fish heads in the mounds with their corn seeds. Manure and fish heads provided something that made the plants grow better.

Scientists experimented by growing plants in water or clean sand instead of soil. These experiments proved that plants need certain chemicals for proper growth. Other experiments showed that **fertile soils** are rich in the chemicals that plants require for growth. In a natural ecosystem the **nutrients**—chemicals needed by the plants—are returned to the soil when the plant decays. Some nutrients are lost from the ecosystem by harvesting, erosion and leaching, but most are recycled.

Plants "rob" the nutrients from the soil. Each year that plants are grown and harvested, more of the same chemicals are removed from the soil's "nutrient bank." Many of the nutrients are transported from the farm ecosystem to the city ecosystem. Farming increases the amount of erosion. Soon the soil's supply of certain chemicals is exhausted. The soil is now **infertile**—unable to support good plant growth. It is "worn out."

Essential Nutrients

Scientists learned that the fertility of the soil depends upon the presence of at least thirteen chemical elements. Plants require large quantities of three nutrients: Nitrogen (N), phosphorus (P), and Potassium (K). These **primary nutrients** are often listed on fertilizer labels as N-P-K. Smaller amounts of other nutrients are needed. These **secondary nutrients** are: Calcium (Ca), Magnesium (Mg), and Sulfur (S).

Seven additional elements have been identified as being necessary for plant growth. Since only very tiny amounts of these nutrients are needed, they are referred to as **micronutrients**. The micronutrients are iron, manganese, boron, copper, molybdenum, zinc and chlorine.

The Primary Nutrients

Nitrogen is necessary for the proper growth of plant leaves and stems. Plants with plenty of nitrogen grow fast in warm, humid weather. They have a rich green color. But the lack of nitrogen is most often the **limiting factor** for the growth of plants. Even with plenty of moisture and warmth, lack of nitrogen results in slow growth and leaves that are yellow-green in color.

Sometimes the elements needed by the plants are present in the soil, but they are not in a form that plants can use. Nitrogen is a good example of this. The air spaces between soil particles contain nitrogen gas (N_2), but it cannot be used by the plants unless bacteria change it into the proper form: ammonium ions (NH_4^+) or nitrate ions (NO_3^-).

Plants remove large amounts of nitrogen from the soil. Since the forms of nitrogen used by plants readily dissolve in water, they are easily leached from the soil. Some forms of nitrogen escape into the air. We are aware of this each time we open a bottle of ammonia or change a baby's diaper.

Just as a lack of nitrogen causes problems, too much nitrogen also causes problems. If too much nitrogen is present, the stems of plants grow very tall, but they are not strong. Heavy winds or rain easily break these stems. An excess of nitrogen also makes plants more susceptible to fungal diseases and to frost.

Although plants are larger, they do not taste as good if too much nitrogen is present in the soil. Cows do not eat the large clumps of grass that grow on the piles of old manure; they prefer the shorter, tastier grass that grows nearby. During dry weather, high levels of nitrogen (nitrates) can accumulate in plants if too much nitrogen is present in the soil. Cattle eating these plants may develop **nitrate poisoning**.

One hundred bushels (3.5 m^3) of corn contain 78 pounds (35 kg) of nitrogen, 16 pounds (7 kg) of phosphorus, and 22 pounds (10 kg) of potassium.

Phosphorus is necessary for good root growth as well as flower and seed formation. If the proper amount of phosphorus is not available, plants produce fewer blooms and less fruit. A lack of phosphorus results in slower growth and makes plants more susceptible to disease.

Potassium is also necessary for proper growth and resistance to disease. Potassium forms strong stems, and it is necessary for the development and ripening of fruit. Stems of plants deficient in potassium will be more likely to fall over during a storm.

Nutrient deficiencies are not always easily recognized. Plants develop purple-tinged leaves when they are lacking phosphorus, but plants turn purple when temperatures are cool, and purple is a natural color for some plants. A lack of potassium may cause "firing" or browning of the edges of leaves, but the edges of leaves on some plants turn brown if there is not enough humidity.

Plants lacking potassium or phosphorus appear stunted in growth. Ears of corn have rows of kernels that are crooked or incomplete when potassium is deficient. A lack of phosphorus prevents the kernels of corn from filling out, and results in "nubbins" instead of well-developed cobs of corn.

Potassium and phosphorus are present in some soils, but they are present as chemical compounds that are not soluble in water. Other forms of potassium readily dissolve in water and are quickly leached from the soil. In both instances the minerals are not available to plants, and nutrient deficiencies may occur.

The chemical compounds in the soil are affected by the **pH** of the soil. If the soil has the proper pH, chemicals are in forms that can be absorbed and used by the plants. If the pH of the soil is too high or too low, the nutrients are locked in compounds that plants cannot use.

Environmental Challenge: Certified Organic

The popularity of organic foods has increased and organic farming has experienced explosive growth in several states during the 1990s. The USDA has established national standards that must be met for foods to be labeled "Certified Organic." Some states have also passed laws concerning similar requirements. To learn more about organic food production and find answers to the questions below, visit these Websites: www.oneplan.state.id.us/ez/Organic/organic.htm, www.nofavt.org and www.ccof.org.

- Make a list of approved fertilizers for the organic food grower.
- Make a list of approved pest controls that can be used on "Certified Organic" foods.
- Can genetically engineered or genetically modified foods be "Certified Organic"?
- Is "Certified Organic" farming a sustainable agricultural practice? Explain.
- List reasons why people might prefer to buy produce that is "Certified Organic."
- Do you think that "Certified Organic" produce is better than other produce? Explain.

www

Soil Testing

Farmers and gardeners must make sure that the soil has the proper amount of each nutrient available for the plants. The nutritional quality of vegetables, fruits and grains is determined by the nutrients present in the soil. The yield is increased if the proper nutrients are present in the soil.

You can tell something about the physical structure of the soil by looking at it and feeling it, but how can you tell if there are enough nutrients for the crop that is being planted? To find out the level of nutrients in the soil, a soil sample is taken and chemical tests are made. There are several ways to do this:

- Send a soil sample to the laboratory at your state university's College of Agriculture. The instructions and kits for mailing the sample are available from the university's Cooperative Extension Office in your county. Check the telephone book.
- Send a soil sample to a private laboratory.
- Buy a soil testing kit from a local garden supply and test your own soil.

The first two methods provide the most accurate and detailed information. Testing at private laboratories will probably be more expensive than at a state university. The cheapest and quickest method is a soil test kit, but it will not be as accurate, and it will not provide as much information.

A Choice of Fertilizers

Once the test results are known, the farmer or gardener must decide which fertilizers to use. The term **fertilizer** refers to any substance, natural or manufactured, that is added to the soil in order to supply one or more plant nutrients. **Synthetic fertilizers** are human-made products. Their production involves chemically changing the nutrients so that they are readily available for the plants.

Organic fertilizers are natural products made from dead organisms or their waste products. Their production may involve physical changes such as grinding, but any chemical changes must occur only through natural processes. Bone meal is considered an "organic" fertilizer because it is natural bone that is simply ground into a powder.

Organic fertilizers are not always organic chemicals. Rock phosphate is considered to be an "organic" fertilizer because it is a natural rock. It is crushed into a powder, but it has not been chemically changed. **Superphosphate** is classified as a synthetic fertilizer because the rock phosphate has been treated with a chemical (sulfuric acid) to make the phosphate more readily available to plants.

Scientists discovered how to change nitrogen gas into chemical compounds that plants could use. In the late 1930s they manufactured the first synthetic fertilizers. Natural gas is needed to make the fertilizer, and large amounts of other fossil fuels are used to supply the energy needed for the chemical reactions. In the 1930s the low price of fossil fuels allowed manufacturers to produce and sell synthetic fertilizers at a relatively low cost.

The nitrogen removed when protein is broken down in the liver becomes a part of a compound called **urea**. The urea and other waste products are filtered out of the blood by the kidneys. Straw used in animal pens absorbs the urea and is a good source of fertilizer. The compound urea is also synthesized from atmospheric nitrogen and natural gas. Urea is an organic chemical, but whether it is a synthetic fertilizer or an "organic" fertilizer depends upon its source.

Farmers found that they could dramatically increase the yield of crops by using synthetic fertilizers on the "worn out" soil. The increased use of synthetic fertilizers, along with other technological advances such as better seeds and pest control, improved both the yield and the quality of the crops.

Did You Know?

George Washington's Mount Vernon Plantation did not prosper because the soil was depleted by continuous planting of tobacco. Washington searched for a good natural fertilizer and even had mud from the Potomac River spread on his fields.

An Unlimited Supply

A constant supply of nitrogen is ensured by the action of the nitrogen cycle. But the availability and cost of synthetic nitrogen fertilizers are directly dependent upon the supply of natural gas and crude oil. Fossil fuels are not renewable resources, so the supply of natural gas and crude oil will one day be exhausted. Long before these supplies run out, a shortage of synthetic nitrogen fertilizers may occur because of political actions such as the Arab Oil Embargo, which limited imports during the 1970s.

Phosphorus, potassium and all of the secondary nutrients are minerals that are found in rocks. Rocks that contain calcium, magnesium, sulfur and potassium are common, but few rocks contain phosphorus. The supply is limited.

Plants we grow for food crops require more phosphorus than the grasses or trees that originally grew in the soils. The soil needs applications of phosphate fertilizers to produce food crops. Ninety-seven percent of the rock phosphate is located in the United States and Russia. Deposits of rock phosphate are being mined and scattered over farmland or used for other purposes.

The phosphorus is either removed from the soil by the plants or is carried away by erosion. Uneaten plant parts may be dumped in a compost pile or buried in a landfill. The plants that are eaten provide phosphate for bones. Some of the phosphate is not absorbed by the digestive system. Along with the uneaten plant parts that pass through the garbage disposal, human waste is also sent to sewage treatment plants. Some of the phosphorus becomes a part of the **biosolids** or sludge that settles out of the sewage.

Some of the phosphorus is carried into streams with the treated wastewater. Here it joins the phosphorus carried away by erosion, and the journey continues to the ocean. The loss of potassium by the same pathway is not as critical because there are more rocks with potassium. It will take millions of years before the phosphate and potassium being deposited in the ocean will accumulate into new rock deposits that could once again be mined.

Environmental Challenge: Compost

Take a quiz, watch a video, and get ideas for a student research project focusing on compost at: www.cfe.cornell.edu/compost/schools.html.

www

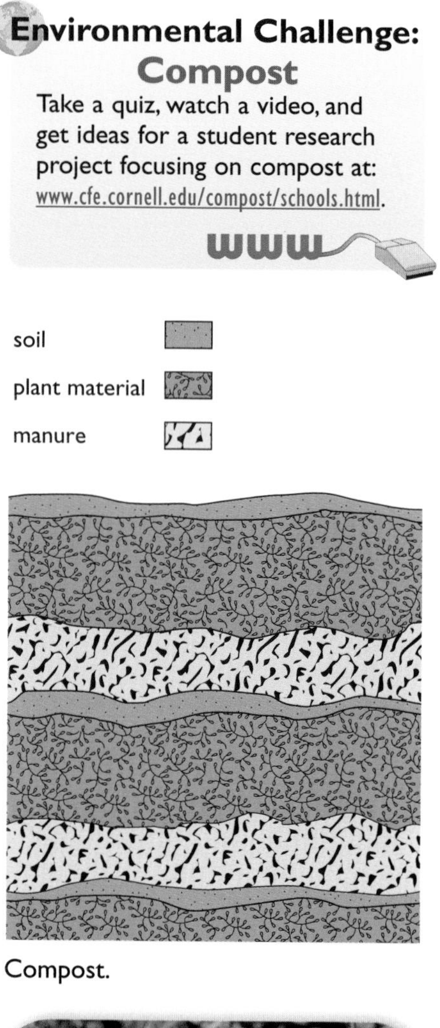

Compost.

Where legumes, such as red clover, are planted, the nitrogen level in the soil increases.

The Organic Way

The organic method of farming and gardening tries to duplicate the continuous recycling of nutrients that occurs in a forest ecosystem. Although the organic method does not eliminate all loss of phosphorus and potassium, it will decrease the loss. For example, organic gardeners recycle plant material instead of "feeding" it to the garbage disposal.

Bacteria must break down organic materials before plants can use them. The bacteria "rob" the soil of nitrogen during the time it takes to break down the organic matter. Organic gardeners speed up the process of decay by making compost piles. A pile is made with alternating layers of soil, manure, and plant material. It is kept moist and turned frequently to provide air. The resulting **compost** is a mixture of soil and decomposed organic materials (humus).

Organic matter feeds the organisms in the soil and provides nutrients for the plants. The fungi in the soil help the plant roots to absorb nutrients. When farmers depend entirely on synthetic fertilizers, the level of organic matter in the soil decreases and the fungi disappear. Without the help of the fungi, larger amounts of fertilizer are needed so that plants can get the same amount of nutrients.

The organic matter also helps maintain good soil structure. The humus increases the water-holding capacity of the soil. This decreases erosion and leaching. The humus particles also increase the ability of the soil to hold nutrients until the plants need them.

More than two billion tons of animal feces, slaughterhouse waste and other organic waste products are produced each year. Putting the material in a landfill takes up valuable space and removes nutrients from their natural cycle. Some of this material is used as fertilizer. Dried blood and bone meal are two examples.

Some farmers use **biosolids**, formerly called sewage sludge, as a soil conditioner and a source of nutrients. Sewage sludge from Chicago, Illinois, was spread on former coal mines in Fulton County, Illinois. It was plowed into the poor soil that remained after the coal was removed by strip-mining. New topsoil was created by the addition of organic matter in the biosolids. The city has leased about 2,000 acres (808 ha) of "reclaimed" land to farmers.

Biosolids recycling is governed by "Part 503" of the Clean Water Act. Class A biosolids are treated to reduce **pathogens** below detectable levels and may be used in place of commercial fertilizers. Class B biosolids have been treated to reduce pathogens. But farmers must wait before harvesting crops from land where Class B biosolids have been applied. Biosolids are not allowed on land that is highly permeable or has a steep slope. Odor problems can be avoided by injecting the biosolids into the soil.

Green manure crops are grown for the purpose of adding organic matter to the soil. If legumes such as clover are planted, the level of nitrogen in the soil is also increased. Rye is a grass that is often sown in the fall for a winter cover crop. The clover or rye is plowed under or killed with herbicides when another crop is planted in spring. By planting rye or clover, the farmer also decreases erosion.

Which is Better—Organic or Synthetic?

Both forms of fertilizer provide nutrients for plant growth. The plant cannot tell the difference between natural and synthetic sources. Both types of fertilizer have advantages and disadvantages.

Organic Fertilizers

Advantages

- Most organic fertilizers are not as concentrated and will not harm the plants. There are some exceptions such as fresh poultry manure and dried blood.
- Organic materials are available for a longer period of time and are less likely to be lost from the soil.
- Many organic fertilizers add humus to the soil.

Disadvantages

- If it is necessary to buy fertilizer, organic fertilizers are more expensive than synthetic fertilizers.
- Nutrient levels of **N-P-K** in most organic materials are usually low, and large amounts of material are required to provide proper plant nutrients.
- The nutrient levels will vary with the materials used.
- Organic materials must be composted before their nutrients are available to the plants.

Synthetic Fertilizers

Advantages

- If it is necessary to purchase the fertilizer, then synthetic fertilizers are more economical than organic.
- The nutrients are concentrated and only small amounts of fertilizer are needed.
- The concentration of nutrients can be easily determined by reading the label and must meet industry standards.
- The nutrients are quickly available; plants do not have to wait.

Disadvantages

- If too much fertilizer is used, or it is placed too close to the plant, the concentrated chemicals will harm the plant.
- Since very small amounts are needed, people often apply too much.
- Since the nutrients are very soluble in water, they are easily leached from the area of the plant roots.
- Synthetic fertilizers do not increase the humus content of the soil.

3.7 Questions for Study and Discussion:

1. Define the following terms: **VOCABULARY**

biosolids	infertile soils	organic fertilizers	superphosphate
compost	limiting factor	pathogens	synthetic fertilizer
fertile soils	micronutrients	pH	urea
fertilizer	nitrate poisoning	primary nutrients	
green manure crops	nutrients	secondary nutrients	

2. What were the first materials that were added to the soil that made the plants grow better?
3. Give three ways that plant nutrients are lost from the soil.

Essential Nutrients

4. List the three primary nutrients.
5. What is the difference between secondary nutrients and micronutrients? Give examples of each.

The Primary Nutrients

6. Which of the primary nutrients most frequently limits the growth of plants? What is the appearance of plants that lack enough of this nutrient?
7. Why do plants need phosphorus and potassium?
8. Why may plants show nutrient deficiencies even though the elements needed by the plants are present in the soil?

Soil Testing

9. Give two reasons why farmers, gardeners, and orchard owners are concerned about the nutrients in the soil?
10. Compare the cost and accuracy of different methods of soil testing.

A Choice of Fertilizers

11. What is the difference between synthetic and "organic" fertilizers?
12. What is the connection between fossil fuels and synthetic fertilizers?
13. Identify the three technological advances that improved the quality and the yields of farmers' crops.

An Unlimited Supply (?)

14. What caused the shortage in the supply of nitrogen fertilizers that occurred in the 1970s?
15. Identify the primary nutrient that is most limited in supply.
16. Explain what happens to the phosphorus that is lost from the soil?

The Organic Way

17. In what ways does the use of organic matter help the soil ecosystem?
18. Why do organic gardeners make compost piles?
19. Give three examples of waste that can be used as organic fertilizers.
20. Give two examples of green manure crops and explain the benefits of growing these crops.

Which is Better—Organic or Synthetic?

21. Which type of fertilizer increases the humus content of the soil?
22. Which type of fertilizer contains the most concentrated nutrients?
23. Which type of fertilizer provides nutrients for a longer period of time?

3.8 Pests and Pesticides—They Both Cause Problems

"I am pessimistic about the human race because it is too ingenious for its own good. Our approach to nature is to beat it into submission."
E. B. WHITE

OBJECTIVES

- **Contrast** behaviors of insects that are beneficial with behaviors of insects that are pests.
- **Relate** changes in pesticide use associated with World War II and with the publication of the book *Silent Spring*.
- **Explain** the relationship between monocultures and pest populations.
- **Identify** problems associated with the use of pesticides and describe ways of reducing or eliminating the problems.

The bacterium that causes bubonic plague is carried from rats to humans by fleas. More than one-fourth of the population of Europe died of the plague in the 14th century. **Pest**, a word that comes from the Latin word for plague, refers to any troublesome, destructive or annoying organism. Insects and other pests have bothered humans for generations.

Some insects carry disease and others compete with humans for food. Mosquitoes are more than just another annoying pest; they carry malaria and yellow fever. These two diseases have killed more people than all the wars throughout history. Insect pests and other organisms destroy large quantities of food each year.

There are many types of fungi that cause disease in plants. In the 1840s more than half a million people starved when a fungus struck the Irish potato crop. Millions of people avoided starvation by immigrating to other countries. So many people died on ships leaving Ireland that they were called coffin ships.

One of the worst insect pests is the grasshopper. Since the beginning of history, plagues of grasshoppers have been attacking the crops which humans grow for food. Indians and grasshoppers were both enemies the settlers faced as they moved west.

The year 1874 would be remembered as "The Year of the Grasshopper." Grasshoppers ate almost everything except the native grass. Great swarms of grasshoppers moved across the Great Plains destroying crops and stopping trains. The bodies of the dead grasshoppers made the rail so slick that the engine couldn't pull the train. Farmers began to expect a plague of grasshoppers about every ten years. Grasshoppers are still serious pests.

According to the Agricultural Research Service, grasshoppers do $400 million worth of damage each year. When the density of grasshoppers is eight per square yard (10/m^2), the grasshoppers damage the plants eaten by livestock and game animals. In 1985, a state of emergency was declared in 14 western states. Idaho farmers fought a two-mile-wide (3.2 km) band of grasshoppers. In some places the population density was 1800 grasshoppers per square yard (2,250/m^2). The land appeared as if massive lawn mowers had cut the plants off where they came out of the ground.

Cotton plants are not only a source of fibers for clothing, but also a source of oil for shortening and meal for livestock feed. The boll weevil entered the United States from Mexico in the 1890s. The quarter-inch (0.6 cm) weevil drills into the cotton bolls and lays its eggs. The boll of cotton provides a home and a source of food for the larvae.

Mosquitoes are more than just annoying; they carry diseases that can kill.

Grasshopper.

The boll weevil is the best-known enemy of the cotton plant.

The boll of cotton has escaped damage from the boll weevil. No doubt pesticides provided the needed protection.

In the early 1900s the boll weevil was such a destructive pest in Coffee County, Alabama, that farmers tried to raise peanuts instead of cotton. The peanut crop was so successful that a fountain was built and dedicated to the boll weevil. Had it not been for the boll weevil, peanuts might never have become the major cash crop in Coffee County.

The boll weevil is not the only enemy of the cotton plant. Farmers that continue to plant cotton must battle aphids, bollworms, cutworms, grasshoppers, nematodes, spider mites, stink bugs, whiteflies and other insects. It is little wonder that cotton growers became dependent upon pesticides.

Miracle Chemicals

People tried magic and banging drums, but they did little to scare off the swarms of insects. Then humans discovered chemicals that kill—**avicides** (bird killers), **insecticides** (insect killers), **fungicides** (fungus killers), **nematicides** (nematode {round worm} killers) and **herbicides** (weed killers). Collectively these chemicals are called **pesticides**.

The first pesticides came from naturally occurring minerals. These included arsenic, copper, lead, mercury, sulfur and zinc. During the 1800s, arsenic compounds were used to control the potato beetle. The **Bordeaux mixture**, a mixture of calcium hydroxide and copper sulfate, is still sometimes used as a fungicide. Wine makers still use sulfur compounds to kill bacteria and wild yeast on the fruit they use for making wine.

Other early pesticides were natural chemicals that were produced by plants. **Pyrethrum** came from the dried flowers of chrysanthemums, **nicotine sulfate** from tobacco plants, and **rotenone** from legumes that grow in the East Indies. These natural chemicals proved to be expensive, and they were not highly effective in controlling certain types of insects.

The fact that human-made chemicals could be used to kill insects was discovered during World War II. Insects were used to test chemicals (nerve gases) which were being developed for chemical warfare. Two groups of chemicals being tested were chlorinated hydrocarbons and organic phosphates. Important insecticides were developed from both types of chemicals.

The chlorinated hydrocarbons became the most important group of insecticides. They were successful because they were cheap and easy to use, they killed many different kinds of insects, they continued to kill insects long after they were applied, they weren't washed away by the rain, and they were not very toxic to humans. The first of the chlorinated hydrocarbons was the chemical dichloro-diphenyl-trichloro-ethane, more commonly known as **DDT**.

To understand chlorinated hydrocarbons we must look at some chemical formulas. A carbon atom with four hydrogen atoms attached is a hydrocarbon molecule called methane. It is the major chemical in natural gas. When hydrogen atoms are removed and chlorine atoms are added, new compounds called **chlorinated hydrocarbons** are formed. A simple example is chloroform—an anesthetic.

Chemists built larger, more complex chlorinated hydrocarbons. All of these molecules are made of carbon, hydrogen, and chlorine atoms. By changing the number and arrangement of atoms, chemists made different insecticides.

Chemists found that by using other atoms such as phosphorus, and sometimes nitrogen or sulfur, instead of chlorine, they could make other types of pesticides. Today chemical companies produce thousands of different products to control insects, weeds, fungi, nematodes, and other pests. Although 90% of Americans use pesticides around their house and yard, farmers use the majority of the pesticides that are sold.

Some of the common insecticides are listed below. It is important to note that today we use more herbicides than insecticides.

Class of Insecticide	Name
Organochlorides (chlorinated hydrocarbons)	• Aldrin • Chlordane • DDD • DDT • Dieldrin • Endrin • Heptachlor • Lindane • Toxaphene
Organophosphates	• Diazinon • Malathion • Parathion • Methyl-parathion
Carbamates	• Sevin® (carbaryl) • Maneb
Naturally occurring (organic pesticides)	• Nicotine Sulfate • Pyrethrum • Rotenone

Not All Are Pests

It is important to remember that all insects, rodents, worms and fungi are not pests. In fact most are helpful. Of the 82,500 species of insects that are estimated to occur in North America, about 10,000 are considered to be pests. This means that only one out of eight insects is a pest. Several of the remaining seven insects are beneficial to humans.

Many worms and fungi are found in "healthy" soil and are important for the process of decay. Penicillin, streptomycin and other antibiotics come from fungi in the soil. Certain molds are responsible for the flavors of different cheeses. Some fungi are necessary for the production of certain foods. Yeast is a fungus used in the making of wine and bread.

One-third of our diet consists of crops that are pollinated by honeybees. The major food in the diet of dairy cattle is alfalfa. The flower structure of some plants, like alfalfa, prevents pollination by wind or other insects. These crops have become dependent upon pollination by honeybees.

Before adding chemicals to the environment, it is important to study their effects upon organisms in the soil, insects, birds, fish and mammals. If this is not done, we may wipe out organisms that are helpful to humans when we only intended to kill an organism we considered a pest.

Methane (Nonchlorinated Hydrocarbon)

Chloroform (Chlorinated Hydrocarbon)

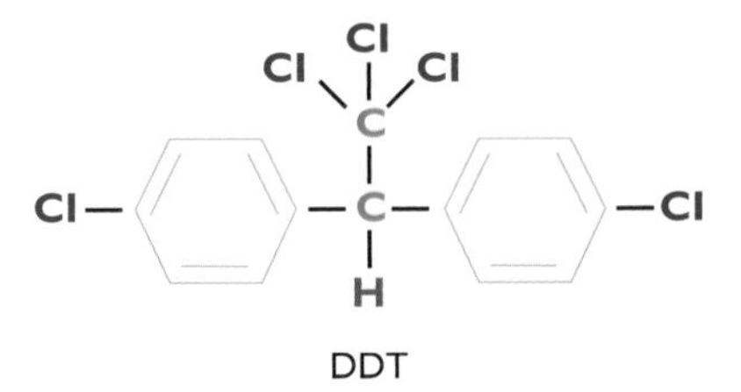

DDT

The picture-perfect lawn that consists of only one kind of grass is more susceptible to attack by fungi and insect pests.

Monoculture—An Invitation to a Picnic

At a picnic you might hear someone say, "Who invited the ants?" It seems the ants have an excellent ability to find food, and there is always plenty of food at a picnic. Farmers and gardeners create picnics for ants and other insects. We call them pests.

A **monoculture**, the growing of one plant species over a large area, provides an abundant food supply for the insects. When there is more food available, more insects survive and reproduce. Scientists have estimated that in some corn fields there have been more than 60,000 European corn borers per acre (0.4 ha).

Humans also create monocultures on golf courses and lawns. Golf courses are treated with large amounts of chemicals to control sod webworm and other pests that feed on turf grass. Well-manicured lawns that support only one kind of grass may be heavily treated with chemicals to control pests.

The farmer who spends long hours in the field and does not have time to pay much attention to the lawn is less likely to have problems with pests or diseases. A closer look at the lawn will probably show that, unlike the cornfield, it is not a monoculture. It has many different types of grasses, and probably some broad-leaf weeds.

Herbicides are used to prevent the invasion of dandelions and other broad-leaf weeds.

Problems Caused by Pesticides

When synthetic pesticides first appeared, doctors had visions of no more diseases spread by pests. Farmers imagined a day when no more pests would harm their crops. Unfortunately, it was only a vision.

At first it was easy to see the significant benefits of synthetic pesticides. DDT saved many lives that would have been lost because of diseases carried by pests. The quantity and quality of food were dramatically improved by the use of pesticides. Without the use of pesticides, an estimated 30–35% of a crop is lost before harvest. Another 10–15% is lost while the food is in storage.

In 1962, the book *Silent Spring* was published. Rachel Carson wrote the book so that the public would be aware of the problems associated with the use of pesticides. The book caused quite an uproar in the pesticide industry. The publication of *Silent Spring* stimulated an evaluation of the risks of using pesticides. Today we are much more aware of some of the problems caused by pesticides. One problem is the creation of superbugs.

Prior to planting, agricultural pesticides are applied to control root worm or other insects in the soil.

Superbugs:

People expected the pesticides to eliminate all pests. That didn't happen. Even before it was approved for public use in 1947, some houseflies were surviving when sprayed with DDT. Changes occur in the DNA of some flies that enable them to produce enzymes that detoxify or make the pesticide harmless. These genetic changes make the insect **resistant**—immune to the pesticide.

Resistance to Pesticides:

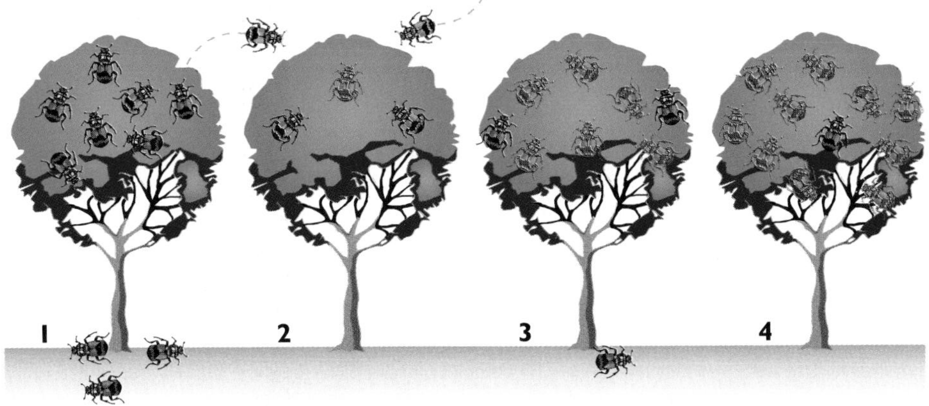

Insect Resistant to Pesticide

Insect NOT Resistant to Pesticide

New Generation Insect Resistant to Pesticide

1. When insects are sprayed, a few of the insects become resistant to the pesticide.

2. The resistant insects may mate with other resistant insects that survived the spray, or they may mate with insects that arrive from areas that have not been sprayed.

3. The new generation of insects will have many more resistant insects. Unaffected by the spray, they breed and produce offspring.

4. More of the insects in the next generation are resistant to the pesticide. When a new spray is used, the process begins again.

Each time a pesticide is used, more insects become resistant to it. These resistant insects breed and produce offspring that are resistant to the pesticide. The life cycle of an insect is short, and they reproduce quickly. During one season there may be as many as six generations of boll weevils in the cotton fields of the southern United States. Most pests develop resistance to a chemical within five years, but sometimes it takes only one season.

Today more than 535 species of insects and mites, and 210 plant diseases, are resistant to pesticides. This number has doubled since 1965. Ten species of insects are resistant to every group of insecticides known. As the use of herbicides increases, weeds become more resistant. Scientists have identified more than 200 weeds that have developed resistance to one class of herbicides.

Persistent Pesticides:

Plastic is persistent; paper is not. If we bury plastic, we can come back years later and dig it up. It will be very much the same as it was when we buried it. If we bury paper, organisms in the soil will break it down, and later when we dig, we will find nothing that looks like paper.

Chemicals that can be broken down by organisms in the environment are **biodegradable**. Like paper, some pesticides are biodegradable. Other pesticides are not easily broken down by organisms in the environment. Like plastic, these pesticides are found in the soil many years after they were used. We say these pesticides are **persistent pesticides**.

Think About It

About one million bug zappers are sold in the United States each year. Bug zappers, which attract bugs to a light and electrocute them using an electrified grid, are like broad-spectrum pesticides. They kill many kinds of pests, both beneficial insects and bothersome ones, which are attracted to light.

Researchers at the University of Delaware found that only 31 of the 13,789 bugs killed in 6 electric traps during a summer were insects that bite or suck blood. After learning the results of a study at Kansas State University, you might want to move the zapper away from your picnic table. The study found that zapping bugs creates a spray of bacteria and viruses that can extend up to 6 feet.

You might want to consider replacing the bug zapper with a bat house. A single little brown bat can catch 600 mosquitoes in just one hour.

bat house.

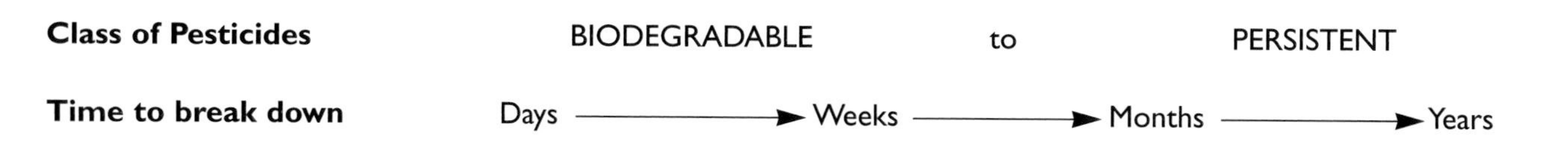

Some pesticides are more easily broken down than others. Some are broken down in a few days. Others are broken down more slowly and remain in the soil for a few weeks or months. The more persistent a pesticide is, the longer it will remain in the environment.

The pesticides classified as **chlorinated hydrocarbons** are extremely persistent. They remain in the environment for many years after they are used. DDT was the pesticide most frequently found in the 1998 FDA market basket survey of 261 different foods. The use of DDT was banned in the United States in 1972, 26 years before the survey.

WWW

For a list and photos of herbicide-resistant weeds, visit: www.weedscience.com.

DDT evaporates from the fields where it is sprayed and is carried by wind and water. Some of the pesticide hitchhikes on dust particles until the rain or snow brings it down. DDT has been spread by the winds and deposited throughout the world by rain and snow. It has been discovered in birds, seals and fish in Antarctica.

Like other animals, humans carry DDT and other chlorinated hydrocarbons in their body fat. A study of 75 humans, who showed no symptoms related to DDT exposure, reported an average of 5.3 ppm of DDT stored in body fat. Infants who are breast-fed are exposed to DDT through their mother's milk. DDT is found in higher concentrations in human milk than in cow's milk or other foods.

At first it had seemed that persistence was good because farmers would not need to reapply the pesticides so often. This would save them both time and money. Then we began to learn of another problem—bioaccumulation (also called biomagnification or bioconcentration).

Bioaccumulation:

Only very small amounts of the pesticides that are chlorinated hydrocarbons dissolve in water, but they easily dissolve in fat. This was first thought to be a major advantage because the pesticides would not be easily washed away by rain.

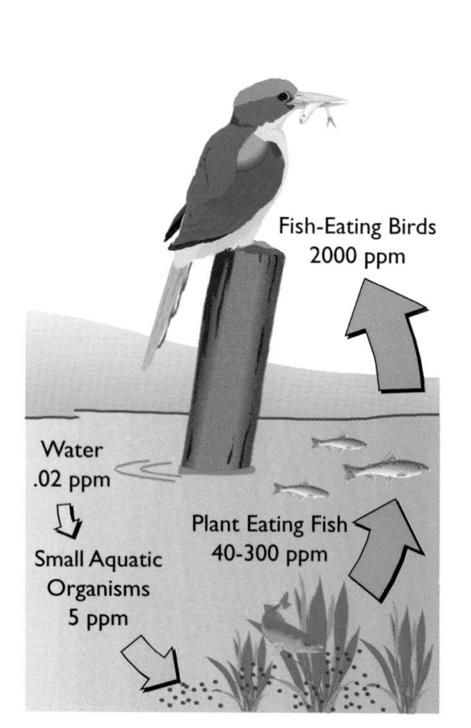

A study (1957) of organisms in California's Clear Lake showed how bioaccumulation of pesticides occurs.

DDT was sprayed on marshlands and croplands. It was carried with runoff into lakes and streams and much of the DDT was deposited in the soil at the bottom of the water or absorbed by organisms living in the water. Cell membranes are made out of protein and fat. The chlorinated hydrocarbons were easily absorbed through the cell membranes of the aquatic organisms.

Few organisms have the enzymes that are needed to break down the pesticides. Since the chemicals dissolve in fat more easily than water, they are stored in the body fat rather than being excreted with wastes through the kidneys. The pesticides accumulate in the organism's body tissues.

As the pesticide moves up the food chain, it becomes more and more concentrated in the body tissues. This is called **bioaccumulation**. When water contains toxic chemicals like DDT, the small aquatic organisms absorb the toxin and store it in their body fat. Fish convert 10 grams of small aquatic organisms into 1 gram of body mass. If the fish cannot break down the pesticide, all of the pesticide that is in the 10 grams of food is then stored in the 1 gram of mass the fish gains.

The populations of some species of fish-eating birds, such as ospreys and eagles, declined. One colony of ospreys, in Connecticut, declined from 200 breeding pairs in 1938 to 12 pairs in 1965. Scientists frequently found broken eggs and eggs that did not hatch. The egg yolks in the unhatched eggs contained high levels of DDT. The fat in the egg yolk provides energy for the developing bird. Evidently DDT interfered with the normal development of the egg. High levels of DDT were also found in fish eggs that did not develop normally.

From collections in museums, scientists obtained eggs, which had been laid before DDT was used as a pesticide. When they compared the shells of these eggs to the broken eggshells collected from the nests, scientists found that the broken eggs had shells that were much thinner. It appeared that DDT was preventing the deposit of calcium in the eggshell.

Birds that fed in areas that had been sprayed with DDT, soon died of insecticide poisoning. In areas that had not been sprayed, the robins were not affected.

DDT has not been used in the United States since 1972. The level of DDT in the water has declined, and the populations of fish-eating birds are once again on the rise. During the 1970s bald eagles were seen in only 39 states. Today they can be found in every state except Hawaii, and their populations have increased significantly. In July 1999, President Clinton proposed removal of the eagle from the lists of threatened and endangered species.

DDT also affected other food chains. Elm trees were sprayed with DDT to control Dutch elm disease. DDT was used to kill the elm bark beetle that spreads the Dutch elm disease fungus. Scientists hoped that this would stop the spread of the disease.

Since DDT is not easily dissolved in water, rains did not wash it away. As the leaves fell and decayed, the DDT accumulated in the layers of organic matter under the trees. When earthworms fed on the decaying matter, they absorbed and accumulated DDT. Robins returned in the spring and began feeding on the worms. Birds that fed in areas that had been sprayed soon died of insecticide poisoning. In areas that had not been sprayed, the robins were not affected.

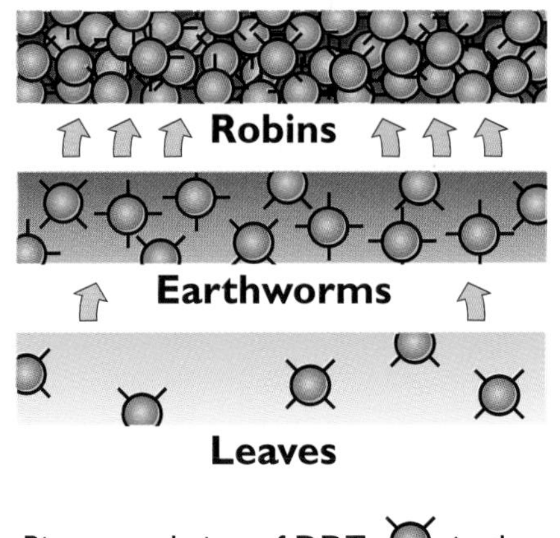

Bioaccumulation of DDT  in the Food Chain.

Pesticides Create Pests:

There are two approaches to killing pests—the rifle approach and the shotgun approach. Imagine yourself as a tiny hunter. Armed with a tiny rifle, you climb aboard your tiny airplane and take off for the nearby potato field. As your copilot flies about the plants you take careful aim and fire. One after another, the striped potato beetles fall from the plants. **Selective pesticides** are like this hunter. Selective pesticides kill only one type of organism. The pesticide does not affect other types of organisms.

Many pesticides are not selective. They do not search out and destroy just one kind of pest. They are like the tiny hunter with a shotgun. Some pellets hit the potato beetle while others hit Ladybird beetles, or other

Fish eating birds like this kingfisher, bioaccumulate pesticides.

beneficial insects. **Broad-spectrum pesticides** kill many different kinds of pests, but they also kill beneficial insects.

Pesticides sometimes make a major pest out of a minor one by eliminating its predators. This was the case with the bollworm. The boll weevil was a major pest in cotton fields. As farmers attempted to destroy the boll weevil, they also destroyed the natural predators of the bollworm. Without predators, the bollworm became a major pest.

Insect pests have predators that keep the population in balance. As the pest population increases, the population of predator insects also rises. The rise in the population of predators occurs more slowly because the predator population depends upon the pests for food. When the food supply (the plants) of the pest becomes limited, the pest population begins to decline. Fewer pests mean less food for the predator insects, and the predator population declines.

This rise and fall of insect populations continues to occur until it is upset. Such an upset occurs when a broad-spectrum insecticide is used. The populations of both kinds of insects experience a drastic decline when the pesticide is used. The surviving pests find themselves in a world with fewer natural enemies. The pests multiply quickly, and a pest population explosion occurs.

3.8 Questions for Study and Discussion:

1. Define the following terms: **VOCABULARY**

avicide	chlorinated hydrocarbon	nematicide	pyrethrum
bioaccumulation	DDT	nicotine sulfate	resistant
biodegradable	fungicide	organic pesticide	rotenone
Bordeaux mixture	herbicide	organophosphate	selective pesticide
broad-spectrum pesticide	insecticide	persistent pesticide	
carbamate	monoculture	pest	
		pesticide	

2. Give two reasons why certain insects are classified as pests.
3. Give examples of at least two pests that are carriers of disease.
4. Not all pests are insects; give examples of other organisms that are pests.

Miracle Chemicals

5. In what ways are nematicides, insecticides, and fungicides alike? What is a herbicide?
6. Give two examples of natural pesticides. What are the disadvantages of using these chemicals?
7. Identify the two types of insecticides that were developed from "nerve gases."
8. Why were the chlorinated hydrocarbons so successful as pesticides?

Not All Are Pests

9. Are most insects pests? What percent of insects are pests?
10. Give three ways in which some fungi are helpful to humans.
11. A decrease in honeybees might mean a decrease in milk production. Explain.

Monoculture—An Invitation to a Picnic

12. What is a monoculture?

13. How does the practice of monoculture increase the population of insects?
14. Why do pests and disease often attack some lawns and golf courses?

Problems Caused by Pesticides

15. How was DDT helpful to humans?
16. Why was *Silent Spring* such an important book?
17. What changes occur in some insects that enable them to survive when sprayed with a pesticide?
18. Explain why insects develop resistance to pesticides more quickly than other pests such as "weeds"?
19. What characteristic of DDT and other insecticides makes them so easily stored in the body?
20. Since DDT is not easily dissolved in water, what happens to it when it is carried into a lake with runoff during a storm?
21. Give two ways in which DDT decreased the population of some fish-eating birds.
22. How did DDT affect the robins?
23. Why do people, robins, and fish-eating birds have more pesticides stored in their bodies than other organisms do, such as crabs and earthworms?
24. What do we call pesticides that are not selective?
25. In a natural environment, what are the limiting factors that limit the number of pests?
26. Why does use of a broad-spectrum pesticide lead to an increased pest population?

Environmental Challenge: Golf Courses — How Green?

Biologists at New York's Department of Environmental Conservation documented numerous cases of birds killed by application of insecticides on golf courses. Seven hundred brant geese died after feeding on a Nassau County, New York, golf course that had been treated with the pesticide diazinon. The U.S. Fish and Wildlife Service has documented more than 150 bird die-offs caused by diazinon. The EPA has banned the use of diazinon on golf courses and sod farms.

In 1990, the Environmental Protection Bureau of the New York Attorney General's Office conducted a survey of 52 golf courses on Long Island. The results of the survey found that 21 different herbicides, 20 fungicides, and 8 insecticides were used each year. The pesticides used contained a total of 50,000 pounds (22,727 kg) of active ingredients. The application rate was 18 pounds per treated acre per year. The application rate of pesticides applied on agricultural land was 2.7 pounds per treated acre per year.

Interview the manager of a golf course near your home.

Find out:

- How many different types of pesticides are used and how do the pesticides used today differ from those used 10 to 15 years ago?
- Are pesticides used on a regular basis or, if not, how is the course monitored to determine the need for application?
- Who applies the pesticides and what steps are taken to ensure their safety?
- Are fertilizers applied on a regular schedule or are soil tests taken to determine the fertilizer needs?
- What type of fertilizer is used?
- Are there fish in the "water hazards" (ponds) and, if so, do fish sometimes die in the summer?
- Do streams flow through the golf course and, if so, how does the water quality above the golf course compare to the quality below the course?
- How many different species of birds have been observed on the grounds?
- Bluebirds prefer cavities in trees near open areas. Have any bluebirds been observed?
- Do you think it would be a good idea to establish a bluebird trail by placing nesting boxes on trees along the fairways?

A Lady Named Carson

OBJECTIVES

- **Contrast** the message in Rachel Carson's book with the message of other books about pesticide use.
- **Compare** pesticide use prior to the publication of *Silent Spring* with pesticide use today.
- **Infer** how Rachel Carson, if she were living, would view our use of pesticides today.

Rachael Carson—for four years she did her homework and then she wrote a book. The subject was pesticides.

"By their very nature, chemical controls are self-defeating, for they have been devised and applied without taking into account the complex biological systems against which they have been blindly hurled."
RACHEL CARSON
in *Silent Spring*

An ecology book, published in 1962, became a bestseller. It stunned the world. *Saturday Review* said that no science-fiction nightmare could be its equal. The Chicago Daily News said that it is "must reading for every responsible citizen." The book was *Silent Spring*, and the author was Rachel Carson. Rachel Carson was a scientist, and the book was an account of what pesticides were doing to the balance of nature.

Rachel Carson had been editor-in-chief of the U.S. Fish and Wildlife Service's publications. As she read about the accomplishments of DDT, she became concerned about the possible long-term effects the pesticide might have on organisms in the environment. In the 1950s research indicated that pesticides were causing problems, but most of the public was not yet aware of this information.

Rachel Carson felt the public should know, and she set out to write a book about the use of pesticides. Her goals were to inform the public and to get the attention of government officials. It took her 5 years to research and write *Silent Spring*.

Ms. Carson was known as a responsible scientist, and the list of references that supported her statements filled 30 pages. When one chemical company asked the publisher to reconsider its plans to publish the book, the publisher hired an independent scientist to check the facts. The facts were confirmed, and the book was published.

Any discussion of pesticides prior to the publication of *Silent Spring* had been based on economics. Greater use of pesticides allowed farmers to grow bigger and better crops. Pesticides were cheap and easy to use, and they increased the profits for the farmer. Chemical companies and the United States Department of Agriculture promoted pesticides with the claim that: "Unrestricted use of pesticides is necessary to grow the food to feed, and the fibers to clothe, the world's millions of people."

The unrestricted use of pesticides and the problems they cause were very controversial subjects. Rachel Carson was the first person to approach the issue from an ecological point of view. Some scientists supported Ms. Carson; others referred to her as "an emotional woman from the garden club." Rachel Carson was not "an emotional woman." She was a professional who had done her homework and knew her subject.

Her book survived the controversy and became the stimulus for amendments to the Federal Insecticide, Fungicide and Rodenticide Act—the law that regulates pesticide use. Before her death in 1964, Rachel Carson offered these recommendations about pesticides to a Senate Subcommittee:

- That all community, state and federal spraying programs be legally required to give adequate advance notice to citizens who will be affected.
- That citizens who are inconvenienced or damaged by their neighbor's spraying be able to "seek appropriate redress."
- That new programs in medical research and education of the medical profession be supported.
- That registration of chemicals be determined by all agencies concerned rather than only the United States Department of Agriculture.
- That new pesticides be approved only when there is no chemical already available or no other method that will work.
- That the government give full support to research on new methods of pest control which will reduce or eliminate the need for chemicals.

Rachel Carson did not campaign against the use of all chemical pesticides, nor did she feel that all environmental problems are due to the misuse of pesticides. If she had been one of the authors of the Bill of Rights, she would have included "the right of every person to be free from poisons distributed by private or public individuals." She felt that this right had been left out only because our forefathers could not foresee the problems that would accompany pesticides (and other toxic chemicals).

Perhaps no other person has influenced environmental policies as much as Rachel Carson. When she died, two years after the publication of *Silent Spring*, Senator Abraham Ribicoff paid her tribute from the floor of the United States Senate. He said: "... this gentle lady ... aroused people everywhere to be concerned with one of the most significant problems of mid-twentieth century life—man's contamination of his environment."

With the publication of *Silent Spring*, Rachel Carson had accomplished both of her goals. She had informed the public and had begun an environmental movement. She had also gotten the attention of government officials. Ten years after the publication of *Silent Spring*, DDT was banned and a new government agency had been created—the Environmental Protection Agency.

Did You Know?

The Chinese may have made the first insecticide in the first century B.C. when they used powdered chrysanthemums to kill fleas. Today these natural insecticides are called pyrethrums. Synthetic compounds, called pyrethroids have been developed that are more effective and less toxic to mammals. Although they are less toxic than many pesticides, they should be used with caution. Some people have allergic reactions to these compounds. Severe poisonings have occurred in infants because they do not have the enzymes to break down these compounds.

Washington Monument, reflected, Washington D.C.

3.9 Questions for Study and Discussion:

1. What was the name of the book written by Rachel Carson?
2. What was the topic discussed in the book?
3. Why did Ms. Carson write a book on this subject?
4. Were the statements in Ms. Carson's book supported by fact?
5. Why do farmers use pesticides?
6. According to the USDA, and the chemical companies that manufacturer them, are pesticides needed? If so, what for?
7. How was Rachel Carson's book different from other books that discussed pesticides?
8. If Rachel Carson had been one of the authors of the Bill of Rights, what "right" would she have added?
9. What were Rachel Carson's goals? Did she accomplish her goals?

Pesticides—How Safe Are They?

OBJECTIVES

- **Identify** factors that contribute to pesticide poisoning.
- **Relate** evidence that pesticide use today is safer than pesticide use prior to 1970.
- **Create** a list of conditions that will reduce environmental damage caused by pesticide applications.
- **Explain** why pesticide use poses higher risks for certain groups of people.
- **Evaluate** the role of consumer opinion in pesticide use.

Firefighters need to know where pesticides are stored.

"Our nation enjoys the safest, most abundant food supply in the world.... Nonetheless, as our scientific understanding of the health risks and environmental effects of pesticides improves, it is becoming increasingly clear that foods can be made even safer, especially for children."

CAROL BROWNER, Administrator
Environmental Protection Agency

The 1970s gave us a new awareness of the problems that were caused by the use of human-made pesticides. Laboratory tests showed some pesticides were causing tumors, liver disorders and changes in the chromosomes of laboratory mice. But the problems extend beyond pesticide resistance, broken eggshells and tumors in mice.

Pesticide Poisoning

Acute pesticide poisoning is a major global health problem. A 1990 World Health Organization/United Nation's report estimated that 1 million people worldwide may suffer acute unintentional pesticide poisoning each year. Inadequate knowledge of safe practices and lack of suitable protective clothing for use by workers contributes to higher rates of poisonings in less developed countries.

Pesticide poisonings are under-reported illnesses. An illness may not be correctly identified as pesticide poisoning, even in developed countries. Health care providers receive little training in the diagnosis of pesticide-related illnesses. Pesticide poisoning may not be recognized because many of the symptoms—sweating, headache, fatigue, nausea and diarrhea—are also the symptoms of other illnesses. In warm environments the symptoms may be mistaken for heat exhaustion.

The American Association of Poison Control Centers reported 22,433 cases of pesticide poisoning in 1996. Nearly one-third of the victims were children under 6 years old. These cases included poisonings caused by common types of disinfectants found in the home. The actual number of poisonings is thought to be much higher because many cases are not reported to poison control centers.

Illness in pets after a pest control application in a home may be a sign that an illegal pesticide has been used. Indoor spraying of methyl parathion has killed both pets and people. Three people died in Mississippi when family members sprayed homes with methyl parathion, an agricultural insecticide. In 1994–1996, unlicensed pest control operators illegally sprayed methyl parathion in more than 1000 homes in several states. Several thousand people were relocated, and cleanup costs exceeded $70 million. Ten people were arrested.

Agriculture uses 80% of all pesticides in the U.S. and the workers are most at risk of acute poisoning or even death. California's Pesticide Illness Surveillance Program, which is considered the best in the nation, reported 4,670 occupational (workplace) cases of illness "likely due to pesticides" between 1991 and 1995. California has the nation's most comprehensive program to regulate pesticide use.

For many uses, organophosphate and carbamate pesticides have replaced the older chlorinated hydrocarbons. In 1997, they were applied to 70% of the crops treated with insecticides in the United States. The organophosphates parathion and methyl parathion are inexpensive pesticides that are highly effective against a broad range of insects, but they are extremely toxic to agricultural workers.

Agricultural workers need information about the chemicals they are using, and they need to understand the risks of exposure to the chemicals. Since 1994, EPA regulations have required employers to train workers in pesticide safety, post safety information, and place warning signs that prohibit entry into sprayed areas for 12 to 72 hours, depending upon the pesticide used. The notices must be posted in English and Spanish.

With the exception of agricultural workers, children who live in agricultural areas are likely to be exposed to higher levels of pesticides than any other group of people. This increased exposure is due to pesticide residue on clothing, in dust, pesticide drift from aerial spraying, and possibly contamination of water supplies. This exposure may affect the development of children.

A study compared 4- and 5-year-old children in the Sonora's Yaqui Valley in Mexico, where pesticides are heavily used, with children in Yaqui ranching villages, where the only major exposure is to DDT sprayed by the government to control malaria. None of the children exhibited obvious symptoms of pesticide poisoning, but those who lived in the valley demonstrated significantly less stamina, 30-minute recall, hand-eye coordination and drawing ability than the children from the ranching villages.

The Regulation of Pesticides

Pesticides were first approved under the **Federal Insecticide, Fungicide and Rodenticide (FIFR) Act of 1947**. This law required manufacturers to test the pesticide for short-term or acute effects. In 1972, Congress amended the Act to require testing for long-term or chronic effects.

Until 1970, the control of pesticide use was the responsibility of the U. S. Department of Agriculture (USDA). The USDA promoted the use of chemical pesticides as an effective way to increase yields and make greater profits. In 1970, the responsibility of regulating pesticide use was taken away from the USDA and assigned to the Environmental Protection Agency (EPA).

In 1972, the U.S. government banned the use of DDT because of its effects on birds and because of its presence in human tissues. The EPA began a review of the active ingredients in pesticides. By the end of the 1970s, most of the chlorinated hydrocarbons had been banned or their use severely restricted by the EPA. Since 1972, more than 50 other pesticides have been banned or their use severely restricted.

The EPA must register new pesticides that are marketed or used in the United States. Many new pesticides have been registered. There are more than 89,000 products containing pesticides in the California Department of Pesticide Regulation database.

Think About It

Not all misuse or overuse of pesticides can be blamed on agriculture. In the United States, homeowners use five times more pesticides per acre on their lawns than farmers do on their own fields. About 67 million pounds of pesticides are applied to lawns every year.

Think About It

Thailand's farmers are exporting more food, but pesticide poisoning is a widespread problem. A nationwide study by the Thai Ministry of Public Health found that more than 69,000 farmers (17% of those tested) had abnormally low cholinesterase enzyme levels. A low enzyme level is evidence of overexposure to organophosphate and carbamate pesticides. The Material Safety Data Sheet for parathion includes this information: "Persons who work with organophosphate materials for long periods of time should have frequent blood tests of their cholinesterase levels. If the cholinesterase level falls below a critical point, no further exposure should be allowed until it returns to normal.

Did You Know?

More than 800 antimicrobial products are currently registered with the EPA. These products destroy bacteria, viruses, or fungi on inanimate objects or surfaces. Antiseptics and germicides that are used in or on living humans and animals are considered drugs and controlled by the Food and Drug Administration (FDA).

WWW

To find the Pesticide Information Profile on the active ingredients in pesticides that you use in your home or garden, visit http://ace.orst.edu/info/extoxnet.

Environmental Challenge: Genetically Modified Insecticide

Scientists modified a naturally occurring insect-killing virus to make a fast-acting microbial pesticide. They gave the virus a gene from the African brown scorpion. The genetically engineered virus kills the caterpillars in 2-3 days. Scientists have not yet been able to produce this virus in commercial quantities.

- If they succeed, what additional information should the EPA consider when making a decision about registration of this microbial pesticide?

Before a pesticide can be registered, the EPA must evaluate the risks and benefits of its use. The risks include danger to humans and the environment. The benefits include protection of crops from pests and the protection of animals, including humans, from disease. The law requires the EPA to balance the risks to the environment and to human health with the benefits of using the pesticide.

Manufacturers spend several years and several million dollars on testing programs to meet EPA guidelines. The decision to register, or not to register, a pesticide is based on results of many tests. The tests must determine the acute and chronic toxicity of the pesticide—whether it could cause cancer, birth defects, nerve damage, or changes in chromosomes. Tests must determine the effects on mammals, birds, aquatic organisms, and bees. The EPA also wants to know what happens to the pesticide in the soil and in surface and groundwater.

Reducing the Risks

Although the chlorinated hydrocarbons (DDT, chlordane, heptachlor) were not very toxic to humans, they are **persistent pesticides**. This persistence increased the risk of damage from their continued use, and the EPA has banned their use. These pesticides remain in the environment for many years posing a risk for wildlife and humans.

Manufacturers produced new **biodegradable** pesticides (pyrethroids, carbamates and organophosphorus compounds) that break down more easily. These pesticides were promoted as "safer." The risk of bioaccumulation in the food chain is reduced, but accumulation is not the only risk.

At first scientists thought that, since the pesticide breaks down quickly, the risk to the consumer would be very small. Now scientists are learning that some of the breakdown products are more toxic than the parent chemicals. Still, the use of biodegradable pesticides presents less risk to the consumer than the use of persistent pesticides that will accumulate in the fatty tissues.

To reduce the risk during application of the pesticide, the EPA has restricted the use of some pesticides. Pesticides classified as **restricted-use** are only available to farmers and commercial applicators who have been certified by the state's department of agriculture. To be certified, a person must take a course in the proper use of chemicals and pass a written examination. They must demonstrate their understanding and ability to use information on the label.

Workers using the pesticide are also required by federal law to follow the directions on the container. This includes wearing protective clothing and sometimes a respirator and goggles. Some pesticides are easily absorbed through the skin even when washed with soap and water immediately after spraying. Wearing protective clothing to prevent pesticide poisoning can sometimes lead to other problems. When applying pesticides in hot weather, workers face two problems—pesticide poisoning and heat exhaustion.

The EPA requires the use of (Signal Words and Precautionary Statements of Hazards) on the labels of pesticides. The EPA, not the manufacturer of the pesticide, determines the words used.

EPA Toxicity Category	PA Required Signal Word	EPA-Required Precautionary Statements for Acute Oral Ingestion and Skin Absorption Hazards
I	DANGER (Skull and Crossbones) POISON	Fatal if swallowed or absorbed through skin. Do not get in eyes, or on clothing. Wear protective clothing and rubber gloves. Wash thoroughly with soap and water after handling and before eating or smoking. Remove contaminated clothing and wash before reuse.
II	WARNING	May be fatal if swallowed or if absorbed through skin. Do not get in eyes, on skin, or on clothing. Wear protective clothing and rubber gloves. Wash thoroughly with soap and water after handling and before eating or smoking. Remove contaminated clothing and wash before reuse.
III	CAUTION	Harmful if swallowed or absorbed through skin. Avoid contact with skin, eyes, or clothing. Wash thoroughly with soap and water after handling.

Following the directions also includes using the correct amount or "dose" of the pesticide. Manufacturers must prove that the concentration of pesticide recommended will kill the pest. Some people believe, "if a little is good, more will be better." When the amount of pesticide used is greater than the amount given in the directions, the pesticide present on the food may exceed the "safe" tolerance levels. Using more pesticide also increases the risk that the water supply may become contaminated, and wildlife may be poisoned.

People who apply pesticides need to check the weather report before applying them:

- Plants may be damaged by some pesticides if the temperature is too warm.
- Pesticides should not be sprayed when the wind will carry the chemical away from its target. Even when there is no wind, some of the pesticide enters the air by evaporation.
- If it rains soon after the pesticide is applied, the pesticide may be washed off the plant before it can kill the pests. If the pesticide is washed off the plant too quickly, it may contaminate bodies of water nearby.

When pesticides are sprayed on crops in the flowering stage, honeybees may be poisoned. Some state laws prevent the spraying of these pesticides while crops are in bloom, to protect the bees. More than 400,000 colonies are destroyed or damaged by pesticides each year. The number of bees killed can be decreased by:

- Selecting pesticides that are less toxic to bees,
- Spraying in the evening or at night when the honey bees are not collecting pollen, and
- Alerting the owners of the bee hives so that the hives can be moved or closed.

Even if these cautions are taken, some pesticides will kill bees. Manufacturers are packaging some pesticides in small capsules. The pesticide is slowly released as if it were a time-released cold medicine

STOP!

ALL PESTICIDES CAN BE HARMFUL TO HEALTH AND THE ENVIRONMENT IF MISUSED. READ THE LABEL CAREFULLY AND USE ONLY AS DIRECTED.

In the United States, agricultural pesticides are often applied by crop dusters.

Think About It

Professional football players always wear a helmet when playing football, but only 44% of farmers always wear gloves when working with pesticides. In some situations gloves can reduce exposure to pesticides by up to 99%. Unlined chemical-resistant gloves are essential to prevent exposure to pesticides, but the well-dressed farmer may also need coveralls, eye protection, and respiratory protection. This information is on the pesticide label.

capsule. The pesticide is effective for a longer period of time. This is an advantage to the farmer. It protects the workers from the poison, and it reduces the number of times they must spray, but it is more deadly to bees. The insecticide pellets are about the same size as pollen. They are picked up by the bee and carried back to the hive. Stored with the pollen, the pesticide continues to kill bees.

Parathion and methyl parathion are among the most acutely toxic pesticides registered by the EPA. Both of these organophosphates are now classified as "Restricted-use-Pesticides." Use of parathion is now limited to only 9 crops (alfalfa, barley, corn, cotton, canola, sorghum, soybeans, sunflower, and wheat). Equipment used to load and mix the pesticide must be in closed systems, and application must be by airplane. No hand labor is allowed in fields where parathion has been applied.

In 1999, the EPA re-evaluated methyl parathion and decided that its use posed unacceptable risks to workers and children. The EPA no longer allows the use of methyl parathion on fruit or on most vegetables that are hand-picked. Use is restricted to 24 crops, and application must be from closed cabs or cockpits.

When pesticides are used on crops that will be eaten by humans or other animals, it is important to follow the directions concerning "days to harvest." **Days-to-harvest** refers to the number of days between the last application of the pesticide and the day the crop can be legally harvested. Crops that are harvested too quickly after spraying may have pesticide residues that exceed the "safe" tolerance levels.

The farmer must allow the proper amount of time for the pesticide to break down before harvesting the crop. The time needed varies with the type of crop grown and the pesticide used. For example, a certain pesticide may be applied one day before harvesting potatoes, but not within four days of harvesting spinach. The manufacturer must include this information with the pesticide when it is sold.

Pesticides in Our Food

According to the National Academy of Sciences, there is "a potential concern" that some children may be ingesting unsafe amounts of pesticides. Certain foods containing pesticides make up a larger portion of a child's diet than an adult's diet, and developing bodies may be more sensitive to changes caused by pesticides. While the Academy found no evidence that pesticides in food have harmed children, scientists say that children may be at greater risk than adults.

Another concern is the effect of pesticides that are combined with other pesticides. Little is known about the effects of pesticides when they are combined with other pesticides. Laboratory studies test the effects of pesticides individually. The foods we eat may have been sprayed with several pesticides. There are more than 100 pesticides registered for use on apples.

The EPA is developing a testing program to screen pesticides for their effects on the endocrine system. If you think of your body as the marching band, the endocrine and nervous systems are the bandleaders. Without clear direction from the leaders, the musicians' motions are not synchronized. There are concerns that some pesticides may be "**endocrine disrupters**," interfering with hormonal messages.

The **Food Quality Protection Act (FQPA) of 1996** is an amendment to the Federal Insecticide, Fungicide and Rodenticide Act (FIFR) and the Federal Food, Drug and Cosmetic Act (FFDCA). This amendment requires the EPA to regulate all pesticides used on foods in a way that provides a "reasonable certainty of no harm." The EPA must set tougher standards to protect infants and children. The law also includes a consumer "right-to-know" clause.

By August 2006, the EPA must re-evaluate 9,721 pesticide tolerances which were in effect when the FQPA was passed. The **tolerance level** is the maximum amount of pesticide residue that is allowed in or on food, or in drinking water. In setting a tolerance level, the EPA must consider the amount of foods consumed by infants and children, their greater susceptibility to effects, and the combined exposure from all sources.

Once tolerance levels are set, the Food and Drug Administration monitors the pesticide levels in foods to be sure that they are below the tolerance level. The FDA conducts random tests, using a multiresidue method that tests for about 200 pesticides on imported and domestic foods. Imported foods must meet the same tolerance levels as domestic foods.

During 1998, the FDA analyzed samples of 3,860 imported foods sampled during its routine surveillance monitoring, and found no pesticide residues on 68%. Three percent violated residual tolerances. Based on one violation, the FDA may "detain without physical examination" other shipments of the food during the same growing season. During 1985-1995, more than 14,000 shipments of produce were stopped at the U.S. border because of excess pesticide residue.

The FDA's 1998 surveillance monitoring of domestic foods found no detectable residues on 65% of samples and 0.8% of samples with residues that violated tolerance levels. In a total diet study of table-ready foods, the FDA found 54 pesticides, but none exceeded the tolerance levels. The most frequently found pesticide was DDT, which was present in 21% of the foods. While DDT is no longer used in the U.S., its use continues in developing countries.

The 1995 marketplace survey in California found illegal pesticide residues on 1.64% of 5,502 samples. Most of the violations were for pesticides not registered for use on the crop sampled. In some cases the pesticide may have been in the soil from treatment of a previous crop or it may have drifted from a nearby field.

Pesticides in Our Water

Some water supplies in agricultural areas contain pesticides. Tolerance levels, called the **Maximum Contaminant Levels** (MCLs) are lower for water than for foods because they are based on the total amount consumed. It is expected that you will consume more water than broccoli, so water is not permitted to contain as much pesticide as broccoli.

The following warning is on the label of a herbicide made by Shell Chemical Company. "BLADEX is a pesticide which can move (seep or travel) through soil and can contaminate groundwater that may be used

Environmental Challenge: Particle Film Technology

Microscopic mineral particles sprayed on fruit trees can form a protective barrier that prevents attack by insects and diseases. Pests are unable to feed or lay eggs, but the particles do not harm beneficial insects like ladybugs and don't affect photosynthesis or pollination.

Particle film technology provides an alternative to synthetic pesticides in controlling insects and diseases. Kaolin is a natural mineral approved by the FDA as an indirect food additive. It is easily removed from plants by weathering or washing. In 1998, the EPA registered three particle film products. It exempted the particle film from pesticide-tolerance regulations.

- Do you think that the EPA should set tolerance levels for mineral particles?
- Which would you prefer, a pear treated with a particle film or a pear treated with synthetic pesticides?

Sekel pears—untreated/treated.

For more information about pesticides in food, visit: www.epa.gov/pesticides/food.

Environmental Challenge: HRC — Herbicide-Resistant Crops

Soybeans are the second most important cash crop in the United States. Soybean oils are found in a wide variety of foods, including margarine, baked goods, cake mixes, and chocolate. Soybean meal is used in livestock and poultry feed.

Monsanto has transplanted a gene from another plant to make soybeans resistant to its best-selling herbicide, Roundup.

- Make a list of potential positive and negative effects of this genetic modification of soybeans.
- Should growers and processors be required to keep genetically modified soybeans separate from other beans?
- Should the label on foods that are made with these genetically modified soybeans include a GM symbol to let consumers know that the soybeans contain genes that are not a natural part of the soybean plant?

as drinking water. BLADEX has been found in groundwater as a result of agricultural use. Users are advised not to apply BLADEX where the groundwater is close to the surface and where the soils are very permeable—well drained soils such as loamy sands."

In Suffolk County, Long Island, New York, the soil is sandy, and the groundwater is only a few feet below the surface. Well water is the only source of drinking water on the island. In 1979 more than 2,000 wells were found to contain a nematicide, Temik (aldicarb), that had been applied to the soil to control **nematodes**. Since its approval in 1975, the pesticide had been used to spray many of the 22,000 acres (8,800 hectares) of potato fields in Suffolk County.

It had been thought that aldicarb would break down in the soil before reaching the groundwater. Now we know that, at least in sandy or sandy loam soils, that does not happen. Since aldicarb was found in the wells on Long Island, it has been found in the groundwater in over 25 counties and 12 states at concentrations that exceed the MCL. In 1990, the manufacturer of Temik (aldicarb) announced a voluntary halt on its sale for use on potatoes, because of concerns about groundwater contamination.

The MCL, set by the New York State Department of Health for Temik in drinking water, is 7 parts per billion (ppb). More than 1,000 wells had levels of Temik above 7 ppb. One well had 515 ppb. The manufacturer provided filters for the contaminated wells. Aldicarb has a half-life of 5 to 10 days in pond water; its breakdown rate is considerably longer in groundwater. Three years after the ban, the pesticide was still present in the water from the contaminated wells.

Risks vs. Benefits

While products of technology provide certain benefits, they also carry certain risks. Airplanes and cars provide the benefit of speed, but there is always the risk of an accident. For every product of technology, we could make a list of risks and benefits.

There is no question that pesticides have saved millions of lives and billions of dollars worth of crops. It has been suggested that overpopulation would not be the problem it is today if pesticides had not saved so many lives. Pesticides benefit us by protecting us from disease and hunger, but the use of pesticides also carries certain risks.

When the EPA approves a pesticide, it must consider both the risks and the benefits of the product. Many people think the benefits of using pesticides justify the risks taken. Others think the risks are too great. While the risks from using poisonous chemicals cannot be eliminated, they can be reduced.

The Perfect Apple

Does the grower really need to use so many pesticides? At first, pesticides were used to protect crops from pests that might destroy them. Some pesticides are still used for that purpose. Other pesticides are used to improve quality. Consumers demand perfection.

It is not likely that the corn earworm will eat more than one or two rows of corn kernels. The rest of the ear of corn is still safe for human consumption, but many people are not willing to cut away the bad part. Consumers want perfect ears of corn, and growers spray with pesticides to perfect the corn.

Some insects that attack fruit do not affect the taste of the fruit, only the appearance. An example is the small insect called thrips. Thrips cause small rusty spots on the skin of oranges. They do not affect the fruit itself, but farmers may not be able to sell the oranges with rusty spots.

Some buyers will not accept fruit if it has more than 1% cosmetic damage. If the growers do find a buyer, they may have to accept a lower price for the blemished fruit. So the spraying continues, even on fruits and vegetables that are going to be crushed into juice.

These apples have not been sprayed with pesticides. Would you eat these apples?

Is There a Better Way?

At this time there is little evidence that the levels of pesticides generally found in the environment are hazardous to human health. This lack of evidence makes some people feel safe. Others are not so secure. They worry about exposing people to small amounts of pesticides. There is little reliable data on the long-term effects of exposure to small amounts of pesticide. Most health studies used short-term exposure to larger amounts of pesticide.

Some people feel that we are wasting time debating which level—10 ppb or 30 ppb—of a pesticide is a "safe" level. They feel that the best policy would be to reduce pesticide use as much as possible. Some pests can be controlled without the use of chemical pesticides. Where these methods are used, the use of pesticides has been drastically reduced. Some alternative methods of pest control are discussed in Section 3.12, IPM—A Better Way to Control Pests.

Did You Know?

The EPA is requiring new studies on approximately 140 pesticides that are thought to have neurotoxic effects. The studies are intended to increase protection for infants and children.

3.10 Questions for Study and Discussion:

1. Define the following terms: **VOCABULARY**

biodegradable	FQP Act of 1996
days-to-harvest	persistent pesticides
endocrine	restricted use
endocrine disrupters	tolerance level
FIFR Act of 1947	

2. What problems were revealed by laboratory studies of pesticides?
3. What problems were being caused by pesticides in the environment?

Pesticide Poisoning

4. List several reasons why pesticide poisoning is a major global health problem.
5. Why are pesticide poisonings often not reported?
6. What group of people is most at risk for acute pesticide poisoning?
7. What has the EPA done to protect farm workers from pesticide poisoning?
8. Which group of children is exposed to higher levels of pesticide and how might the exposure affect them?

The Regulation of Pesticides

9. What is the significance of the 1972 amendment to FIFR?
10. How did the regulation of pesticide use change in 1970?
11. In what class were most of the pesticides that were banned or restricted in the 1970s?
12. Identify the kinds of information that the EPA must evaluate before a pesticide can be restricted.

13. Identify four types of changes that might be observed in laboratory animals being tested for pesticides?
14. What types of organisms are tested for pesticides?

Reducing the Risks

15. Why were the organophosphates considered safer than the chlorinated hydrocarbons?
16. What is required of people who apply pesticides classified as restricted-use?
17. Which of the following words—CAUTION, DANGER or WARNING—is required on labels of the most toxic pesticides?
18. List three risks that are increased when the amount of pesticide applied is greater than the concentration recommended on the label.
19. What weather conditions should be avoided when applying pesticides?
20. How can the danger to bees be reduced?
21. How has the EPA reduced the risks associated with the use of parathion and methyl parathion?
22. Why is it important that a pesticide user know the information about the number of days-to-harvest?

Pesticides in Our Food

23. List three concerns that exist about the presence of pesticide residues in food.
24. What is the major goal of the Food Quality Protection Act of 1996?
25. What factors must the EPA consider when setting tolerance levels?
26. Do you think that domestic foods are safer to eat than imported foods? Explain.

Pesticides in Our Water

27. Why are levels of pesticides allowed in food higher than the levels allowed in water?
28. Explain why the use of BLADEX® has been restricted.
29. Identify two situations where pesticides should not be used.
30. Why didn't the pesticide Temik break down in the soil before reaching the groundwater in Suffolk County, Long Island?
31. Do you think that aldicarb should be banned or should it be a Restricted-Use pesticide?

Risks vs. Benefits

32. What are the benefits of using pesticides?
33. Do you think that the benefits of using pesticides outweigh the risks?

The Perfect Apple

34. Explain the statement: "You are one of the reasons why farmers use so many pesticides."
35. Would you be willing to use oranges with "rust spots," if the damage was only skin deep and the fruit was not affected?

Is There a Better Way?

36. Are the pesticides in the environment today harmful to human health? Are you sure? Explain.

Environmental Challenge: Insect Repellents

Should you or shouldn't you use insect repellents? That is the question that must be answered each year when bug season arrives. The active ingredient in 192 of the 212 insect repellents registered by the EPA is n,n-diethyl-3-methylbenzamide, commonly known as deet.

Deet was developed by the Department of Agriculture for the Army in 1946 and first approved for public use in 1957. Since deet was originally approved when government standards were less strict, the EPA recently re-evaluated deet and concluded that it is safe when used correctly. The EPA did require companies to make some changes in label directions and claims.

The benefit of using an insect repellant with deet is its ability to repel insects and ticks that may transmit disease. The Centers for Disease Control (CDC) receives nearly 10,000 reports of Lyme disease (transmitted by deer ticks) and 1,000 reports of encephalitis (transmitted by mosquitoes) each year. The CDC recommends the use of insect repellents when out-of-doors in areas where these diseases are present.

Soldiers depend upon deet and another insecticide, permethrin, as well as antimalarial drugs. In March 1993, there were 47 cases of malaria among U.S. troops in Somalia. Most were because people had not used insecticides or taken drugs. A computer model predicted that, without protection, there could have been 3,000 cases among 16,000 troops in just 60 days.

The Banning of Pesticides

"No one says you shouldn't worry about people first; but if you really do, you need to protect fish and wildlife. Fish and wildlife are more sensitive; they always die first."
TED WILLIAMS

OBJECTIVES

- ✓ **Relate** the conditions that cause the banning of a pesticide.
- ✓ **Describe** circumstances in which you would allow an exemption to the ban of a pesticide.
- ✓ **Explain** how exported pesticides used in other countries can affect people in the country that exported the pesticide.
- ✓ **Evaluate** the effects of a total ban on persistent pesticides.

The History of Heptachlor and Chlordane

Heptachlor and chlordane are chlorinated hydrocarbons. They were used extensively as insecticides in agriculture and in the home to control a variety of insects, including ants, cutworms, maggots, and termites. Use of chlordane is no longer allowed in the U.S., and heptachlor is restricted to one very limited use.

Animal studies reported liver tumors, decreased fertility, and decreased survival of offspring. Heptachlor breaks down to form heptachlor epoxide, which is more toxic and more persistent than heptachlor. It is highly toxic to aquatic organisms and it **bioaccumulates** in fish. There is insufficient data to evaluate its long-term effects on birds or other land animals.

Although information on health effects in humans is limited, the EPA classifies chlordane and heptachlor as probable human carcinogens. Inhaling these pesticides can affect the central nervous system causing abnormal behavior, tremors and convulsions. Ingesting the pesticides can cause changes in the liver and the blood. Heptachlor may also damage the kidneys and it may be transferred across a placenta and affect development of a fetus.

1978—Ban Proposed but...:

After nearly five years of hearings, the EPA cancelled nearly all registered uses of heptachlor and the use of chlordane on food crops. The use of existing supplies was allowed if certain restrictions were followed. Use would be phased out during the next five years. Some exemptions to the ban were allowed where no alternative pesticide was available.

1978—"Export Only" Registrations Granted:

Velsicol Chemical Corporation, Memphis, Tennessee, the only company in the world to produce chlordane and heptachlor, was granted "export only" registrations for two products: Velsicol Technical Chlordane and Technical Heptachlor. Between 1991 and 1995 at least 10,000,000 pounds (4,545,455 kg) of these pesticides were exported from the United States to Africa, Asia, South America and Northeastern Australia. According to Velsicol, the pesticides were used for crop protection in South America and for termite control in other countries.

1988—Prohibition with One Exception:

From 1983 to 1988, the only approved use of chlordane in the U.S. was for control of termites in homes. With one exception, the sale, distribution, and shipment of all cancelled products containing chlordane and heptachlor were prohibited in the United States.

The only commercial use of products containing heptachlor still permitted in the United States is to control fire ants in pad-mounted electric power transformers and in cable television and telephone cable boxes. Homeowners are allowed to use existing products that contain heptachlor for termite control.

1995—Registrations Cancelled:

Velsicol Chemical Corporation requested voluntary cancellation of "export only" registrations granted in 1978.

1997—Production Ceases:

Velsicol Chemical Corporation announced that it was permanently ceasing production of chlordane and heptachlor and that it would not make the technology available to any other company.

An Exemption Caused Trouble in Hawaii

The pineapple industry of Hawaii was granted an exemption from the original EPA ban of the insecticide heptachlor. Pineapples were grown on more than 11,000 acres (4,400 ha) in Hawaii. The mealy bug is an insect pest that damages the pineapple plant. The bug feeds on the pineapple plant and produces a substance called honeydew that is a favorite food of a certain species of ant.

The ants protect the mealy bug from their natural predators (ladybird beetles, wasps, and lacewings). No insecticide was effective against the mealy bug, so pineapple growers attacked the ants. The growers said heptachlor was the only insecticide effective against the ants, so the EPA gave the growers permission to continue using heptachlor.

The chopped leaves of the pineapple were fed to dairy cows until tests showed bioaccumulation of heptachlor.

When the pineapples were harvested, the leaves of the plants were chopped and fed to dairy cows. The EPA set certain guidelines for growers to follow. The maximum amount of heptachlor that could be sprayed was less than two pounds per acre. The chopped leaves were to be stored for one year before feeding. Both the chopped leaves and the milk had to be tested for pesticide levels.

The leaves were never tested, and the milk was only tested twice a year. In 1982, samples of milk were found to contain 2.7 ppm heptachlor. This was far above the .03 ppm tolerance level that had been set. Dairy products were recalled. The sale of milk, butter, ice cream, cottage cheese and yogurt was banned.

The feeding of the pineapple leaves—"green chop"—was stopped and the use of heptachlor was banned. A year later, in 1983, the cows were still producing milk with high levels of heptachlor. It may be difficult to identify heptachlor as the cause of any future health problems that occur. Tests of milk from Hawaiian women showed the presence of several other pesticides including DDT, DDE (a breakdown product of DDT), chlordane and dieldrin.

A Costly Mistake in the Midwest

It was March 1986. Approximately 100 dairy farmers in Arkansas, Oklahoma and Missouri were told that they could no longer sell their milk. It was contaminated with the pesticide heptachlor. Thousands of gallons of milk were recalled from a region that included portions of eight different states.

The dairy farmers were surprised to learn about the contamination because none of them had used heptachlor. The FDA discovered the heptachlor in a feed supplement, during routine tests on feed produced by Valley Feeds in Van Buren, Arkansas. The supplement is normally a cheap source of feed for dairy cattle, but this time buying the less expensive feed was a costly mistake.

Grain used to make alcohol was contaminated with the pesticide. The alcohol was not intended for human consumption; it was used in the production of gasohol. The part of the grain that remains after the alcohol is produced is called mash. The mash still contains nutrients and is used as a supplement for cattle feed. Unaware that the mash was contaminated, Valley Feeds bought it and then sold it to the dairy farmers.

The farmers were concerned about the health of their families and about the possibility of losing their farms. Their income depended upon the sale of the milk. The heptachlor contamination did not produce any short-term health effects in humans. Infants, whose liver and immune system were still developing, were at greatest risk.

Thousands of gallons of milk were recalled when tests showed that it contained heptachlor.

A Deadly Mistake in Florida

During the 1998 Christmas bird count, a record 173 species of birds were observed on Lake Apopka in central Florida. By March it was obvious that something was terribly wrong: the fish-eaters (including great blue herons, great egrets, wood storks, and white pelicans) were dying. The events that created the massive bird-kill had begun more than 50 years earlier.

Vegetable growers had been allowed to **dike** and drain the saw grass marshland around the lake. They grew three crops each year in the rich muck soil. To protect sweet corn from earworms and fall armyworms, farmers sprayed with DDT. One farmer claimed he got 98% control by spraying everyday. The fields were irrigated with lake water, and they were flooded in summer for weed and nematode control. When the water was pumped back into the lake, it carried a load of pesticides and massive amounts of phosphorus, which stimulated the growth of aquatic plants.

The Florida legislature decided the lake should be restored. The farmers were paid for their land so that the wetlands could be replaced. For the first time ever, the fields were flooded in the winter, and the migratory birds came by the thousands. The fish-eaters filled their bills with tilapia, an introduced fish species from Africa. The toxic chemicals (including DDT, DDE, toxaphene, dieldrin and chlordane) in the tilapia were passed up the food chain. Analysis of fatty tissue from one great blue heron found 23,041 ppm of DDE.

The cleanup of Lake Apopka continues. Plans include a 3,500-acre (1414-ha) marsh that will filter the water in the lake twice each year. The restored wetland must be designed so that it is less attractive to fish-eating birds. Perhaps in another 50 years the lake will once again be clean enough to support bass as it did 50 years ago.

Birds attracted to flooded fields near Lake Apopka were poisoned by pesticides that accumulated in the fish.

Environmental Challenge: Exemptions to a Pesticide Ban

Discuss the following questions and make a decision that reflects the majority position of the group. Support your position.

- Should the EPA permit exemptions to the banning of a particular pesticide?
- If so, what circumstances should warrant an exemption?
- If not, what might be the positive and negative impacts of the exemption?

Methyl bromide is used worldwide as a pesticide to destroy pests in the soil, to control many pests on crops, and to protect crops during storage after harvest. Methyl bromide is a potent ozone-depleting substance. Find out more about methyl bromide by visiting the EPA's methyl bromide phaseout website at: www.epa.gov/spdpublc/mbr/mbrqa.html.

Made in the U.S.A.

A pesticide that is banned by the EPA cannot be sold for use in the United States, but the EPA has no authority to ban the export of pesticides. If the EPA does not ban the production of a pesticide, the manufacturer can continue to produce the pesticide and may legally export it to other countries. In some countries, use of these high-risk pesticides has caused serious health and environmental problems.

Two United Nations organizations, the Environment Program (UNEP) and the Food and Agriculture Organization (FAO) have developed a Prior Informed Consent (PIC) procedure, which is similar to the "right-to-know" law. The UNEP/FAO notifies countries of any restrictions the exporting country has placed on hazardous chemicals and pesticides, and it provides information that helps the countries understand the risks of importing and using these chemicals. The countries then decide whether or not they will allow the chemical to be imported, and the UNEP/FAO communicates the country's decision to the exporting countries.

In 1998, 5 industrial chemicals and 22 pesticides, including PCBs, DDT, chlordane, and heptachlor were on the PIC list. Companies exporting such chemicals must make sure that the containers are properly labeled and have safety data sheets. Unfortunately, this may have little effect on how they are used in other countries. One problem is the difference in language and another is that the farmers are often poorly trained. Even those pesticides that are acceptable by U.S. standards may result in poisoned food and poisoned people if they are not properly stored or used.

People in other countries use DDT or heptachlor even though the EPA banned their use in the U.S. New varieties of high-yield rice and wheat are dependent upon the use of agricultural chemicals—fertilizers and pesticides. In many countries newer pesticides are used, but they are more expensive. In less developed countries, cost is an important factor. DDT is the cheapest weapon for controlling insects that cause malaria and other diseases that kill millions of people each year.

People in the developed countries are concerned about the persistence of DDT and other persistent organic chemicals and their long-term effects upon the environment. People in third world countries are more interested in preventing the short-term effects of starvation and the immediate threat of disease, but the use of pesticides in those countries has a widespread effect on those and other countries.

Many of the countries that import pesticides export food. A pesticide that is banned in the U.S. may be used in another country to grow food, and that food may be exported to the United States. About one-fourth of all fruits and vegetables that are sold in the United States are imported from other countries. Nearly one-half of all fresh and frozen produce that is imported comes from Mexico. Tests have shown that pesticide residues are lower in foods that are grown in the United States than in foods that are grown in other countries.

3.11 Questions for Study and Discussion:

The History of Heptachlor and Chlordane

1. Heptachlor and Chlordane belong to what class of insecticides?
2. Make a list of the benefits and risks of using these pesticides.
3. What type of registration did the EPA grant in 1978? Did the EPA later cancel this registration?

An Exemption Caused Trouble in Hawaii

4. Why did the pineapple industry request an exemption?
5. Why didn't the growers use natural predatory insects instead of the pesticide?
6. How were humans endangered by the use of the pesticide?
7. We may never know if any health problems are caused by heptachlor. Why?

A Costly Mistake in the Midwest

8. How was the situation in the Midwest like the situation in Hawaii? How did it differ?
9. Did the heptachlor cause any health problems? Are you sure?

A Deadly Mistake in Florida

10. How did the lake become contaminated?
11. Describe the series of events that led to the death of the birds.

Made in the U.S.A.

12. Chemical companies can sell pesticides that have been banned or restricted and pesticides that have not been approved by the EPA. Who buys them?
13. List two ways that the government regulations try to protect people in countries that buy the pesticides.
14. Give two reasons why the exported pesticides are often the cause of pesticide poisoning.
15. Why do farmers in other countries use pesticides like DDT when less persistent pesticides are available?
16. Why aren't people in third world countries as concerned as people in developed countries about the long-term effects of pesticides?
17. How might pesticides that are used in other countries affect you and your environment?

Environmental Challenge: A Total Ban

About 14% of all Danish women develop breast cancer. The rate has more than doubled since the 1960s. A study of blood samples showed women who had the highest concentrations of dieldrin, an estrogen-mimicking pesticide, had more than double the breast-cancer risk of those whose blood samples had little or no dieldrin.

In 1999, atrazine was one of the two most widely used agricultural pesticides in the U.S. The 1996 Food Quality Protection Act required the EPA to re-evaluate food tolerances for atrazine, a herbicide used on corn, wheat, pineapples, sugarcane and lawns. The EPA considers cancer to be the potential adverse health effect of greatest concern. Atrazine is classified as a possible human carcinogen based on an increase in mammary gland tumors in female laboratory animals.

Denmark banned the herbicide atrazine in 1994. Denmark's EPA phased out or severely restricted 30 pesticides between 1994 and 1997. In 1996, the Danish EPA announced plans to phase out approximately 100 agricultural chemicals that have estrogenic effects. Some members of parliament want the country to be totally organic by 2010.

- If you were a member of parliament, would you vote for a total ban on synthetic pesticides?
- How do you think a total ban on synthetic pesticides would affect the agricultural industry? The food supply?
- Do you think a total ban would make the country a healthier place to live?
- What do you think? Would you prefer that the EPA ban atrazine or would you be comfortable if the EPA's decision was to lower the tolerance levels for atrazine in food?

Environmental Challenge: AZM

The sugar in products that satisfy your craving for something sweet probably comes from sugar cane or sugar beets. Although sugar is the most obvious product of sugar cane, it is possible to produce more than 30 other products including paper, chemicals, and biodegradable plastic. Sugar cane grows quickly and is a renewable resource. It produces energy—electricity and ethanol—without any net increase in carbon dioxide.

The pesticide endrin protected the sugar cane crop from the corn borer. When endrin was banned, it was replaced with the pesticide azinphos-methyl (AZM). It appears that AZM is causing problems. Are the problems severe enough to justify the banning of AZM? That is the question that must be answered.

Some of the most massive fish kills in U.S. history occurred in Louisiana in 1991. One estimate places the loss at one million fish. The cause of death—pesticide poisoning. The pesticide AZM was responsible for 15 separate fish kills in 1991 and 6 fish kills in 1992.

AZM is an organophosphate, which is a neurotoxin. It overstimulates the nervous system, interfering with the normal flow of nerve impulses, and causes muscles to contract in random motion. The body of a fish appears to vibrate in the water. In humans it causes nausea, dizziness, confusion, and at high exposures it causes death. Death comes from respiratory failure.

There were 27 health complaints filed with the Louisiana Department of Agriculture and Forestry (DAF) between July 10 and September 19, 1991. One complaint represented a number of people who reported symptoms of pesticide poisoning within hours of spraying near their village. Symptoms reported included acute asthma, eye irritation, severe rashes and vomiting. The use of AZM was temporarily suspended.

In addition to its importance in the sugar cane industry, AZM has been used on a wide variety of fruits and vegetables, cotton, and on ornamental plants, Christmas trees, forest trees, and shade trees.

- If you were a member of the EPA Risk Management Team, would you further restrict or ban the use of AZM? Consider the environmental and economic impacts of your decision.
- What additional information would you need to know before making the decision?

To find out the current legal uses for azinphos-methyl, visit the EPA Office of Pesticide Programs at www.epa.gov/pesticides.

Environmental Challenge: A World-Wide Ban

Representatives of 92 nations met in Montreal, Canada, in June 1998 to plan for the phaseout of 12 chemicals that are persistent organic pollutants (POPs). POPs readily evaporate, are carried by the winds around the globe, and bioaccumulate. They are:

Chemicals	Pesticides		
Dioxins	aldrin	dieldrin	hexachlorobenzene
Furans	chlordane	endrin	mirex
PCBs	DDT	heptachlor	toxaphene

In the future, other chemicals may be added to the list. These persistent chemicals travel long distances and remain in the environment and in body tissues for many years. Their use has been banned in most developed countries, but they are still manufactured in several countries including the United States. They are exported to less developed countries for controlling insects and pests. In many tropical regions, DDT is still used to control insects that transmit diseases.

- Write the names of the following countries on cards. Then draw a card to determine which country you will represent. Additional countries may be added to the list. Make sure that both developed and less developed countries are represented.

Australia	China	Nigeria	South Africa
Bangladesh	India	Russia	United Kingdom
Brazil	Japan	Saudia Arabia	United States
Canada	Mexico	Somalia	

- Research the country you represent to find information about the country's economy, agriculture, population, and health-related issues.
- Choose a chairperson and a recorder for the convention.
- Create a plan for a phase-out of persistent organic chemicals. For the plan to become a treaty, which has the force of an international law, it must be signed by three-fourths of the countries at the convention.
- As you discuss the plan, be sure the needs of the country that you represent are considered. Sign the treaty only if you feel the needs of your country are met.

> *"We should no longer accept the counsel of those who tell us that we must fill our world with poisonous chemicals; we should look about and see what other course is open to us."*
>
> RACHEL CARSON
>
> *Silent Spring*

OBJECTIVES

- **Cite** evidence that pesticides are not eliminating pests.
- **Explain** how scientists are trying to decrease the loss of crops while reducing or eliminating the use of pesticides.
- **Compare** the use of biological controls to the use of chemical insecticides.
- **Identify** important components of an IPM program.

Despite the use of chemicals, corn is still attacked by 70 different insect pests. The chlorinated hydrocarbon mirex was used against red fire ants for 15 years, but banned in 1978. Despite this attack, the ants spread from Alabama to Texas and to North Carolina. Safer methods of control were needed for this aggressive pest.

We have doubts about the safety and long-term effectiveness of insecticides, yet we must control insect pests. Pests still take about one-third of our food every year. Not long ago we thought that if all farmers quit using pesticides, there would be no commercial production of important crops like apples, lettuce, and strawberries. Now growers are producing some crops with fewer pesticides, and in some cases none at all.

Integrated Pest Management (IPM) involves the use of not one, but several different methods of control to reduce the population of a particular pest. The goal is to select a combination of nonchemical methods and, if necessary, less harmful chemicals for pest control. Because of consumers' concerns, large industries like Campbell and Del Monte have developed IPM programs.

The EPA, FDA, and the USDA are working together to expand the use of IPM in agriculture. In 1994, the USDA set a goal of implementing IPM on 75% of the nation's farmland by the year 2000. Nine Asian countries now have IPM programs sponsored by the UN.

Crop consultants are working with farmers to reduce their use of toxic insecticides. In some cases IPM is also saving the growers money. An IPM Program might include the use of:

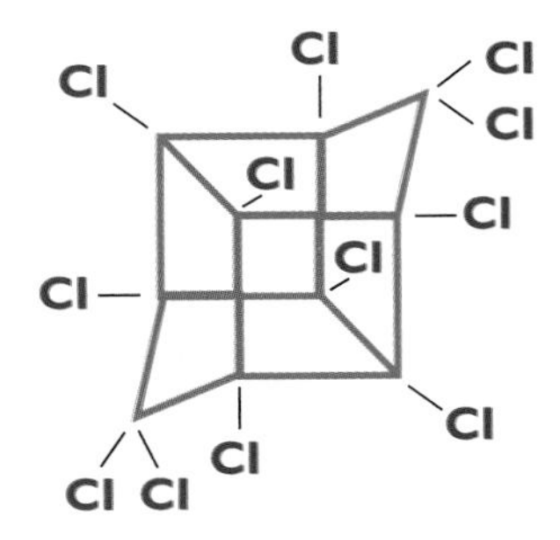

Structural formula for Mirex.

Resistant Varieties:

Some plants are naturally resistant to insects. Some produce their own pesticides. The natural odor of herbs and evergreens comes from chemicals that discourage pests from attacking the plants. Some plants produce chemicals, similar to caffeine and nicotine, which interfere with the flow of messages in an insect's nervous system. Tannins and other chemicals that are found in some plants make an insect unable to digest food.

Scientists are developing varieties of crops that are resistant to attack by specific pests. Resistant varieties have some type of built-in protection. It may be a natural pesticide, or it may be a physical barrier such as spines or hairy leaves. This is an ideal solution to insect control because it reduces the need for spraying synthetic pesticides.

Did You Know?

A huge number of birds are killed each year by pesticides applied legally on farms in the United States. No one knows how many, but estimates are in the millions. Just two chemicals used on corn, carbofuran and terbufos, create the most serious risks. Farmers can reduce the risk by using Integrated Pest Management.

The Hessian fly is one of the most serious pests of wheat.

Varieties of wheat have been developed that are resistant to the Hessian fly. The Hessian fly is one of the most serious pests of wheat. Varieties of alfalfa are being developed that are resistant to attack by weevils. Scientists are also interested in developing varieties of crops that are resistant to attack by insects while the food is in storage.

The development of **resistant varieties** is a time-consuming and expensive process. Plant breeders began a program to develop apple varieties that were resistant to the major apple diseases—scab, rust, fire blight and mildew. The resistant varieties developed had to also produce high-quality fruit. No one would want a disease-resistant apple tree if the fruit tasted like cardboard. The breeding program that began in the 1940s finally produced apple trees resistant to these diseases in the 1970s. New processes developed in the field of genetic engineering may someday reduce the time needed to develop new varieties.

Environmental Challenge: A Sticky Situation

Imagine a plant that secretes a sticky chemical that traps and kills mites. Some plants do excrete chemicals that make the plant resistant to mites. Scientists have identified the chemical excreted by some varieties of geraniums and are now working on biosynthesis of the chemical in the laboratory. If scientists can identify the genes responsible for this resistance, they may be able to transfer it to other plants.

- What risks, if any, would offset the benefits of this genetic engineering?

Beneficial Insects:

Wasps are the most useful insects for control of other insects. The beneficial species of wasps are much smaller than the familiar wasps that build paper nests and are feared for their sting. Most live alone and the females hunt insects to provide food for their young.

The female wasp lays her eggs inside the eggs or larvae of insect pests. The wasp eggs hatch, and the wasp larvae feed on the egg or the inside of the host larva. When they are mature, they eat their way out of the host and spin a cocoon. In the cocoon they gradually change into adult wasps. Parasitic wasps and some parasitic flies help control the populations of important insect pests like the gypsy moth larvae, cutworms, boll weevils, and hornworms.

The root crop cassava and the cassava mealy bug were introduced to Africa from South America. Cassava is now an important food for more than 200 million Africans. Without its natural enemies, the cassava mealybug threatened the cassava crop. In 1995, a Swiss scientist won the World Food Prize award for his role in the introduction of the Paraguayan wasp, a parasite of the mealy bug, into 30 African countries.

Insects like the ladybugs and the larvae of the green lacewing are important insect predators, but not all insect predators are good biological

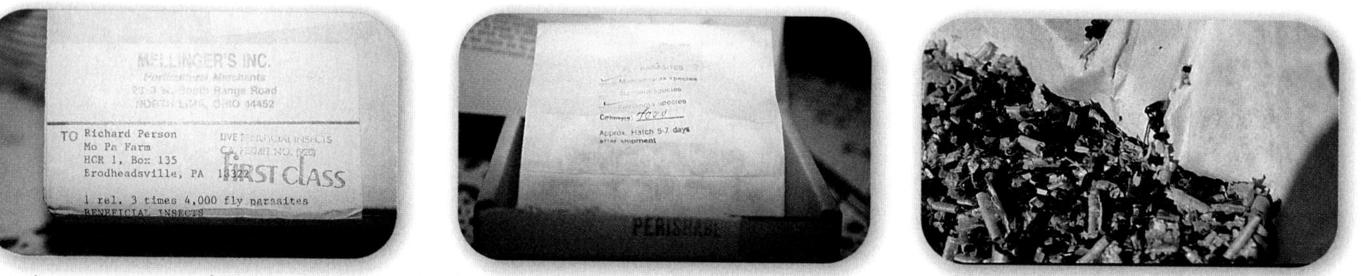

Imagine getting a package in the mail, and when you open it you find it contains 4,000 wasp larvae. Dairy farmers are finding that mail-order wasps can do the job that poisons once did — control the fly population. The ant-sized wasps insert their eggs in the fly larvae. One cow patty can hide as many as 2,000 fly larvae, and an insect control program using two species of parasitic wasps can reduce fly breeding by 99 percent.

This tomato hornworm is carrying the eggs of a parasitic wasp. When the eggs hatch, the larvae will feed on the worm.

This lady beetle (commonly called ladybug) helps farmers by feeding on other insects that damage crops.

This aphid lion, which is the larva of the green lacewing, is feeding on a cabbage looper larva.

controls. The praying mantis has a big appetite for insects, but it is not selective. Beneficial insects, insect pests and other praying mantises are a part of its diet. Buying praying mantises for your garden will do little to reduce the population of insect pests.

Microbial Pesticides:

Viruses, protozoa, bacteria, fungi, parasites and predators can be used to control certain insect pests. Certain types of fungi strangle some harmful nematodes in the soil. *Nosema locustae* is a one-celled protozoan that lives as a parasite in grasshoppers. As it feeds and multiplies in the stomach of the grasshopper, the grasshopper slowly becomes ill and dies.

A very small rod-shaped bacterium ***Bacillus thuringiensis*** **(B.t.)** may be the safest insecticide that is used today. It does not harm honeybees or other beneficial insects, spiders, fish, birds or humans. Vegetables sprayed with B.t. may be eaten immediately after spraying. There is no required waiting period or "days-to-harvest." B.t. is also exempt from the requirement of a "safe" tolerance level.

B.t. is a very selective insecticide. A specific strain of B.t. produces a poison that affects a specific type of insect. B.t.i. is effective against mosquito larvae and blackflies. When the larvae mistakenly eat it as food, it causes the cells of their digestive system to explode. B.t. san diego is effective against certain beetles and the boll weevil.

B.t.k. bacteria produce a chemical that is toxic to caterpillars (larvae of moths and butterflies). When these caterpillars feed on leaves that have been sprayed with B.t.k., the toxic chemical produced by the bacteria begins to break down the insect's stomach wall. The caterpillar stops feeding within 24 to 48 hours and will die within several days. When the caterpillar dies and decays, the B.t. bacteria also decay. This prevents any build-up of the bacteria in the environment.

Japanese beetles can be controlled by another bacterium that causes milky spore disease (*Bacillus popillae*). It is sprayed on the soil where the beetle larvae live. When the larvae die, the spores of the bacteria are

Environmental Challenge: Distribution of Beneficial Insects

IPM Laboratories supplies predatory insects and mites to farmers. They are shipped in small containers that may contain 1,000 to 20,000 predators. Farmers need to dispense these predators across large areas that may be 100 to 200 acres (a football field is approximately an acre). Your job is to design a device that will decrease the labor costs of distribututing the beneficial predators. Keep in mind that some insects, such as wasps and ladybugs, are flying insects while other insects and mites are crawlers. Your device may be designed for one or both of these predators.

released into the soil. These spores continue to control the beetle larvae once they have become established. There are two disadvantages to control with milky spore disease. It is expensive to establish the spores and they are effective only if used in the entire neighborhood.

Birth Control:

Birth control is another method of controlling insect populations. Males that have been sterilized by radiation are released in the fields. When these males mate with untreated females, the females lay eggs that do not hatch. This reduces the population of the new generation.

The screwworm fly, a parasite that lives in the open wounds of cattle, was eliminated from Florida, and is controlled in the Southwest, by releasing masses of sterile male flies. This method of birth control is also used to eliminate introduced pests before their populations become large. This technique works only when the pest population is small and is not widespread.

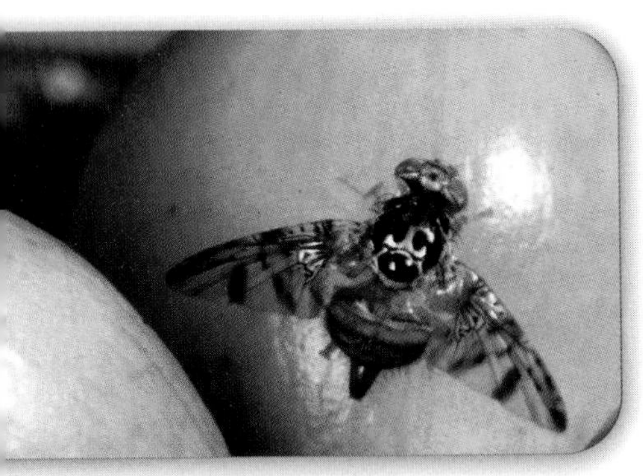
Mediterranean fruit fly.

The codling moth larva can be a devastating pest in apple and pear orchards.

Biochemical Pesticides:

Biochemical pesticides are naturally occurring substances that control pests by nontoxic methods. Some insects can be attracted to and caught in traps that are baited with sex attractants called **pheromones**. Male insects often find a female of the same species by the way she smells. The females produce a chemical that can be identified by a male, when the male is a mile or more away. This sex attractant increases the chance of reproduction.

Researchers have isolated and identified several of the chemicals that produce these odors and can now make synthetic sex attractants. In 1957, bait containing a sex attractant and an insecticide, were used to eliminate the Mediterranean fruit fly from Florida. Since then, it has been used to control fruit flies introduced in Florida and California.

On 760 acres of commercial Bartlett pear orchards in California, hollow tubes that look like telephone cords dispense the pheromone from the female codling moth. The males find the pheromone dispensers instead of the female moths, and the eggs are deposited without being fertilized. The use of the nontoxic sex attractant has totally replaced the highly toxic pesticide Guthion in some fields. Costs are about the same and average yields are equal to those fields treated only with chemicals.

For the gypsy moth, there is no practical or economical way to hang dispensers, containing the female pheromone, high in the trees in the forest. That is where the male moths find the flightless females. The USDA is experimenting with aerial drops of dispensers that look like tiny beads or flakes of confetti. The correct distribution of the pheromone is necessary to disrupt the mating process. Cost is also an important factor.

Scientists are perfecting inexpensive ways to dispense the gypsy moth pheromones so that there will be fewer caterpillars to defoliate the trees.

Cultivation Practices:

Timing the planting and the harvest to avoid pests can reduce damage to some crops. In some cases planting should be delayed until the region is free of the insect pest. Delaying the planting of wheat prevents Hessian flies from laying eggs on the young wheat plants. Faster growing varieties of cotton allow harvest before the pests arrive.

Growing cotton plants become winter nurseries for boll weevils. Plowing under the cover crop residue eliminates winter habitat for some insect pests. This reduces the population of pests and the damage to the crop in the next growing season. In Texas, a plowdown law requires growers to shred and destroy all standing residue after cotton harvest. Following cotton with corn can break the cycle of a disease called root rot.

The practice of monoculture has allowed the rootworm to affect thousands of acres. Planting corn in the same field year after year ensures a food supply for the rootworm. Rotating corn with soybeans removed the food supply and helped reduce the pest population, but the rootworms have adapted and are now laying eggs in the soybean fields. Farmers need new controls, and one of the newest is a pesticide called SLAM!

The adult stage of the western corn rootworm is the target of an IPM program that may reduce the amount of insecticides used on corn.

Synthetic Pesticides:

Synthetic pesticides, such as SLAM, are a part of the IPM program. SLAM may help farmers in the Corn Belt reduce the amount of pesticide they need to control the western corn rootworm. SLAM is a low-insecticide bait made from powdered wild buffalo gourd root and carbaryl insecticide (one ounce per acre). Chemicals in the gourd are like candy to the rootworm beetle. They eat so much of it that it takes little insecticide to kill them. Farmers only spray when needed.

This apple tree shows signs of damage from Japanese beetles.

Male Japanese beetles are attracted to a chemical that smells like a female beetle. They cannot cling to the slick plastic surface and are trapped when they fall into the bag.

Environmental Challenge: Grapefruit

Did you know that Caribbean fruit flies (and other insects) are attracted to the color yellow? A scientist has discovered that a natural growth hormone (gibberellic acid) disappears as a grapefruit turns yellow. When scientists spray grapefruit with a solution containing 10 ppm of the hormone, it prevents the grapefruit from losing its chlorophyll and turning yellow. The fruit flies tend to ignore the green fruit. The fruit continues to ripen. Growers already treat the grapefruit with another growth hormone, ethylene, to turn grapefruit yellow during storage. The growth hormone doesn't harm beneficial insects.

- Do you think that you have the "right-to-know" how your grapefruit has been treated?
- Would you pay more for a grapefruit that has been treated with a natural growth hormone instead of a synthetic insecticide?

Did You Know?

Native American apples (crab apples) were not edible unless cooked. The favorite fruit in America, the apple, was introduced into this country more than 300 years ago. You would need to eat more than an apple a day if you tried to sample all of the 3,300 varieties grown at the New York State Agricultural Experiment Station.

Apples can require more chemicals per acre than any other crop grown in the United States. Scientists at Cornell University are developing strains that are naturally resistant to insects and to the most common apple diseases. Two disease-resistant apples developed at Cornell are the dark-red Liberty and the red and yellow-striped Freedom. Both have been grown with few or no fungicides.

Recently U.S. plant scientists found one of the earth's oldest apples growing wild in a remote region of Kazakhstan. Scientists are growing the *Malus sieversii* because they believe it contains genes that can resist serious diseases.

Apples can require more chemicals per acre than any other crop grown in the United States.

Biological controls have significantly reduced the amount of synthetic pesticides used to control certain pests, but they have not replaced the use of pesticides entirely. After pesticides eliminated the predators of the planthopper in Indonesia, the pest destroyed $1 billion worth of rice during the 1970s. Indonesia developed an IPM policy which banned 57 pesticides for use on rice. Pesticide subsidies were eliminated and farmers were trained. Now Indonesia uses only 18% of the pesticides it used before the IPM program.

Computer Programs:

Computer programs are helping farmers reduce the amount of pesticides they use. When farmers spray using the calendar as a guide, they spray at a specific time. There may be few insects present. Computer programs are helping farmers reduce the amount of pesticide they use. Texas farmers can use an IPM program called BUGNET. Farmers sweep the cotton fields with bug nets and report the number of boll weevils found.

A computer at Texas A & M University uses the information from the sweep to determine when the weevils will reach damaging levels. This allows the farmer to spray only when necessary. During the 1960s, 20 million pounds ($9x10^6$ kg) of insecticides were used to grow cotton in Texas. Since 1976, the use of insecticides for Texas-grown cotton has decreased, and at the same time profits have increased.

The spring flight of the codling moth, a devastating apple pest, begins on the first day when there is a 62°F (17°C) temperature at sunset. Control of this pest is accomplished by spraying when the insect is in the larval stage. Farm advisors enter the date of the first spring flight in a computer, and the program calculates the dates for each stage in the life cycle. With this information, the farmer can avoid spraying after the larva has spun its cocoon, when it is too late.

Some insects develop only when the temperature is within a specific range. The development stops if the temperature is too low or too high. An IPM program at the University of California is linked to the National Weather Service. Using the average daily temperature and the minimum and maximum temperatures for the development of the species, a computer program calculates the **growing degree days**—the daily accumulation of heat—and tells farmers when the insect will be in each stage of its life cycle. The farmer can select the most appropriate time to spray.

The Benefits and Disadvantages of Biological Controls

It would cost $200 an acre to control citrus red scale insects using chemical insecticides. The cost of control using the *Aphytis melinis* wasp is $20 per acre. Biological controls are usually cheaper to use than chemical controls, and biological controls don't pollute the environment.

Biological controls often kill only the pest, not the innocent insects that may offer a beneficial service to humans. With these advantages, it would seem that farmers would not need chemical controls, yet farmers are spending about $10 billion on chemical controls each year. Here are some of the reasons:

- Biological controls are often more expensive to develop than chemical controls. Our most destructive pests have been imported from other countries. It is necessary to travel to the country where the pest originated to find its natural predators and diseases. The natural predators or diseases must be brought to the U.S. and studied under strict quarantine to make sure it will attack only the pest. This makes research on biological controls very expensive.
- Companies may not be able to make large amounts of money selling biological controls. Without a financial incentive, most companies will not invest the time and money necessary to research biological controls. Universities and the federal government conduct most biological control research, and they must depend on Congress to appropriate funds.
- Although biological controls may exist for most insect species, the research has not been done to identify and test them. Effective biological controls are not yet available for many insect pests.
- In order for biological controls to be effective, farmers must identify the pest and plan a course of action to prevent a population explosion. Some farmers are not planners. They find it easier to use chemical pesticides.
- Some biological controls are not effective unless they are applied over a large region. This requires the cooperation of the surrounding neighbors. Milky spore disease is not effective against the Japanese beetle unless used over a wide area.
- Chemical pesticides are fast-acting and biological controls are slow-acting. It may take a few days or weeks for a biological control to reduce the pest population. A worm may quit eating within an hour of being sprayed with bacteria, but it remains upon the plant for several days before dying. This leads some people to think that the bacteria doesn't work. A chemical pesticide kills a worm almost instantly.

Application of pesticide is not necessary if there are fewer than 14 western corn rootworm beetles on the trap.

Pest Control Does Not Mean "No Pests"

An insect is a pest only when its population is large enough to damage or at least bother other organisms (including humans). The goal of IPM is not to eliminate the pest, but to manage the pest population. Pests can seldom be eradicated. It is necessary to accept a certain number of pests. For IPM to be acceptable to the farmer, the money lost because of the surviving pests must be less than the cost of using pesticides to eliminate them.

The presence of insects does not always mean there is a problem. It has been shown that one insect "pest" is actually helpful when its population is small. A large population of *Lygus* bugs decreases the yield of a cotton crop, but a small population of these bugs increases the yield. The bugs remove some of the cotton bolls that would normally drop off anyway. This early removal allows the remaining bolls to grow larger. The bug is like a gardener who removes some pumpkin flowers so that the remaining flowers can produce larger fruit or pumpkins.

Environmental Challenge: Genetic Engineering

The fungus *Phytophthora infestans* wiped out the Irish potato crop in the eighteenth and nineteenth centuries. It is still the most destructive disease of potatoes worldwide. A new potato hybrid appears to be resistant to the fungus. If scientists can identify the gene responsible for the resistance, they can clone it and transfer it to commercial potato varieties.

- What risks, if any, would offset the benefits of this genetic engineering?
- Do consumers have a right to know if the potatoes in the supermarket have been genetically engineered?

www

For information on IPM in schools, visit: www.ifas.ufl.edu/~schoolipm.

3.12 QUESTIONS FOR STUDY AND DISCUSSION:

1. Define the following words: **VOCABULARY**

   Bacillus thuringiensis (B.t.)
   growing degree days
   integrated pest management
   pheromones
   resistant varieties

2. Give evidence that pesticides are not eliminating the pests.
3. What is the goal of IPM and how does the farmer reach this goal?

Resistant Varieties

4. Explain ways in which plants protect themselves from pests.
5. Identify two major crops that are attacked by insects and diseases, and explain how scientists are protecting them.
6. Give two reasons why we have not developed more varieties of crops that are resistant to pests. What development may change this?

Beneficial Insects

7. Identify the type of insect most beneficial for controlling pests and describe how it reduces the pest population.
8. What characteristic makes an insect predator a good biological control? Give an example.

Microbial Pests

9. Give examples of microbial pesticides.
10. What characteristics make Bt an ideal insecticide?
11. What are the two disadvantages of using milky spore disease to control the Japanese beetle?

Birth Control

12. Explain how radiation is used as a form of birth control for some insect pests.
13. What are two limitations of this means of pest control?

Biochemical Pesticides

14. Explain how pheromones are used to control insect populations.
15. Give examples of insects that are being controlled with pheromones.
16. Explain why the gypsy moth pheromone has not yet been effective in controlling populations.

Cultivation Practices

17. List three cultivation practices that will help reduce the population of insect pests.

Synthetic Pesticides

18. How has the use of pesticides changed in Indonesia? What caused this change?
19. How does SLAM differ from conventional insecticides?

Computer Programs

20. How is Texas A & M helping farmers reduce the use of pesticides? What information must the farmers provide?
21. How can a computer program help the orchard owner control the population of codling moths on the apple trees?
22. Why is it more important for a farmer to know the number of degree days than it is for him to know what day of the year it is?

The Benefits and Disadvantages of Biological Controls

23. List three advantages of biological controls.
24. Why haven't more biological controls been developed?
25. Why is it difficult to convince some farmers that biological controls really work?

Pest Control Does Not Mean "No Pests"

26. Complete this statement: "An insect is only a pest when …"
27. What is the goal of IPM?
28. Why doesn't a cotton farmer want to kill all *Lygus* bugs?

UNIT FOUR
Water As An Ecosystem

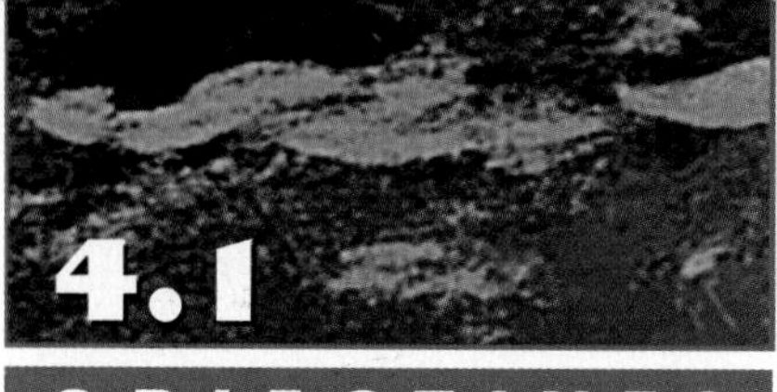

4.1 Aquatic Environments

OBJECTIVES

- ✔ **Locate** major watersheds on a map and find the watershed in which you live.
- ✔ **Classify** freshwater ecosystems.
- ✔ **Contrast** the upper, middle and lower reaches of a stream.
- ✔ **Describe** the aquatic habitats found in a freshwater ecosystem.

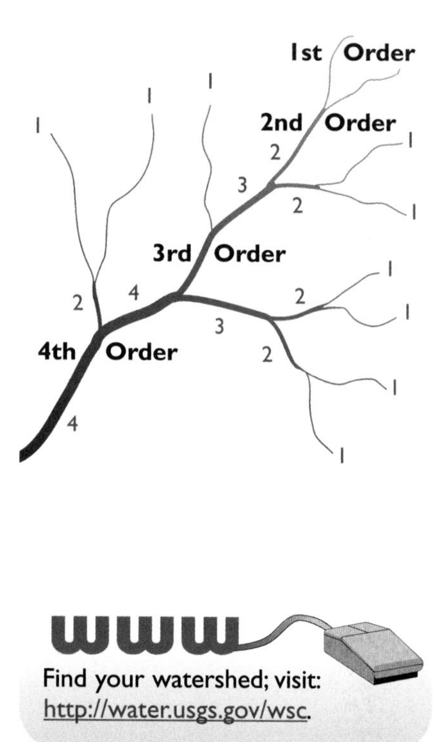

WWW
Find your watershed; visit: http://water.usgs.gov/wsc.

Watersheds

A watershed is the land area that is drained when drops of rain join others to flow to a particular stream, river, lake, or wetland. It is also called a **drainage basin**. The **watershed boundary** is the line along the highest elevation that divides two watersheds. Large watersheds are made up of many smaller or sub-watersheds. Two watersheds within the Mississippi River watershed are the Missouri River watershed and the Ohio River watershed.

What happens on the land in a watershed affects the quality of the water in the aquatic environments and the organisms that live there. There are many different types of aquatic environments. There are saltwater ecosystems and freshwater ecosystems.

Freshwater ecosystems can be divided into two groups: those with relatively fast moving water or **lotic** ecosystems, and those with relatively slow moving water, where water seems to stand still, called **lentic** ecosystems. Lentic bodies of water include lakes, ponds, and wetlands. A **lake**, which is usually larger than a pond, has areas that are too deep for rooted plants to grow. **Ponds** are so shallow that rooted plants grow across the entire bottom.

Lotic ecosystems include rivers, streams, brooks, creeks and human-made channels through which water moves. Streams are sometimes called creeks or brooks. A body of flowing water that is much larger and deeper than a stream is called a **river**. The smaller feeder streams or rivers that empty into a larger stream or river are called **tributaries**.

Streams are classified by their size. The smallest streams are **first-order** streams. When two first-order streams meet they form a **second-order** stream. The place where the two streams meet is the **confluence**. The stream formed at the confluence of two second-order streams is a **third-order** stream. The process continues until the stream or river empties into a lake or the ocean. The place where the river system ends is its **mouth**.

Reaches

River systems are divided into three different regions—upper reaches, middle reaches and lower reaches. The beginning of a stream is called the **headwaters**. As the water moves from the headwaters to the mouth of the river system, the physcial characteristics of the stream change. The characteristics of the **riparian zone**—the ecosystem along a stream or river that is strongly affected by water—also change.

The **upper reaches** include the regions of the stream with the greatest slope. The **channel**, the natural path where the water flows, is straight and "V"-shaped. The riparian zone is narrow and the trees form a canopy shading the stream. Little sunlight reaches the stream. Leaves and woody

debris that fall into the stream provide food and cover for organisms in the stream.

Rapids, riffles and waterfalls are abundant in the upper reaches of a stream. In many places the water appears white because its surface is broken as it flows over rocks. These areas are called **rapids**. There are also many shallow areas where the swiftly flowing water forms small waves. These areas are called **riffles**. The fast-moving water causes constant erosion. **Boulders** (greater than 10 inches/4 cm) and **cobble** (2–10 inches/0.8–4 cm), rocks that are too large to be carried by the water, cover the bottom of the stream. The rocks are worn by the force of the water and the load of sand and gravel that it carries.

Organisms that live in the upper reaches must constantly fight the fast current. Rocky projections and woody debris create small **pools** or areas of slower moving water. Although the fish living in this region of the stream are strong swimmers, they spend most of their time in these pools. They dart from the pool to feed on insects that are carried by the current and then return to the pool to wait for the next meal.

Organisms that are not good swimmers must hold on. Algae, insect larvae and other organisms attach themselves firmly to the surfaces of rocks so that they will not be washed away. The small animals either strain microscopic food from the flowing water, or feed on the algae that cling to the rocks or on the plant matter that falls into the water.

The upper reaches of the stream contain fewer species of plants and animals than other regions of the river system. The populations of those species present are smaller than populations found in regions with slower moving water.

The **middle reaches** include the sections of the river system with third or fourth-order streams. Here the slope is moderate and the "U"-shape channel is wider. The bottom of the stream is covered with boulders, cobble and gravel. The riparian zone widens to form a **floodplain**, and the path of the stream has more curves or **meanders**.

Trees and other rooted plants growing along the stream's edges provide food and shelter for some species. The trees provide shade along

www

To find out more about riparian ecosystems managed by the Bureau of Land Management and the Columbia River Basin (watershed), visit: www.blm.gov/education/index.html.

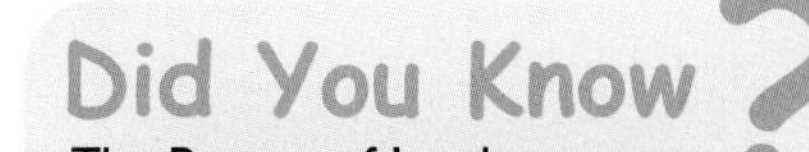

The Bureau of Land Management estimates that 80% of all fish and wildlife in the Columbia River Basin at some time in their lifetime depend upon the riparian zone.

the edges, but sunlight reaches some areas, increasing the growth of algae and aquatic plants.

The middle reaches have the greatest variety of habitats with a combination of shallow areas of riffles and deeper pools. There are fewer rapids and less erosion than in the upper reaches. The pools are larger and more plentiful than in the upper reaches. Silt (fine particles of soil) is deposited in some pools.

Most organisms are found in the pools and the shallow areas at the water's edges. The number of species found in the middle reaches is greater than the number found in the upper reaches. The population densities are also greater—there are more organisms per unit area.

The **lower reaches** include the sections of the river system with a gentle, steady flow. The slope has a low slant and the river meanders across a wide valley. The "U"-shape channel is deeper and wider than the middle reaches. The eroded material from the upper and middle reaches is deposited here. The bottom of the stream is covered with gravel, sand and silt.

There are no rapids, riffles, or waterfalls; the surface of the water is smooth. The riparian zone is a broad **floodplain**, often several miles wide. Seasonal flooding deposits sand and soil over this land and there is a mixture of marshes and swamps. The river is wide so much of the surface is not shaded. The **turbidity** of the water prevents the sunlight from reaching the bottom and limits photosynthesis. The community of plants and animals of the lower reaches is very much like the community of a pond.

These scenes are found along the upper, middle, and lower reaches of the river.

Habitats

Each ecosystem has its own community of organisms. Each species has a **niche** to fill—a job to do. The complex interactions between the species keep the aquatic ecosystem in balance. There are a variety of **habitats** or places where organisms can live in an aquatic ecosystem. The habitats found in streams depend upon the volume of flowing water and the slope of the channel. Aquatic habitats include:

- **Surface film**—the place where the water meets the air. Animals found here include air-breathing insects that may walk on or hang from the surface of the water.
- **Open water**—the area where the rooted plants do not reach the surface of the water. In this habitat you may find large fish, turtles and birds. Microscopic plants and animals float in the open water. These organisms are known collectively as **plankton**.
- **Bottom**—the area of rocks, sand or mud that is the habitat for a variety of small organisms including bacteria, snails, worms, sponges, crayfish and the larvae of some aquatic insects. Fish create nests on the bottom of the stream where the eggs are deposited.
- **Water's edge**—is where the water meets the land. This area is home for the greatest number of species of plants and animals. Many small organisms can be found on the leaves and stems of plants. The plants

provide many hiding places where small fish and other organisms find some protection (cover) and a place to breed.

Human-made channels are straight box-like ditches that have been dug to move water more efficiently. Human-made channels do not offer wildlife the variety of habitats that can be found in natural streams and rivers.

The great blue heron walks slowly through the shallows at the water's edge looking for prey that might be hiding beneath the vegetation.

Channels — box-like ditches — are dug to move water more efficiently. Although they provide habitat for some species, like this anhinga, they do not provide the variety of habitats found in a natural stream.

The rocky bottom of this fast-flowing stream is habitat for a variety of small organisms.

4.1 Questions for Study and Discussion:

1. Define the following terms: **VOCABULARY**

boulders	lake	plankton	tributary
bottom	lentic	pools	upper reaches
cobbles	lotic	pond	water's edge
confluence	lower reaches	rapids	watershed
drainage basin	meanders	riffles	watershed boundary
floodplain	middle reaches	riparian zone	
headwaters	mouth of river	river	
human-made-channel	open water	surface film	

Watersheds

2. What is the relationship between tributaries and watersheds?
3. What characteristic is used to classify a body of water as a lake rather than a pond?
4. What characteristic is used to distinguish between a lotic and a lentic ecosystem? Give 2 examples of each.
5. Describe how the bottom habitat changes as you move downstream from the headwaters to the mouth of the river.

Reaches

6. Compare the riparian zones in the upper, middle and lower reaches.
7. Explain why the middle reaches have a greater number of species and greater population densities than the upper or lower reaches.

Habitats

8. Identify the habitat of the pond or lake that will contain the most species and the largest populations.
9. How do human-made channels differ from natural streams and rivers?
10. In which habitat would you expect to find the fewest organisms?

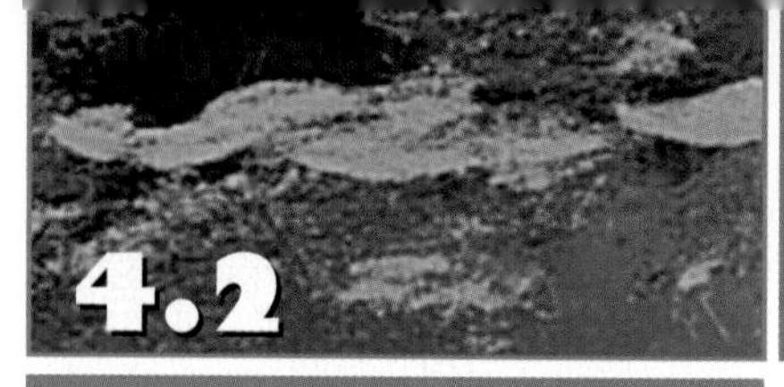

4.2 Creatures that Live in the Water

OBJECTIVES

- ✔ **Identify** benthic macroinvertebrates that are index species and explain what their presence indicates about the water quality.
- ✔ **Describe** adaptations that allow macroinvertebrates to survive in an aquatic ecosystem.
- ✔ **Draw** a food web and **identify** the niche of each organism in the web.

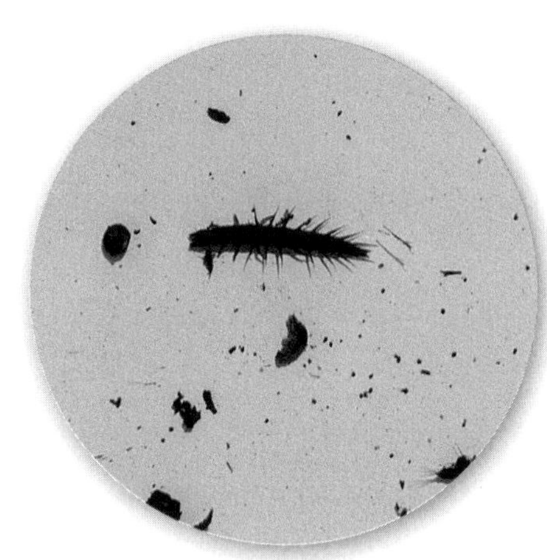

Dobsonfly larva.

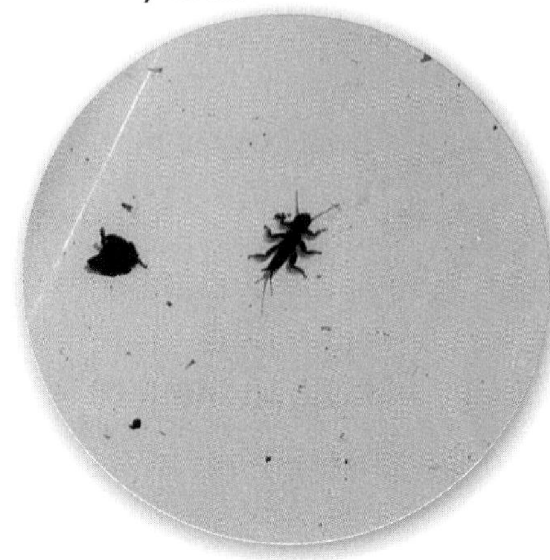

Stonefly nymph.

Macroinvertebrate surveys are an important part of monitoring the water quality of an aquatic ecosystem. The **benthic macroinvertebrates** are aquatic insects or other small organisms that have no backbone and that are large enough to be seen without a microscope. **Benthic** means that their habitat is the bottom of the aquatic ecosystem.

A benthic macroinvertebrate survey can tell us if the aquatic ecosystem is healthy. Since these organisms do not move very far or very fast, they cannot escape pollution. Chemicals dumped in the water may be carried quickly downstream, wiping out populations of sensitive species. Fish may be more tolerant or may be able to escape by moving into a tributary until the chemical passes.

While chemical tests are important, they give only a snapshot of the water quality at the time the water sample was collected. Macroinvertebrates indicate the quality of water in the stream over a long period of time. Some immature insects live in the stream for two to four years before they mature and leave the stream.

Some macroinvertebrates are **clean-water** organisms, or sensitive to pollution, while others are **pollution-tolerant**. Certain organisms are called **index species** because their presence in large numbers can tell us whether the water is clean or polluted. The diversity of macroinvertebrates is a strong indicator of the health of the aquatic ecosystem.

The macroinvertebrates are essential to healthy fish populations. They are eaten by most of the smaller fish. Larger fish may eat both the macroinvertebrates and the smaller fish. After a chemical spill, fish should not be stocked in a stream until the macroinvertebrate populations have recovered.

Feeding Groups

The macroinvertebrates can be grouped according to what they eat and how they eat it. The feeding group, in which an organism is placed, describes the **niche**, or job that the organism does in its aquatic environment.

- **Collectors:** feed on decomposing organic matter. This includes **feces**, fragments of dead plants and animals, and the bacteria on their surface. There are two types of collectors:
  - **Gathering collectors:** feed on the bottom where organic matter accumulates.
  - **Filtering collectors:** also called "filter feeders" use structures to trap and strain small particles out of the water.

Students collect macroinvertebrates using the kick screen method.

Students use the magnifying lens to identify the tiny invertebrates placed in bug boxes.

Once the sample is collected, the students and their teacher look for creatures moving among the debris.

- **Scrapers:** graze on algae that is attached to surfaces of submerged rocks and other objects.
- **Shredders:** break large pieces of dead plant material into smaller pieces. They get nutrition from the algae, bacteria, and fungi that coat the plants.
- **Predators:** have adaptations for capturing other organisms.
- **Parasites:** have structures for attaching to and drawing fluids from other organisms.

There is much we can learn by studying the creatures that live in the water. Some macroinvertebrates are included in this section because their identification is important when assessing the water quality. Others are included because they are an important part of the food web.

Tubifex Worms "sludge worms" (Segmented Worms) Length to 3 cm

Activity: They burrow headfirst into the bottom sediment. The tail end waves back and forth in the water increasing the exchange of oxygen between the water and the body of the worm. They mix the bottom sediments as they ingest sediments and deposit fecal matter on the surface of the bottom sediments.

Eat and Eaten by: Like their cousin, the earthworm, *Tubifex* worms are gathering collectors. Waterfowl, fish, and many invertebrates eat them.

Environmental Factors: *Tubifex* worms are index species—indicators of organic pollution. Their presence in large numbers indicates large amounts of organic matter—sewage or decaying vegetation. They can tolerate low levels of **dissolved oxygen** (DO) and high levels of heavy metals, insecticides, herbicides and fungicides. Their tolerance and uptake of these dangerous chemicals can result in large amounts of these chemicals in organisms that feed on the *Tubifex* worms.

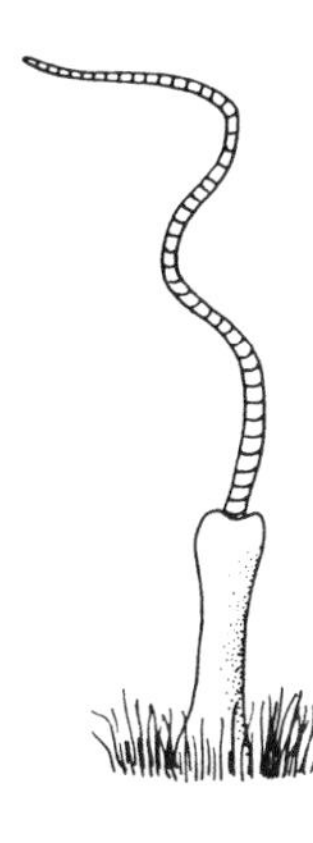

Tubifex worm.

Leeches (Segmented Worms) Length to 7 cm

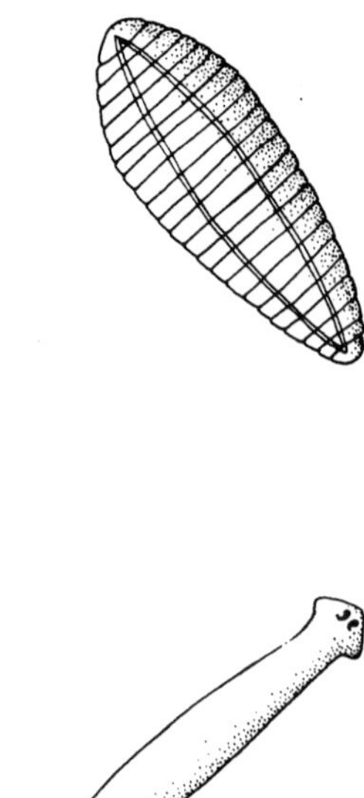
Bloodsucking Leech.

Activity: Leeches prefer quiet water. They are sensitive to light and to vibrations. They move toward vibrations. They are usually attached to aquatic plants unless they are searching for food.

Eat and Eaten by: Some species are parasites. Many leeches are predators on other **benthic** organisms. Some species are gathering collectors. They are an important fish bait.

Environmental factors: Leeches are seldom found in acidic waters, but they are tolerant to organic pollution (waste from untreated sewage, feces, and food processing).

Planaria (Flatworms) Length to 2 cm

Planaria (Free-living Flatworm).

Activity: Planaria cling to plants and stones in shallow water. They are sensitive to light and avoid it by hiding under objects.

Eat and Eaten by: Some species are parasites. Others are predators. Some species are gathering collectors. Leeches, insects and crustaceans eat them.

Environmental factors: Planarians are somewhat sensitive to pollution.

Crayfish (Crustaceans) Length to 15 cm

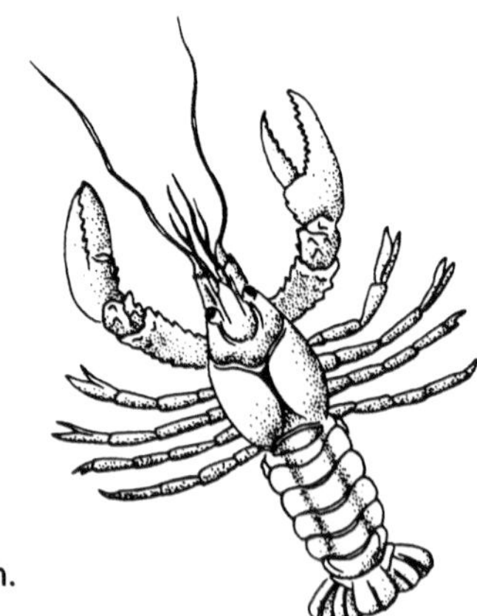
Crayfish.

Activity: Crayfish may be found in wet meadows or shallow water. They spend the day in burrows that can be identified by "chimneys" made of mud balls piled high from digging the burrow. They may burrow down 6 or 7 feet to reach water during dry spells. They are active at night.

Eat and Eaten by: Crayfish are gathering collectors. They are an important fish food and are also eaten by frogs, turtles, raccoons, otter, mink, humans, and wading birds such as little blue herons.

Environmental Factors: Crayfish are somewhat sensitive to pollution. About half of the 330 known species are endangered or at risk. The majority of crayfish eaten by humans are grown in farm ponds in Louisiana. If eaten, they must be cooked thoroughly because they are sometimes a host for a lung fluke that is a parasite in humans.

Scuds "Sideswimmers" (Crustaceans) Length to 2 cm

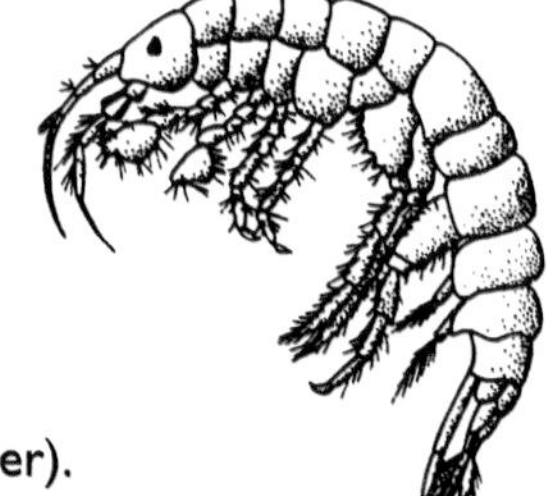
Scud (Sideswimmer).

Activity: Scuds swim on their sides. They avoid light and usually live close to the bottom.

Eat and Eaten by: Scuds are shredders. They are food for small fish and many other aquatic animals.

Environmental Factors: Scuds are somewhat sensitive to pollution and may be found in large numbers in clear, clean waters.

Aquatic Sowbugs (Crustaceans) Length to 2.5 cm

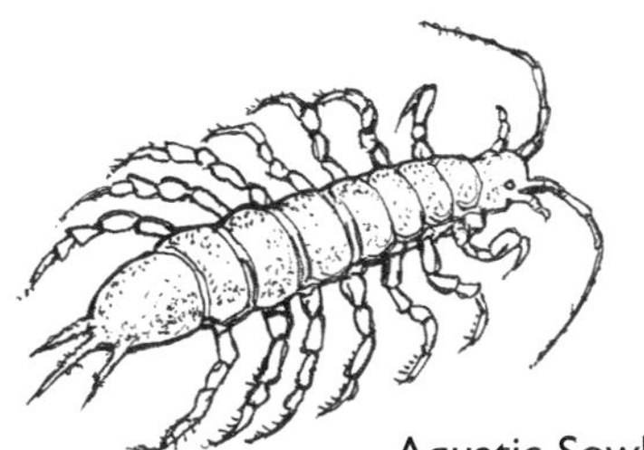
Aquatic Sowbugs.

Activity: Sowbugs crawl slowly across the bottom on 7 pairs of legs. They appear flat when viewed from the side. The female carries her eggs under her abdomen.

Eat and Eaten by: Sowbugs are shredders. They are food for small fish and many other aquatic animals.

Environmental Factors: Sowbugs are somewhat sensitive to pollution.

Water Fleas (Crustaceans) Length < 1 mm

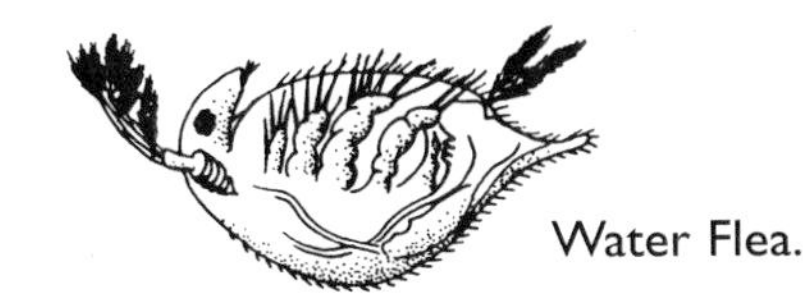
Water Flea.

Activity: Water fleas sweep food into their mouths with their 5 pairs of "legs." They swim with a jerky motion using the antenna.

Eat and Eaten by: Water fleas are filter feeders. They may provide as much as 90% of the diet of small fish. Hydras, insects and wading birds also eat them.

Environmental Factors: Water fleas are abundant in all types of water except rapid streams and polluted waters.

Spiders (Arachnids) Length to 2.6 cm

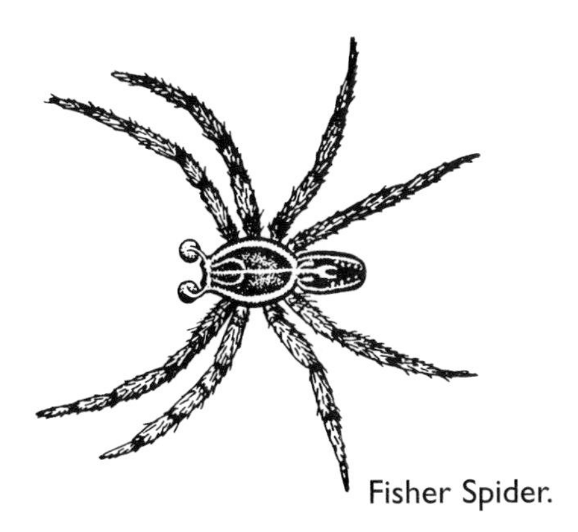
Fisher Spider.

Activity: The fisher spider can dive and remain below the surface of the water for long periods of time. It is covered with body hair that traps a coat of air around its body. Other spiders live near the shore and may be seen skating across the water.

Eat and Eaten by: Spiders are predators feeding mainly on insects, but they sometimes eat a small fish or tadpole. They feed by sucking the fluids from the body of the chosen victim.

Water Mites: (Arachnids) Length to 2 mm

Water Mite.

Activity: Most water mites crawl about on submerged plants or on the muddy or sandy bottom of quiet pools. They must surface for air.

Eat and Eaten by: Most water mites are predators; but a few are parasites. They are the prey of hydras, insects and small fish. Sometimes they are the main food found in a fish's stomach.

Environmental Factors: Some biologists feel that water mites are valuable as a control for mosquitoes. A mosquito that is host to several mites will not feed, and without blood the mosquito cannot reproduce.

Mosquitoes (Insects) Length to 8 mm

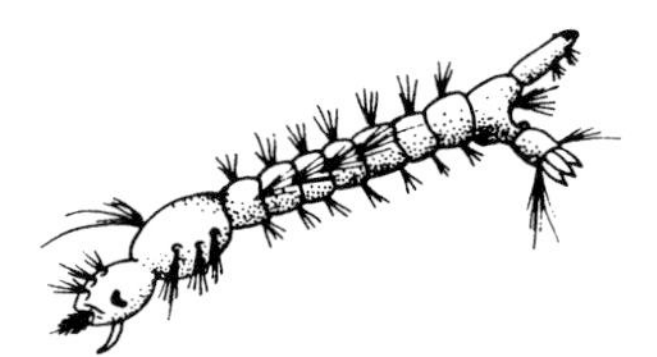
Mosquito Larva.

Activity: Mosquito **larvae** cling to the surface of the water and breathe air through a breathing tube much like a snorkel. They are often called "wrigglers" because of the wriggling motion they make as they move through the water while feeding. After seven days of feeding, they change into **pupae** shaped like question marks. The pupae cling to the surface of the water for two days while changing into the adult form. The female mosquito returns to the water where she deposits a small raft of eggs.

Eat and Eaten by: Mosquito are filter feeders. The pupae do not eat. The adult females need a dose of protein for development of the eggs. Thus, it is only the females that feed on human blood. The adult males may not eat at all, or they may feed on the nectar of flowers and ripe fruit. Mosquito larvae and pupae become food for some small fish. One mosquito-eating fish, the gamusia or mosquito fish, has been released in the California rice fields and the Reflecting Pool in Washington, D.C.

Learn how participants in the Save Our Streams Program collect and identify macroinvertebrates; practice using an identification key and assess stream quality using practice samples at: www.people.virginia.edu/~sos-iwla.

Environmental Factors: Mosquitoes carry the parasites that cause malaria and the viruses that cause yellow fever and encephalitis. In North America, viruses carried by mosquitoes cause five different kinds of encephalitis. They also carry organisms that cause diseases in other animals, such as heartworm in dogs.

Midge Flies (Insects) Length to 1.5 cm

Activity: Midge flies resemble mosquitoes but have a thinner body. They are attracted to light at night. They do not bite.

Midge Fly Larvae.

Eat and Eaten by: Midge fly larvae are gatherer collectors. They may be the most important source of food for young fish and other aquatic carnivores. No other single genus of insects is so important as a food source for so many different fish.

Environmental Factors: The larvae of the bloodworm midge are much larger than other midges (30 mm). Abundant hemoglobin gives them their blood-red color. Midges are pollution tolerant and can survive where the oxygen supply is very low.

Crane Flies (Insects) Length to 5 cm

Activity: Adult crane flies are often seen swarming near ponds. They are poor fliers and often become food for some carnivore. The larvae breathe by pushing a disk through the surface of the water.

Crane Fly Larva.

Eat and Eaten by: Crane fly larvae are shredders or predators. Larger aquatic animals eat them. Birds, amphibians, spiders, and other insects, especially dragonflies, eat the adults.

Environmental Factors: Crane fly larvae are somewhat sensitive to pollution.

Black Flies (Insects) Length to 8 mm

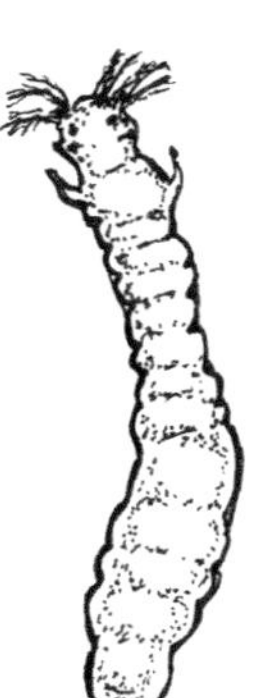
Black Fly Larva.

Activity: The enlarged end of the larva is attached to a rock by silken threads and tiny hooks. As they sway with the current, tiny hair-like structures at the opposite end capture food. Sometimes these insects are so abundant they form a black carpet on the rocks.

Eat and Eaten by: Black fly larvae are filter feeders. The adult flies feed on the blood of warm-blooded animals.

Environmental Factors: Black fly larvae are pollution-tolerant.

Backswimmers (Insects) Length to 2 cm

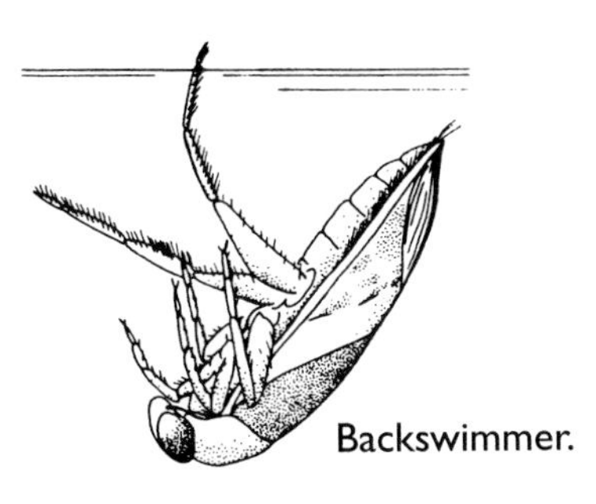
Backswimmer.

Activity: When resting, backswimmers hang head-downward from the surface of the water, or they hold onto plant stems with their front legs. They must come to the surface for a new supply of air. Carried underneath their wings and on the lower side of their body, the air appears as a silver film. They have a beak that can inflict a painful bite.

Eat and Eaten by: Backswimmers are predators, usually feeding on small crustaceans that they hold with their front legs. Sometimes they attack small fish. Young backswimmers are eaten by other insect predators.

Water Boatman (Insects) Length to 2 cm

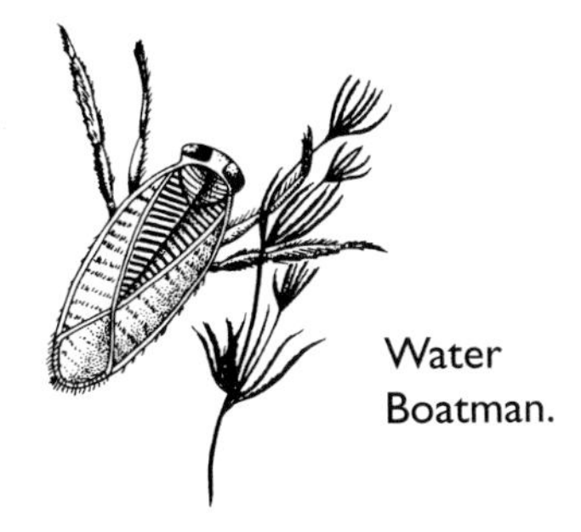
Water Boatman.

Activity: Water boatmen must surface for air, but they always break the surface of the water with their head-end, and they always swim with their backs up. They must cling to water plants to remain submerged.

Eat and Eaten by: Water boatmen are omnivores. Often they are shredders, but sometimes they pierce the cell walls of algae and plants with their beaks, and drink the liquid from the cells. They also feed on mosquito larvae and other small organisms. Fish and other predators readily eat them.

Water Scorpions (Insects) Length to 6 cm

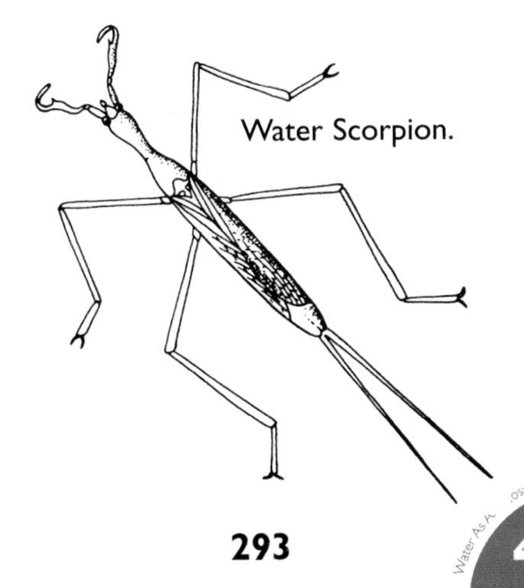
Water Scorpion.

Activity: Water scorpions usually can be found among the muddy leaves and stems of plants at the edge of the pond or stream. They remain underwater lying in wait for their prey. They often back up a stem of a plant and breathe through the long air-tube made with the long tail filaments. They can inflict a painful bite.

Eat and Eaten by: Water scorpions are predators. They clutch the prey with their powerful front legs and suck the juices from the body.

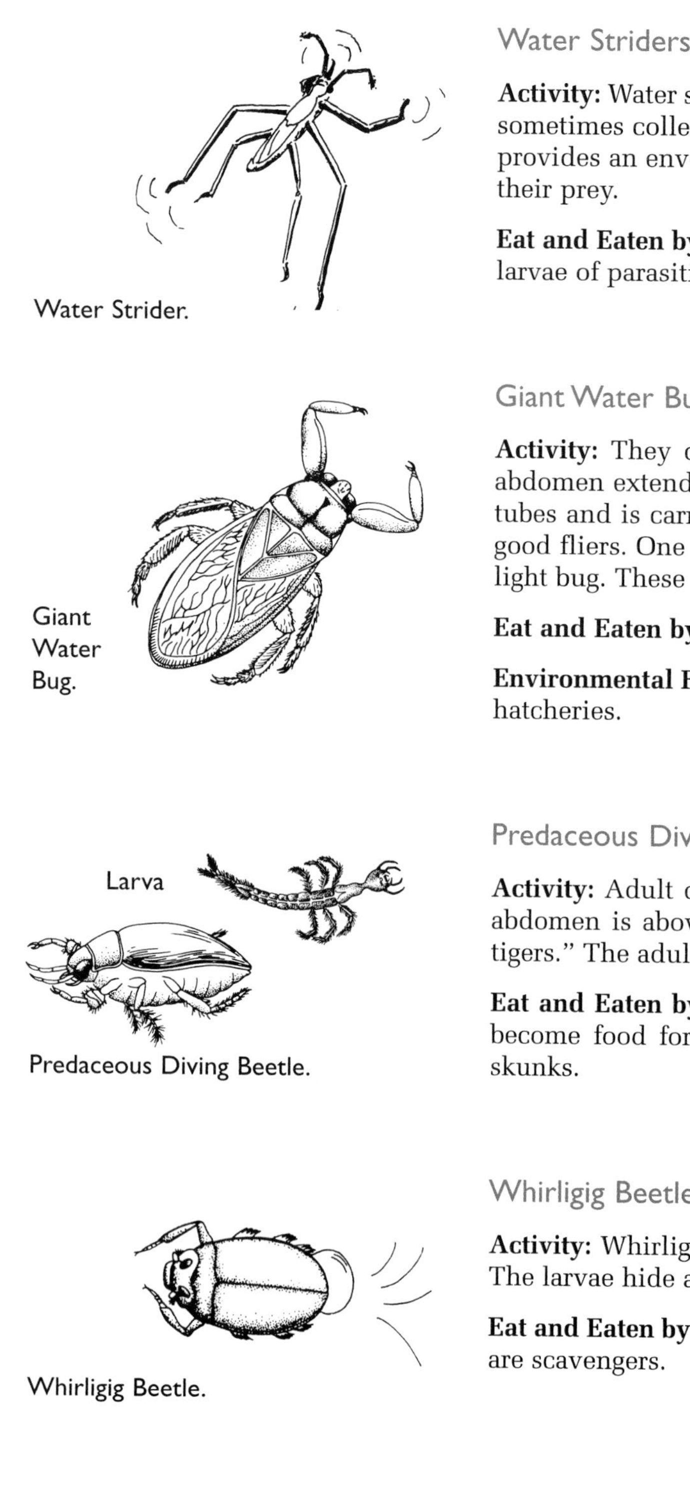

Water Strider.

Giant Water Bug.

Predaceous Diving Beetle.

Whirligig Beetle.

Water Striders (Insects) Length to 1.5 cm

Activity: Water striders or pond skaters skim rapidly over the surface. They sometimes collect in schools. Their body is covered with short hairs. This provides an envelope of air when they dive beneath the surface to capture their prey.

Eat and Eaten by: Water striders are predators. They are often hosts for the larvae of parasitic water mites.

Giant Water Bugs (Insects) Length to 7.5 cm

Activity: They often rest on the bottom, or they sit with the tip of the abdomen extended above the surface of the water. Air fills a system of air tubes and is carried in the space beneath the wings. Giant water bugs are good fliers. One species that is attracted to lights is known as the electric-light bug. These bugs sometimes bite swimmers.

Eat and Eaten by: Giant water bugs are fierce predators.

Environmental Factors: Giant water bugs can become a serious pest in fish hatcheries.

Predaceous Diving Beetles (Insects) Length to 2.5 cm

Activity: Adult diving beetles often hang head down. Only the tip of the abdomen is above the surface of the water. The larvae are called "water tigers." The adults use their hind legs as oars when swimming.

Eat and Eaten by: Both larvae and adults are very active predators. They become food for reptiles, amphibians, fish, wading birds, raccoons and skunks.

Whirligig Beetles (Insects) Length to 2.5 cm

Activity: Whirligig beetles are easily recognized by their whirling motion. The larvae hide and hunt on the bottom. The larvae look like centipedes.

Eat and Eaten by: Most adults and all larvae are predators, but some adults are scavengers.

Dragonflies (Insects) Length to 6 cm

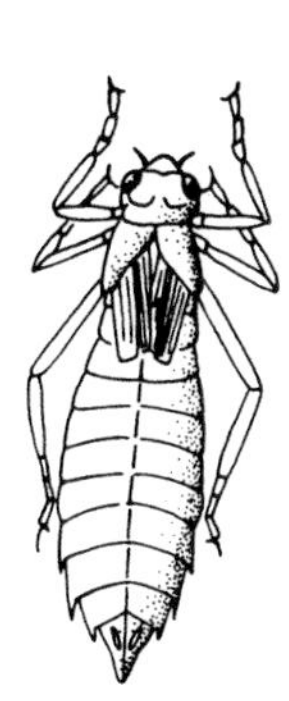
Dragonfly Nymph.

Activity: Adult dragonflies hold their wings in a horizontal position when at rest. Damselflies fold their wings when at rest. This difference can be used to identify the adults.

Eat and Eaten by: Adult dragonflies are predators. They fly about, patrolling the weedy edges of ponds. The **nymphs** patrol the muddy bottoms of ponds and seize their prey with an extended lower lip that has hooks. The lip is used as a long arm. Although they compete with young fish for food, they are important food in the diet of adult fish. The adults are a favorite food of birds.

Environmental Factors: Both the nymphs and adults feed on mosquitoes. In some areas of the country, the adults are called "mosquito hawks." Most species are somewhat sensitive to pollution.

Damselflies (Insects) Length to 3 cm

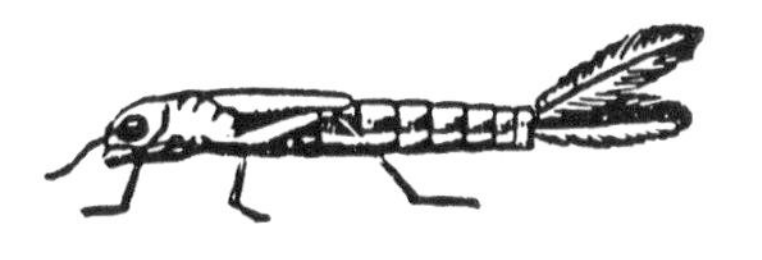
Damselfly Nymph.

Activity: Damselflies are much more delicate-looking than dragonflies, but looks don't tell the entire story. Their activity is very much like that of the dragonflies except that they fold their wings when at rest. The nymphs can easily be identified by the two respiratory organs, which look like the blades of canoe paddles.

Eat and Eaten by: same as dragonfly.

Environmental Factors: Some species are somewhat sensitive to pollution.

Mayflies (Insects) Length to 2.5 cm

Mayfly Nymph.

Activity: Mayflies can be identified by the 7 pairs of gills along the abdomen. They have a single claw on each foot. Clouds of adults are often seen on early summer evenings. The adults have only one purpose in life—to reproduce. A few hours or days after becoming an adult, they mate and deposit eggs in the water. Death soon follows.

Eat and Eaten by: Mayfly nymphs are sometimes called the "cattle" of the stream. Some are scrapers while others are filtering collectors. Most species are gathering collectors. Most aquatic predators eat them. Both adults and nymphs are an important food source for fish. The adults do not eat, but they are frequently the prey of birds, frogs, and adult dragonflies.

Environmental Factors: Mayflies are often the most abundant macroinvertebrates found in clean streams. Some mayflies are **index species**—an indicator of clean water. Most mayflies are sensitive to pollution, except for members of two families which are fairly pollution-tolerant.

Stoneflies (Insects) Length to 5 cm

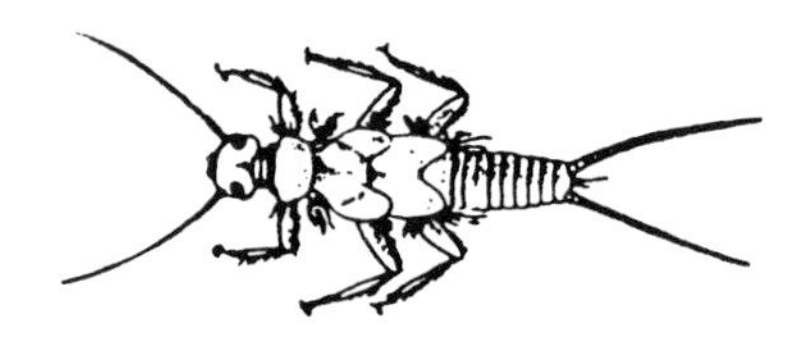

Stonefly Nymph.

Activity: The flattened nymphs cling to rocks with two strong claws. The adults hide among leaves of shrubs close to the water. Some species require two or three years to mature.

Eat and Eaten by: The nymphs of most species are shredders. In small streams many species feed on leaves that fall in the stream. A few species are predators. Stoneflies are one of the most important foods in the diet of trout and many other fish. Frogs also eat them. The adults of most species do not feed, but birds eat them.

Environmental Factors: Stoneflies are sensitive to pollution. Their presence indicates clean water and high levels of oxygen. When they are not getting enough oxygen, they do "pushups" to push more water across their gills.

Caddisflies (Insects) Length to 2.5 cm

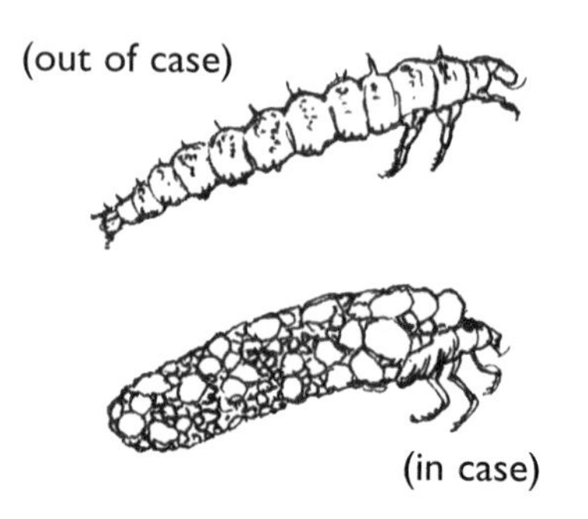

Caddisfly Larvae.

Activity: Most caddisfly larvae live in cases made of mud, sticks and stones. They usually creep along the bottom in search of food. Some species that live in streams build nets to catch food. The adults are active at night and are attracted to lights; but they are not very strong fliers.

Eat and Eaten by: Most caddisfly larvae are scrapers or filtering collectors. A few species are gathering collectors and others are predators. They are an important food in the diet of trout and other fish. The adults do not feed.

Environmental Factors: Most species of caddisfly larvae are sensitive to pollution and are indicators of clean water. Some species are moderately tolerant of pollution.

Dobsonflies (Insects) Length to 9 cm

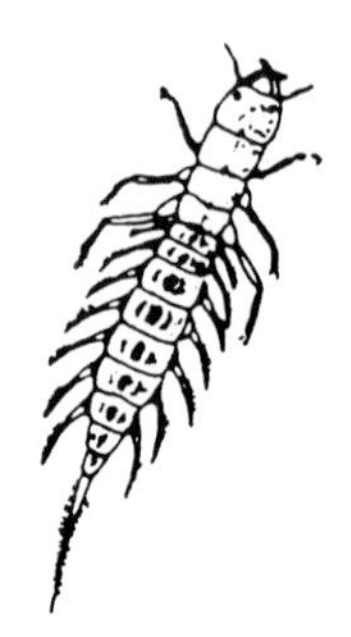

Hellgrammite (Dobsonfly Larva).

Activity: The larvae, commonly called **hellgrammites**, avoid the light and are seldom seen unless stones are quickly pulled from the stream. When threatened they often swim backwards. The adults are short-lived and are usually nocturnal and are often attracted to lights. The female lays eggs on leaves overhanging a stream. When the eggs hatch, the larvae fall into the water and begin to feed.

Eat and Eaten by: The larvae are predators. They are eaten by fish and are considered one of the best bass baits available.

Environmental Factors: Dobsonfly larvae are sensitive to pollution.

Water Pennies (Insects) Length to 1.2 cm

Activity: The flat, copper-colored larvae of a water penny cling to the underside of rocks in the riffles. When a rock is pulled from the water, the water penny will remain motionless and can easily be overlooked. They must be removed from the rock and turned on their back in order to see their legs and gills.

Eat and Eaten by: The water pennies are scrapers. They are food for the dragonfly larvae, other predaceous beetles, water birds and even turtles.

Environmental Factors: Water pennies are sensitive to pollution.

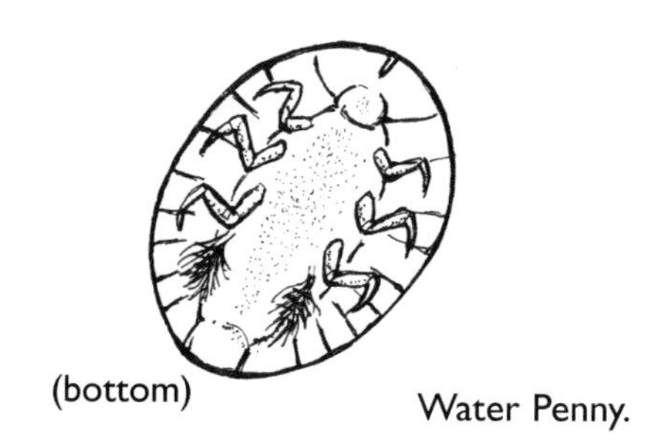

Water Penny.

Riffle Beetle (Insects) Length: adult to 6 mm/larva to 12 mm

Activity: Most beetles live in quiet waters with submerged or emerging plants where they hide while waiting for their prey, but not the riffle beetle. The riffle beetle prefers to crawl on rocks and deposit eggs on plant material in fast-moving water.

Eat and Eaten by: The riffle beetles are scrapers or gathering collectors. They are food for the dragonfly larvae, other predaceous beetles, water birds and even turtles.

Environmental Factors: Riffle beetles are sensitive to pollution.

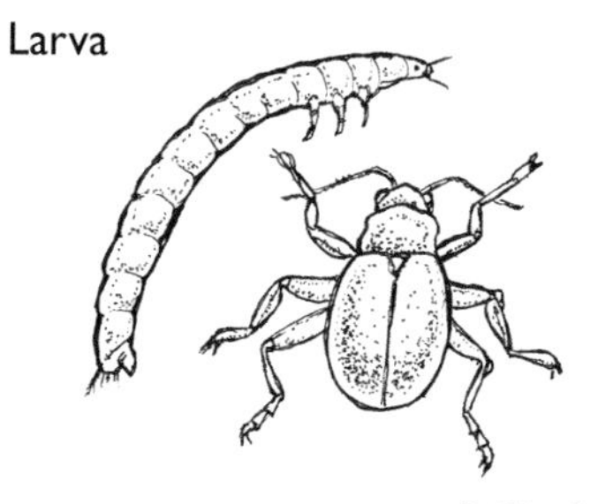

Riffle Beetle.

Snails (Mollusks) Length to 2.5 cm

Activity: Snails glide slowly, on their muscular foot, over the surfaces of all objects beneath the water.

Eat and Eaten by: The snails are scrapers. Many larger animals eat them.

Environmental Factors: Gilled snails are less tolerant to pollution than others. The shells of gilled snails usually open on the right (when the tip of the shell is up and the opening is facing the viewer) where an operculum (plate-like door) covers the opening. Lung-breathing snails, also called pouch snails, (opening on the left/no operculum) are pollution-tolerant.

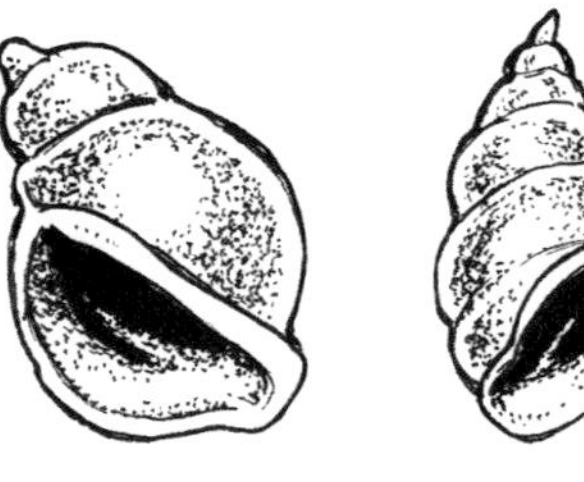

Pouch Snail. Gilled Snail.

Mussels/Clams (Mollusks) Length to 25 cm

Activity: Clams are more symmetrical than mussels. Mussels have a flat, oblong shell. They have a foot that they use for digging into the bottom and siphons that take in water and small particles of food. The larvae (glochidia) develop in the gills of the female clam. Once they develop their first shell, they leave the female through the siphon and attach to the fins or gills of fish. Some species require a specific fish and if they attach to the wrong species they drop off.

Mussel.

Clam.

These clams were the victims of the drought of 1999. When water from Beltzville Lake was released to maintain the flow of the Delaware River, they were exposed to the air and to predators.

Did You Know?

A person who studies fresh water mussels (clams) is called a macologist.

Eat and Eaten by: The larvae remain as parasites on fish for several weeks. The adults are filter feeders. Fish, ducks, and raccoons eat them.

Environmental Factors: Because mussels live long lives (4 to 40 years) and their movement is limited, they are excellent indicators of water quality. Clams are somewhat sensitive to pollution but more tolerant than mussels. Mussels can tolerate only low levels of pollutants. Some species are extremely pollution-sensitive and will die in water that is clean enough for mayflies.

Scientists analyze their shells, which accumulate pesticides and heavy metals, to determine past and present levels of these pollutants. Dams that have interfered with the migration of fish have reduced mussel populations. More species of mussels are in jeopardy than any other type of aquatic organism.

Did You Know?

During the Gulf War, Iraqi forces blew up oil wells and pipelines. The oil formed ponds in low places. The surface of the oil reflected more polarized light than the surface of water and was more attractive to insects. The "ponds" were a death trap for the adult insects as they deposited their eggs in the oil.

4.2 Questions for Study and Discussion:

1. Define the following terms: **VOCABULARY**

benthic	feces	nymphs	pupae
benthic macroinvertebrates	filtering collectors	parasites	scrapers
clean-water organisms	gathering collectors	pollution tolerant organisms	shredders
collectors	index species	predators	
	larvae		

2. What group of organisms is the best "indicator of water quality?"
3. Why are living organisms sometimes better indicators of water quality than chemical tests?
4. List several types of macroinvertebrates whose populations would increase as the level of organic pollution increases. Refer to Environmental Factors.

Feeding Groups

5. List several types of macroinvertebrates that you would expect to find in a "clean water" stream. Refer to Environmental Factors.
6. Give examples of macroinvertebrates that you would expect to find in each habitat: bottom, water's edge, surface, open water.
7. Explain why more shredders are found in the upper reaches and more gathering collectors are found in the lower reaches.
8. Create a chart with a column for each of the feeding groups. List 3 examples of organisms for each category. Note: organisms may be listed in more than one group.
9. List several organisms that are important food sources for small fish.
10. List several organisms that are air breathers and describe how they get air.
11. Give three examples of index species.
12. What type of organism could provide information about the quality of water from 10 years before?
13. Create a food web using at least 15 of the organisms described in this section. Make sure that you begin each food chain with a producer, and organisms have choices of food to eat. Include other organisms to make the food chains complete.

Plants in an Aquatic Ecosystem

4.3

OBJECTIVES

- **Explain** the importance of algae and plants in an aquatic ecosystem.
- **Classify** algae and aquatic plants based on differences in their structure.
- **Relate** changes in the growth of algae and aquatic plants to human activities.

- **Evaluate** methods of controlling the growth of algae and aquatic plants.

In another course, you may have learned that algae are members of the **Protista** kingdom. Although biologists classify most algae as protists, many people refer to algae as plants. Many references include algae as a type of aquatic plant. Whether algae are classified as protists or plants is not an issue that concerns the ecologist. The ecologist is most interested in the role that algae play—their **niche**—in the ecosystem.

Types of Algae

Very small, usually microscopic, types of floating algae are known as **plankton algae**. When present in large numbers, plankton algae give the water a brown, yellow, red or pea-soup green color. Although they are not flowering plants, when enough algae are present to color the water, it is called an **algal bloom**. When there is an algal bloom, each milliliter of water contains thousands, or perhaps millions, of alga cells.

Pond scum is a floating mat of filamentous algae. **Filamentous algae** grow as long strands or filaments instead of individual floating cells. Some filamentous algae form a green fur-like covering on stones in fast-moving streams.

Another type of alga, sometimes mistaken for a flowering plant, is often found on the bottom of ponds or lakes in areas with limestone soil. **Stonewort algae**, easily identified by a central stem with **whorls** of branches, may grow to a length of 2 or 3 feet (0.6–1 m). They are sometimes called **muskgrass algae** because of their appearance and odor.

The Importance of Algae

Algae are the most important **producers** in any aquatic ecosystem. Some species of algae serve as the first link in many food chains. Another important role for algae is the production of oxygen. Algae use carbon dioxide and produce oxygen during photosynthesis. They produce most of the dissolved oxygen in standing or slow moving water. Much of the oxygen escapes into the atmosphere.

Most organisms, including algae, use oxygen for **respiration**. When there are too many algae competing for a place in the sunlight, many of the algae die and decay. This creates a great demand for oxygen. When the weather brings a series of warm, calm and cloudy days, the algae cannot produce enough oxygen to meet the needs of all the aquatic organisms.

Some fish require high levels of dissolved oxygen. When the amount of dissolved oxygen in the water is not sufficient to meet their needs, the fish die. Too many algae may cause a **fish kill** (the death of many fish at one time). The cause of the fish kill may be the lack of oxygen, or the algae may produce toxic chemicals.[See nitrates and nitrites on page 310.]

Some species of algae damage the gills of fish. Excessive concentrations of certain algae can be a problem for other animals as

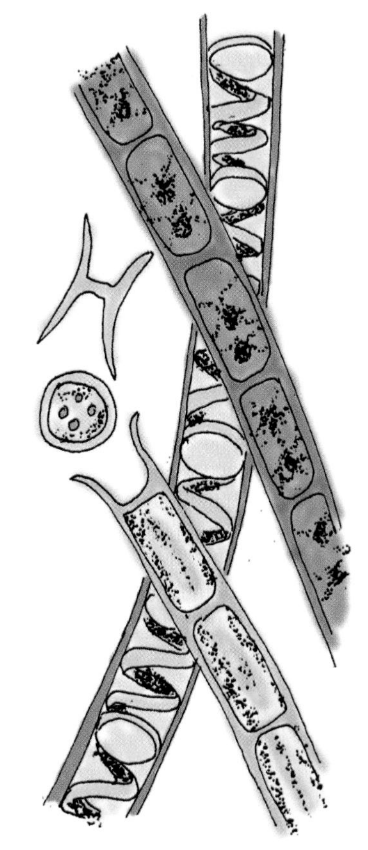

Filamentous and Plankton Algae.

The algal bloom in this aging pond is due to millions of microscopic cells in each milliliter of water.

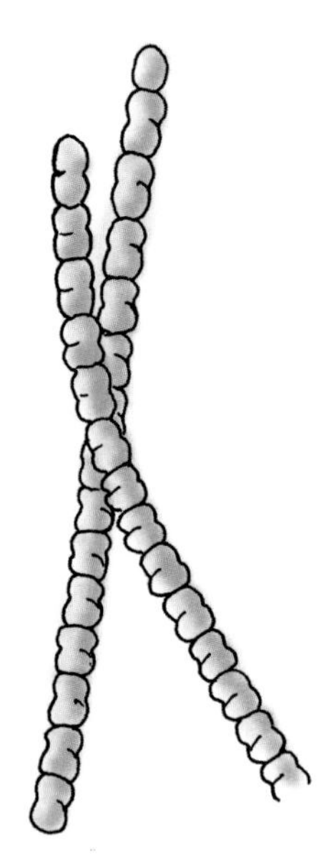

Anabaena Algae.

well. Algal blooms have caused the deaths of sheep, horses, dogs, ducks, and cattle.

Some types of algae make swimmers sick. Some algal blooms are toxic to humans. *Anabaena*, a blue-green alga, can cause an allergic reaction. Swallowing water with high concentrations of *Anabaena* causes cramps, diarrhea, nausea, headaches, muscle pain, weakness and sore throats. Water with a pea-soup green color is not safe for swimming.

In lakes and reservoirs, certain species of algae are the most frequent cause of taste and odor problems. A "fishy" odor in a water supply is frequently due to the presence of certain algae rather than fish. One species of algae gives the water the odor of a "pig pen."

Water treatment plants remove algae and other particles by filtering the water through sand. As water passes through the filter, the particles are trapped in the spaces between the grains of sand. When algae are present in large numbers, the filters quickly become clogged.

As the particles fill the spaces between the grains of sand, the flow of water slows. The direction of the water is reversed and the sand is stirred to remove the algae and other particles. This process is called a **backwash**. Normally filters are cleaned every twenty-four to thirty-six hours. During an algal bloom, the filters must be washed more frequently. An algal bloom increases the cost of cleaning the water.

Types of Flowering Plants

There are three types of flowering plants that grow in aquatic ecosystems.

- **Submerged plants**—grow in deep water and usually are rooted in the muddy bottom. Except for the flower, these plants grow entirely below the surface of the water.
- **Emerging plants**—grow in shallow water. Most of the stems, leaves and flowers grow above the water.
- **Floating plants**—have floating leaves and flowers, or their leaves and flowers rise only slightly above the surface.

The Importance of Flowering Plants

The submerged stems and leaves of flowering plants provide habitats for many small organisms. The surfaces of leaves and stems provide homes for bacteria, fungi, algae, diatoms, protozoa, insect larvae, aquatic worms and other small organisms. Fish and amphibians deposit their eggs among the plants. The plants provide protection from predators. The coating of slime is dinner for the small creatures that are scrapers. They, in turn, are a source of food for the young fish and frogs.

The emerging plants along the shore prevent erosion and provide cover for fur-bearing animals such as beaver, muskrats and mink. Muskrats and beavers feed on the roots and stems of plants such as cattails and water lilies. The plants at the water's edge provide nesting sites for many species of waterfowl and other birds, such as the red-winged blackbird. The seeds provide an important source of food.

The surfaces of leaves and stems of these water lilies provide cover and food for many small aquatic organisms.

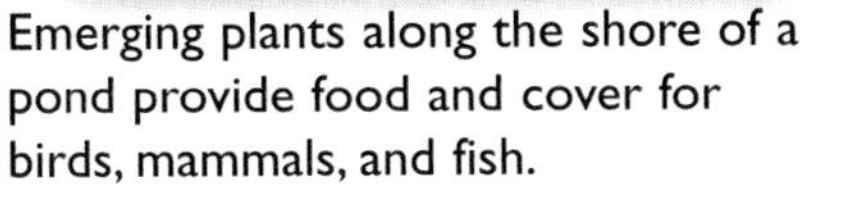

Emerging plants along the shore of a pond provide food and cover for birds, mammals, and fish.

A large pond can provide many hours of relaxation and maybe even fish for dinner.

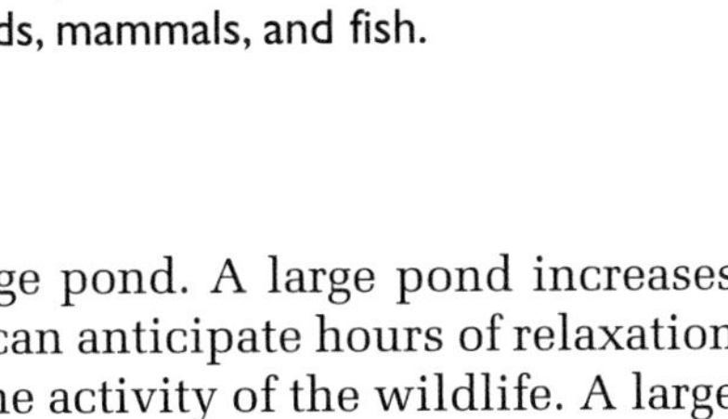

It is easy to see the benefits of a large pond. A large pond increases the value of a property. Potential buyers can anticipate hours of relaxation fishing, swimming or simply watching the activity of the wildlife. A large pond may also provide dinner.

Small ponds that dry up in the middle of the summer are important, too. Ponds less than four feet deep may dry up during the summer, freeze solid in winter, or both. Such temporary ponds cannot support a population of fish. They are usually too shallow and weedy for swimming, and too small for ice-skating.

A small, shallow, weedy pond provides excellent salamander and amphibian breeding habitat. The "weeds" provide places for egg-laying as well as hiding places for the larvae. It is the lack of fish in these temporary ponds that makes them the ideal place for salamanders and amphibians to breed. Fish eat eggs and larvae, and they compete with reptiles and amphibians for food. The absence of fish greatly increases the chance that an egg will survive to become an adult.

This pond dries up every summer, but it is just what 26 of Missouri's 42 species of amphibians need—a fish-free pond.

Water Pollution and Plant Growth

Some pollutants inhibit the growth of aquatic plants while other pollutants stimulate growth. Both types of pollutants can create serious problems. Chemicals that affect the growth of aquatic plants may enter an aquatic ecosystem when there is an industrial accident or from daily operations at an industrial plant or sewage treatment plant—**point sources** of water pollution. Herbicides and fertilizers enter aquatic ecosystems in storm water runoff from lawns, farms, and construction sites— **nonpoint sources** of water pollution.

Many aquatic ecosystems, especially ponds and lakes, are polluted with chemicals that stimulate plant growth. This is due to increased levels of certain chemicals that are plant nutrients (fertilizers). The primary chemicals that stimulate growth are **nitrates** and **phosphates**.

Major sources of nutrients are sewage treatment plants, developments with individual home septic systems, food processing plants, the application of fertilizers, and animal wastes.

Plants along the edge of the lake provide food and cover for wildlife, but too many plants can create problems.

Water Use and Plant Growth

For some uses, plant growth is essential. Aquatic plants attract ducks and geese. Fishermen like a limited number of aquatic plants that provide cover, food and a spawning site for the fish. Plant growth at the water's edge is also needed to control erosion.

The intended use of a body of water determines whether the growth of plants is desirable. For some uses, there may be too many plants. If the major use for a body of water is recreation that includes boating, swimming and water skiing, too much plant growth is undesirable and may be hazardous. In some situations it is necessary to control plant growth.

Too many aquatic plants interfere with operations at fish hatcheries. Excessive plant growth slows the flow of water in irrigation systems, and the plants steal water intended for farm crops. Intake pipes for factories and water treatment plants may become clogged with floating plants. If the water is to be used for drinking, controlling certain species of algae that give water an unpleasant odor and flavor will reduce treatment costs.

Controlling Plant Growth

When the presence of aquatic plants interferes with the planned use of the water, it is necessary to control their growth. Control of submerged plants may not be necessary in water that is more than ten feet (3 m) deep. There is not enough sunlight at this depth to allow much plant growth. When necessary, the following methods can be used to control plant growth:

- Physical Removal: This method is most effective for small quantities of plants at the water's edge. Pulling or cutting must be repeated to prevent new growth. The physical removal of submerged plants is often not practical because fragments of the stems left in the water will frequently grow into new plants.
- Animals: Animals that eat aquatic plants are not usually very helpful in controlling plant populations. Fragments left behind develop into new plants. Ducks and geese feed on certain floating and submerged plants, but their wastes provide fertilizers that cause algal blooms.

  Some exotic species of fish have been introduced to control aquatic vegetation. In some situations they have created problems. Today a bioengineered (triploid) grass carp that is incapable of reproducing, is used to control weeds in some lakes. The release of these fish is prohibited in some states. In other states a permit is needed.
- Chemicals: Many aquatic weeds can be controlled with chemicals. Chemicals that kill unwanted plants are called **herbicides**. The

following steps must be taken to provide the most effective control and the least damage to the environment:

- Identify the plants causing the problem.
- Select the correct herbicide.
- Determine the time of application that will provide the most effective control. It is usually late spring or early summer.
- Calculate the surface area and the average depth of the pond or lake. This is necessary to determine the amount of the chemical to be used.

To find out more information about the use of grass carp to control aquatic vegetation, visit: www.ces.ncsu.edu/nreos/wild/aquatics/weed/grasscarp.

In some states, permits are required to chemically treat any waters. In Pennsylvania, both the Pennsylvania Fish Commission and the Department of Environmental Resources must approve permits for the use of aquatic herbicides.

Many herbicides are toxic to fish and other animals. Many organisms may be affected by the lack of food and oxygen that results from the death of the plants. A chemical used to control plant growth may poison fish, or they may die because of a lack of other organisms that serve as food. The decay of the dead plants may lower the **dissolved oxygen** content of the water to a level that is harmful to fish, causing a fish kill.

4.3 QUESTIONS FOR STUDY AND DISCUSSION:

1. Define the following terms: VOCABULARY

algal bloom	floating plants	nonpoint sources	producer
backwash	herbicides	phosphates	Protista kingdom
emerging plants	muskgrass algae	plankton algae	stonewort algae
filamentous algae	niche	point sources	submerged plants
fish kill	nitrates	pond scum	whorls

2. As an ecologist, which of the following true statements would you consider most important? a. Algae are protists. b. Algae are not plants. c. Algae are producers.

Types of Algae

3. Compare stonewort, filamentous and plankton algae.

The Importance of Algae

4. Algae are not flowering plants. Describe what you would see in a lake with an "algal bloom."
5. Give two reasons why algae are so important in an aquatic ecosystem.
6. Give several problems caused by excessive growth of algae.

Types of Flowering Plants

7. Compare emerging, submerged, and floating plants, and give an example of each.

The Importance of Flowering Plants

8. Briefly explain how flowering plants are important aquatic organisms?
9. Explain why a temporary pond may be a better habitat for some species of frogs than a bigger permanent pond.

Water Pollution and Plant Growth

10. Name the two chemicals that are plant nutrients.
11. Give an example of a point source and a nonpoint source pollutant.

Water Use and Plant Growth

12. Identify three uses of water that might make it necessary or at least desirable to control plant growth.
13. Explain why it is desirable to have plants growing along the water's edge.

Controlling Plant Growth

14. Why isn't physical removal a successful method of controlling submerged plants?
15. Give two reasons why the use of ducks and geese is not a successful method to control plant growth.
16. List the steps that should be followed when using herbicides to control growth of aquatic plants.

Environmental Challenge: Imported Plants

Lake Istokpoga is a shallow, nutrient-rich, 27,000-acre (10,900-hectare) lake in south Florida. Federal, state and local governments have spent nearly $4 million on herbicides to control a weed problem in the lake. The weed is hydrilla—an aquarium plant imported from Africa—that escaped into the wild in the late 1950s. Hydrilla was discovered in Lake Istokpoga around 1980.

In 1992, nearly 2,500 acres (1000 hectare) of the lake were treated with the hydrilla-killing herbicide Sonar. The herbicide slowly kills the hydrilla by interfering with its growth process. It does not affect fishing or other recreational uses of the lake. Farmers, who use water from the lake for irrigation, were notified to avoid using the water for seven days after the herbicide was spread.

Other attempts to use herbicides, to control the growth of hydrilla, were not effective. After each treatment, the hydrilla grew back, and it seemed the money was being wasted. To prevent the hydrilla from bouncing back this time, the Florida Game and Fresh Water Fish Commission added a biological control—fish.

After the Sonar reduced the growth of hydrilla, the state released 125,000 Chinese grass carp. The hydrilla-eating fish live for about 10 years and grow to about 70 pounds. The fish were sterilized so they were unable to reproduce. Regulations make it illegal for fishermen to keep the carp if they are caught.

- What type of plant is causing a problem in Lake Istokpoga? Why do you think this plant has become a problem?
- Identify the methods of control used by the Florida Game and Fresh Water Fish Commission to control plant growth.
- Evaluate the action taken to control the growth of hydrilla in Lake Istokpoga. Do you think this plan will work? Do you think this is a good idea?
- You are to develop a policy for a local government concerning the use of herbicides in bodies of water. Under what conditions would you grant a permit for herbicide use?

Water Quality — Chemical and Physical Factors

4.4

OBJECTIVES

- ✔ **Identify** chemical and physical factors that affect water quality.
- ✔ **Relate** the temperature of the water to the level of dissolved oxygen (DO).
- ✔ **Contrast** ecosystems with hard and soft water.
- ✔ **Evaluate** the condition of an aquatic ecosystem based on chemical and physical conditions.

How do we determine quality? Factors such as size, color, and flavor might be used to determine the quality of an apple. The intended "use" is another factor that is important when judging the quality of apples. Some varieties of apples are good for baking, others for eating, and still others are good for making applesauce.

Water quality is determined by a number of chemical, physical, and biological factors. The designated "use" is also important when judging the quality of water. High-quality drinking water with 0.4 ppm chlorine would not be high-quality water for a goldfish. Most fish cannot live in water with even small amounts of chlorine. Brook trout and brown trout cannot survive in water with more than 0.02 ppm chlorine.

The ability of an organism to survive and reproduce in an aquatic ecosystem depends upon the quality of the water. The water quality depends on certain physical, chemical, and biological conditions. Water is **polluted** when substances are present in the water in amounts that are harmful to the organisms living in or using the water.

In this section we will study some of the conditions that affect the water quality of aquatic ecosystems. Such studies are not simple. Changing one condition will often cause other conditions to change. For example, a change in temperature will affect the amount of dissolved oxygen that the water can hold. **Synergistic effects** also occur. Some chemicals are more poisonous when certain other chemicals are present. Keeping this in mind, let's investigate water quality.

Dissolved Oxygen

Aquatic organisms do not break water molecules apart to get oxygen for respiration. The oxygen they absorb, through their skin or special respiratory structures, is oxygen gas (O_2) that is dissolved in the water—**dissolved oxygen** (DO).

Dissolved oxygen enters water by **diffusion** from the atmosphere. When water is mixed with air as it falls over rocks and waterfalls, the level of DO is greatly increased. Standing or slow-moving bodies of water have lower DO levels than fast-flowing water or bodies of water with wave action. The types of organisms in a pond or lake may be limited by the amount of DO. This is not usually a problem for organisms living in a rapidly flowing stream with clean water.

Photosynthesis in algae and aquatic plants produces oxygen, which increases the level of dissolved oxygen during daylight hours. At night and on cloudy days, the oxygen level falls as all organisms, including algae and aquatic plants, use oxygen for respiration. The water at the bottom of a deep lake has very little DO. Decomposers use any oxygen that reaches the bottom by diffusion.

Water polluted with organic matter has less dissolved oxygen than clean water because the bacteria and other decomposers use much of the

Students measure the dissolved oxygen level of the water in the creek.

Dissolved oxygen is not a problem for organisms living in this fast-flowing creek.

oxygen for the process of decay. When there is not enough oxygen for decomposers, other decomposers not dependent on oxygen take over the job of decomposition. The waste products produced by these organisms give the water an unpleasant odor.

Dissolved oxygen may be the most important factor affecting aquatic organisms. A large variety of organisms usually indicate water with a high level of DO. Fewer types of organisms are found in water with low levels of DO. Many of these, such as the water boatmen, are air-breathers and must come to the surface to breathe.

A balanced aquatic ecosystem usually contains between 5 and 10 ppm of DO near the surface. Only a few species of fish can survive in water with less than 4 ppm DO. Carp and catfish may be able to survive in water with only 1 or 2 ppm DO, but they will be more active if the DO level is higher. Bluegill, bass, and pike need at lest 4 ppm DO. Trout and salmon require much higher levels of DO, usually 6 ppm or more.

Temperature and Dissolved Oxygen

Solubility is the ability of a substance to dissolve in a liquid. The solubility of a gas decreases as the temperature of the liquid increases.

Maximum Level of DO (ppm) Over Temperature (°C)

DO (ppm) in Water
20
15
10
5
0
14.6
10.1
7.5
0
15
30
Temperature (°C)

After several warm and cloudy days, the dissolved oxygen level may drop to dangerously low levels in this weedy Florida lake.

As the temperature of the water increases, the water retains less DO. In contrast, cooler water can hold more DO. Fish, such as trout and salmon which require high levels of DO, are found in cold water. Warm water fish, like carp and catfish, can survive in water with very low levels of DO.

Fish are cold-blooded animals. As the temperature of the water rises, the body temperature of cold-blooded animals increases. As the temperature increases, more oxygen is needed to maintain their normal bodily functions. The warmer water may not hold enough oxygen to supply the fish's needs. The insufficient amount of DO found in some water now causes more fish kills than any other single event, including oil spills.

Most water used by factories, especially electrical power plants, is used for cooling. Pollution occurs when hot water is dumped into aquatic ecosystems. The warmer water cannot hold as much DO. Water quality standards strictly limit industrial activities that increase the temperature of a natural aquatic ecosystem. To meet the requirements, some companies build cooling towers or holding reservoirs that permit the water to cool before it enters the natural aquatic ecosystem.

Cooling towers at this nuclear power plant allow the water to cool before it is returned to the river.

Rainbow Falls, Hawaii

Yellowstone Falls, Wyoming.

In which of these rivers would you more likely find fish with gas bubble disease?

Can There Be Too Much Oxygen?

We have already seen that the amount of gas that can be dissolved in the water is dependent upon the temperature. When a liquid holds all of the gas that can be dissolved at a given temperature, it is **saturated**. If it holds less than it can possibly hold, the amount of gas dissolved is described as the **percent oxygen saturation**. For example, if water holds half of the DO that it can hold at a given temperature it is 50 percent saturated.

Under certain conditions more gas is dissolved in water than normally would be dissolved at a given temperature. When this situation occurs, the water is supersaturated. **Supersaturation** of water usually occurs in rivers below dams or waterfalls. As water falls it mixes with air, and in the deep pool below the dam or waterfall, the pressure increases.

The dissolved gases **diffuse** across the fish's gills, and the gases come out of solution forming bubbles in the blood vessels or the body tissues. This condition is known as **gas bubble disease**. This condition is most likely to occur in spring when large amounts of cold water flow over the dam or waterfall. Fish that do not die of gas bubble disease are frequently in a weakened state and often die of other diseases.

A healthy aquatic ecosystem should have water that is between 80 and 125% oxygen saturation. A low saturation level indicates that there is a demand for DO, perhaps due to decaying vegetation or untreated sewage. The amount of oxygen consumed (demanded) by microorganisms

Did You Know?

Several times a year fish, crabs, and shrimp come ashore in Alabama's Mobile Bay. It happens on warm, still nights when the DO level is low. The rising tide brings the hypoxic (low oxygen) water toward the shore, and the fish swim ahead of it. When the fish reach shallow water, they are an easy catch for local residents who call it a jubilee.

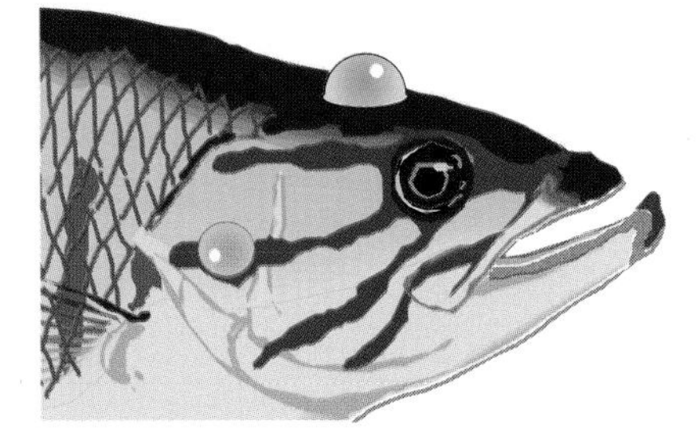

Gas Bubble Disease.

and combined with chemicals in the water is called the **biochemical oxygen demand (BOD)**. If the BOD is 5 mg/L or higher, the water quality is poor.

pH

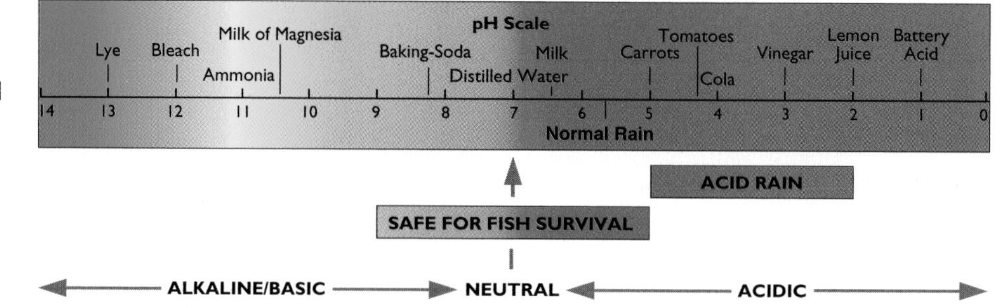

The pH Scale: The color distribution of the chart represents the indicator colors of pHydrion paper that is used to determine the pH of liquids.

Few organisms live in water with a **pH** lower than 4 or higher than 9. Although some organisms live in water with a very low or very high pH, most species have a narrow range of pH where they can grow and reproduce. Some species are very sensitive to small changes in pH and a sudden change in the pH can be deadly.

The pH of water often determines the kinds of animals and plants that can live there. Water with a pH between 6.5 and 8.2 usually supports a good variety of plant and animal life. At 6.5 snails and tadpoles begin to die, salmon and trout reproduction declines, and mayfly and caddisfly populations decline. At 5.5 the decomposers begin to die. A pH above 9.0 can be harmful to salmon, trout and perch.

For background information on pH, visit: http://ga.water.usgs.gov/edu/.

The pH of the water is affected by several factors. Lakes and ponds are usually basic (alkaline) when they are first formed. Living organisms produce carbon dioxide during respiration. When organisms die, more carbon dioxide is produced during the process of decay. **Carbonic acid** is formed when carbon dioxide combines with water. The higher the amount of carbonic acid dissolved in the water, the lower the pH.

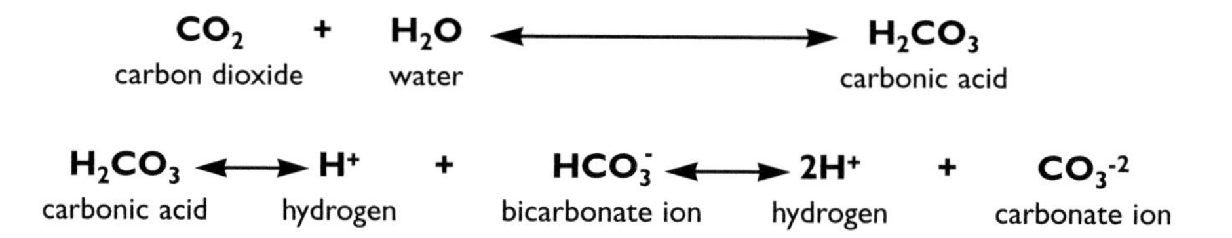

$$\underset{\text{carbon dioxide}}{CO_2} + \underset{\text{water}}{H_2O} \longleftrightarrow \underset{\text{carbonic acid}}{H_2CO_3}$$

$$\underset{\text{carbonic acid}}{H_2CO_3} \longleftrightarrow \underset{\text{hydrogen}}{H^+} + \underset{\text{bicarbonate ion}}{HCO_3^-} \longleftrightarrow \underset{\text{hydrogen}}{2H^+} + \underset{\text{carbonate ion}}{CO_3^{-2}}$$

Water entering aquatic ecosystems from industries may contain chemicals that alter the pH. Accidents involving trains and trucks sometimes result in chemical spills that affect the pH of the water. For example, a massive detergent spill from a tanker truck did not affect the aquatic insect life in a small creek nearby, but it caused the death of more than 32,000 fish.

There are many places where coal has been removed from the ground by strip mining. Some coal deposits and the surrounding rock formations contain sulfur. When the sulfur is exposed to air and water, **sulfuric acid** is formed. For many years after the mining has ceased, sulfuric acid is produced with each rain. Acid mine drainage, from abandoned coal mines, is the single biggest pollutant of Pennsylvania's streams. Over 2,400 miles of streams don't meet water quality standards because of acid mine drainage.

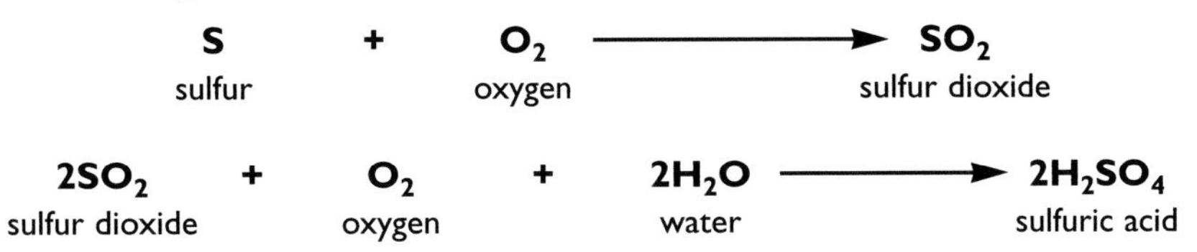

Acid lakes are formed in the old strip mine pits. During heavy rains, these lakes overflow and drain into nearby creeks. Old strip mine lakes lie in the watershed of Cedar Creek, near Columbia, Missouri. As many as sixty thousand fish have been killed when a lake overflows, and a slug of acid moves down the creek. Once the acid is diluted, fish once again move up the creek from the Missouri River. These fish will be the next victims when heavy rains cause another acid lake to overflow.

Two rivers in western Pennsylvania show the effect of pH on an aquatic ecosystem. The Little Conemaugh River that runs through Johnstown, PA, once supported trout, bass, pike, shad and pickerel. Now most of the river is severely polluted with large amounts of acid mine drainage. The upper reach of Stoneycreek River, a tributary of the Little Conemaugh, has benefited from mine **reclamation**. The upper Stoneycreek now supports 22 species of fish, including brook, brown and rainbow trout and smallmouth, spotted and rock bass.

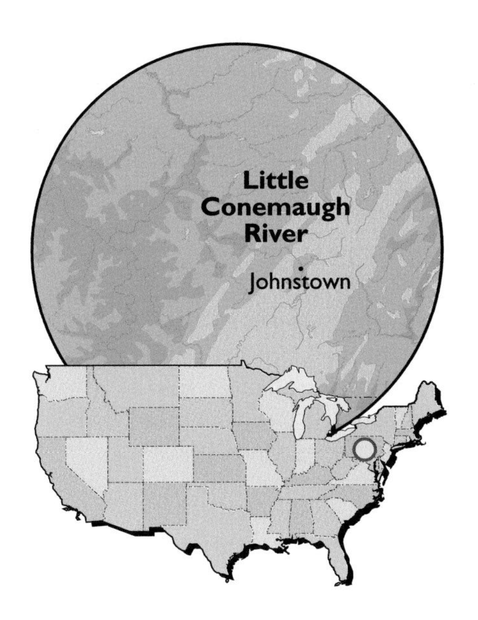

Strip mining can be done without damage to nearby streams. To prevent the formation of acid, the sulfur minerals left behind must be covered with soil. This reduces the amount of acid in the runoff. These new lakes can be stocked for fishing, and plantings can be made to provide more habitats for wildlife.

Streams that drain watersheds with rocks and soils containing natural buffers may have a pH greater than 7. A **buffer** is a substance that, when placed in water, prevents large changes in the pH. Buffers neutralize the acids that enter the water. The **alkalinity** is a measure of the buffering capacity of the water. Freshwater aquatic ecosystems with an alkalinity between 100 and 200 ppm will have a stable pH.

Hardness

The rocks and soil in the watershed also determine the hardness of a body of water. If the area contains granite rocks that do not dissolve easily, the water will contain few minerals. Water that lacks certain minerals is said to be **soft water**. Water with a hardness of less than 10 ppm can support very little plant or animal life.

In areas where there is limestone, the carbonic acid in the water dissolves the calcium and magnesium compounds from the rocks. Water that contains high levels of calcium and magnesium is said to be **hard water**. Calcium is essential for the making of cell walls in plants, and shells and bones in animals. Magnesium is an element in the chlorophyll molecule.

Hard water also contains mineral compounds that act as buffers. Aquatic ecosystems in streams and lakes with hard water are less affected by acid rain than those aquatic ecosystems that contain soft water. The buffers prevent large changes in pH that would harm the aquatic organisms.

The water test most used by industry is the total hardness test. Minerals in the water interfere with many industrial processes. The manufacture of steel and synthetic rubber requires water with less than 50 ppm calcium carbonate. It is often necessary for industries to "soften" the water or remove excess minerals.

The abundant growth of algae in this stream indicates a high level of nutrients. The nutrients come from malfunctioning septic systems in addition to animal waste and fertilizers in run-off.

Nitrates and Nitrites

Most fertilizers, used by farmers and homeowners, contain **nitrates** (NO_3^-). All nitrates are soluble in water. When it rains, the nitrates from fields and lawns are carried into nearby streams and lakes. Another major source of nitrates is sewage produced by humans and other animals. One cow produces waste equal to the sewage produced by 4.5 humans. Nitrogen is also released by the decomposition of organic matter. [See Section 1.7, Nitrogen Cycle, page 31].

The nitrates in a body of water are nutrients for algae and aquatic plants. This increased growth of algae and build-up of dead plant material causes an increase in the BOD and lowers the DO level of the water. The EPA has identified nitrogen as the main factor causing low oxygen levels (less than 3 ppm) in the western part of Long Island Sound.

Unpolluted waters generally have a nitrate-nitrogen level below 1 ppm. Fast-flowing water will prevent the growth of floating aquatic plants and plankton algae even when nitrate levels are high. In the lower reaches where the water is warmer and slower moving, the nitrate causes abundant growth of algae, an **algal bloom**. The algae die and settle to the bottom and their decay causes the DO level to fall.

Water that is used for drinking should be tested for nitrates. The national drinking water standard for nitrate-nitrogen is 10 ppm. Wells can be contaminated with nitrates from fertilizers and sewage. Nitrate levels in the water of farm wells, and wells in areas with septic systems, can be high enough to cause the death of infants. Special bacteria in the baby's digestive system change nitrate to **nitrite**. Nitrites enter the bloodstream causing a condition called **methemoglobinemia** (met-hemo-glo-bin-emia). When nitrites are present, oxygen cannot combine with hemoglobin. The "blue baby" condition that results is sometimes fatal.

Phosphates

Phosphorus, in the form of **phosphates** (PO_4^{-3}), is a plant nutrient and stimulates the growth of algae and aquatic plants. In most aquatic ecosystems the phosphate level is low, and this makes it the "growth-limiting" factor for aquatic plants and algae. The maximum level of phosphates recommended for rivers and streams is 0.1 ppm. A level of 0.03 ppm increases the growth of algae and plants in ponds and lakes.

Inorganic phosphates, the type found in fertilizers used by farmers and homeowners, are attracted to soil particles and organic matter in the soil. When erosion occurs, the soil particles with the attached phosphates enter the water. Organic phosphates are present in human and animal wastes. Phosphates are also present in some detergents and wastewater from certain industrial processes. Many states have banned or limited the use of phosphates in detergents.

Turbidity

Carol Browner, head of the EPA during the Clinton Administration, said that the products of soil erosion are our greatest water-quality problem. Soil erosion increases the **turbidity**—the solid particles suspended in the water. The phosphates attached to the particles and the nitrates dissolved in the water increase the growth of plankton algae, which also increases the turbidity. As the turbidity increases, less light penetrates the water and photosynthesis decreases.

There may be abundant life in the turbid water of some rivers, but there is less diversity of species than there is in the clearer water upstream. Suspended particles create problems for aquatic life. They clog the gills of fish and smother the benthic organisms. Fish eggs and the larvae of clams, crabs, and aquatic insects that are coated with silt do not develop.

Erosion makes water in this stream turbid and smothers aquatic organisms.

4.4 QUESTIONS FOR STUDY AND DISCUSSION:

1. Define the following terms: **VOCABULARY**

algal bloom	dissolved oxygen	pH	supersaturation
alkalinity	gas bubble disease	phosphates	synergistic effects
biochemical oxygen demand (BOD)	hard water	polluted	turbidity
buffer	methemoglobinemia	reclamation	
diffusion	nitrates	soft water	
	nitrites	solubility	

2. List three types of factors that affect water quality.
3. Under what conditions is oxygen considered a pollutant?
4. Why are studies of aquatic ecosystems often complicated?

Dissolved Oxygen

5. What is the source of oxygen used by aquatic organisms?
6. What are the two major sources of the dissolved oxygen in water?
7. Explain why the level of oxygen is low when the water is polluted with organic matter.
8. What is the minimum amount of DO that you would expect to find in an aquatic ecosystem with a large variety of organisms?

Temperature and Dissolved Oxygen

9. What is the relationship between the temperature of a liquid and the amount of gas that can be dissolved in the liquid?
10. Give two reasons why fish may not be able to get as much oxygen as they need if the water is warm.

Can There Be Too Much Oxygen?

11. Describe the condition that exists when fish get gas bubble disease.
12. Give the location and the time of year when gas bubble disease usually occurs.
13. What is the range of saturation levels that indicates a healthy aquatic ecosystem?

pH

14. Give the pH range that supports a good variety of organisms.
15. Explain why the pH of a body of water changes as it ages.
16. Explain why fish kills sometimes occur in streams that receive water from abandoned coal mines.
17. What is the relationship between the alkalinity level and the pH of a stream?

Hardness

18. What determines the hardness of a body of water?
19. Compare water in a lake within a watershed that has granite rocks with the water in a lake within a watershed that has limestone.
20. Why will hard water be affected less by acid rain than soft water?

Nitrates and Nitrites

21. How will excess nitrates affect a body of water?
22. List three problems caused by excess algae growth.
23. Explain why a high level of nitrates in water can be dangerous.

Phosphates

24. How do excess phosphates affect lakes and streams?
25. What is the connection between erosion and phosphate levels in a stream?

Turbidity

26. Describe the effects of turbidity on an aquatic ecosystem.

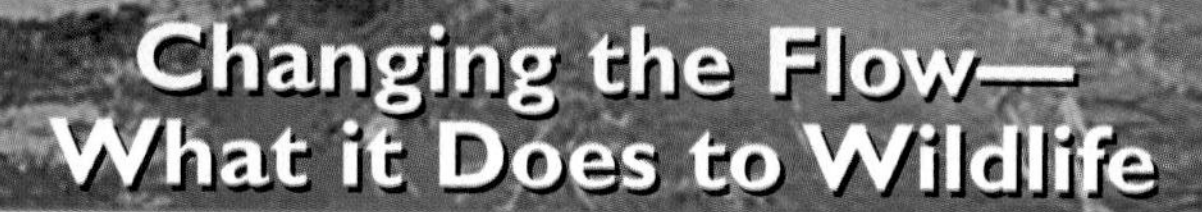

Changing the Flow—What it Does to Wildlife

4.5

Nature's Engineers

Although they are not highly intelligent animals, beavers are excellent engineers. They create deep ponds by damming a stream. Their building supplies consist of mud, stones and small trees. Although they will cut most species of trees, they prefer willows, aspens, poplars, cottonwood, or birch. Because it's easier to float a log than to carry it, beavers sometimes dig a canal system to the pond site.

Beavers will stay in an area until the food supply is exhausted. Beavers left southwestern Wyoming after cattle destroyed the trees they needed for food and dam building. Without beaver dams to slow the flow of water, the free-flowing streams carved deep ditches in the meadows. Scientists measured the amount of silt carried by the water in free-flowing streams and in streams with beaver dams. In one stream with beaver dams, the water carried away four tons (3.6 metric tonnes) of silt each day. In a nearby stream without beaver dams, the water carried a much heavier load, 109 tons (98 metric tonnes) of silt daily.

The Bureau of Land Management and ranchers sometimes slow erosion by building rock chip dams, but building and maintaining these dams is expensive. Now in southern Idaho ranchers have a new plan for stream recovery. The first step is to remove the cattle that have damaged the **riparian** ecosystem. Then they live-trap and move beavers into the area. When the area has recovered, the cattle will be allowed to graze, but only in the spring and fall. Eventually it will become necessary to control the beaver populations.

The beaver dams help conserve water and improve the water quality. When the snow melts, a series of beaver ponds on a stream store the water. By allowing more time for **infiltration**, the beaver ponds increase

OBJECTIVES

- ✔ **Contrast** a stream with beaver dams to a stream without dams.
- ✔ **Describe** the features of human-made dams that are detrimental to wildlife.
- ✔ **Explain** the differences between the life-sustaining ability of a natural stream and a stream that has been channeled.
- ✔ **Relate** the restoration of the Kissimmee River to the water supply in southern Florida.

A healthy riparian ecosystem is important to wildlife.

Dam builder.

Trees cut like this are a sign that beavers are nearby.

Environmental Challenge: Beavers

- Research the history of the beaver. If beavers live in your area, find out how their populations have changed.
- Find out how the beaver is adapted for its job as an aquatic engineer.

Think About It

On November 5, 1996, voters in Massachusetts approved the Wildlife Protection Act, which banned all body-gripping traps. Before the ban, the population of beavers was growing even though trappers were taking 1,800 beavers a year. Three years after the ban, the population of beavers in the state had exploded from 18,000 to nearly 55,000. Now wildlife managers are spending more time addressing complaints about beavers. Both humans and beavers alter each others' habitats, but they often don't agree on the plan.

Engineers designing large hydro-electric dams, like this one in Washington State, must consider the possibility of supersaturation.

the amount of water returned to the aquifer, and the water table rises. The plant growth in the pond filters the water, improving the water quality in the stream below the dam.

Beaver ponds change the habitat, eliminating some species and making it better for others. They create valuable habitat for mink, muskrats, otters, raccoons, turtles, frogs, waterfowl, and bass. A study in central Idaho found three times as many songbirds along streams with beaver ponds than along streams without ponds. There was also a greater diversity of songbird species.

Beavers bring large amounts of plant materials to a pond. The decay of these materials makes nutrients available for algae and plant growth. These nutrients increase the productivity of the stream, and many organisms benefit from the increased food supply. In addition to providing food, the plant material deposited by the beavers also provides protective cover for small fish. In some river systems, most fish depend upon a few streams that are shaped by beavers to provide nurseries for their young.

Some property owners love beavers; others hate them. Beavers don't seem to mind a few people nearby, but people often don't like the way that beavers alter the habitat. Property owners and lumber companies object when beavers cut down trees. City officials object when beavers block storm sewers. More and more beavers are moving to suburban areas. Because natural predators have been wiped out, populations of beavers are increasing, and the beavers are expanding their range.

Danger Below the Dam

Supersaturation—too much air dissolved in water—caused the worst fish kill recorded in Missouri. Nearly 500,000 fish were killed in the first two years following the 1978 completion of the Harry S. Truman Dam on the Osage River. There were no previous reports of supersaturation causing the death of fish below dams, on large rivers in the Midwest. The engineers probably did not consider the possibility of supersaturation in designing the dam. Later a lip like a waterslide was added to the dam to prevent fish kills.

Water pressure increases with depth, and the amount of air that can be dissolved in the water increases as the pressure increases. At a depth of thirty feet (9m), the amount of air that can be dissolved in the water is twice the air normally found in water. As it tumbles over the dam, the water is mixed with air. The water captures air bubbles, carries them deep into the pool below the dam, and the water becomes supersaturated.

Most aquatic organisms need some air dissolved in the water, but too much can be as dangerous as too little. If the amount of air dissolved in water is 10% more than is found in the water naturally, it can be harmful to aquatic life. The amount of air dissolved in the water below Truman dam was more than 30% above natural levels. At this level, fish cannot survive more than a few hours.

The blood absorbs the dissolved gases as water passes over the gills. Small bubbles of air form in the blood when some of the dissolved gases come out of solution. The fish develop a condition similar to the bends called **gas bubble disease**. Biologists can easily identify the problem by blisters formed by the air bubbles under the skin. Another symptom, called popeye, occurs when bubbles collect behind the eye and push it out of its socket. If air bubbles cause blood vessels in the eye to burst, the fish will be blind. The fish die if air bubbles block blood vessels carrying blood to the heart or other vital body organs.

Barriers for Fish

Supersaturation is not the only problem that dams create for fish. Although the adults live in salt water, some fish must have access to fresh water streams for reproduction. Salmon, shad and other species of fish migrate from the ocean to spawn in the same fresh water stream where they were hatched. The instinct to return to their native stream is so strong that the fish fight powerful rapids to get to the spawning beds.

As they return from the Pacific Ocean, salmon must detour through fish ladders built around nine dams on the Columbia River. **Fish ladders** are pools of water arranged as a series of steps. Some water is diverted around the dam and flows through the pools. Fish can jump from one pool to the next as they make their way around the dam.

Even though the words are not written on the massive concrete or earthen structure, high dams and even some low dams are a "dead end" for fish. Fish can bypass low dams by using fish ladders, but fish ladders cannot move fish over dams like Grand Coulee Dam in northeastern Washington, which is as tall as a 55-story building. Dams on the Columbia prevent salmon from using almost one-half of their original spawning areas.

A female salmon that reaches the spawning bed may deposit 2,000 to 6,000 eggs, which develop into minnow-like smolts. The smolts are dependent upon currents to take them out to sea. Dams can be deadly to the young fish. The current is slow and the water is warm. The power turbines on hydroelectric dams kill millions of young fish as they make their way to the ocean. The installation of screens reduces this loss, but screens are expensive to install and maintain.

A study showed that several major dams in the Northwest are costing more in lost fish and recreation than they are providing in irrigation or power supply. Savage Run Dam, on Oregon's Rogue River, was built to provide irrigation water for agriculture, but most of the farms have been replaced by developments. Although the dam has two fish ladders, biologists say the old dam is "a real fish-killer."

A government study shows that it will cost millions of dollars to remodel the ladders in order to improve fish passage. The alternative to remodeling the ladders is to dynamite the dam. The Fish and Wildlife Service calculate that if the dam were removed, 26,700 more fish would return to the river in a typical year. This would add more than $6 million to the local economy.

Old dams that no longer serve their original function block many rivers in the United States. Although these old dams block fish migration,

This fish ladder allows salmon and other migratory fish to bypass the dam that forms Lake Washington.

Machinery at the old mill is silent and the dam is no longer needed. Many old dams, like this one, prevent fish from migrating up streams in the Northeast.

WWW

More than 120 dams have been removed from America's rivers since 1930. For a list of these dams and the story behind the removal of selected dams, visit: www.amrivers.org.

A habitat restoration project for the Brodhead Creek. After a devastating flood in 1955, the U.S. Army Corps of Engineers created a straight, wide channel in the creek. In 1992, the local chapter of Trout Unlimited hired contractors who built deflectors to create pools and habitat for trout. Aquatic specialists use before-and-after electroshocking to study changes in fish populations, and results show far more fish present in streams after habitat improvement projects like this one. Project cost: 500 yards (450 meters) of stream habitat $20,000.

they have been there for so long that the river's potential to support fish has almost been forgotten. History was made in 1999 when the 162-year old Edwards Dam, on the Kennebec River near Augusta, Maine, was removed against the owner's wishes. Removal of the dam will allow 9 species of migratory fish to spawn in the free-flowing waters of the Kennebec.

Channeled Streams and Wildlife

The natural bed of a stream or river where the water usually flows is called the **channel**. The natural channel of an old river twists and turns as it wanders to the sea. The channels are often deepened and straightened to increase the flow of water and prevent flooding. Rivers are also channeled to make them better highways for transportation.

Channeling a stream is not good for wildlife. As channels are dug, the trees and shrubs along the stream's banks are usually removed. Channeled streams have few, if any trees to shade the water and protect it from the hot summer sun. Some species of fish are not able to tolerate the warmer temperatures.

Fish in channeled streams also face other problems. The roots of trees and shrubs growing along the stream bank help hold the soil in place. Once they are removed, there is nothing to protect the stream bank from the force of the flowing water. The rate of erosion increases. As the stream banks are eaten away, the gravelly bottom becomes covered with silt.

Silt and clay increase the **turbidity** or cloudiness of the water. The clay and silt particles cover the bottom of the stream and fill the deep pools. The lack of food, oxygen and good breeding places become limiting factors for some species of fish. The turbidity also makes it more difficult for predators, such as otters and herons, to locate their prey.

The making of channels decreases the productivity of the aquatic ecosystem. It also destroys the habitat of deer, squirrels, wood ducks, otters, eagles and other wildlife species. Figures, released by the Fish and Wildlife Service, show that straightening the Missouri River resulted in the loss of 127 miles (203 km) of shoreline and destroyed 475,000 acres (190,000 hectares) of wildlife habitat.

The Kissimmee—Repairing a River

The Kissimmee River once meandered nearly 100 miles (160 km) through the central part of Florida. That was before Congress approved a major project to convert wetlands along the river to farmland. The project included a 200-foot (60 m) wide, 30-foot (9 m) deep channel with five gates to control the flow of water. The Army Corps of Engineers took the natural bends out of the river and changed it into a 56-mile-long (90-km) canal.

Along the river's natural channel were 45,000 acres (18,000 ha) of wetlands that were frequently flooded. The canal drained more than three-fourths of these wetlands. The wetlands that remain are changed. Plants that grow in the pools created by the engineers are not a good source of food and cover for wildlife. Gone are the small fish and freshwater shrimp that were food for the birds. Many species have nearly disappeared. Waterfowl populations have declined by 90%. Nesting bald eagles have declined 70%.

After many years of draining wetlands and reducing wildlife habitat, we have begun to realize the importance of wetlands. Changing the winding river into a straight canal was a big ecological mistake. Now, as part of the "Save Our Everglades" program, canal C-38 is being changed back into a river. Cattle pastures are being changed back to wetlands.

It took ten years and $32 million to take the kinks out of the Kissimmee and another 15 years and $276 million to put the bends back into the Kissimmee River. Restoring the river will benefit wildlife, and it will also benefit people. The program to save the Everglades is also a program to save the water supply for the people of southern Florida. Without the wetlands to absorb the water and return it to the aquifer, the people of Miami are in danger of running out of fresh water.

Channeling the Kissimmee River resulted in great ecological damage. The goal of a $1.4 million demonstration project is to see if the river ecosystem can be restored.

What Have We Learned?

Changing the natural flow of water affects both the quality and the quantity of habitats available to wildlife. It also affects the quantity and quality of water available for our use. When we plan changes in the ecosystem, we must remember that the ecosystem is a complex puzzle, and we must carefully study all of the pieces and how they fit together.

4.5 Questions for Study and Discussion:

1. Define the following terms: **VOCABULARY**

channel	riparian
fish ladders	supersaturation
gas bubble disease	turbidity

Nature's Engineers

2. In what way is the beaver a conservationist?
3. Explain how the beaver dams affect the water cycle.
4. Give two ways that the beavers help other organisms.
5. Explain why many humans consider the beaver a pest.

Danger Below the Dam

6. Describe how water becomes supersaturated.
7. What causes the death of a fish with gas bubble disease?

Barriers for Fish

8. How do dams decrease the population of fish?
9. Give possible solutions to the problem listed in question 8.
10. What criteria should be used when making a decision about removing a dam?

Channeled Streams and Wildlife

11. Describe how the natural channels are changed when a river or stream is channeled.
12. Give two reasons why rivers and streams are channeled.
13. Describe several ways in which channeling a stream might affect fish.
14. Describe how channeling a stream affects other wildlife.

The Kissimmee—Repairing a River

15. How did the Army Corps of Engineers change the Kissimmee River?
16. Although the river was only 100 miles long, the changes made by the Army Corps of Engineers affected thousands of acres. Explain how this was possible.
17. What changes are being made in the Kissimmee River as a part of the "Save Our Everglades" program?
18. Explain how the changes will affect: (A) wildlife and (B) people.

What Have We Learned?

19. How does changing the natural flow of water affect wildlife?
20. How does changing the natural flow of water affect humans?

Environmental Challenge: The Everglades

Marjory Stoneman Douglas, a pioneering conservationist, worked tirelessly during much of her life (1890-1998) to save Florida's Everglades. In her book, she described the Everglades as a "river of grass." Although sawgrass is its best known feature, the Everglades is actually a complex of grassland and forest ecosystems that are dependent upon cycles of flooding and periodic fires. The Everglades has been designated an "International Biosphere Reserve," a "World Heritage Site," and a "Wetland of International Importance." As Ms. Douglas said, "There are no other Everglades in the world."

National Parks are greatly affected by what happens outside of their boundaries. The Everglades National Park is no exception. During the normal wet season, which begins in May, most of the park is covered by water. During the dry winter season, the wildlife crowds around the few remaining open areas of fresh water. Many plants and animals that live in the Everglades are adapted to alternating wet and dry seasons. When water levels are too high, nests are flooded and wading birds can't find enough concentrated sources of food to feed their young. When the water level is too low, there is a lack of small aquatic organisms, which disrupts the food chain.

Only one-fifth of the historic Everglades has been protected as a national park and even that area is threatened. The population in Florida increases by 900 people each day, and as the population increases, so does the demand for water. Manipulating water to meet human needs reduces the water in the shallow aquifers that feed the Everglades. Water that does reach the Everglades is polluted with nutrients from agricultural runoff.

The rich biodiversity of the Everglades is now severely threatened. The fate of both the Everglades and the species that live there is uncertain, but the National Park Service is working with the U.S. Army Corps of Engineers to find solutions to the problems facing the Everglades.

Congress has extended the park boundary to protect nesting populations of wading birds. In July 1999, President Clinton proposed an $8 billion plan to restore the Everglades. It is intended to balance the environmental concerns with the water supply and flood control needs of the people living in central and southern Florida. Saving the Everglades is one of the world's largest ecosystem restoration projects.

To find out more about this unique wilderness and the restoration project, visit www.nps.gov/ever/home.htm.

- Snails normally reproduce during the wet season. What is likely to happen to the snail population if water managers release excess water into the Everglades and water levels are higher than normal?
- Does the Everglades situation support or refute the statement that "National Parks are not islands of land." Explain.
- What responsibility do we have to restore the Everglades? Do you think we can meet the needs of the environment and the needs of the people?

Trouble at Mono Lake

"We've already lost in California most of our wetland habitat, and with that an incredible diminishment of birds and other wildlife, ...So with increasing population pressures, I think places like Mono Lake are going to be cherished because they are the last of the last."
MARTHA DAVIS
Board Member, Mono Lake Committee

OBJECTIVES

- **Compare** and **contrast** Mono Lake to the ocean.
- **Draw** a food web that shows the relationship between organisms in the lake and organisms that depend upon the lake for food.
- **Relate** the changes in Mono Lake and the growth of Los Angeles.
- **Evaluate** the impacts of the Supreme Court decision on the lake, wildlife, and the people of California.

There is a large depression just east of Yosemite National Park, on the eastern slope of the Sierra Nevada Mountain Range. It is called Mono Basin. Here in the desert climate, not far from Lake Tahoe, is the largest natural lake that lies entirely in the state of California. It is one of the oldest lakes in North America.

The Inland Sea

For at least 760,000 years, water from melting snow in the mountains has tumbled down the mountainside into Mono Lake. In winter, clouds of steam rise from the lake at places where water bubbles out of hot mineral springs beneath the lake's surface. Water also enters the lake from cold freshwater springs.

Mountains surround the lake. Water entering the lake has reached a dead end, for there are no rivers or streams that carry water from the lake. The water remains in the lake until it evaporates, leaving behind its load of minerals. Except for the water from freshwater springs, water in the lake is not fit to drink. It is about 7% salt—twice as salty and 100 to 1000 times more **alkaline** than the ocean.

Life in Mono Lake

Mono Lake has been called the Dead Sea of California. With a pH near 10 it is too alkaline for fish, but the lake is not dead. In spring the growth of algae makes the lake look like a large bowl of green soup. Then in May, between four and six trillion brine shrimp hatch and begin to feed on the algae. By August these tiny crustaceans have so drastically reduced the algae population that the lake is once again a clear blue.

In *Roughing It* (1872), Mark Twain described brine shrimp as "white feathery worms, one half-inch (1.3 cm) long, which look like bits of thread frayed out at the sides." The brine shrimp, about the size of a thumbnail, are a valuable source of food, though not for humans. A local company harvests some of the brine shrimp to be used as food for tropical fish and hatchery-raised trout, but birds harvest most of the brine shrimp. In addition to brine shrimp, alkali flies are an abundant food source for the nearly 100 species of birds that are found at Mono Lake.

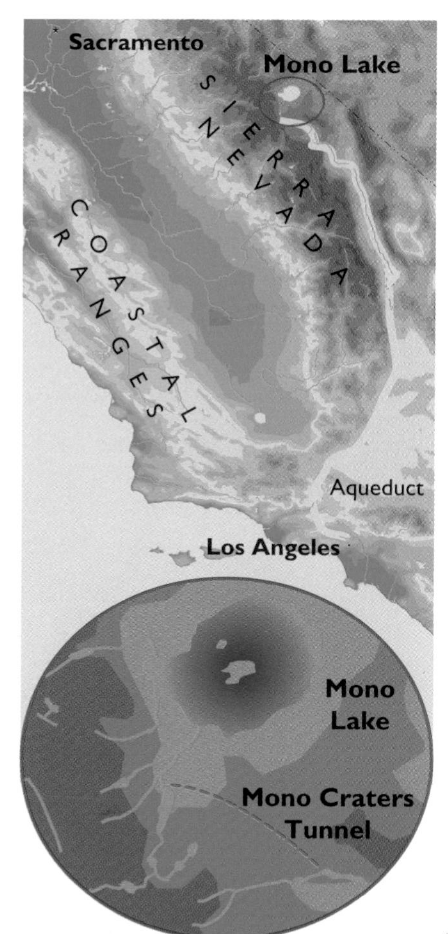

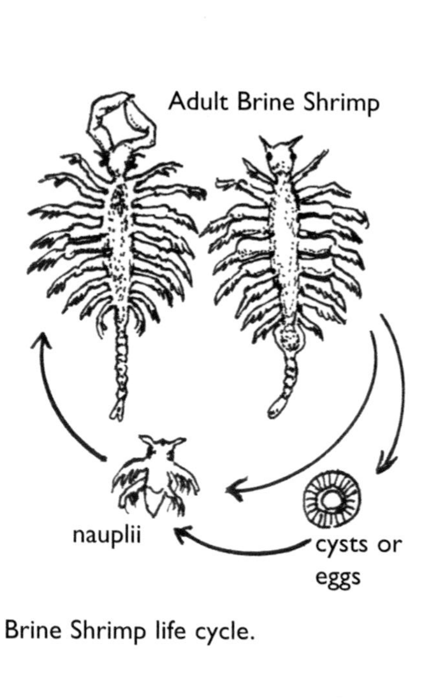

Brine Shrimp life cycle.

During the summer, millions of tiny black alkali flies swarm near the shores of the lake. The bodies of the adult flies are covered by tiny hairs, which trap air when they dive into the shallow water to lay eggs or to feed on the algae. The eggs develop into algae-eating larvae. The larvae and pupae as well as the adult flies are important sources of fat and protein for the birds.

The pupa of the alkali fly was once an important food in the diet of a group of hunter-gatherers who lived in the Mono Basin. The Kutzadika'a (koo-zah-di-ka-ah) Paiute people made their home near the lake during the spring and summer months. The women used winnowing baskets to skim the pupae and larvae from the shallow water near the shores of the lake. They were laid in the sun to dry and used in stews.

Prepare for Take Off

Mono Lake is an essential resting and feeding stop for millions of water birds migrating across Mono Basin. After spending the summer at their breeding grounds in the northern U.S. and Canada, 100,000 Wilson's phalaropes (a member of the sandpiper family) and nearly 2 million eared grebes (a diving, duck-like bird) along with many other species of migratory birds come to Mono Lake. It is here that they rest and prepare for their nonstop flight to their wintering grounds.

The birds stay at Mono Lake a month or more, feeding on brine shrimp or the larvae and pupae of the alkali fly. This abundant food supply provides the fuel that the birds will use during their long journey. Some of the adult birds double their weight before they head south to their winter habitat.

As the birds put on the layers of body fat, they also shed their summer coat and grow new feathers. This process, called molting, also requires large amounts of energy. The birds spend much of their day feeding and grooming their new coat of feathers. As August approaches, the Wilson's phalaropes depart on their 3,000-mile (480 km) non-stop flight to their winter home in the Andes Mountains of South America. In early fall, other migratory species leave Mono Lake for their winter homes.

Adult Alkali fly
pupa
egg
larva

Alkali fly life cycle.

Don't Step on the Eggs

Mono Lake is the primary nesting site for more than 80% of the state's population of California gulls. Volcanic islands in the lake provide the ideal habitat for the nesting gulls. The freshwater springs provide drinking water and the lake provides plenty of brine shrimp to eat. Islands provide protection from coyotes and other predators. The majority of gulls used to nest on Negit Island, but things have changed.

Concrete dams were built on the mountain streams that flowed into Mono Lake and, beginning in 1941, the flow of water was diverted into an aqueduct or artificial waterway. This water diversion caused the water level to drop dramatically. In 1979, the level of the lake was so low that a portion of the lake bottom was exposed, forming a landbridge that connected Negit Island to the lake's shore.

Coyotes crossed the landbridge, the adult gulls abandoned the island, and most of the 34,000 chicks were killed. Attempts to destroy the landbridge with explosives were unsuccessful. In 1980 a chain link fence was erected across the bridge, but only a few gulls returned to the island. Although the level of the lake is higher now and the landbridge is once again flooded, no gulls had returned to nest on the island as of 1998.

The Wilson's phalarope feeds off brine shrimp to build body fat that will supply energy for migration.

Tourists at Mono Lake—Then and Now

By the 1880s Mono Lake was a popular resort area. Mono Inn and other motels were busy in the 1930s. Some visitors were attracted by the claims that the mineral rich water had healing properties. There were conventions, beauty pageants and boat races. Tourists could enjoy a boat ride and a tour of Paoha Island. While some people came to swim and water ski, others came to fish in the creeks that fed Mono Lake.

Tourists no longer come to Mono Lake to swim or watch boat races, but they do come to see the wildlife and the unique landscape left by the shrunken lake. The National Forest Service has declared the Mono Basin a National Forest Scenic Area. More than 100,000 people visit the area each year.

In 1941 the level of water in Mono Lake was 6417 feet (1925 m) above sea level. Fifty years later in 1991, the water level in the lake was 6374 feet (1912 m) above sea level, a vertical drop of 43 feet (12.9 m). At some places, the shoreline was nearly a mile (1.6 km) from the lake's original edge. **Tufa** towers (too'-fah), irregular columns of limestone, stand along the lake's shores and pierce the surface of the lake near the shoreline.

These unusual limestone columns form beneath the water's surface. Fresh water (rich in calcium) enters the lake from freshwater springs and mixes with lake water that contains carbonates (as in baking soda). The chemical reaction creates limestone (calcium carbonate) which is deposited near the mouth of the spring. Eventually the deposits form columns, some as high as 30 feet (9 m). In 1981 the California legislature established the Mono Lake Tufa State Reserve to protect these unusual rock formations.

Before water was diverted from the lake, the islands provided ideal habitat for nesting gulls.

As the level of the water in the lake dropped, land that was once at the bottom of the lake was exposed to the air. Nothing grows on this land because of the high concentrations of minerals that accumulated in the lake's bed. Winds pick up the alkaline dust, making it difficult to see and dangerous to breathe. When the winds blow, the air on the eastern shore of the lake does not meet state and federal air quality standards.

Where Did the Water Go?

The city of Los Angeles (LA) lies in the southern part of California. An average of 15 inches (38 cm) of rain falls on the city each year. This is not enough to meet the needs of the city's growing population. In the early 1900s, the city bought land in the Owens Valley and built a 200 mile (320 km) aqueduct to provide additional water for the city, but that was not enough.

A study in 1920 concluded that the city could continue to expand if the Owens Valley Aqueduct was extended into the Mono Basin. The

Diversion of water from Mono Lake's tributaries threatens the wildlife that depends upon the lake ecosystem.

Formed by chemical reactions in the lake water, Tufa Towers were exposed when diversions of water to LA lowered the level of the lake.

Federal Government owns most of the land in the basin, and the government gave the "water rights" to the city. Some property owners were poor and very willing to sell their land to the city. The land owned by people who would not agree to sell was condemned.

Water from four of the five creeks that once flowed freely into Mono Lake was diverted into aqueducts that carried water to the city of Los Angeles. The fifth creek was too small to divert. Each year between 1941 and 1989, the 340-mile-long (544 km) aqueduct delivered 32 billion gallons (1.2x10^{11}L) of water from Mono Basin to LA— about 15% of LA's annual water usage.

Most of the water used in Los Angeles comes from the Owens Valley, and the diversion turned Owens Lake into a dry lakebed. Additional water used in LA is bought from the Metropolitan Water District. Water sold by the MWD comes through aqueducts from Northern California and the Colorado River. The remainder of the city's water supply comes from its own wells.

A Violation of the Public Trust

In the 1970s, scientists began to study Mono Lake and its tributary streams. They became concerned about the effects of the water diversion. The streambeds were dry; cottonwoods, willows, and other plants along the streams were dead. The stream banks were threatened by erosion. Animals that depended upon the streams or the **riparian** habitat were gone. Wetlands had disappeared and populations of waterfowl that depend on fresh water had nearly disappeared.

In 1980, the scientists found that the salinity of the lake had doubled, and they predicted that if diversion of the streams continued salinity would triple by 2012. If the increase in salinity prevented the reproduction of the brine shrimp and the alkali flies, millions of migratory birds would not have food. Another concern was the threat of predators on the reproduction of California gulls.

The Federal Government owns most of the Mono Lake Basin. In the opinion of some, the government, as owner, should care for the lake in a way that would benefit "the people." In other words, land owned by the public should be managed to benefit the public, not the City of Los Angeles. They argued that allowing the destruction of Mono Lake was a violation of the Public Trust Doctrine — a law that says all people have a shared right to enjoy certain natural resources.

A Day in Court

In 1978, some of the scientists who had conducted scientific studies at Mono Lake formed the Mono Lake Committee. The goal of the Mono Lake Committee was to protect Mono Lake while helping Los Angeles get the water that it needed. Lawyers for the Mono Lake Committee, the National Audubon Society and residents of the Mono Lake area sued the City of Los Angeles in 1979. The lawyers asked the court to decide the question: "Does the Los Angeles Department of Water and Power (LA DWP) have the right to divert water from Mono Lake if it will destroy the lake?" On the other side of the issue, the LA DWP defended the right of the city to divert water from Mono Basin.

In 1983, the California Supreme Court ruled that the LA DWP must consider the environmental effects of the diversion of water from the Mono Basin. It was the opinion of the court that a state must balance the commercial value of water and the interest of the public trust when granting water rights. The court ruled that Mono Lake's public trust values—"the purity of the air, the scenic views of the lake and its shore, the use of the lake for nesting and feeding birds..." must be protected.

Although the Supreme Court had ruled that Mono Lake must be protected, the court did not say how this should be done. Over the next 11 years scientific studies continued and other lawsuits were fought in court. During this time the courts ordered the restoration of the stream's fisheries and prohibited the diversion of water when the lake was below 6377 feet (1913 m).

Finally in 1994, after 16 years of scientific research and many days in court, the State Water Resources Control Board issued a landmark decision that would protect Mono Lake and its tributaries. The Water Board's decision (Decision 1631) set permanent stream flows for Mono Lakes tributaries. The LA Department of Water and Power was ordered to restore streams and waterfowl habitat damaged by the water diversions. Over the next 20 years the lake level will be raised to a minimum of 6,392 feet (1918 m), which is 25 feet (7.5 m) below the pre-diversion level.

www

For an update on the lake level and other information about Mono Lake, visit www.monolake.org.

The Need for Water

LA can buy additional water from the Metropolitan Water District (MWD) to replace the water diverted from Mono Basin. The reason LA prefers water from the Mono Basin is because the water flows by gravity through an aqueduct system built by the city. Water bought from the MWD must be pumped over the mountains, and this makes it more expensive.

Mono Basin water offers another advantage. As the water flows to the city, it passes through 11 hydroelectric generators that provide the city with electricity. Other sources of electricity are more expensive, and they produce more air pollution.

The Mono Lake Committee has helped Los Angeles get more than 80 million dollars in state and federal funds to pay for water projects that would eliminate the need for the water diverted from Mono Lake. These projects have been so successful that even though the city's population has grown by almost one million, the city is using no more water than it did in 1972. Recycling projects are saving millions of gallons of water each day. In 1999 the city used 100,000 acre-feet ($1.2x10^{11}$L) less than it did in 1990.

Los Angeles, CA.

Will the Lake Survive?

The landmark decision issued by the State Water Resources Control Board allows Los Angeles to divert some water from Mono Basin. Once the lake reaches the 6392 feet (1918 m) level, the city can divert about 1/3 of the water that was diverted prior to the decision. The Water Board can always review and modify the 1994 decision. The decision does not guarantee protection for Mono Lake.

Although there is hope that the lake ecosystem will survive and its streams and wetlands will be restored, its future depends upon the ability of LA to meet the needs of a growing population. There is some concern that the problems created at Mono Lake may be transferred to other ecosystems if the potential environmental impacts are not carefully considered.

4.6 Questions for Study and Discussion:

1. Explain how the climate of Mono Basin is affected by its location. [See page 106.]

The Inland Sea

2. Identify the sources of the water in Mono Lake.
3. Explain why the lake is sometimes called the Inland Sea.

Life in Mono Lake

4. Create a food web that includes only the producers and consumers found in and around the lake.
5. What commercial product is harvested from the lake? Draw the food chain that includes this product.

Prepare for Take Off

6. Explain the importance of Mono Lake to the existence of the Wilson's phalarope and other migratory birds.
7. What are two important changes that take place during the bird's stay at Mono Lake?

Don't Step on the Eggs

8. Identify the bird that nests at Mono Lake and explain why the islands on the lake provide ideal habitat.
9. What changes have occurred in the past to make the island habitat less suitable for nesting?

Tourists at Mono Lake—Then and Now

10. Describe the changes in the lake that make it less suitable for some tourists.
11. Explain how tufa towers are formed.

Where Did the Water Go?

12. Describe how the city of Los Angeles obtained water rights for the Mono Basin.
13. List the sources of the water supply for the city of Los Angeles.

A Violation of the Public Trust

14. What were the effects of the diversion of water from the Mono Basin to LA?
15. In what way was the diversion of water a violation of the Public Trust doctrine?

A Day in Court

16. How did the Supreme Court ruling and Decision 1631 affect the Mono Lake ecosystem?

The Need for Water

17. Explain why water from Mono Basin is cheaper than water supplied by the Metropolitan Water District from the Colorado River.
18. In addition to cost, give another advantage of using water from the Mono Basin.
19. How does the water use in LA today compare to the water used prior to Decision 1631?

Will the Lake Survive?

20. Under what circumstances can water be diverted from Mono Lake?
21. Do you think that Mono Lake will survive? Support your position.

"Waters of the United States" and Other Wetlands

The Clean Water Act, passed by Congress in 1972 and strengthened in 1977, created several programs to control water pollution. Congress gave the U.S. Environmental Protection Agency (EPA) the responsibility of enforcing the programs. **Section (§) 404** of the Clean Water Act requires anyone planning to place dredged or fill materials in the "waters of the United States" to obtained a permit from the **U.S. Army Corps of Engineers (COE)**. Since 1977, regulations have also required §404 permits for isolated wetlands, lakes, prairie potholes, and other waters.

Often it is not easy to determine where land ends and water begins. The "**waters of the United States**" are defined as navigable waterways, streams and lakes that flow into navigable waterways, and wetlands that lie beside these bodies of water. **Wetlands** are areas that normally have plants adapted for life in soil that is saturated or inundated with water for part of the growing season.

The EPA and COE identify wetlands by studying the plants, the soil type, and water in the area. Wetland soils, called **hydric soils**, can be identified by their color and texture. Most plants cannot survive in hydric soils, which contain little or no oxygen. Plants that are adapted to grow under these conditions include marsh grasses, cattails, sedges, cottonwood trees, and willows. The presence of water is not always a good indicator of a wetland because water levels fluctuate with the season and the amount of precipitation.

Wetlands are not always wet. **Prairie potholes** are shallow basins that are found in the Great Plains states. They are filled with water each spring just at the time when ducks and other water birds are migrating through the region. The potholes often dry up before fall. **Wet meadows** are seldom flooded, but the soil is usually saturated with water. Although **bottomland hardwood forests** (often called swamps) are periodically flooded, they may be dry for half of the year. **Tidal marshes** are regularly flooded by ocean tides.

The Value of Wetlands

Until recently, people thought of wetlands as wastelands. The **Swamp Lands Act of 1849** gave 65 million acres (26 million ha) of federal wetlands to states for the purpose of "reclaiming." Wetlands were considered useless, unless they were drained or filled to create land for housing developments, industry, or farming. They have sometimes been used for landfills or garbage dumps.

Congress and the courts have concluded that wetlands should be protected under §404 because they affect the water quality and aquatic ecosystems in the following ways:

- Wetlands slow the flow of runoff helping to prevent erosion.
- Wetlands store floodwater and reduce flooding downstream.

OBJECTIVES

- ✔ **Identify** characteristics that are used to identify wetlands and **give** examples of different types of wetlands.
- ✔ **Compare** the impacts of the Swamplands Act and §404 of the Clean Water Act on wetlands.
- ✔ **List** valuable functions that wetlands perform for people and wildlife.
- ✔ **Evaluate** the impact of the §404 permit process and the effects of wetland mitigation.

When wetlands are not wet they can be identified by the plants. The broad base of the cypress tree and the cypress knees are adaptations for life in wet soils.

Although they may be dry for long periods of time, wetlands like this cypress swamp support plants that are adapted for soil that is saturated with water.

Trees growing in wetlands have no need for deep roots. Such trees are supported by roots that spread out near the surface, but are more easily blown over in a storm than trees with deep roots.

Wetlands provide habitat for wildlife.

- Wetlands protect the shoreline from erosion during storms.
- Wetlands filter and purify water that drains into lakes, rivers or streams. Wetlands have been called "nature's kidneys."

In addition to improving water quality and recharging the groundwater, wetlands provide:

- Spawning, nesting, rearing and resting sites for aquatic species. Two-thirds of U.S. commercial fishes depend on estuaries and salt marshes. In 1991, Louisiana's marshes produced commercial fish and shellfish worth $244 million.
- Habitat for wildlife and plants. According to the World Resources Institute, wetlands provide habitat for as many as 600 wildlife species and 5,000 plant species. At least 45% of the animals and 26% of plants listed as endangered need wetlands.
- Timber—bottomland hardwood, black spruce, cypress.
- Recreation—hunting, fishing, bird watching, canoeing, hiking. In 1991, these activities added an estimated $59.5 million to the national economy.

More than half of the 220 million acres (88 million ha) of wetlands in the lower 48 states were "reclaimed" before we recognized that wetlands are not wastelands. In both the United States and Canada, 85% of the wetlands have been converted for agricultural uses. Wetlands remaining in the lower 48 states cover only 5% of the land surface. Wetlands cover 14% of Canada's land surface.

In the United States, thousands of acres of wetlands are still lost each year, but the rate of loss is slower now. Between 70,000 and 90,000 acres (28,280–36360 ha) of wetland are lost each year, mostly for development. **Mitigation** of wetland loss is the process of creating a comparable human-made wetland in the region where a wetland is destroyed by a project. The following examples show how §404 has slowed the disappearance of wetlands in the United States.

Riverside Bayview Homes, Inc.

Riverside Bayview Homes, Inc. owned 80 acres (32 ha) of low-lying, marshy land near Lake St. Clair in Michigan. In 1976, as they prepared to start the construction of houses, they began placing fill material on their property. The developer did not obtain a §404 permit from the Corps of Engineers.

The Corps of Engineers filed suit in U.S. District Court to stop the developer from filling the wetlands without a §404 permit. The court ruled that the property was a wetland and a §404 permit was required. The developer appealed the court's decision.

The Court of Appeals reversed the lower court's decision. The court ruled that the developers were not required to obtain a §404 permit because the wetlands were not subject to flooding by navigable waters. This decision was appealed to the U. S. Supreme Court.

The U.S. Supreme Court ruled that Congress wrote the Clean Water Act to protect water quality and aquatic ecosystems. The court concluded that it was the intent of Congress to include wetlands next to navigable waterways as "**waters of the United States**." The court also found that the land owned by Riverside Bayview Homes, Inc. had been properly identified as wetland. In addition, the court found that the wetland extended to Black Creek, a navigable waterway. The court ruled that the developers were required to obtain a §404 permit from the U. S. Army Corps of Engineers before placing fill on their property.

Moving a Marsh

The purpose of §404 of the Clean Water Act is to protect water quality and aquatic ecosystems, not to prevent development of wetlands. No discharge of dredged or fill material can be permitted in "waters of the U.S." or wetlands, if a practical alternative exists that is less damaging to the aquatic environment or if it will significantly degrade the waters. Normal activities on agricultural wetlands that were previously converted do not require §404 permits, but a new use of the wetland does require a §404 permit.

The permit process is designed to make sure that each project is carefully evaluated. Less than 5% of all requests submitted for permits are denied each year. Where possible, the Corps of Engineers tries to find alternatives to development of wetlands. When this is not possible, they work with the developer to make sure damage to the wetlands is minimized. Landowners may be required to mitigate or compensate for the loss of wetlands by creating or restoring wetlands in another location.

Before the Clean Water Act was passed, road builders simply hauled truckloads of fill and built roads across wetlands. Highways in many states, including a section of a four-lane highway in Wisconsin, are built through wetlands. When the Wisconsin Department of Transportation (DOT) needed to expand the highway to six lanes, a §404 permit was required. The Corps of Engineers required the Department of Transportation to submit a plan that showed how they would minimize damage to the marsh.

The DOT proposed a plan that included hiring an environmental scientist to construct five wildlife ponds and create 25 acres (10 ha) of new marshland. After evaluating the plan, the COE agreed that there was no alternative to developing the marsh. They issued a permit to fill the marshland and expand the highway.

The road builders dug up and moved 22 acres (8.8 ha) of the Upper Mud Lake Marsh. The peat contained roots of wetland plants. Plants and topsoil were removed from the area of the new marsh and replaced with the peat. The road was built and the impact on the marsh was minimized.

Loss of Wetlands in Selected States

State	Acres Lost	Percent*
CA	4,546,000	91
OH	4,517,200	90
MO	4,201,000	87
IL	6,957,500	85
OK	1,892,900	67
PA	627,986	56
TX	8,387,288	52
FL	9,286,713	46
NJ	584,040	39
ME	1,260,800	20
NH	20,000	9
AK	200,000	0.1

*Estimate of original wetlands lost between 1780s and 1980s.

For more facts about wetlands, visit: www.epa.gov/owow, and the Louisiana Coastal Restoration Website at: www.lacoast.gov.

Did You Know?

Wetlands are such efficient filters that cities and industries are building artificial wetlands to clean their wastewater.

Environmental Challenge: Defining a Wetland

In 1992, there was an attempt to rewrite wetland identification manuals and redefine wetlands. Compare the two definitions below:

What is a wetland (the EPA/COE definition since 1970s)? Property is classified as a wetland if:

- Water floods the area or soil is saturated at a frequency and duration that limits the types of plants growing in the area.
- Main plant types are those that can live in soil saturated with water.
- Hydric soils have characteristics created by saturation with water.

What is a wetland (a definition proposed in 1992)? Property is classified as a wetland if all of these conditions exist:

- Water floods the area for 15 consecutive days during the growing season, and number of days in defined growing season is reduced.
- Fewer types of plants would be classified as wetland plants.
- Soil must be saturated at the surface for 21 consecutive days.

Consider the following:

- An important goal has been "no net loss of wetlands." Evaluate the proposed definitions. If adopted, will there be a net loss?
- Compare the environmental and economic impacts of the two definitions.

Swamp or Shopping Center

Pyramid Companies of Boston owned land near Interstate 95 in Attleboro, Massachusetts. Locally the area is known as Sweeden's Swamp. The COE refused Pyramid's request for a permit to build a 150-store shopping center on 50 acres (20 ha) of the swamp. The decision made by the New England COE office was overruled by the COE headquarters in Washington. Washington instructed the New England Office to issue the permit, with the requirement that Pyramid would minimize the loss of swamplands by building an artificial swamp nearby.

The EPA is required by law to review decisions made by the Corps. After reviewing the permit application, the EPA vetoed the request for a permit. The request was vetoed because a practical alternative existed that would be less damaging to the aquatic environment. An alternative site was available for the proposed shopping center. The available site was only one mile away from the swampland owned by Pyramid. Since 1979, the EPA has vetoed only 11 of the estimated 150,000 permit applications reviewed.

Put it Back the Way it Was

In cases where owners or developers have placed fill in wetlands without obtaining the required §404 permit, they may be ordered by the courts to restore the site to its original condition. This requires the removal of the fill, restoring the normal flow of water, and replanting of wetland plants. The goal of the restoration plan is to re-create the wetlands.

While the EPA and the COE prefer to resolve §404 violations without criminal proceedings, it is sometimes necessary to go to court. John Pozsgai bought property with wetlands at a reduced price and began filling without a §404 permit. He ignored warnings by the EPA and COE and defied a temporary restraining order issued by a federal judge. Neighbor's homes were being flooded because of the filling of wetlands. Mr. Pozsgai was convicted of 40 counts of knowingly filling wetlands, assessed a fine, sentenced to 3 years in jail, and ordered to restore the site.

The destruction of 86 acres (34 ha) of wetlands on Maryland's Eastern Shore cost one landowner $2 million in fines. Paul Tudor Jones, a wealthy New York businessman, pleaded guilty when he was charged with negligent violation of the Clean Water Act. Mr. Jones had hired William Ellen as project manager to convert his 3,000-acre (1212-ha) estate into a private retreat for duck hunting. Both consulting engineers and the COE told Mr. Ellen that permits were needed, but he did not obtain the proper permits.

When work continued, even after repeated warnings, the landowner was notified. The owner fired the project manager and hired a conservationist to restore the wetlands. The retreat, which borders the Chesapeake Bay, is now recognized as a model for wetland development. The project manager was sentenced to six months in jail and one year supervised release.

Can Humans Imitate Mother Nature?

Ecologist Joy Zedler is monitoring a new wetland created to mitigate or compensate for the loss of a part of San Diego's Sweetwater Marsh. The marsh was disturbed to build a new interchange for Interstate 5 and a flood-control canal. The §404 permit required the road builders and ditch diggers to create a new marsh in another location.

After studying the new marash for 5 years, Zedler concluded that it was not functioning like the original marsh. Creating a functioning marsh requires finding all the parts, and we do not know all of the parts. When an important predatory insect is not introduced to a new marsh, there may be a population explosion of insects that feed on marsh plants. The Sweetwater Marsh is home to the endangered light-footed clapper rail. Although birds still nest in sections of the marsh that weren't disturbed, they are not nesting in the newly created marsh. No one knows why.

POPULATION LINK

The National Research Council has also concluded that restoring wetlands is a "trial-and-error" process. While it may work in some places, replacing wetlands is not always a success. The council recommended that restoration projects should not be used to justify the destruction of other wetlands. But it is often difficult to say "No" to development, especially when the human population is expanding.

Environmental Challenge: Coastal Development

More than 100 beach-front homes that were damaged by a storm cannot be rebuilt. New federal and state laws prohibit rebuilding homes in coastal wetlands when:

(1) The damage is more than 50% of the home's value, and

(2) Septic and water systems have been affected.

Consider the environmental and economic impacts of the laws:

- Is this law fair to property owners?
- Are there alternatives?
- Should the law be changed?
- What additional information do you need to know to make these decisions?

4.7 Questions for Study and Discussion:

1. Define the following terms: **VOCABULARY**

bottomland hardwood forests	prairie potholes	U.S. Army Corps of Engineers (COE)	wet meadows
hydric soils	Section (§)404	"waters of the United States"	wetlands
mitigation	Swamp Lands Act		
	tidal marshes		

2. What department of the Federal Government is responsible for enforcing the Clean Water Act?
3. Who must obtain a Section 404 permit? What department of the Federal Government is responsible for granting Section 404 permits?
4. When is a body of water classified as "waters of the United States?"
5. What is a wetland? What are the three factors that the EPA and COE study in order to identify an area as a wetland?

The Value of Wetlands

6. List the ways that wetlands improve water quality.
7. What was the purpose of the Swamp Lands Act?
8. We know that wetlands improve water quality; list four additional reasons why wetlands are valuable.
9. What percentage of the wetlands in the lower 48 states have been reclaimed? How does the loss of wetlands in Canada compare to the loss in the United States? What is the major reason for wetland loss in both countries?

Riverside Bayview Homes, Inc.

10. Why did the Corps of Engineers file suit against Riverside Bayview Homes, Inc.?
11. What was the reason that the Court of Appeals reversed the decision of the District Court?
12. According to the decision of the U.S. Supreme Court, are wetlands a part of the "waters of the United States?" Was the land owned by Riverside Bayview Homes, Inc. wetland? Were the developers required to obtain a §404 permit?

Moving a Marsh

13. What is the purpose of Section 404 of the Clean Water Act?
14. Most requests for section 404 permits are denied. [True/False]
    If there is no alternative, development of wetlands is allowed. [True/False]
15. Describe how the Wisconsin Department of Transportation built a road through a marsh without destroying it.

Swamp or Shopping Center

16. Why did the Environmental Protection Agency veto a permit that would have allowed Pyramid Companies of Boston to build a shopping center in Sweeden's Swamp?

Put it Back the Way it Was

17. What happens if a developer or private landowner fills in the "waters of the United States" without a permit?
18. What three requirements must be met in order to restore a wetland that has been damaged by placing fill in the wetland.
19. Do you think the fine for violations of the Clean Water Act at the Maryland estate was appropriate? Explain your answer.

Can Humans Imitate Mother Nature?

20. What makes it difficult to create a new wetland that functions like the old one?
21. Why don't we "just say no" to the development of wetlands? Do you think we should?

Environmental Challenge: Government Regulations

Nearly half of the potholes in the "duck belt" across Minnesota and the Dakotas are less than a quarter-acre (0.1 ha) in size. One study showed that 75% of the prairie country's breeding ducks and 96% of its breeding shorebirds are raised on these seasonal ponds.

A study in Massachusetts revealed that, during the spring and summer, black bears spend 60% of their time feeding in small, forested wetlands.

Many state and local governments have recognized the importance of small wetlands and have passed laws that regulate activities in wetlands. Some state regulations are more restrictive than federal laws.

- Consider the following national permits and check the regulations in your area to see if they are more restrictive than these federal regulations:

(1) A permit is automatically issued for construction or expansion of single-family homes that affect up to one-half acre of nontidal wetlands.

(2) A streamlined permit process allows small landowners, farmers and small businessmen to carry out routine projects that affect less than 2 acres of wetlands.

In fiscal 1995, approximately 62,000 people applied to the Corps for a §404 permit. Over 83% were covered by general permits like those described in (1) and (2) above. Only 8% were required to go through an extensive review that took an average of 123 days. Only 274 applicants (0.5%) had their permits denied.

- What definition of wetlands do you think is best?
- Do you think that wetlands should be classified and protected based on their value?
- Do you think that the effort to protect wetlands has been balanced between the value of the wetlands and the needs of the people?
- Under what conditions should mitigation of wetland loss be required?
- If you owned a prairie pothole or a small forested wetland, could you fill it?

Can We Save the Chesapeake?

"The preservation of our soil and water resources must be one of our national priorities. History has shown us that when the soil or water resources of a society diminish, so does that society."

CHARLES S. ROBB
former Governor of Virginia

OBJECTIVES

- ✔ **Locate** the Chesapeake Basin and the Chesapeake Bay on a map.
- ✔ **Explain** the relationships between the people, the wildlife and the bay.
- ✔ **Relate** the water quality in the bay to human activities in the bay's watershed.
- ✔ **Justify** the description of Submerged Aquatic Vegetation as keystone species.
- ✔ **Develop** a list of criteria that must be assessed to determine the water quality of the bay.
- ✔ **Create** a plan that will improve and protect the water quality and the organisms that depend upon the bay.

The area where fresh water from a river mixes with salt water from the ocean is called an **estuary**. The largest estuary in North America is the Chesapeake Bay. People living in Maryland and Virginia simply call it "The Bay," as if it were the only one. There are many other bays, but no other bay is as complex or as productive as the Chesapeake.

The Bay's 64,000-square-mile (166,000-sq.-km) watershed lies in six different states [Delaware, Maryland, Virginia, West Virginia, Pennsylvania and New York] and the District of Columbia. Although the Bay does not reach into Pennsylvania, almost half of Pennsylvania is in the Chesapeake Basin (watershed). The Susquehanna River flows 440 miles (700 km) from Cooperstown, New York, through Pennsylvania and into Maryland. It supplies nearly one-half of the Bay's freshwater and as much as 90% of the water in the upper Bay.

The People's Bay

The Bay extends for almost 200 miles (320 km) from southern Virginia to northern Maryland. Two major shipping ports on the Bay are connected with many smaller ports farther inland. The ease of transportation has encouraged the development of many industries including shipbuilding, agriculture, steel making, paper manufacturing and chemical production. Jobs provided by these industries have attracted many people to the area.

The Bay also supports a large recreational industry that attracts many tourists to the area. Recreational fishing in Maryland and Virginia brings in more than $1 billion each year. More than 175,000 sailboats and motorized pleasure boats were registered in 1993.

Development and human activities along Chesapeake Bay and the rivers and streams which enter the Bay are threatening its ability to produce food for people and wildlife.

The Susquehanna River supplies one-half of the Bay's freshwater and 90% of the water in the upper Bay.

Chesapeake Bay.

Motorists travelling on Interstate 80 see this sign as they enter the Susquehanna River watershed. The Susquehanna River provides most of the water in the upper part of Chesapeake Bay.

The edges of the Bay provide habitat for so many humans that the Bay is sometimes called the "People's Bay." Since 1950, the population along the Bay has more than tripled, and it continues to grow. Fifteen million people live in the Chesapeake Bay watershed and the population is expected to grow to 18 million by the year 2020. Each year thousands of acres of forests and pastures are converted to urban or residential developments.

Habitat for Wildlife

The wetlands, along the 4,400 miles (7,080 km) of the Chesapeake Bay's shoreline, provide critical habitat for many wildlife species. While many are permanent residents, some species spend only part of their life cycle there. The Bay's wetlands provide winter homes for approximately one million migratory birds.

More than one-half of the Bay's wetlands have been filled, drained, or converted to open water. In the past, wetlands were considered worthless unless they could be used for farmland or developed. Today scientists see wetlands as important nurseries for fish and vital habitat for wildlife. On the basis of their ability to produce food, wetlands are worth more than most farmland. They also improve water quality by filtering storm water runoff.

Thirteen species of underwater grasses, known as **Submerged Aquatic Vegetation (SAV)**, once carpeted vast areas of the Bay's shallow waters. These underwater grasses are considered keystone species and indicators of water quality. SAV provides essential cover for fish, crabs, and other invertebrates. SAV also provides food for waterfowl. It is the most important producer in many of the Bay's food chains because the dead SAV is eaten by the zooplankton, which are essential to the survival of young fish and some adult fish.

Estuaries are important protein factories. Two-thirds of the commercially important fish and shellfish harvested along the Atlantic Coast depend on estuaries and their wetlands. Of the ten most commercially valuable species [shrimp, salmon, tuna, oysters, clams, menhaden, crabs, lobsters, flounders and haddock], seven species depend on estuaries. Only tuna, lobsters and haddock do not. For some species the estuary is an important source of food. For other species the estuaries provide places to spawn and a nursery for their young.

Fish and Wildlife in Trouble

The Chesapeake Bay supports more fish and wildlife than any other estuary. Although it still provides most of the seafood for the Atlantic coast, the Bay is no longer producing as much protein as it once did. As the human population has increased, the quality of water in the Bay has declined.

The oyster harvest fell to 592,000 pounds (269,091 kg) in 1993, which is less than one percent of the harvest in the late 1800s. Overharvesting was the initial cause of the decline in the oyster population. Loss of habitat (a clean hard surface where oysters can attach) and two parasites (which kill the oysters before they reach a harvestable size) are also contributing to the decline in the oyster population.

Adult blue crabs live in the upper and middle parts of the Bay. After mating, the female blue crab migrates toward the mouth of the Bay to spawn in water where pollutants are more diluted than they are in the upper region of the Bay. Underwater grasses are important to the survival of the young crabs.

Blue crabs are still plentiful and the population is healthy, but scientists are concerned that watermen are still overharvesting the blue crabs. Watermen take about 75% of the adult crabs from the Bay each year. Both Maryland and Virginia have regulations that limit the taking of crabs.

The catch of valuable fish is also declining, and commercial fisheries are in difficulty. In 1969, more than one million pounds ($4.5x10^5$kg) of shad were taken from the Chesapeake. Ten years later the take was only 20,000 pounds ($9x10^3$kg). Over-harvesting, organic pollution, and hydroelectric dams have reduced shad populations.

Steps are being taken to reverse the decline in the shad population. A moratorium prohibits the sale, capture or possession of shad in the Chesapeake Bay. Passageways are being constructed around some dams and others are being removed. Fish ladders and passageways on the Susquehanna River, costing $50 million, allowed 100,000 shad to return to their spawning grounds in 1997. By 2005, more than 1,300 miles (2,080 km) of rivers in the Chesapeake Basin will be accessible to migratory fish like the shad.

Although overfishing with commercial nets is partly responsible for the decline in fish populations, another problem is the poor quality of the water in the upper part of the Bay. The tidal freshwater tributaries of the Chesapeake provide the spawning habitat of the striped bass. Here the young bass feed on the zooplankton. As the water quality declined, fewer adult fish spawned, fewer eggs hatched and fewer young survived.

The commercial harvest of striped bass fell from nearly 15 million pounds ($6.8x10^6$kg) to less than 2 million ($9x10^5$kg) in a decade. In 1984, the striped bass, or rockfish, was listed as a "threatened species." The states of Maryland, Delaware and Virginia banned striped bass fishing, and fishing restrictions were implemented along the entire Atlantic Coast. The ban on fishing has helped to rebuild the population and a limited fishing season is once again permitted. There is concern that the adult fish are now thin with little or no body fat.

Menhaden spawn in the ocean, and then they move into the Bay where they feed on the abundant algae. Menhaden are now the most economically important fish in the Bay. About 90% of the annual Atlantic Coast catch is processed into fishmeal and oil, while the rest is used for lobster, crab and fish bait. The menhaden are an important source of food for striped bass and other fish in the Bay. Although they are still abundant, the population of menhaden in the Bay has decreased.

Oysters are an important Bay creature. By filtering the water in the Bay, oysters improve the water quality.

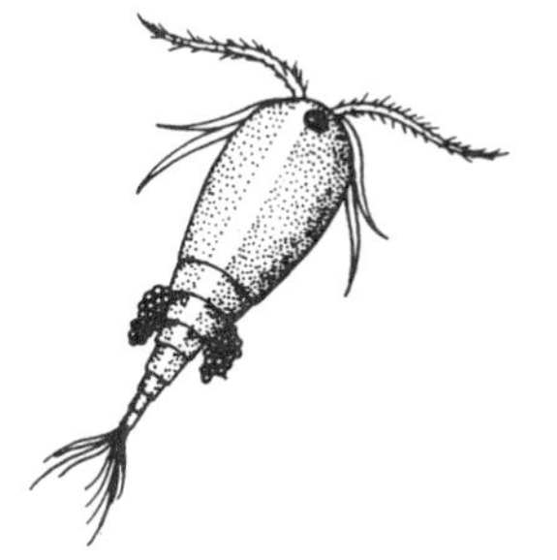

Copepods are a common form of zooplankton that are an important link between phytoplankton (algae) and many fish species.

Submerged Aquatic Vegetation (SAV) that grow in the shallow water of the Bay are the most important producers in the Bay's food chains. Much of the submerged vegetation has disappeared.

Identifying the Problems

In 1975, the U.S. Congress asked the EPA to begin a major study of the Bay's water quality and its wildlife. Congress wanted to know what was causing the decline in water quality in the Bay, how serious the situation was, and what could be done to improve conditions in the Bay. In 1983, the EPA published the results of the $27 million study that took seven years to complete.

The study confirmed the theory that the Bay acts as a sink without a drain. Some pollutants that enter the Bay are attached to particles of clay. As the water flows through the Bay to the ocean, the clay particles sink to the bottom of the Bay. Studies were conducted on two types of pollutants—nutrients and toxic substances.

Nutrients:

POPULATION LINK

Nutrients are the major pollution threat to the Bay. Population growth and farming practices have increased levels of nutrients, mainly nitrates and phosphates, in the upper and middle parts of the Bay. Nutrients come from both point and nonpoint sources. **Point sources** are those that are discharged through a pipe or ditch—mainly sewage treatment plants and industries. In New York, Maryland, Virginia, and D.C., most nitrogen and phosphorus comes from point sources, mainly sewage treatment plants.

Nonpoint sources are those that flow directly from the land. Nonpoint sources include runoff from farmland, residential lawns, developments, construction sites, and abandoned mines. In Pennsylvania, most nutrients come from nonpoint sources, mainly agriculture. Precipitation is also an important nonpoint source of pollution. Atmospheric deposition is a major source of nutrients (nitrogen oxides), pesticides and toxic chemicals, such as mercury and lead, entering the Bay.

The nutrients "fertilize" the Bay and stimulate the growth of algae. The increased growth of algae, and particles of soil suspended in the water, reduce the amount of sunlight that passes through the water. Without sunlight the SAV dies, and an important source of food and cover is missing.

When the algae and SAV die, they sink to the bottom and begin to decay. The process of decay uses the dissolved oxygen faster than it is

The shad spends most of its life in the ocean, but each spring it travels through the Bay and into fresh water to spawn.

Menhaden live in the open water of the Bay feeding on abundant phytoplankton.

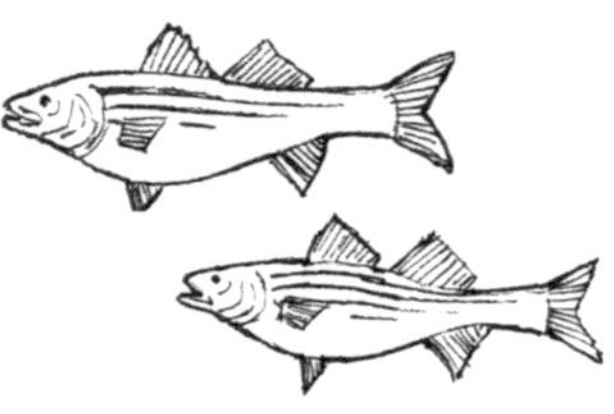

Striped bass spawn in the tidal fresh water areas of the Bay or the tributaries. The adults may remain in the Bay or migrate to the ocean.

While living, Submerged Aquatic Vegetation (SAV) is important as food for ducks and cover for shedding crabs. When it dies, it is food for many small organisms. SAV is essential to a healthy Bay.

replaced by photosynthesis. The low level of oxygen becomes a limiting factor for fish and shellfish. Widespread areas in the upper and middle regions of the Bay have low levels of dissolved oxygen from May until September. Due to the reduced flow of water during the severe drought of 1999, the number of fish kills increased.

Toxic Substances:

Toxic substances are those chemicals that can harm living organisms. Toxic metals include arsenic, cadmium, chromium, copper, lead and zinc. Organic compounds that are toxic include hydrocarbons, pesticides and other industrial chemicals that contain carbon.

More than 5,000 point sources dump wastewater into the rivers and creeks that flow into the Bay. Much of the wastewater contains low levels of nutrients and/or toxic chemicals. Toxic chemicals accumulate in the Bay, and in some localized areas high concentrations of certain toxic chemicals are threatening organisms.

Areas with highly contaminated sediments are near urban areas with high levels of industrial activity. The highest levels of toxic chemicals are found in the upper Bay, in the Baltimore Harbor and in some rivers, posing a significant risk to aquatic organisms in these areas.

Toxic chemicals also enter the Bay through storm drains that carry runoff away from urban areas. Used motor oil poured into a storm drain eventually enters an aquatic ecosystem. Oil contains certain toxic chemicals that slowly dissolve in the water. Some of these chemicals are carcinogens while others produce toxic effects.

The four quarts (3.8 L) of oil from a car engine can form an oil slick that covers nearly 8 acres (3.2 ha) of an aquatic ecosystem. An **oil slick**—a layer of oil on the surface of the water—reduces the amount of dissolved oxygen that can enter the water from the atmosphere. The oil also smothers fish by coating the surfaces of their gills. **Benthic** organisms and SAV are smothered when mixtures containing oil settle to the bottom of the Bay.

Many household, auto, lawn and garden products (such as paints, paint thinners, pesticides, and antifreeze) are improperly dumped or flushed down the drain. The standard sewage treatment process does not remove these toxic substances, and they flow into the Bay with the treated wastewater. During heavy rains, many of the chemicals used on lawns and gardens are carried into storm drains with the runoff.

Areas of the Bay that are contaminated with toxic chemicals support fewer types and numbers of bottom-dwelling organisms. In areas with high levels of toxic chemicals, fish tissue contains abnormal cells. Even though the levels of some toxic chemicals present in the aquatic ecosystem are low, some chemicals **bioaccumulate**, and much higher levels are found in fish.

What are the environmental impacts of this oil sprayed along a Pennsylvania highway? Some of the toxic chemicals evaporate, but some of the oil is carried by runoff into the storm drain. Eventually it will have an impact on an aquatic ecosystem like the Chesapeake Bay.

Working Together to Save the Bay

Government officials and the public were alarmed by the information revealed by this EPA study. If the living resources of the Bay were to be saved, immediate action was needed. In 1983, officials from Maryland,

Virginia, Pennsylvania, the District of Columbia, and the EPA signed the **Chesapeake Bay Agreement**. The agreement was the beginning of a cooperative effort to "improve and protect the water quality and living resources of the Bay."

The states and the EPA worked together to develop a plan for the entire Chesapeake Basin. One of the goals of the plan was a 40% reduction in the nutrients entering the Bay by the year 2000. The plan included changes in the following areas:

Point sources like the pipe shown here dump toxic pollutants into rivers that flow into the Bay.

Industry:

Toxic chemicals must be removed by pretreatment of wastewater before it is sent to the sewage treatment plant or discharged directly into the Bay. The amount of toxics that industries released to the Bay decreased by 67% between 1988 and 1996.

Storm Water Control:

Projects are being implemented to slow the velocity of storm water runoff and reduce erosion. This will help protect aquatic life from being smothered by sediment. In some places it is necessary to pretreat storm water to reduce the levels of toxic chemicals, nitrogen and phosphorus.

Agriculture:

Much of the nitrogen enters the Bay as nitrates that are **leached** from cropland and animal waste. There are 600 million chickens on farms along the eastern side of the Bay. Most of the phosphorus is carried into the Bay as phosphates on eroded soil particles. Soil and water tests in southeastern Pennsylvania show that farmers often apply more nutrients than their crops need. The excess is carried into the Bay.

Pennsylvania, Maryland and Virginia have nutrient/manure management programs. These programs are beginning to reduce nutrients entering the Bay through use of the **Best Management Practices** (BMPs). These practices not only help reduce pollution in the Bay, but they also reduce the cost of raising a crop. BMPs include:

- Using soil tests to determine the actual amount of nutrient needed.
- Timing the application of nutrients to correspond to the crop's needs.
- Reduced tillage, crop rotation, contour farming, strip cropping.
- Using integrated pest management (IPM) on cropland.

Land Use:

Human activities [including agriculture, logging and development] on land along streams increase runoff and contribute to erosion. Forests provide the best protection against erosion. While 60% of the watershed is forested, the land closest to the Bay and the lower reaches of its tributaries is developed.

Planting a buffer strip to separate human activity from streams can reduce erosion and decrease the suspended sediment and nutrients carried into the stream. Maryland has restricted development by

Environmental Challenge: Save the Bay

The Chesapeake Bay Foundation began issuing a "State of the Bay Report" in 1998. Visit their website at: www.savethebay.cbf.org to view the latest report.

The Chesapeake Bay Program is the regional partnership that is directing the restoration of the Bay. Visit their website at: www.chesapeakebay.net.

- How do the levels of pollution—nutrients and toxins—in the Bay compare to 1998 levels?
- How has land use changed since 1998?
- How has the quality of the habitat— SAV, DO, turbidity—changed?
- How have the populations of shad, stripped bass, oysters, crabs and menhaden changed?

The CBF set goals for Year 2010:

- Do you think that we will Save the Bay if we reach these goals?
- Are we doing enough or should we be doing more to Save the Bay?

www

requiring a thousand-foot (76 m) buffer zone along most remaining natural shorelines. The Riparian Forest Buffers Initiative calls for restoring 2010 miles (3216 km) of riparian buffers on streams and shoreline in the Chesapeake Basin by the year 2010.

Many of the nutrients in the Chesapeake Bay come from cows and other farm animals.

Sewage Treatment Plants:

The use of detergents containing phosphorus has been banned in the entire Chesapeake watershed. Between 1985 and 1996 phosphorus entering the Bay was reduced by 51%, but nitrogen was reduced by only 15%. Installation of Biological Nutrient Removal technology at sewage treatment plants will further reduce the load of nitrogen entering the Bay.

As storm water increases the volume of sewage to be treated, the quality of treatment is reduced and more nutrients flow into the Bay. Repair of some cracked sewer pipes is needed to prevent storm water from flowing into the sewer systems.

Restoring Declining Populations:

SAV is being replanted. The goal of restoring 114,000 acres (46,056 ha) of grasses should be met by 2005. Hatcheries are producing larval oysters, and oyster habitats are being created. In some areas striped bass have been restocked.

Monitoring:

Physical and chemical conditions in the Bay must be measured and recorded in order to determine how the Bay responds to natural variations caused by changing seasons, storms, and droughts. The data collected will also reveal how the Bay is responding to the attempts to restore it. In 1984, the EPA began measuring 19 water-quality variables at 50 different stations on the Bay. The states are responsible for monitoring the same variables on the major rivers that empty into the Bay.

Scientists cannot predict the outcome of the program to save the Bay, but there is hope. They expect the living resources to increase as the water quality improves. It may take years before water analysis and population studies reveal trends that reflect the changes in human activities. We must remember that it has taken years to pollute the Bay, and it will take years to restore it.

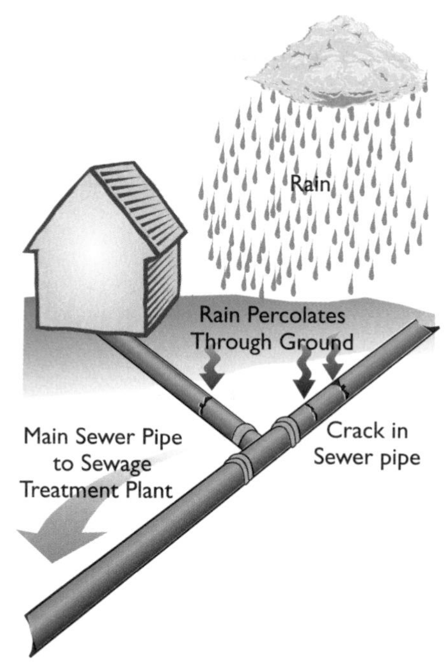

The rain water percolates through the soil and enters the sewer pipes through cracks in the walls of the pipe. The additional water overwhelms the sewage treatment plant.

Lessons Learned

Lesson 1: The solution to pollution is not dilution of toxics; the solution is control of contaminants at their source.

Lesson 2: When you no longer want it, you can't simply throw it or wash it "away." There is no "away." It will go somewhere else.

Lesson 3: Political boundaries do not stop pollution. Eroded soil from New York and Pennsylvania, sewage from Washington, D.C., toxic chemicals from Baltimore, and acid rain from power plants in the Midwest all affect the quality of the water in the Chesapeake Bay.

Hopefully it is not too late to save the Chesapeake Bay.

You Can Make a Difference

It has taken us a long time to learn these lessons, and hopefully it is not too late for the Bay. You can help. You may be contributing toxic chemicals to the Chesapeake Bay or to another aquatic ecosystem. By following the suggestions listed below, you can help keep toxic chemicals out of aquatic ecosystems.

- Use laundry detergent and other cleaning products that contain little or no phosphates.
- If you have a septic system, see that it is properly maintained.
- Control runoff and prevent soil erosion around your home.
- Use the least amount of fertilizers and pesticides possible.
- Promote the protection of wetlands.
- Recycle oil and antifreeze.
- Do not pour toxic substances down the drain.

Check the phone book for the phone number of a government agency that can provide information about how to dispose of toxic substances. The Cooperative Extension Service in your county may be able to provide the information you need.

4.8 Questions for Study and Discussion:

1. Define the following terms: **VOCABULARY**

benthic	Chesapeake Bay Agreement	nonpoint sources	toxic substances
Best Management Practices (BMPs)	estuary	oil slick	
bioaccumulate	leached	point sources	
		SAV	

2. What is the relationship between the Chesapeake Bay and the Chesapeake Basin?
3. Describe the geographic location of the Chesapeake Bay and describe the important relationship between the Bay and the state of Pennsylvania.

The People's Bay

4. Explain why many industries and people are attracted to the Bay.
5. How has the increase in population changed the land around the Bay?

Habitat for Wildlife

6. List several reasons why wetlands may be the most valuable type of ecosystem bordering the Bay.
7. Draw a food chain that includes SAV.
8. List several species of fish and shellfish that depend upon estuaries.

Fish and Wildlife in Trouble

9. Why is the Chesapeake Bay sometimes considered the most important estuary?
10. Explain why the oyster population is declining but the blue crab population is still healthy.
11. What factors had caused the decline in the shad population?
12. Explain why the stripped bass population is in greater difficulty than the menhaden.

Identifying the Problems

13. Explain how clay particles affect the level of pollutants in the Bay.
14. Identify the two major nutrients in the Bay and identify both point and nonpoint sources of these nutrients.

15. Compare the major source of these nutrients in Pennsylvania's Susquehanna River with the major source in Maryland's Potomac River.
16. Explain how the increased nutrients cause the SAV to die.
17. Explain how soil erosion also leads to the death of submerged aquatic plants.
18. Explain why increased growth of algae can create problems for fish and shellfish.
19. Give examples of toxic substances that enter the Bay.
20. What evidence makes scientists think that toxic chemicals may be affecting bottom-dwelling organisms?
21. Even though the level of some toxic chemicals present in the water is low, much higher levels are found in fish. Explain why.

Working Together to Save the Bay

22. What is the goal of the Chesapeake Bay Agreement?
23. Explain how industry can help clean up the Bay.
24. Describe what can be done to reduce the level of these pollutants in runoff.
    A. sediment B. nitrogen and phosphorus
25. Why does reducing erosion also reduce the level of phosphorus in the Bay?
26. List several best management practices that a farmer might use and explain how each will help the Bay.
27. What is the best way to protect streams from human activity?
28. Identify two ways that sewage treatment plants can be upgraded to improve the quality of water entering the Bay?
29. How will we know if the steps taken to restore the Bay are improving the quality of water in the Bay?

Lessons Learned

30. What lessons have we learned from our study of the Bay?

You Can Make a Difference

31. List several things you can do personally that will save the estuary that is downstream from your house.

Environmental Challenge: Menhaden

The season is always open and there are no limits on menhaden taken from the ocean beyond one mile of the beach. Regulations vary within one mile of the beach and within estuaries. In 1991 there was one commercial fisherman taking menhaden from New Jersey's Raritan Bay, using purse sein technology. By 1998 there were 4 additional boats aided by spotter planes. A law was proposed to eliminate purse seining from Raritan Bay.

- Would you vote for or against this law?
- Should regulations be placed on menhaden in the Chesapeake Bay? Support your position.

4.9 Dam the Rivers or Let Them Run Free

OBJECTIVES

- ✔ **Compare** the flow of water in river systems today with the flow when the rivers were discovered by the early explorers.
- ✔ **List** the advantages and disadvantages of damming a free-flowing river or stream.
- ✔ **Relate** the role of dam building to the growth of cities.
- ✔ **Evaluate** the environmental and economic impacts of the construction of a hydroelectric dam.
- ✔ **List** criteria that should be used in making decisions about the construction of a new dam or the removal of an old dam.

"The river is an ever-changing environment dominated by flowing water. At least it was until someone decided to build a dam."

The Army's Dam Builders

One of the nation's first schools of engineering was the Army's Military Academy at West Point. The United States government depended on the West Point engineers for the technical knowledge that was needed to harness the nation's rivers. Today the **U.S. Army Corps of Engineers (COE)** is the largest engineering firm in the world.

Many of the nation's rivers are no longer the wild, free-flowing rivers that were discovered by the early explorers. The Yellowstone is the only large river in the United States that flows free for its entire length. With the approval of Congress, rivers are dammed, dredged and straightened by the Army's engineers. The Corps has been given the responsibility of maintaining the nation's navigable waterways and protecting its wetlands.

Rivers are often the subjects of controversy. Wars have been fought over rivers. More recently, the courtroom has become the scene of battles fought over the use of a river. Individual citizens and environmental organizations have challenged projects planned by private developers and industries in court.

Groups of interested citizens have challenged dams and other projects proposed by the Corps of Engineers. Some of the projects have been stopped. For other projects, the court case only delayed the completion date and increased the project cost. Critics claim the Corps of Engineers often underestimates the cost of a dam and the value of the land to be flooded, while they overestimate the benefits and the useful life of the dam.

Worldwide more than 800,000 dams have changed the flow of rivers. Making changes in an ecosystem may offer certain benefits for humans. Unfortunately these benefits always carry a price tag. Along with the cost in dollars, the price tag includes another cost—the value of the ecosystem that is lost. The question that must always be asked is: "Which is greater, the cost or the benefit?"

Thanks to the Army Corps of Engineers the Mississippi River is navigable for most of its length.

Dams Provide Flood Control

Dams are often a part of flood-control plans. Frequently dams flood areas that are sparsely populated in order to protect areas downstream that have a greater population density. The Flood Control Act of 1936 included plans for 243 dams as a part of the Comprehensive Flood Control Plan for the Ohio and Mississippi Rivers. The flood-control dams were to be built on tributaries of these rivers.

Two of the dams would be built on the Meramec River in Missouri. Located near St. Louis, the valley along the lower reaches of the river supported a steadily increasing population. Towns that had been built on the broad floodplain were frequently flooded. The dams would help protect the densely populated region of the Meramec Valley.

Congress first voted funds for the Meramec Dam and Meramec Park Lake proposal in 1968. Construction of the first dam was to be completed in 1978, but the dam was never built. Missouri citizens fought long and hard to keep the flow of the Meramec River from being blocked by dams. It was their opinion that the costs were greater than the benefits.

The Corps of Engineers has often proposed dams for flood control in areas that have been devastated by major floods. Monroe County, Pennsylvania, sustained $28.5 million in property damage during the 1955 flood. The flood killed 78 people in the county.

In 1960, the Corps recommended the construction of 14 small dams on tributaries of the Brodhead Creek. Another dam was to be built at Tocks Island on the Delaware River. This dam would permanently flood land in Monroe County, but it would decrease flood damage for eight communities on the lower reaches of the Delaware. Only two of the proposed dams were built.

This Dam was built along the Little Miami River in Ohio. Its purpose is flood control for the cities downstream.

Save the River

Dams create lakes, and lakes provide an opportunity for flat-water recreation and a water supply. The lake created by Meramec Dam would have provided 12,600 acres (5,040 ha) of flat-water recreation near the densely populated St. Louis area. Figures provided by the Corps of Engineers showed that the lake could support 3.7 million visitors annually. According to the Corps, recreational opportunities offered by the lake would include motor boating, water skiing, bird-watching, picnicking, sightseeing, fishing, swimming, camping, field sports and ice skating.

Opponents of the dam suggested that the undammed stream already provided most of the recreational activities that would be offered by the lake. They questioned the need for additional flat-water recreation facilities. Lakes, within a 100-mile radius of St. Louis, already provided 134,000 acres (53,600 ha) of flat water for recreation. According to Missouri's Statewide Outdoor Recreation Plan (1976), the supply of flat-water recreation already exceeded the demand. The plan also suggested that the demand for recreational facilities provided by free-flowing streams would soon exceed the existing supply.

Dams provide flat-water recreation such as sailing, but opponents of the Meramec Dam questioned the need for additional flat-water recreation facilities.

The Meramec River was one of only seven free-flowing streams remaining in the state. The Corps of Engineers pointed out that more than 30 miles (49 km) of streams above the lake would still be available to canoeists. They also suggested that the uniform flow created by the dam would increase the number of days that canoeists could float the 108 miles (173 km) of river below the dam. The project, they said, would also improve public access to the river. Opponents argued that the dam would flood the most beautiful stretch of the free-flowing stream.

Tocks Island on the Delaware River.

The Corps of Engineers also planned to build Tocks Island Lake and Dam on the Delaware River. It was to be a multi-purpose project that would provide recreation, flood control, hydroelectric power and water supplies. The environmental cost of the Tocks Island Project would be the loss of one of the few unspoiled free-flowing sections of river in the northeastern United States. Interested citizens and environmental groups rallied to "Save the Delaware" as Missourians had rallied to "Save the Meramec."

The weather cooperated with the plan to save the Delaware River. During the years of debate about the dam, there were no floods, and there were no major water shortages. An evaluation showed that the need for additional power supplies was uncertain, and a need for free-flowing recreational facilities was demonstrated. In addition, federal money that was once available for dams and other federal projects was needed for the Vietnam War.

Finally Congress voted to shelve the $325 million Tocks Island Project and protect the river. They declared the 37-mile (59-km) section, that would have been covered by the reservoir, a part of the National Wild and Scenic Rivers System. Land purchased for the project was transferred to the Delaware Water Gap National Recreation Area. The Tocks Island Project was finally killed in 1992 when Congress deauthorized the proposed dam.

The proposed dam at Tocks Island was not built. This section of the river and its floodplain are now a part of the Delaware Water Gap National Recreation Area. Visitors still enjoy canoeing the free-flowing river.

Dams Provide a Water Supply

Had the Meramec Dam been built, the lake it created could have supplied 207 million gallons (7.9×10^8 L) of water per day for communities nearby. Opponents of the dam said this additional water supply was not needed. According to the Missouri Geological Survey, ground water supplies in the area are sufficient to meet the needs of the area until the year 2076. The Corps of Engineers argued that drilling deep wells is expensive and Meramec Lake would provide growing communities with a cheaper source of water.

Lakes that store a supply of water for future use are often called **reservoirs**. Many communities depend upon reservoirs to provide their water supply. More than 22 million people, or about 10% of the nation's population, live in the region extending from New York City to Philadelphia. Most of these people depend upon the 12,765-square-mile (33×10^9 km^2) watershed of the Delaware River for their water supply.

The area that drains into a river is the river's watershed or basin. Water in the Delaware River Basin is shared by four states: New York, New Jersey, Pennsylvania and Delaware. In 1931 and 1954, disputes over use of the water were settled by the Supreme Court.

In 1961, the governors of the four states signed the Delaware River Basin Compact. The Compact recognized the Delaware River Basin as a regional resource, and it created the Delaware River Basin Commission to manage the resource. The Commission consists of the four governors and a commissioner who is appointed by the President of the United States.

The Compact requires the Delaware River Basin Commission to adopt a comprehensive plan for managing the water resources in the Delaware Basin. The Commission also sets policy for the floodplain, sets water quality standards, and approves projects that would affect water resources in the basin. An important part of this plan has been the building of dams to increase the basin's capacity to store water supplies.

New York City's more than 9 million residents use about 1.5 billion gallons ($5.7x10^9$ L) of fresh water each day. While some residents of Queens get their water from wells, most people living in New York City get their water from the 18 reservoirs and 4 controlled lakes that are owned by the city.

Although New York City is not in the Delaware River Basin, the city owns three reservoirs on the upper reaches of the Delaware River. The 1954 decision of the U.S. Supreme Court allows New York City to divert 800 million gallons ($3.0x10^9$ L) daily from the Delaware Basin. This is about one-half of the water needed by the city.

New York City is not the only city to divert water from one watershed to another. The Colorado River is about the same size as the Delaware River, and it is the only major source of surface water in the Southwest. Water held behind dams on the Colorado River is diverted to cities like Los Angles, Phoenix and Denver. Some of the water flows into irrigation canals in Southern California.

Because it lies east of the Cascade Mountain Range, the Columbia Basin in the eastern part of the state of Washington receives less than twelve inches of rain a year. Although the soil in the Columbia Basin is fertile, farming would not be possible without irrigation. The water needed for irrigation is pumped from a reservoir behind Grand Coulee Dam. The dam forms a 151-mile-long (242-km) lake on the Columbia River.

In Canada where the Columbia River begins, it snows almost every day of the winter. By winter's end the Rockies are covered with 30 or 40 feet (9–14 m) of snow. Most of the water flowing in the high reaches of the Columbia River comes from the melting snow. Grand Coulee Dam blocks the flow of water, and stores it for the farmer's thirsty crops.

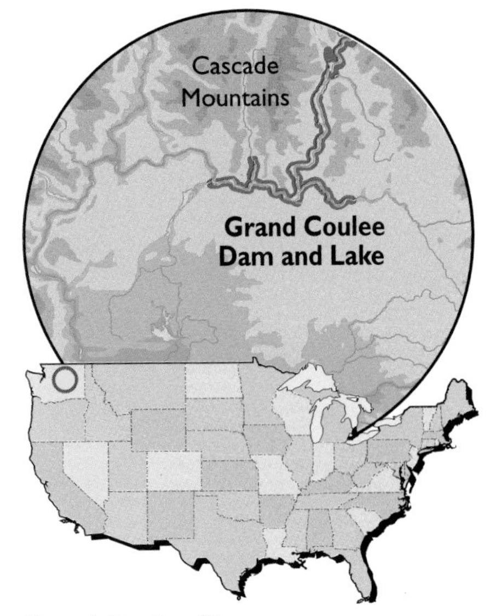

Grand Coulee Dam.

Dams Provide Water to Increase the Natural Flow

Droughts, during the mid-1960s and again in the early 1980s, created water shortages for many communities throughout the northeastern United States. Low flow in the Delaware River threatened the drinking and industrial water supplies of Camden, New Jersey and Philadelphia, Pennsylvania. The problem was not the absence of water but the presence of salt.

The flow of fresh water in the Delaware River normally keeps the **salt front**—the line where fresh water from the river meets the ocean water—near Wilmington, Delaware. In January 1981, the Delaware River Basin Commission declared a drought emergency. The salt front had moved 30 miles (48 km) upstream near Camden, New Jersey.

Philadelphia's Torresdale water treatment plant takes water directly from the Delaware River. The water treatment plant was not designed to

Delaware River Basin.

Dam in Zimbabwe.

remove salt, because the salt-removal process was expensive. The advancing salt front threatens the city's water supply. Even though Camden draws its water supply from wells, when the river's flow is low, salt and other chemicals move upstream from the ocean. Water from the river flows into the aquifers that provide Camden's water supply.

High salt content in a water supply damages pipes, plumbing and machinery. It ruins products produced with the water, and it is a threat to human health. The 1954 Supreme Court ruling that allowed New York City to divert water from the Delaware River also required the city to release water from its reservoirs during periods of low natural flow. The city must release enough water to guarantee a minimum flow of 1,750 cubic feet per second (49 m^3/s) at Montague, NJ.

Before New York City built the reservoirs, and releases were made to increase the natural flow, the flow at Montague was sometimes only 175 cubic feet per second (4.9 m^3/s). Thus during droughts, the release of water from New York City's reservoirs and reservoirs on tributaries of the Delaware helps to maintain a minimum flow of water in the river. By regulating the flow of the Delaware, the salt front is kept at a safe distance downstream during low-flow periods.

Drought conditions, a growing population, and a rising sea level are factors that led the Delaware River Basin Commission to conclude that the existing reservoirs did not have adequate water storage capacity. In order to ensure the ability to control the salt front, the commission recommended the following:

- Enlarge New York City's Cannonsville reservoir.
- Enlarge two flood-control dams in Pennsylvania's Pocono Mountains to provide water storage and recreation.
- Construct a reservoir in New Jersey.
- Hold the Tocks Island project in reserve for development after the year 2000 if it is needed for a water supply.

After the Tocks Island Project was deauthorized by Congress, the Delaware River Basin Commission ordered seven electrical utility companies that draw water from the river to build a reservoir to hold water that can be released into the river during low flow. Construction of the dam forming the Merrill Creek Reservoir, in Harmony Township, New Jersey, was completed in 1988. Water is pumped from the Delaware River when the flow is high and re-released into the river at times of low flow. The reservoir diminishes the threat of salt water intruding into the lower sections of the river.

Dams for Navigation

The cheapest way to ship cargo is by water. The Allegheny and Monongahela Rivers meet at Pittsburgh, Pennsylvania, to form the Ohio River. In 1977, more freight was hauled on the Ohio River, between Pittsburgh and Cairo, Illinois, than was hauled through the Panama Canal. The city of Pittsburgh claims to be the largest inland port in the United States.

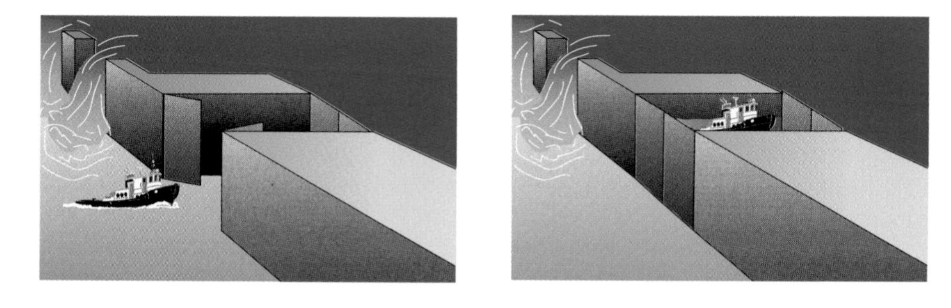

Operation of a Lock.

Travel on the Ohio River has not always been smooth. At Pittsburgh, the Ohio River is 700 feet (210 m) above sea level while at Cairo it is only 250 feet (75 m) above sea level. The natural river elevation sometimes changes abruptly with the water forming rapids and waterfalls. Early settlers traveling the Ohio River met an obstacle near Louisville, Kentucky—a mile (1.6 km) long area of rapids known as "The Falls." The elevation dropped 19 feet (5.7 m) at The Falls making it the greatest hazard to navigation on the Ohio River.

In 1824 Congress directed the U. S. Army Corps of Engineers to improve the nation's rivers for navigation, and six years later the Corps finished a dam and a canal around The Falls. The dam controls the river's flow, and a canal at one end of the dam is fitted with a series of locks. A **lock** is an area between two massive steel gates. Barges enter the lock, and the water is raised or lowered to the river on the opposite side of the dam.

By 1929, the Ohio River had been channeled to a depth of nine feet (2.7 m) and fitted with 46 locks and dams. Today powerful diesel towboats push as many as seventeen barges from Pittsburgh to Cairo, in less than a week. At Cairo the barges are joined with others and are pushed down the Mississippi by larger towboats.

Barges move through the locks at a dam on the Mississippi River. Dependable navigation on the nation's large rivers provides the least expensive means of transporting products.

Dams for Hydroelectric Power

Dams may be used to change the energy of moving water to electrical energy. Some of the newer hydroelectric dams are 90% efficient. Although less than 40% of the hydroelectric potential in this country has been developed, it is not likely that many new dams will be built for hydroelectric power. Most new hydroelectric generation will come from the installation of generation equipment at existing dams.

Bonneville Dam fish hatchery, rainbow trout, Oregon.

Columbia River, Bonneville Dam, first spillway.

Satellite image of Colorado River Basin.

Nineteen dams on the Columbia and Snake Rivers supply half of the Pacific Northwest's electricity. All but 80 vertical feet (24 m) of the Columbia River has been dammed to provide power for the Northwest. Computers monitor and regulate the flow of water in the rivers. At one time the ability of the Columbia River to provide water and electricity may have seemed unlimited, but today there is competition for both of these resources.

When water is taken from the river for agriculture or other uses, it reduces the power that can be produced down-river. Additional dams could provide more clean electrical power for the Northwest. Conservation groups have fought power company proposals for dams that would flood the section of the Columbia River known as Hell's Canyon. According to some people, Hell's Canyon provides the best white water rafting in the United States.

Hydroelectric dams are deadly to fish populations. In the reservoirs behind the dams, the temperatures are sometimes too high and the **dissolved oxygen** levels too low. To get to the spawning areas, salmon must use fish ladders to by-pass 8 federal dams on the Columbia and Snake Rivers. The journey downstream is a treacherous one for the juvenile salmon. Millions of young fish are killed as they pass though the powerful turbines at the hydroelectric power plants.

All five species of Snake River salmon and steelhead trout are listed under the Endangered Species Act.

Before the era of dam building on the Columbia and Snake Rivers, the rivers were home to millions of salmon. Now only 5,000 wild salmon return to the Snake River to spawn. All five species of Snake River salmon and steelhead trout are listed under the Endangered Species Act. In March 1999, 206 Northwest scientists signed a letter sent to President Clinton, stating the salmon populations couldn't recover unless normal river conditions are restored. This would require partial removal of the lower four dams.

Saving the salmon is important to the Northwest fishing industry. Salmon fishing is an important part of the Northwest's economy, but so is cheap electricity. The aluminum manufacturers were drawn to the Northwest by the promise of cheap electricity. Changing the flow of water to protect the salmon will increase the cost of electricity and eliminate the use of the river for irrigation and navigation.

In Canada, Hydro-Quebec has built a series of dams on rivers that empty into the James Bay. The dams produce as much energy as 30 nuclear power plants. Hydro-Quebec sells electricity to other Canadian provinces and the northeastern United States. Native Cree Indians are fighting a proposal by Hydro-Quebec to dam the Great Whale River. The Chief of the Cree community says they will fight to "prevent the destruction of the land, water and our way of life."

Dam Safety

The US Army Corps of Engineers cataloged approximately 75,000 dams greater than 5 feet (1.5 m) on the nation's waterways. Two dam failures in 1976 and 1977 caused national concern over the safety of dams. The disasters resulting from the dam failures led the President to direct the

Corps of Engineers to inspect the nation's dams for potential hazards. State governments are responsible for nonfederal dams. The Dam Safety Office in the state of Washington is responsible for 857 dams. Inspectors found safety deficiencies at 17% of 99 dams classified as "high hazard potential."

The safety of dams is dependent upon the geological features of the area and the structure of the dams. There are some places where dams should never be built. These include earthquake-prone areas and areas where the rock is porous.

Over a period of many years, water flowing beneath the earth dissolves limestone rock leaving openings called caves. Some of the passageways may be filled with clay. If a lake lying over this type of porous rock structure develops a leak, the water pressure may force the clay plug out of the cavity. If the plug is removed, the lake may be drained in the same manner as a bathtub. This would be devastating for the communities downstream.

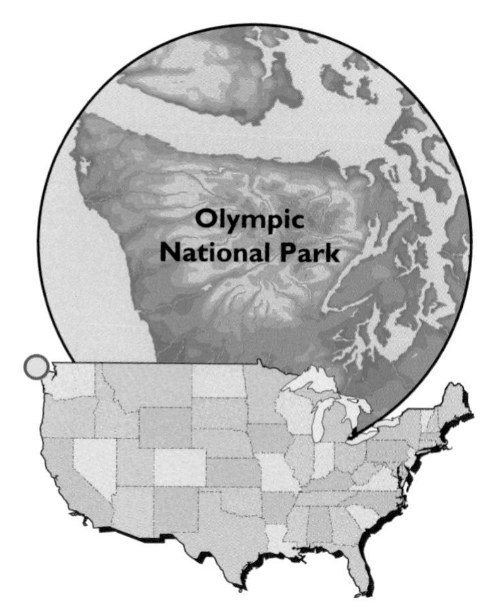

Environmental Challenge: The Elwha Dam

Washington's Elwha River was home to large populations of 8 species of salmon and trout. Dams have devastated the populations. The Elwha's king salmon population is extinct. Construction of the Elwha Dam, between 1910 and 1926, violated state law because it did not include any mechanism to allow fish to pass. There is increasing pressure from local residents, environmentalists, and Native Americans to restore the fish runs.

The construction of Elwha and Glines Canyon Dams has left fish with only 5 miles of their original habitat. The only way to restore the biodiversity of the river is to remove the dams. Removal of the dams would provide spawning fish with access to 70 miles of habitat in the Elwha River and its tributaries. Federal studies have concluded that fish runs cannot be restored without removal of the dams.

The majority of the Elwha River and its watershed are within the boundaries of Olympic National Park. According to an Environmental Impact Statement produced by the National Park Service in 1995, removal of both dams could restore the fish populations to their historic levels within 30 years. A restored fishery would create approximately 450 local jobs in recreation and tourism, and it would improve the economy for the Lower Elwha S'Kallam Indians who once depended upon the river.

The dams provide 28.6 megawatts of electricity to the Daishowa American paper mill, an important employer, and the city of Port Angeles. The Federal Energy Regulatory Commission issues licenses for privately owned dams. The Glines Canyon Dam's license expired in 1976. The Elwha Dam has never been licensed.

In 1992, Congress passed the Elwha River Ecosystem and Restoration Act, which suspended the license and directed the Department of the Interior to restore salmon to the upper Elwha. In the 2000 appropriations bill, Congress allocated $22 million for this project. The estimated cost associated with removing the dams will be more than $100 million.

Consider the question: "Should the dams be removed?"

- What factors must be considered in making this decision.
- What additional information is needed?
- If you had to make a decision, would you appropriate the funds for removal of the dams or license both dams?

For information about removal of dams on rivers in several states, visit: www.amrivers.org/hydro.html.

4.9 Questions for Study and Discussion:

1. Define the following terms: **VOCABULARY**

Delaware River Basin Commission	reservoir
Delaware River Basin Compact	salt front
lock	U.S. Army Corps of Engineers (COE)

The Army's Dam Builders

2. How did the U.S. Army Corps of Engineers (COE) improve transportation in America?
3. List two responsibilities that Congress has assigned to the COE.
4. In the past, wars have been fought over rivers. Where are battles fought over rivers today?
5. What question should always be asked when plans are being made to change an ecosystem?

Dams Provide Flood Control

6. Dams have often been proposed to protect areas from floods. What area would the Meramec dams have protected? What areas would have been flooded?
7. What "event" caused the COE to propose 14 dams on tributaries of the Brodhead Creek in Monroe County, Pennsylvania?

Save the River

8. In addition to flood control, what additional benefits would the Meramec Dam have provided?
9. What benefits would have been provided by the Tocks Island Dam on the Delaware River?
10. What valuable resource would have been lost if these dams had been built?

Dams Provide a Water Supply

11. List the four states that share the water in the Delaware River Basin.
12. Why was the Delaware River Basin Compact important?
13. Is New York City in the Delaware River Basin? Explain the relationship between New York City's water supply and the Delaware River.
14. What is the only major source of surface water in the Southwest? Name a major city that depends on this source that does not lie within its watershed?
15. Explain the following statement: Without snow in the Canadian Rockies there would be no farms in the Columbia Basin.

Dams Provide Water to Increase the Natural Flow

16. What is a salt front? Where is the salt front normally located?
17. Why doesn't the city of Philadelphia simply remove the salt at the water treatment plant?
18. What is the source of drinking water for the people of Camden, New Jersey? Why are they so concerned about the salt front?
19. Would the salt line remain further downstream if New York City did not divert water from the Delaware River Basin? Explain.
20. List three factors that might cause the Delaware River Basin Commission to bring the Tocks Island Project back to "life."

Dams for Navigation

21. Why have rivers been such an important means of transportation? What city claims to be the largest inland port? What river begins at this port?
22. How was the Ohio River changed to improve transportation?

Dams for Hydroelectric Power

23. New fossil-fueled power plants are 40% efficient. How do hydroelectric power plants compare?
24. In what region of the country is most of the hydroelectric power produced?
25. What is the environmental cost of hydroelectric dams on rivers in the Northwest?

Dam Safety

26. What events caused the President to call for an inspection of the nation's dams?
27. List two factors that determine how safe a dam will be.
28. List two places where dams should not be built.

Environmental Challenge: An Inflatable Dam

The Susquehanna River has four hydroelectric dams built between 1904 and 1992. Some Pennsylvanians want to add at least one more. The Conowingo Dam, located just 10 miles upstream of the Chesapeake Bay, is 95 feet high. The proposed dam at Harrisburg, Pennsylvania would be only 17 feet high, and it would be an inflatable dam with two fish ladders. There are more than 1,000 inflatable dams in use worldwide, including one along the Susquehanna in Sunbury, Pennsylvania.

The proposed dam would be inflated except during high-flow conditions. During normal flow at Harrisburg, the river is 3.5 feet deep with a chain of islands along the river. With the dam inflated, the water level would be 13 feet higher at the dam and 5 or 6 feet higher at Wade Island. The flooding of this island would endanger one of the largest great egret nesting sites in Pennsylvania. Great egrets are a threatened species in Pennsylvania. Black-crowned night herons, which also use the island, are a "species of concern."

According to a Pennsylvania Fish and Boat Commission biologist, the Susquehanna at Harrisburg is a nationally recognized smallmouth bass fishery. There is a small population of walleyes. People in the area wade into the river to fish. The city's project manager for the dam, who is also a fisheries biologist, says that the dam might enhance the bass fishery and create a walleye fishery. A biologist with the Fish and Boat Commission isn't sure that the changes would increase the walleye population.

- What would be the benefits of the dam?
- How will the dam affect people living upstream? Downstream?
- What are the potential environmental impacts?
- Do you think that a Section 404 permit should be issued for this project?
- What additional information do you need before making a decision?
- If you had to make a decision now, would you vote for or against a bill that would provide funds for the dam?

Further upstream, at Wilkes-Barre/Kingston, the river level drops during the summer months. The water recedes from the river banks and creates mudflats which prevent access to the river. These cities want to install an inflatable dam that would stabilize the water level of the river.

This plan is part of a project to make a more attractive waterfront. A recent study, of cities (including Baltimore and Pittsburgh) that have beautified their waterfronts, reports that waterfront property is valued up to 30% higher than in-land property.

- Would you vote to fund this project? Write a reaction statement that supports your position.

4.10 Rivers on the Land

OBJECTIVES

- ✔ **Diagram** the water cycle showing the role of the floodplain.
- ✔ **Explain** how development of a floodplain affects the water cycle.
- ✔ **Compare** the impacts on the local community and on communities downstream of channeling rivers and building dikes.
- ✔ **Identify** the environmental and economic impacts of developing a floodplain.
- ✔ **Evaluate** the effects of the Natural Valley Storage Plan and the Federal Flood Disaster Protection Act.

"We need to start giving land back to the river. If we don't, sooner or later the river will take it back."
LARRY LARSON
Director, Wisconsin's Floodplain Program

Sometimes rain falls gently and disappears into the soil, but often it strikes the earth with great force, loosening tiny particles of silt and clay from the earth. If the earth cannot absorb the water, it begins a journey across the land carrying some of the particles with it.

The force of the moving water loosens more particles, and the water cuts a path as it moves across the land. The water with its **load**—the clay and silt particles that it carries—flows into a stream. The streams dump the water into a river until the river can hold no more, and then there is a flood.

The Water Drops its Load

Floods occur when water reaches the top of the banks of a river (or a stream) and flows across the low, flat land that lies along the river. The low, flat land that is periodically flooded is called the **floodplain**. Some of the standing water slowly sinks into the soil restoring the supply of groundwater. Much of the floodwater slowly returns to the river as the water level drops.

As the water stands on the floodplain, it drops some of the silt and clay particles that it carried. When the water is gone, a thick new carpet of fertile loam soil is left behind. Some of the world's best farmland is found along the banks of rivers where seasonal floods bring a new supply of fertile soil to the land.

Along the coast where the rivers reach the ocean, the slope of the land is often gentle and the velocity of the water is slowed. Here, at the mouth of the river, the water drops its load of silt and clay, forming an area of land called a **delta**. During the last 6,000 years, the load dropped by the Mississippi River has added some 30,000 square miles (7.8×10^4 km^2) to the state of Louisiana. But now, because of structures built to protect New Orleans from floods, the Mississippi Delta is shrinking.

This floodplain has been converted from a bottomland hardwood forest to a farm.

Cities Along the River

The valleys along rivers and streams are the most convenient and profitable places to live, especially in mountainous areas. Two-thirds of the state of Pennsylvania is mountainous. Of the 2,800 communities in Pennsylvania, 2,468 are located on floodplains that lie along rivers and streams in the valleys.

People chose to live along rivers because the river provided a cheap and easy means of transportation. The river also provided a source of water, and the rich level land of the floodplain was the most suitable land for farming. Farmers cleared timber and sometimes dug ditches to drain water from the swampy lowlands.

The river also provided waterpower that attracted industry to the river communities. The force of flowing water was first used to turn waterwheels that provided the power to grind grain. Later dams were built, and now water flows through turbines to turn generators that make electricity. Although most electricity is not produced by waterpower, large electrical power plants still require huge amounts of water. The 33 coal-fired power plants along the Ohio River withdraw more than twice as much water from the river than all other users.

In regions with a good supply of raw materials, small communities grew into large cities. One of the world's most productive industrial and agricultural regions is the Ohio River Valley. The valley supplies clay, limestone, and sandstone for industries and coal for electrical power plants. The river supplies the water and an efficient means of transportation.

Sattelite image of Rivers in Northwestern Brazil.

Raindrops Falling on the City

As more land is developed, the amount of water that can be absorbed by the earth decreases. Buildings, streets and parking lots cover the land and prevent infiltration of the water. When it rains, the **runoff** now flows through large pipes beneath the ground called **storm sewers**. The storm sewers, which replaced the natural streams, carry the runoff water to the nearest river.

Because of the huge demand for water, coal-fired power plants are built on the floodplains of major rivers.

As the number of buildings, parking lots, and roadways increases, the runoff increases.

Storm sewers collect runoff from city streets and carry it to the creek through outlet pipes like this one in the dike.

Did You Know?

The Federal Emergency Management Agency says that nearly half of all flash flood fatalities are auto related. Water typically flows downstream at 6 to 12 mph. When a vehicle stalls, each foot of water exerts 500 pounds of force against the vehicle. Since the vehicle is buoyant, each foot of water effectively reduces the weight of the car by 1500 pounds. Do not try to drive through water; only a foot or two of water can cost you your life.

More development means more runoff. When the storm sewers can't carry the water away fast enough, city streets are flooded. When storms bring large amounts of rain in a brief period of time, any natural streams that remain in the developed area are quickly filled, and low-lying areas of the city are flooded.

According to the Red Cross, **flash floods** are the number one weather-related killer in the United States. Flash floods occur within a few minutes or hours of excessive rainfall or a sudden release of water, such as a dam or levee failure or the break-up of an ice jam. Factors that contribute to flash floods are intensity (rate) and duration of rainfall, saturation of soil by a previous rainfall, the **topography** (surface features of the region), and the type of ground cover. Replacing forests with parking lots and buildings will increase runoff and the possibility of flooding.

Straight and Narrow Channels

To carry away the excess water, the meandering paths of rivers or streams are sometimes replaced with human-made **channels**. The channels are shorter, straighter and have a steeper slope than the natural channels of the river or stream. This increases the amount of water that can be carried away. In the area where there are human-made channels, the amount of flooding is reduced.

Channels may solve the problem of flooding for one area, but they increase the risk of flooding in other areas downstream. As the increased volume of water reaches an area that has not been channeled, its flow is slowed, and any low-lying areas are likely to be flooded. As more miles of the river are channeled, larger areas downstream are flooded.

Johnstown, PA—City on a Floodplain

The city of Johnstown, Pennsylvania, is located at the point where two mountain streams meet to form the Conemaugh River. The city quickly became an important manufacturing area in western Pennsylvania. By

This dike protects this office building and other businesses built along the creek.

Natural River Channel

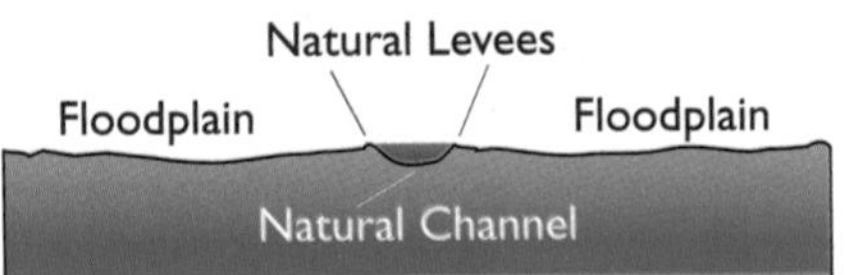

River flows in natural channel. Water level is below floodstage.

Floodplain Unprotected / **Floodplain Protected**

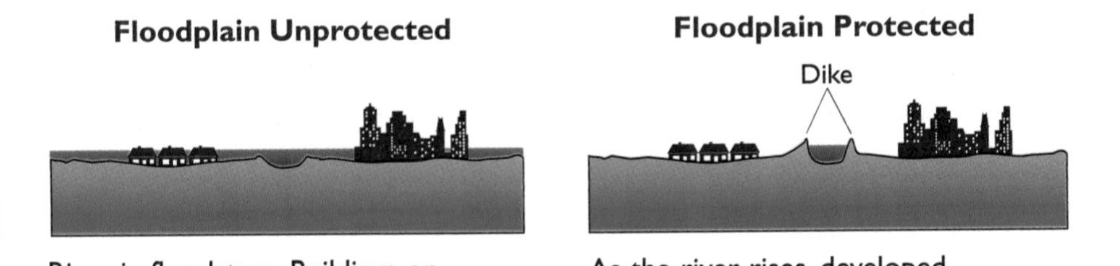

River in floodstage. Buildings on floodplain damaged by floodwater.

As the river rises, developed floodplain is protected by dikes.

1889, its population had reached 30,000. Like other towns built on floodplains, Johnstown was regularly flooded.

The area of Johnstown has received national attention because of the many lives lost in three major floods. Of the 3,500 Pennsylvanians who died in major floods during the last 100 years, at least 2,300 people were killed in floods that hit the Johnstown area.

The first major flood occurred on May 31, 1889, when six to eight inches (15-20 cm) of rain fell in a 24-hour period. Normally a three-inch rain was enough to cause flooding in Johnstown. It had been the wettest May on record, and the soil was saturated. Even then, it would probably have been "just another flood" except for an old earthen dam on the south fork of the Little Conemaugh River.

The 900-foot (270 m) long and 70-foot (21 m) high dam held water in a 500-acre (200-hectare) lake. The dam was originally built to provide water for the state canal system, but the system was no longer used. A group of wealthy businessmen from Pittsburgh bought the lake and a large area of land. The dam needed repairs, and the new owners hired a contractor (with no experience in dam construction) to rebuild the dam. For several years the new owners enjoyed their private lake. Then the heavy rains came.

The repairs made on the dam did not meet the engineering standards for a large earthen dam, and the dam was weak. Little water could flow from the lake because the spillway had been partially blocked and a fish gate installed. Soon the water began to flow over a low area in the center of the dam. After a few hours, it burst through the weakened dam, and a 40-foot (12 m) wall of water moved toward Johnstown. In just a few hours 2,100 people were drowned.

The city rebuilt, and each time the river flooded the residents cleaned up the silt and clay that the floods left behind. Then on March 17, 1936, an unusually heavy rainstorm melted the snow covering the mountains. The resulting flood killed 25 people. The city once again rebuilt.

After the city cleaned up and rebuilt, the U.S. Army Corps of Engineers straightened the channels of the two mountain streams and built **dikes**—massive sloping concrete walls—to protect the city. They thought this would put an end to the city's flood problem, and Johnstown began to promote itself as "flood-free."

Johnstown remained flood-free for 41 years and 124 days—until July 19, 1977. Then during a 12-hour period, thunderstorms dropped nearly 12 inches (30 cm) of water in the Johnstown area. This large amount of water caused five small earthen dams, built on streams above the town, to collapse. The human toll was 75 people dead and 26 people missing.

Just before the flood, one of the dams had been inspected and declared "safe." How could a dam that was declared "safe" collapse? Dams are not built to withstand unusual storms like the 12-inch (3 cm) in 12-hour rainfall. A storm like this is likely to occur in any given place

Johnstown, Pennsylvania, has been flooded many times and many lives have been lost.

Monuments in the cemetery's Unknown Plot honor the memory of those whose bodies were never recovered after the flood of 1889.

Water cascading over the broken dam on the South Fork of the Little Conemaugh River. In only a few hours the wall of water hit the city of Johnstown.

Now the National Park Service Flood Museum overlooks the site of the broken dam and the dry lake bed.

The natural channel of the river has been straightened and massive concrete dikes have been built to reduce the chances of flooding within the city.

only "once in 500 years." Officials tell us that it would be too expensive to protect against the risk of such rare storms.

The U.S. Army Corps of Engineers flood protection project had been designed to protect the city of Johnstown from a flood like the one seen in 1936. The 1977 flood was a bigger flood. The engineers said the flood protection project had protected the city. Without the deeper, straighter channels and the concrete walls, flood damage would have been even greater.

The Value of a Floodplain

Some people feel the floodplain belongs to the river. The floodplain provides a natural storage area for the excess water that the river cannot carry. It is also an important recharge area for the groundwater supply. Although these are extremely important functions, they are not uses that make the land a financial asset for the owner.

In our society, the value of land is not determined by the role it serves in its natural ecosystem. It is the money that can be gained if the land is sold or developed that determines the value. An acre (0.4 ha) of swampy forested land along a river might be worth $400. The same acre (0.4 ha) that has been cleared and drained for farmland might sell for $1,400.

If this land is located near a large city and has potential for residential or commercial development, it might sell for $10,000 per acre. After it is developed, it may be worth $40,000 per acre. Unfortunately when floodplains are developed, the value of property damaged during a flood also increases. Buildings may be destroyed, or a flood may damage a building and its contents.

The Cost of Using a Floodplain

By 1986, 50 years after the adoption of a national flood control policy, the Federal Government had spent $23 billion dollars for flood protection. In spite of this fact, losses from floods continue to increase. The Johnstown flood of 1889 caused $17 million worth of property damage. In 1936, the developed area had doubled in size and damage was $41 million. In spite of the $7 million flood protection project, the 1977 flood caused an estimated $350 million worth of property damage.

Floods are the major cause of disasters. A major flood occurs somewhere in the United States nearly every year. In the four years between 1993 and 1997, floods killed nearly 500 people and destroyed $33 billion in homes and property.

The "Great Flood of '93" began in April and continued through August. Spring was unusually wet, and the summer months, that are normally dry, were filled with frequent and sometimes violent thunderstorms that dropped unbelievable amounts of water in the upper Midwest. More than 50 lives were lost and property damage cost almost $15 billion. President Clinton declared many counties in 8 Midwestern states disaster areas.

A region is eligible for federal assistance if the President of the United States declares it a disaster area. In September 1999, major disaster declarations were issued for 8 states along the East Coast due to damage caused by Hurricane Floyd. There were more than 50 storm-related deaths.

The state that suffered the most damage was North Carolina. In early September, Hurricane Dennis dropped 16 to 18 inches (6.5–7.2 cm) of rain on North Carolina. Hurricane Floyd added as much as 24 inches (9.6 cm) of rain before moving up the Atlantic Coast. The drenching rain caused 8 dam failures, and flooding and washouts closed more than 200 roads.

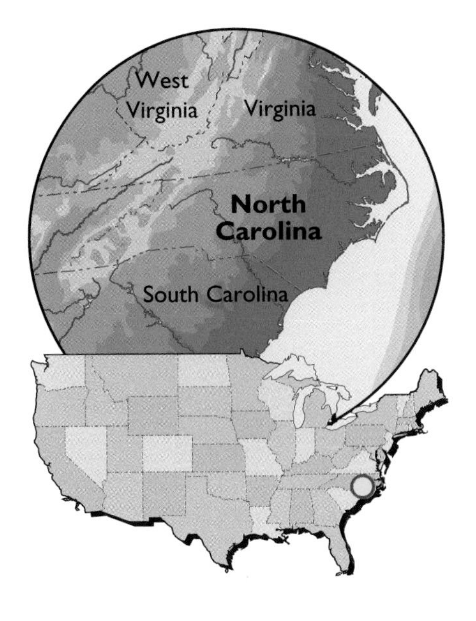

The cost of using the floodplain is determined by the land use selected. Many large cities—including Boston, Kansas City, St. Louis, Pittsburgh and New Orleans—are built on floodplains and depend upon floodwalls or levees for protection from floodwaters. The national flood control program, which began in 1936, involves channeling streams, building up-stream dams to store runoff water and building levees to protect developed areas. But channels, dams and levees cannot guarantee the protection of developed areas.

In 1951, over 200,000 homes were lost in levee-protected areas. A new $8 million levee protected Mark Twain's hometown of Hannibal, Missouri, during the great flood of 1993, but other towns weren't so fortunate. In spite of efforts to strengthen levees with millions of sandbags, about 1000 levees failed. In some places, the force of the water breaking through the levee caused flash floods that uprooted trees, demolished houses, and moved grain bins and propane tanks off their foundations.

A lone man on the beach surveys the intense waves as hurricane Floyd approached. Damage from flooding devastated North Carolina.

In addition to property damage and loss of life, floodwaters also disrupt normal functions such as transportation. Floods destroy bridges, roads and railroads. More than 300 roads in Missouri were impassable during the flood of '93, and barge traffic was halted on the Missouri and upper Mississippi Rivers. People were laid off when industries ran out of parts or couldn't deliver their products.

Another problem in flooded areas is the lack of a safe supply of drinking water. Floodwaters often carry raw sewage, dead animals and toxic chemicals that contaminate community water supplies. Floods from hurricane Floyd killed 6,000 hogs and 945,000 poultry and caused sewage lagoons to overflow in North Carolina. Both surface and groundwater supplies were contaminated.

Satellite image of cyclone.

Different Approaches to Flood Control

Some people feel that the best kinds of flood protection are those that restrict land use so floods cause less damage. When floodplains are used for agriculture, seasonal floods may destroy growing crops, but the farmer's loss is reduced by the nutrients in the silt and clay particles that are deposited by the flood. The financial loss when cropland is flooded is much less than the loss when floods destroy developed land.

It might seem that a simple answer to prevent the high cost of damage from floods would be to prevent farming or development of the floodplains. Let the floodplains remain as wetlands. The problem with this idea is that wetlands and wildlife compete with people for the limited space available, especially in urban areas. Wetlands and wildlife do not provide as many jobs or generate as much tax revenue as farms, industrial parks and housing developments.

Equipped with levees, holding ponds, and pumping stations, Earth City avoided flood damage during the great flood of 1993. How do you think this affected areas downstream?

In 1960, St. Louis County, Missouri, adopted a land-use plan in which all land subject to flooding by major rivers or streams [including the Meramec, Missouri and Mississippi Rivers] was zoned as open space. The use of this land for open space, agriculture or parks would not be severely affected by periodic flooding. The planners felt that the floodplains would best serve humans if they were left to fulfill their natural role of flood control.

In 1970, a development corporation asked the St. Louis County government to rezone a 1,200-acre (480-ha) site on the floodplain of the Missouri River. The developer's proposal included an industrial complex and housing for 16,000 residents. The new development would be named Earth City, and it would be protected by levees, drainage ditches and pumping stations.

St. Louis County hired two engineering firms to study the technological and environmental aspects of the proposed city. In its report to the county government, one of the firms concluded that it was technologically possible to build Earth City. They suggested that the question that should be asked was not could it be done, but should it be done. Modified plans were finally approved, and the industrial complex was built on the floodplain along the Missouri River.

In 1965, Congress asked the Corps of Engineers to develop a plan to control flooding along the Charles River in eastern Massachusetts. The river flows through Cambridge and Boston where it empties into the harbor. All of the marshes along the bay have been filled and developed. Walls have been built along the river to protect the cities, but storms still bring floods.

After a five-year study, the Corps recommended that the best way to control flooding was to buy 8,442 acres (3,377 ha) of undeveloped wetlands in the Charles River watershed near Boston. Left in their natural state, the wetlands absorb excess water and provide better protection than any additional levees or reservoirs.

Congress approved the **Natural Valley Storage Plan**, and the Federal Government bought the wetlands in order to guarantee that they will remain in their natural state. Purchase of the wetlands was less expensive than construction of flood-control structures. The Corps estimated that preserving the wetlands prevents $17 million in flood damage each year.

An Act of Congress

The loss of life and property to floods continues to increase each year. Structures built to control floods fail to hold back floodwaters. The presence of flood control structures gives people a false sense of security and may encourage them to build on the floodplain. In 1973, Congress responded to the increasing cost of flood damage by passing the Federal Flood Disaster Protection Act.

The law encourages communities to use floodplains in ways that will not result in the loss of life or property damage when floods do occur. Communities must follow federal regulations for floodplain development in order for developments to be eligible for federal funding and federal flood insurance. Buildings in areas that are prone to flooding must be elevated or flood-proofed. Floodways must be constructed so that water can pass through the community without causing damage.

In a pamphlet celebrating the 50th Anniversary of the Flood Control Act of 1936, the U.S. Army Corps of Engineers included the following statement: "Many flood control experts today advise that structural flood control projects should be built only if a nonstructural solution is not feasible. The nonstructural solutions generally involve moving people rather than controlling water.

In Missouri, floods in 1993 and 1995 destroyed dozens of levees and damaged thousands of acres of farmland so badly that it was too costly to reclaim. When levees break, the force of the water scours the land, removing the topsoil. The sand carried by the floodwater is deposited on the farmland. After the flood of 1993, deposits of sand at least two feet deep covered more than 60,000 acres (24,240 ha) along the Missouri River.

After the floodwaters returned to the rivers, private property owners and government officials were left with difficult decisions concerning reclaiming the land or giving the land back to the river. The Missouri Conservation Department and federal agencies offered some landowners cash incentives or buyouts to convert damaged farmland to floodways and wetlands. Missouri will never restore the 4.5 million acres (1.8 million ha) of wetlands that have been lost, but restoring some of the wetlands has already made a difference.

In October 1998, torrential rains caused the Missouri River to rise, but when the river crested at Jefferson City, it was six feet below the level predicted. The floodwaters covered 16,000 acres (6,400 ha) that was previously protected by levees. Having this additional land available for storage of floodwater prevented flooding and financial loss for property owners downstream. The restored wetlands are also providing important wildlife habitat and giving people opportunities for outdoor recreation.

The 1993 flood deposited more than two feet of sand on thousands of acres of farmland along the Missouri River.

The Susquehanna River Commission headquarters building, located on the floodplain, is designed to withstand a 100-year flood by allowing water to pass through the flood control arches.

4.10 QUESTIONS FOR STUDY AND DISCUSSION:

1. Define the following terms: VOCABULARY

channels	load
delta	Natural Valley Storage Plan
flash flood	storm sewers
flood	topography
floodplain	

2. What is the load that is carried by the water?

The Water Drops Its Load

3. Describe the relationship between the river and the floodplain.
4. Explain why some of the best farmland lies along the banks of rivers.
5. Explain how a delta is formed, and how the Mississippi River Delta is changing.

Cities Along the River

6. List several reasons why the early settlers chose to locate along rivers?
7. Why do industries and electrical power plants often build along rivers?
8. Why has the Ohio River Valley become one of the most productive industrial areas in the nation?

Raindrops Falling on the City

9. Describe the effect of development of land on infiltration of water.
10. List several situations that might cause a flash flood.

Straight and Narrow Channels

11. How do human-made channels differ from the natural paths of rivers or streams?
12. How do human-made channels affect the amount of flooding: (A) in the area where the channels were made? (B) in the area downstream from the channels?

Johnstown, PA—City on a Floodplain

13. Compare the floods of 1889 and 1936.
14. What changes were made in the river to reduce the risk of flooding?
15. How many years passed after the 1936 flood before another disastrous flood hit the Johnstown area? What events caused this flood to be so destructive?
16. What makes "safe" dams collapse?
17. How could the COE claim that the flood-control project was a success when the city had flooded and lives were lost?

The Value of a Floodplain

18. List two natural functions of a floodplain.
19. Why do landowners and developers continue to develop floodplains?

The Cost of Using a Floodplain

20. Compare the amount of property damage in the Johnstown floods of 1889 and 1936.
21. Did the COE flood protection project reduce the amount of property damage in the 1977 flood? If not, why?
22. Compare the major disasters that occurred in 1993 and 1999.
23. List several large U.S. cities that are built on floodplains, and describe the ways in which these and other cities have been protected from floods.
24. List several ways that a flood might disrupt your daily routine even though your home was not destroyed and no lives were lost.

Different Approaches to Flood Control

25. List several uses of floodplains that will not result in high costs when flooding occurs.
26. How does a flood partially compensate a farmer for the crops that are lost when flooding occurs?
27. Give several reasons why floodplains are developed.
28. Compare the land-use plan for floodplains that was adopted by the St. Louis County planners in 1960 with the Natural Valley Storage Plan.

An Act of Congress

29. Describe how flood control structures may increase the loss of life and property.
30. Describe two ways that the 1973 Federal Flood Disaster Protection Act will decrease the amount of federal money spent for damages from flooding.
31. Explain how the flood of 1993 reduced flooding in some areas along the Missouri River in 1998.

The Mississippi — River on the Move

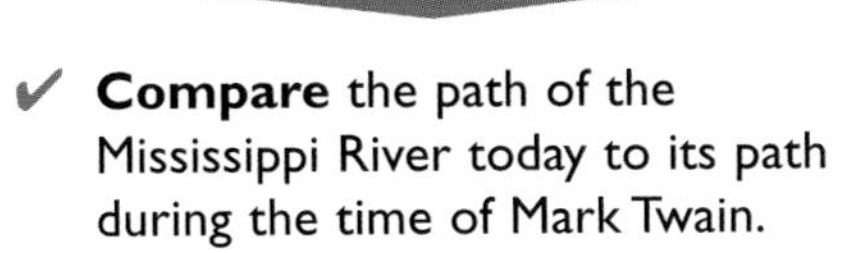

OBJECTIVES

- **Compare** the path of the Mississippi River today to its path during the time of Mark Twain.
- **Relate** the flow of the Atchafalaya River to the flow of the Mississippi River.
- **Predict** the success of the U.S. Army Corps of Engineer's efforts to control the river's flow.

"This river used to meander all over its floodplain. People would move their tepees, and that was that. You can't move Vicksburg."
JOHN MCPHEE
The Control of Nature

The Mississippi River flows from lake Itasca in northern Minnesota for some 2,340 miles (3,744 km) to the Gulf of Mexico. It receives water from 31 states and two Canadian provinces. The length of the river varies as it changes course, which it has done hundreds of times.

The River as a Highway

Today the Mississippi River and its floods are not like those described by Mark Twain in *The Adventures of Huckleberry Finn.* At one time it was possible to wade across some sections of the upper Mississippi, and there were no barriers to slow the flow of water. During the last 100 years the river has been remodeled. Dams have been built, channels have been dug, and both industries and cities have polluted the Mississippi.

When Mark Twain lived along the Mississippi, he watched as hogs, cattle, tobacco, corn, wheat, flour and concrete were loaded on steamboats at Hannibal, Missouri. Hannibal once had the largest concrete plant in the world. It supplied most of the concrete that was used to build the Panama Canal. Today barges and tugboats have replaced the steamboats, but the economy of the Midwest is still linked to the traffic on the Mississippi.

Today the Army Corps of Engineers manages the "monstrous big river" that Huck Finn enjoyed. The COE is assigned the task of preventing floods and assuring that the Mississippi River is navigable from Minneapolis to the Gulf of Mexico. The Corps built levees to prevent flooding and cut nine-foot (3 m) channels in the riverbed to allow barge traffic. The COE built 29 locks and dams between Minneapolis and St. Louis, to keep the flow of water constant.

Changing Rivers

In the spring of 1865 the steamboat Sultana was traveling up the Mississippi River. It carried a load of cattle and hogs, sugar in wooden barrels, and passengers. Most of the passengers were Union soldiers who had been freed from Confederate prisons in the South. Seven miles (11 km) up river from Memphis, Tennessee, a boiler on the overloaded steamboat exploded. The boat sank and many people drowned.

Attempts to salvage the boat were not successful. Later the river cut a new path, leaving the boat partly buried in the old riverbed. Today the boat is buried beneath tons of silt and clay deposited by annual spring floods. Each year, an Arkansas farmer plants and harvests crops in the rich soil that has covered the boat.

Distribution of Flows

Date	Mississippi River	Atchafalaya River
1900	88 %	12 %
1940	80 %	20 %
1950	70 %	30 %

Mississippi River.

It is not an easy task to keep a big river from taking a new path.

Rivers that flow across land with a gentle slope naturally move back and forth, changing their path every hundred years or so. There have been at least six major changes in the path of the Mississippi, and it is once again trying to shift its course. Many years ago the Mississippi shifted its course making a large curve or meander which connected the Mississippi to the Atchafalaya River in Louisiana.

The amount of water flowing into the Atchafalaya increased. Instead of following the Mississippi to the Gulf of Mexico, the water followed the shorter, steeper route of the Atchafalaya. By the 1950s, 30% of the Mississippi's water was flowing into the Atchafalaya. If nothing were done, most of the water in the Mississippi would eventually take the new route.

The River vs. the Corps

Although it is normal for old rivers to change their flow, the Army Corps of Engineers is trying to keep the river in its present bed. Seventy miles (112 km) north of Baton Rouge, Louisiana, the COE built a set of levees and water control gates, known as the **Old River Control Complex**. The structure is designed to keep 70% of the water in the Mississippi River channel during normal flow and to send more water into the Atchafalaya during floods.

The flow of the Mississippi River directly affects the lives of nearly 3 million people living in Louisiana. If the Mississippi River shifts its course, the economic impact will extend far beyond the borders of Louisiana. A 1980 study made by Louisiana State University pointed out some of the changes that will occur if the Mississippi shifts its course.

- The largest complex of port facilities in the world lies along the Mississippi River between Baton Rouge, Louisiana and the Gulf of Mexico. Nearly half of the U.S. grain exports pass through these ports. Barge traffic between New Orleans and the Midwest will be cut off unless the silt that will be deposited by the river is removed.
- The bottom of the Mississippi River is below sea level for 350 miles (560 km) upstream from its mouth. A discharge of 120,000 cubic feet/second (3.4×10^6 L/s) is needed to keep the salt water below New Orleans. If the Control Structure fails, salt water will move up the river channel and contaminate New Orleans' water supply.
- Morgan City, Louisiana, an oil town of 20,000, and the surrounding area where 30,000 people live would be flooded. This area will become a part of the Gulf of Mexico.
- Seven major interstate gas pipelines cross the Atchafalaya Basin. Broken pipelines will cause a shortage of natural gas in several eastern states.
- Transportation on four major highways and four railroad lines crossing the Atchafalaya Basin would be interrupted.
- The increased flow of water through the Atchafalaya Basin would expand the areas in which shrimp and oysters can survive.

It is not an easy task to keep a big river from taking a new path. The engineers must constantly fight erosion that would cause the Old River Control Structure to collapse. The structure was severely tested and almost failed during the flood of 1973. Emergency repair work cost more than $15 million. The cost of maintaining the structure is $5 million a year.

The mighty Mississippi again demonstrated the power of water during the "Great Flood of 1993." Water reached record levels and caused billions of dollars in damage on the upper Mississippi Basin. They say that the likelihood of a flood like that occurring is once in 500 years. There is concern that the river control structure will not hold if a 500-year flood hits the lower Mississippi Basin.

Some people think that, no matter what the Army Corps of Engineers does, the Mississippi will eventually take the easier route to the Gulf. The consensus among geologists is that the Atchafalaya will win this war, but the COE still believes that they can keep the Mississippi in its present channel. Only time will tell who will win this battle—the Army Corps of Engineers or "Ol' Man River."

4.11 Questions for Study and Discussion:

1. Where does the Mississippi River begin?

The River as a Highway

2. List several ways that humans have changed the Mississippi River during the last 100 years.
3. List the two jobs that have been assigned to the Army Corps of Engineers.

Changing Rivers

4. Explain how a steamboat, called the Sultana, was buried on a farm in Arkansas.
5. Identify the Louisiana River that receives water from the Mississippi River.

The River vs. the Corps

6. What is the purpose of the river control structure built by the Army Corps of Engineers?
7. How would a change in the path of the Mississippi River affect the people in these places: the Midwest? the city of New Orleans? Morgan City, Louisiana? the eastern states?
8. Do you think that maintaining the flow is worth the high cost of maintenance?
9. Do you think the COE will be able to prevent the Mississippi River from changing its course?

4.12 Cleaning Up the Rivers

OBJECTIVES

- ✔ **Relate** the development of technology to the water quality of rivers and streams.
- ✔ **State** the goal of the Clean Water Act and **describe** the changes that are necessary to reach the goal.
- ✔ **Compare** primary and secondary sewage treatment.
- ✔ **Compare** the processes of treating sewage in lagoons, septic tanks and at sewage treatment plants.
- ✔ **Identify** appropriate uses of biosolids and sewage effluent.
- ✔ **Evaluate** the effectiveness and **compare** the cost of different methods of sewage treatment.

For many years our rivers were used to carry wastewater away from the cities. The industrial revolution and the invention of the water closet (the first indoor toilet) increased the river's load of wastes. The rivers smelled of sewage, and **water-borne diseases**—diseases caused by organisms in the water—were common. For example, the smell of sewage from the Thames River near Parliament, was so bad that Parliament's draperies were dipped in disinfectant before being hung in the windows to protect Parliament members from the smell!

Reviving the Thames

In the mid-1800s, some 25,000 people living along the River Thames in the vicinity of London, died of cholera. This was caused by a bacteria (*Vibrio cholerae*) in wastes in the Thames. Sewers were built to take the waste out to sea, but the sewers did not solve the problem. They only moved it from one location to another.

During World War II, bombs damaged sewage treatment plants that had been built in the 1930s. The River Thames was declared dead by 1950. Salmon had disappeared, and only a few eels remained in the river. Following a ten-year study, the sewage treatment plants were rebuilt. Wastewater was treated before it entered the Thames, and the solid waste was dumped at sea.

This water closet is in the servant's bathroom of a mansion constructed in 1861 by Asa Packer, founder of Lehigh University.

The Thames River as it flows through London is no longer a sewer. Today it is home to many species of fish including salmon.

Salmon have returned to the Thames, an indication that it is a clean river. Today the River Thames is the site of a variety of recreational activities including boating, sailing, rowing and fishing. A walk along the river no longer requires a "pocket full of posies" to mask the stench, and cholera is no longer a threat in London.

Environmental Challenge: Dr. Snow

In the mid-1800s, no one knew that cholera was caused by a bacterium transmitted in drinking water. Find out how Dr. John Snow used maps of London, England, to stop the cholera epidemic in 1854.

Restoring America's Rivers

Not long ago America's rivers were very much like the Thames. The first sewers were constructed in New York City during the 18th century. They carried untreated sewage and dumped it into the rivers. Every day during the 1970s, 290 million gallons ($11x10^8$ L) of raw sewage flowed into the Hudson and East Rivers. Now the city has 14 sewage treatment plants that treat about 1.5 billion gallons ($5.7x10^6$ L) of wastewater every day.

The price of progress in Boston was the death of the Charles River. By 1900 the river was so polluted that shad had disappeared. People were warned about the dangers of falling into polluted rivers such as the Hudson and the Charles. Members of Harvard's rowing teams practiced on the river. Their friends joked that if the boat overturned, they should not yell for help because: "... if a teaspoon of the Charles gets in your mouth when you open it, you're done for." But it was no joke. The Charles River was not a healthy environment for humans or for fish.

To view the results of daily and monthly monitoring of the Charles River and a color-coded map showing sites where red flags signal water quality that does not meet swimming and boating standards, visit the CRWA website at: www.crwa.org.

The Charles is still polluted by raw sewage and storm water runoff, but there is good news for the rowing teams. The condition of the river is improving. The Charles River Watershed Association (CRWA) has played a key role in reviving the Charles. Every month the CRWA tests water for fecal coliform bacteria at 37 sites along the entire length of the river. Water quality samples taken by CRWA in 1998 were significantly cleaner than samples collected in 1997.

In 1896, some 15 million pounds (6.8 million kg) of shad were caught in the Delaware River. By the early 1940s, the Delaware was black with untreated sewage and chemical wastes. Chemical fumes often overcame dockworkers in Philadelphia. In the early 1950s, the level of **dissolved oxygen** (DO) in the Delaware Estuary was zero, and migrating shad either suffocated or turned back to the ocean. Now sewage flows through wastewater treatment plants before entering the river, and anglers are once again catching shad. States along the Delaware have issued fish consumption advisories because certain species of fish are contaminated with toxins.

Sewage treatment plants, like this one on a tributary of the Delaware River, are removing oxygen-demanding wastes that once polluted the river.

In 1927, workmen refused to work on construction along the "ugly and filthy" Willamette River in Oregon. All major cities along the river discharged untreated sewage directly into the river, and there was no treatment for industrial wastes. Between 1947 and 1967 the state's population doubled. The citizens of Oregon were fed up with the polluted river.

With strong citizen support the State Legislature passed laws to control pollution. By 1967, most cities had built plants to provide primary and secondary treatment of their sewage. Although the sewage was treated, the riverbed was still lined with decaying matter, and globs

To find out the percentage of surface waters in your watershed that are fishable and swimmable, visit: www.epa.gov/ow/states.html; click on your state map and then on the 305B fact sheet.

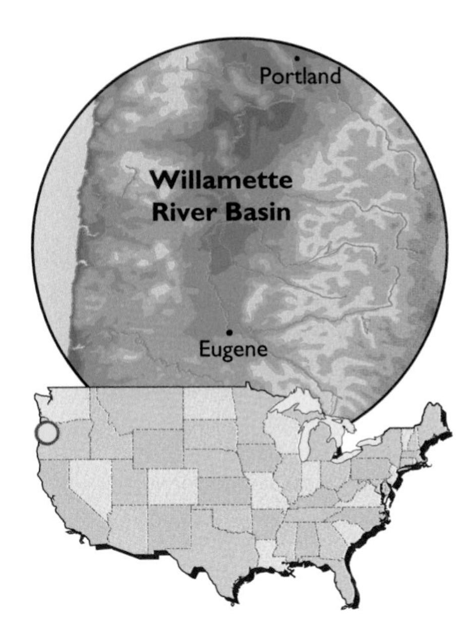

Construction at a water treatment plant.

of slimy material floated down the river. At a public hearing, the river was described as a "stinking, slimy mess, a menace to public health—a biological cesspool."

A study reported that the DO level in the Willamette River was 2.5 ppm. The study also found that 90% of the oxygen-demanding wastes were coming from the pulp and paper industries. New state regulations required all pulp and paper mills to provide primary and secondary treatment of wastes. The slime disappeared, and fish began to thrive in water that had 5 ppm DO.

Development and population growth continues in the Willamette River Basin. The population is expected to double again within the next 25-30 years. A four-year study of water quality, completed in 1995, showed that the health of the Willamette is better than it has been at any time during the last 100 years. Even so, the governor's task force described the river's health as "slightly better than marginal." Concerns about the river's health include mercury and **polychlorinated biphenyls** (PCBs) in fish, sediment mainly from agriculture, and bacteria from sewage treatment plants that lack the capacity to handle sewage and runoff during heavy rains.

Fishable and Swimmable Rivers

There is no river so small or so polluted that it is not worth saving. The water in all rivers should be "fishable and swimmable." This was the belief of Congress when it passed the 1972 Clean Water Act. The new federal water quality standards required cities to treat their sewage before dumping it into rivers and streams. Industries were also required to use the "best practicable" technology to stop pollution.

Lobbyists and some lawmakers objected to the first laws passed to improve the quality of water in Maine's rivers. They feared that the paper companies would be forced to shut down and thousands of jobs would be lost. It could cost cities and industries more than one billion dollars to build wastewater treatment plants.

The paper companies spent millions of dollars for larger, more modern plants, but it was worth it. Today the rivers are clean and Atlantic salmon have returned. Recreational use of the rivers brings millions of dollars to Maine's economy. The problem facing the legislature today is not how to control pollution, but how to regulate the use of the restored rivers.

Much of the wastewater that once flowed into our rivers from **point sources**—mainly industries and sewer pipes—is now being treated to remove the pollutants. Since 1972, billions of dollars have been invested in wastewater treatment systems. In the majority of cases, rivers and streams are safe for fishing and swimming. According to the EPA's 1995 National Water Quality Inventory of surface waters, 74% of the areas tested are safe for fish and shellfish consumption, and more than 77% of the areas met the standard for swimming.

To improve the water quality in the Hudson River, the City of New York designed and constructed the North River wastewater treatment plant on a concrete platform over the Hudson River. The rooftop of the 28-acre (11-ha) treatment plant is the Riverbank State Park, which includes swimming pools, athletic fields, an amphitheater and a restaurant. The treatment plant began operation in March 1986 ending the daily discharge of raw sewage into the Hudson River.

Some communities have yet to meet the Clean Water Act's goal of fishable and swimmable. In 1998, the Charles River was clean enough for boating 83% of the time, and it was clean enough for swimming 51% of the time. The goal of the EPA is to restore the river so that it is fishable and swimmable by Earth Day 2005.

One of the nation's most polluted coastal areas has been Boston Harbor. The Massachusetts Water Resources Authority (MWRA) serves 2.5 million people in 60 communities. Courts found the authority in violation of state and federal clean water laws. Due to outdated sewers and treatment plants, 500 million gallons (1.9×10^9 L) of improperly treated sewage poured into the harbor each day.

The MWRA built a massive multibillion-dollar sewage treatment plant on Deer Island in Boston Harbor. The treatment facilities on Deer Island provide primary and secondary treatment for sewage from 43 communities. There are concerns about the impact of the treated wastewater on plankton in Massachusetts and Cape Cod Bays.

Charles River Bacteria Data*

	1996	1997	1998
Overall			
Boating	57	70	83
Swimming	21	34	51
Dry Conditions			
Boating	94	87	98
Swimming	40	56	85
Wet Conditions			
Boating	45	61	74
Swimming	15	22	31

*percent of days meeting water quality standard

At the Sewage Treatment Plant

Primary Treatment:

As sewage enters the sewage treatment plant, it usually flows through a vertical bar screen that removes rags, sticks and other large solids. The trash is automatically scraped from the bars and then taken to a landfill. At some sewage treatment plants the water passes through a grinder, something like a gigantic garbage disposal. The sewage is then piped to a grit chamber where gravel and other heavy particles settle out.

Primary treatment mostly involves physical separation of liquids and solids. One-third of the suspended solids (organic matter) settles out of the water in the primary settling tanks. The solids that sink to the bottom of the tank are called **sludge**. Floating grease and oils are skimmed off the surface of the water. The sludge and the **effluent**, the partially treated wastewater, are piped to separate tanks for further treatment.

Raw sewage is mostly water. The suspended solids fall to the bottom of settling tanks (foreground). The effluent flows over the baffles and into the trough. It travels to the activated sludge tanks (background).

Secondary Treatment:

This type of treatment is required in all U.S. municipal sewage treatment plants. **Secondary treatment** is a biological process that usually increases the oxygen in the wastewater and allows time for organisms to remove organic matter.

There are three processes that provide secondary treatment. Some cities must treat large volumes of sewage in a very limited space. Although it is more expensive, the **activated sludge process** is often used for secondary treatment. It requires less space than the alternative processes: trickling filters or lagoons.

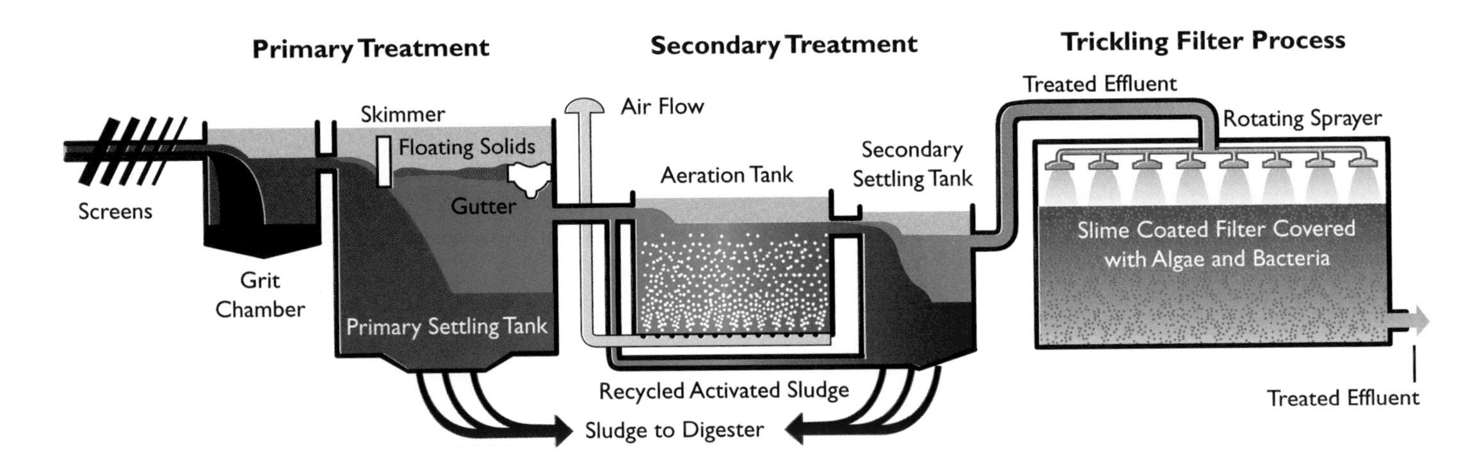

The nutrients in the effluent feed the pollution-tolerant organisms growing in this trickling filter.

In the activated sludge process, wastewater is piped to large tanks where air is pumped into the tank. The air supplies bacteria with the oxygen they need to break down the organic matter in the sewage. After several hours in the aeration tanks, the wastewater is then pumped to secondary settling tanks where the remaining solids settle out. Some of this activated sludge, which contains millions of bacteria, is returned to the aeration tanks where the bacteria help "eat" the organic matter in the wastewater.

Where space is not a problem, trickling filters are used for secondary treatment. A **trickling filter** is a tank filled with a rock-like or grid system that is coated with slime, which contains algae, bacteria, and other pollution-tolerant organisms. The effluent from the primary settling tank is sprayed over the tank, and as it trickles over the organisms, they remove most of the organic matter and nutrients from the wastewater. The purpose of primary and secondary treatment is to remove organic matter and nutrients—food for algae and bacteria—from the sewage. Primary and secondary treatment can remove 85% of the organic matter and nutrients from the sewage.

Sludge from the primary and secondary settling tanks is piped to **digesters**—large tanks that are heated to 95°F. The sludge is held in the digesters for 15 to 20 days so that anaerobic bacteria in the waste can digest more of the organic material. Natural gas or **methane** is a waste product of this digestion process. Some of the methane gas is burned to provide the heat needed for the digestors. At large treatment plants, the excess gas produced also supplies heat for buildings nearby.

It's Not Sludge—It's Biosolids

It used to be called sludge, but since that seemed like a dirty word, a decision was made to rename the solids that are removed from sewage. Now after the water is removed from sludge, it is known as biosolids. Whether you call it sludge or **biosolids**, the issue that must be addressed is what to do with it.

Disposal can be a problem, especially for large cities. In 1928, New York City began loading the digested sludge on special barges and dumping it in the ocean. The EPA approved a site 12 miles (19 km) off the coast as a dumpsite for sewage sludge from treatment plants on Long Island and in New Jersey. The EPA closed the 12-mile site in 1988, and approved a new Deepwater Municipal Sludge Dumpsite 106 miles (170 km) off the coast of New Jersey.

The City of Boston asked the EPA for permission to dump its sludge at the new Deepwater Dump. The EPA said no to Boston and required New York City and other communities to phase out the dumping of sludge. On June 29, 1992 the final load of New York City's sludge was dumped at sea. Now the sludge is dried with heat, or a process called dewatering that mechanically removes the water. The resulting biosolids are used as fertilizers or soil enhancers.

This is the action in the activated sludge tank.

Chicago solved the sludge disposal problem by buying several thousand acres of land in Fulton County, Illinois. The strip mining of coal had ruined the land. Chicago shipped sludge to Fulton County and stored it in reservoirs. During the spring and summer months, the sludge was sprayed on the land. Now the reclaimed land is leased to farmers.

Farmers can reduce their fertilizer costs by applying biosolids, but they must be properly treated and tested to make sure that they are safe. It is unlikely that biosolids will cause disease. Most disease-causing organisms and parasites can't survive the no-oxygen environment in the digester.

Biosolids used to grow crops should be tested for their nutrient **(N-P-K)** content. If too many biosolids are applied to the land, the excess nitrogen leaches into the water supply or nearby streams. The farmer must know the nutrient level of the biosolids and the soil in order to calculate the amount that can be safely applied.

Sludge can also be used to make compost. In 1970, a treatment plant at Hollands Landing, Canada, began using earthworms to compost sewage sludge and food processing wastes. Worms are used in Japan to compost sludge from the pulp and paper industry. At the sewage treatment plant in Lufkin, Texas, earthworms live in beds of aged sawdust and feed on sewage sludge. Sludge is sprayed over the sawdust beds for 3 to 5 minutes once a day. Fresh bedding, lime and water are added as needed. The Department of Parks and Recreation uses the compost.

The Need for Pretreatment

Since heavy metals prevent normal plant growth, sewage sludge must be tested to determine the levels of heavy metals it may contain. Soil tests must also be taken to find the level of heavy metals in the soil. If the soil already contains high levels of heavy metals, sludge should not be applied to the land. Most heavy metals interfere with plant growth at levels well below those that are toxic to humans and other animals, but this is not true of cadmium. Levels of cadmium that are toxic to humans do not affect plants.

Pretreatment and proper testing is necessary to ensure that toxins don't kill the organisms at the sewage treatment plant or concentrate in the sludge.

Industry is the major source of heavy metals found in sludge. To prevent high levels of heavy metals in sludge, industries must pretreat wastewater before dumping it into the sewers. Heavy metals in sewage combine with the organic matter and become concentrated in the sludge. Proper **pretreatment** and laboratory testing can ensure that the sludge is safe.

The purpose of primary and secondary sewage treatment is to reduce the organic matter and lower the **biochemical oxygen demand (BOD)** of the effluent. Sewage treatment plants are designed to provide an ideal environment for the bacteria present in the sewage to do their job. The bacteria break down the organic matter, but they do not have the enzymes that are necessary to break down toxic wastes. Toxic wastes flushed into the sewer may kill the bacteria and stop the treatment process. Industries are required to pretreat wastewater so that toxic wastes don't interfere with the treatment process.

Chlorine is added and reacts with the treated effluent as it flows through the maze in the chlorination tank.

Chlorination

After secondary treatment, the wastewater is usually disinfected before it is discharged through an **outfall pipe** into a body of water nearby. The least expensive and most common method of disinfection is **chlorination**. Sodium hypochlorite, the same chemical found in household chlorine bleach, is added to the effluent to kill any disease-causing bacteria that might remain in the water. If properly treated, more than 99% of the harmful bacteria are killed.

One disadvantage of chlorination is that chlorine reacts with organic compounds in the water to form **trihalomethanes**, which are **carcinogenic**. Another disadvantage is that chlorine is also toxic to organisms in the aquatic environment. Since bacteria are less likely to survive in cold weather, some regions do not require chlorination during the winter months. If the effluent is discharged near shellfish beds, year-round chlorination is required.

The chlorinated effluent flows from the outfall pipe into the creek.

Combined Sewers

In 1965, the river that flows through our nation's capital was a "national disgrace," according to President Lyndon Johnson. In the 1970s, the Potomac River was considered a "severe threat to the health of anyone coming in contact with it." Today the Potomac River flowing through Washington, D.C., is not "swimmable" because of bacterial pollution from combined sewer outlets.

Combined sewers carry both sewage and storm water. When combined sewers were built, no one anticipated the problems they would eventually cause at sewage treatment plants. During average rainfalls the volume of water entering the sewers can be 5–15 times greater than the normal flow. Sewage treatment plants are not designed to process this massive volume of water.

When storms hit cities with combined sewers, untreated sewage and storm water may flow directly into the river. Our nation's capitol is just one of many older cities that have combined sewer overflow pipes which dump untreated water into rivers. New sewer systems must have separate storm and sanitary sewers.

The Effluent—Additional Treatment

Secondary treatment at some sewage treatment plants does not produce effluent that meets EPA standards for nitrates and phosphates. Without further treatment, the effluent will pollute streams and cause algal blooms, but it can be a valuable resource as irrigation water for golf courses, farmland or forests. Natural or artificial wetlands can also be used to remove nitrates and phosphates from effluent.

Water hyacinths and other aquatic plants remove nitrates and phosphates from wastewater in lagoons.

Lagoons and Aquaculture

Where land is available, wetlands may replace trickling filters or activated sludge processes. Another method that provides primary and secondary treatment is a lagoon. Although lagoons require large amounts of land, they are much less expensive to build and maintain than the conventional sewage treatment plant. A **lagoon** is a shallow pond where sewage is held for 20 to 30 days. In warm climates, algae and bacteria in a series of lagoons can provide acceptable primary and secondary sewage treatment.

Water in a lagoon may need to be recirculated to prevent odors that are produced when there is a lack of oxygen. Mosquitoes cause problems at lagoons, but this problem may be reduced by adding fish that eat mosquito larvae and bats that feed on the adults. Water hyacinths were added to lagoons to help control odors. These lagoons produce cleaner wastewater because the hyacinths use the nitrates and phosphates, and the roots filter the water.

Water hyacinth treatment ponds are being used in several southern states. The hyacinths can be used as food for cattle. Although hyacinths can only be used in warm climates, other aquatic plants—duckweed, watercress, or cattails—can be used in areas with cooler climates.

One of the most popular spots for bird watchers in western Michigan is the Muskegon Wastewater Treatment Facility. More than 10,000 acres (4,000 ha) of land around the treatment facility have been cleared and planted with crops. The fields are fertilized and irrigated with the recycled wastewater that is stored in two 800-acre (320-ha) lagoons.

It may look like a lake, but it is one of two lagoons that provide primary and secondary treatment for sewage from the Muskegon, MI, area.

After several months of treatment in the lagoon, the wastewater flows through ditches to fields where crops are growing.

After several months in the lagoon, the treated wastewater is used to irrigate field crops like corn.

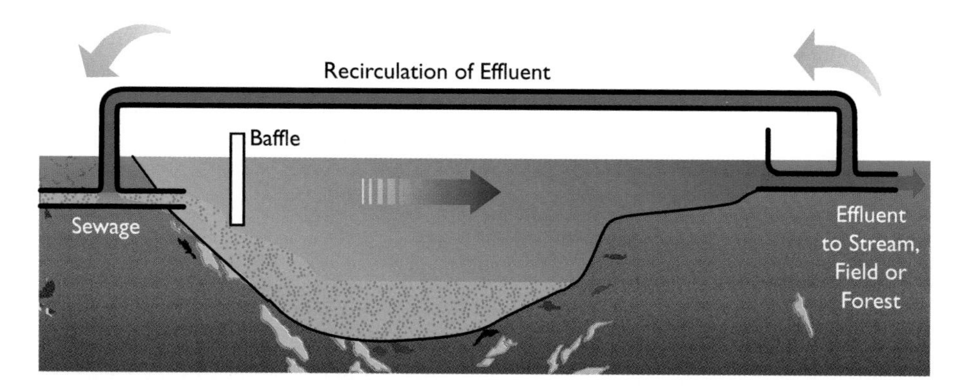

On-Site Sewage Treatment

Septic tank-soil absorption systems are the most common type of wastewater treatment used in rural areas. One-third of housing units in the United States use this form of wastewater treatment. A **septic tank** is simply a large tank buried in the ground to treat sewage from an individual home or business. Solids settle to the bottom, bacteria break down organic matter, and the effluent flows through pipes into the **soil absorption field** (drain field).

Sewage should remain in the tank for at least 24 hours to allow solids to settle out of the wastewater. The size of the septic tank is based on the number of bedrooms in the home. In Pennsylvania, the formula for calculating tank size assumes a minimum daily flow of 400 gallons (1.5×10^3 L) per day for a home with three or fewer bedrooms. An additional 100 gallons is added for each additional bedroom. The flow rate assumes the use of automatic washing machines, garbage disposals and dishwashers.

The effluent from the septic tank flows through a system of perforated pipes in the absorption field. The size of the soil absorption field is determined by the size of the house and the soil's percolation rate. The soil must be a good filter—not too porous and not impermeable to water. The **percolation rate**—the rate at which water moves through the soil—must not be too fast or too slow. For a subsurface absorption field, the percolation rate must be between 6 and 90 minutes per inch (2.5 cm).

In Pennsylvania, a minimum soil depth of 60 inches (120 cm) is required for a **subsurface absorption field**. If the site selected for the absorption field does not meet the requirements for a standard or **subsurface system**, the absorption field must be placed in a mound above the soil's natural surface. In an **elevated sand mound**, a layer of sand is placed on the soil to increase the depth of the absorption area. The depth of the natural soil determines the depth of the sand required.

The drain pipes are placed in a layer of gravel. Building paper is placed over the gravel before the field is covered with topsoil. This prevents the soil from clogging the system. Grease should never be poured down the drain since it will also clog the absorption field.

In a standard septic system, the septic tank and drain field are below ground level. Regular maintenance ensures proper functioning.

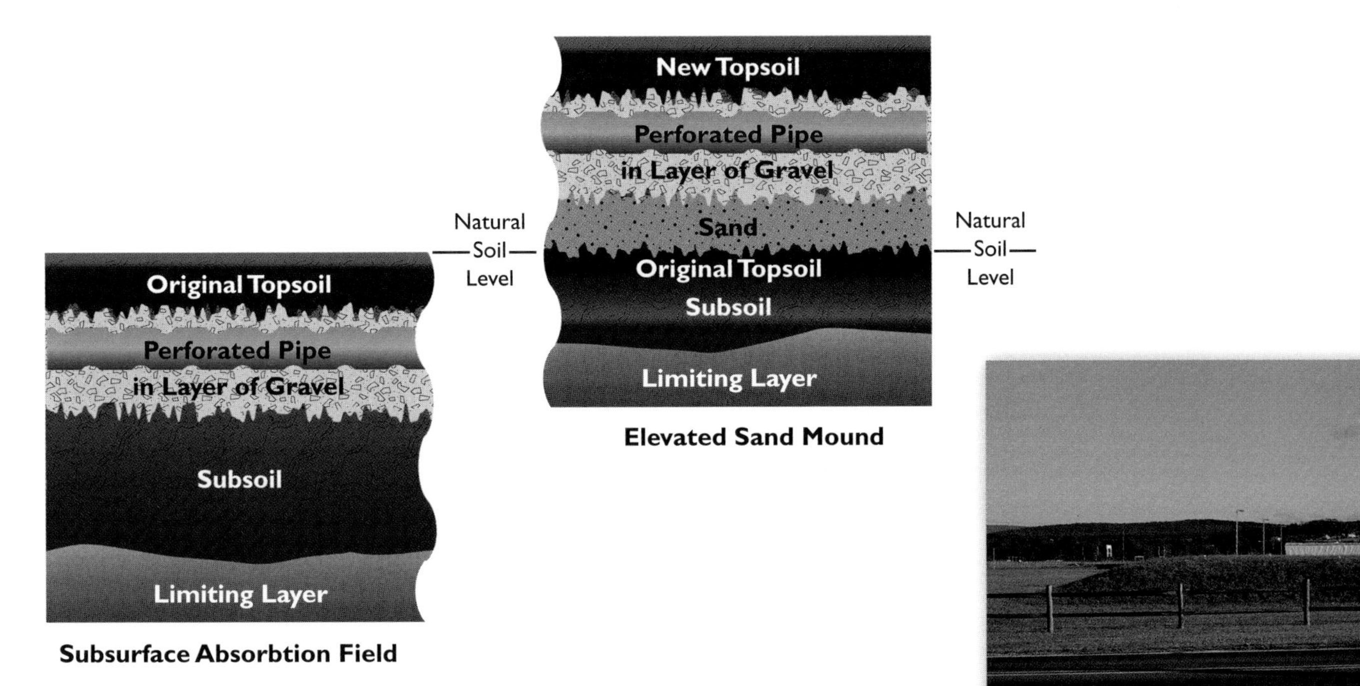

Elevated Sand Mound

Subsurface Absorbtion Field

An elevated sand mound is required if the natural soil depth does not meet requirements.

Inside the Septic Tank

The bacteria normally digest about 50% of the solids that remain in the tank; the remainder will accumulate in the bottom of the tank as sludge. Large amounts of disinfectants may kill the bacteria and stop digestion of the sludge.

Unless it is regularly removed from the tank, sludge will build up and clog the absorption field. The frequency of pumping depends on the size of the tank and the number of people in the household. Garbage disposals may double the amount of solids to be digested, and should not be used with septic systems. If garbage disposals are used, the size of the tank should be doubled.

The mixture of fluids and solids (3–5%) pumped from the tank is called **septage**. Septage contains disease-causing organisms and can contaminate water supplies. The usual method for disposal of septage is to spray it on farmland.

Farmland used for septage disposal should be in one of the following USDA soil texture classes: sandy loam, sandy clay loam, silty clay loam, or silt loam. The site must also meet the following requirements:

- There must be a soil depth of at least 20 inches (50 cm) to bedrock.
- The water table must be at least 4 feet (1.2 m) below the surface.
- The slope of the field must not exceed 12%.
- There must be no visible sinkholes.
- It must not be subject to flooding or erosion.
- It must be more than 300 feet (90 m) from a water supply and 100 feet (30 m) from a spring.
- The soil must not be frozen.

Perforated pipes are laid under the layer of gravel during the construction of an elevated sand mound.

Septic Tank—Side View Below Ground Level

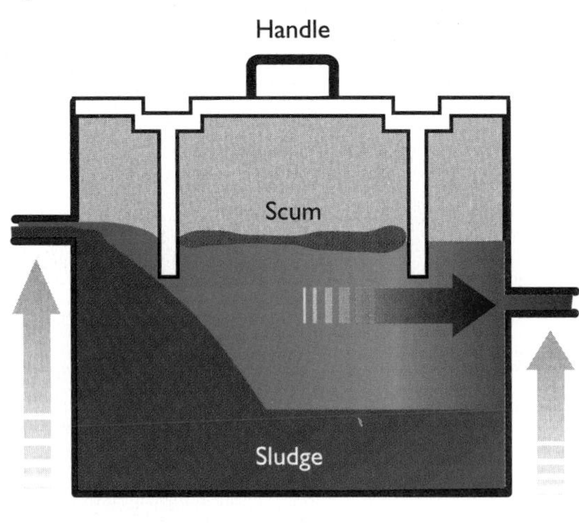

Septic Tank—View From Above

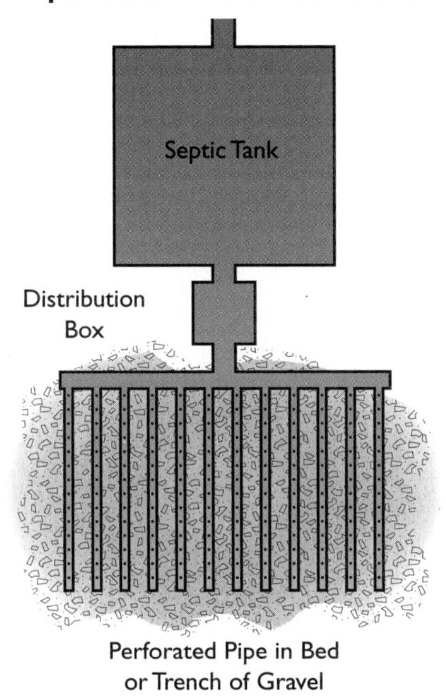

Livestock should not feed on the crops that have been sprayed with septage for at least 60 days after application. The septage applied on dairy farms must be plowed down before crops are planted. Dairy cows are not allowed to feed on crops sprayed with septage. Septage should not be used on home gardens or land that is used for commercial production of food that will be eaten raw. If applied properly, septage can be beneficial. If it is not applied properly, it can be dangerous.

In more densely populated areas, with limited farmland, the usual method of septage disposal was in lagoons. After many years, the nitrates leaching from the lagoons were polluting the groundwater in many communities. The use of lagoons for septage disposal is being phased out. The septage from septic systems in Harwich, Massachusetts, is being treated in a solar aquatic greenhouse with artificial wetlands and aquaculture ecosystems. The effluent is treated with UV light to kill any harmful microorganisms. According to the Massachusetts Department of Environmental Protection, the effluent met Class I drinking-water standards.

Environmental Challenge: Spruce Lake Retreat

Design a sewage treatment system for Spruce Lake Retreat, a campground where 500 youngsters will reside for a 6-week summer camp. The campground will be used on week-ends and holidays during the fall and spring, but be closed during the winter months.

Since the camp does not operate year-round, controlling costs is an important factor. Due to environmental regulations, the treated effluent cannot be discharged into Spruce Creek or the lake.

Is it Worth the Cost?

Wastewater entering the river upstream becomes drinking water downstream. Improperly treated wastewater not only makes water unfit to drink, it also makes it unfit for fish and other aquatic organisms. Effective wastewater treatment is essential to human health. Effective treatment of wastewater and proper disposal of sludge is essential to meet the goal of "fishable, swimmable" waters.

Modern treatment methods are expensive. New York City water and sewer rates increased by 20% and more increases are expected. While it cost $20 million a year to dump sludge in the ocean, the first year of the city's land disposal was $250 million. While there are some scientists that believe that the oceans can assimilate our wastes, others disagree. Regulations, like the ban on ocean dumping, provide increased protection for the ocean ecosystem. The ocean is a source of food and, in some places, drinking water. Like the rivers and the streams, the ocean water quality needs to be fishable and swimmable.

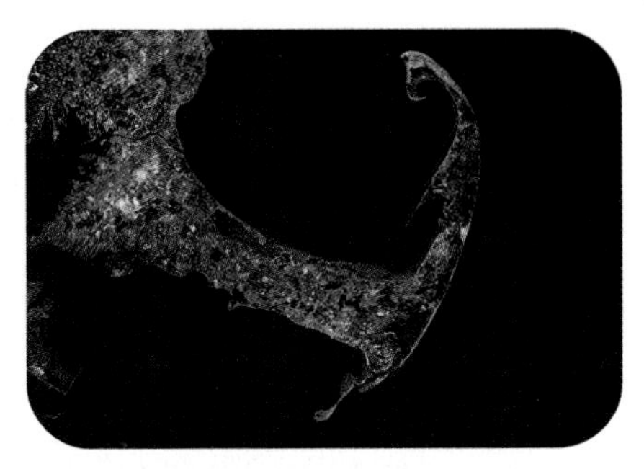
Satellite image of Cape Cod.

4.12 Questions for Study and Discussion:

1. Define the following terms: **VOCABULARY**

activated sludge process	dissolved oxygen	Polychlorinated biphenyls (PCBs)	soil absorption field
biochemical oxygen demand (BOD)	effluent	pretreatment	subsurface absorption field
biosolids	elevated sand mound	primary treatment	subsurface system
chlorination	lagoon	secondary treatment	trickling filter
combined sewers	methane	septage	trihalomethanes (THMs)
digesters	N-P-K	septic tank	water-borne diseases
	outfall pipe	sludge	
	percolation rate		

Reviving the Thames

2. Identify two major events that increased the river's load of wastes.
3. What disease carried by the water caused the death of many people living in London in the 1800s?
4. Compare the condition of the Thames River in the 1950s with the condition of the river today.

Restoring America's Rivers

5. Identify the type of pollution that created problems in the Hudson, the Charles and the Delaware Rivers. How did this pollution affect the level of DO and the fish populations in the Delaware River?
6. Identify the two types of pollution that created problems in Oregon's Willamette River. What action was taken to clean up the river?
7. After the treatment plants were built, what was the level of DO in the river? What was the source of the pollution that caused the low DO level?
8. What action was taken to solve the problem? What is the level of DO in the river now?

Fishable and Swimmable Rivers

9. What was the goal of the 1972 Clean Water Act?
10. Compare the water quality of Maine's rivers with the water quality of the Willamette River in Oregon.
11. What did the federal water quality standards require of cities? Of industries?

At the Sewage Treatment Plant

12. What processes occur in the primary treatment of sewage?
13. Distinguish between sludge and effluent.
14. Is primary treatment of sewage a biological or physical process?
15. Describe a trickling filter.
16. What is the purpose of primary and secondary treatment of sewage? How effective is primary and secondary treatment?
17. Compare the way in which organic matter is removed from the wastewater in the activated sludge process with the way it is removed in the trickling filter process.
18. What part of the sewage receives further treatment in the digesters? What is the purpose of this digestion process?

19. How do the bacteria working in the digester differ from the bacteria working in the activated sludge or trickling filter processes?

It's Not Sludge—It's Biosolids

20. How did the city of New York dispose of its sludge prior to 1992? What does the city do with its sludge now?
21. Why is it unlikely that sludge from a digester will cause disease?
22. What test results must a farmer have before using sludge as fertilizer? What dangerous situation may result if a farmer applies too much sludge to the field?
23. What organism is being used in several countries to compost sewage sludge? Identify two other types of wastes that can be composted by the same process.

The Need for Pretreatment

24. Explain why sludge should be tested for heavy metals. Why are soil tests also needed?
25. What is the source of most heavy metals found in sludge? How can the problem of heavy metals in sludge be avoided?
26. Explain why toxic wastes are not removed by primary and secondary sewage treatment. Explain how toxic wastes may interfere with the primary and secondary sewage treatment processes.

Chlorination

27. How effective is chlorination? What are the disadvantages of chlorination?
28. During what time of the year are some sewage treatment plants allowed to release effluent without chlorination?

Combined Sewers

29. How do combined sewers contribute to the pollution of the Potomac River in Washington, D.C.?
30. What is the advantage of separate storm and sanitary sewers?

The Effluent—Additional Treatment

31. Despite primary and secondary treatment, the effluent from some sewage treatment plants still contains excessive levels of nitrates and phosphates. How will these chemicals affect the stream?
32. Identify a beneficial use of effluent that has excessive levels of nutrients.
33. What is the advantage of pumping effluent that doesn't meet the water quality standards for nutrients into a wetland?

Lagoons and Aquaculture

34. Describe how lagoons provide primary and secondary treatment of sewage.
35. Identify the plant that is being added to lagoons in warm climates to aid the treatment processes. What plants could be used in colder climates? Describe how these plants purify water.

On-Site Sewage Treatment

36. Identify the most common type of sewage treatment found in rural areas.
37. Identify the two parts of a septic system. Briefly describe what happens to the wastewater as it passes through the system.
38. How does the treatment of sewage in a septic tank differ from the treatment that occurs in an activated sludge tank and a digester?
39. Why is the percolation rate in the absorption field important?
40. Describe how a soil absorption field is made if the natural soil level does not meet the minimum depth requirement.

Inside the Septic Tank

41. What type of material might interfere with the normal digestion processes in the septic tank?
42. What will happen if a septic tank is not emptied regularly? List three factors that determine how often the septic tank should be emptied.
43. What is septage? What is the usual disposal site for this material?
44. Describe the technology that is being used in Harwich, MA, to purify the septage from septic systems. How pure is the effluent?

Is it Worth the Cost?

45. Is it possible to have rivers that are "fishable and swimmable"? Explain.
46. Do you think that the ocean should be used as a disposal site for human wastes? Justify your position.

UNIT FIVE
Water For The People

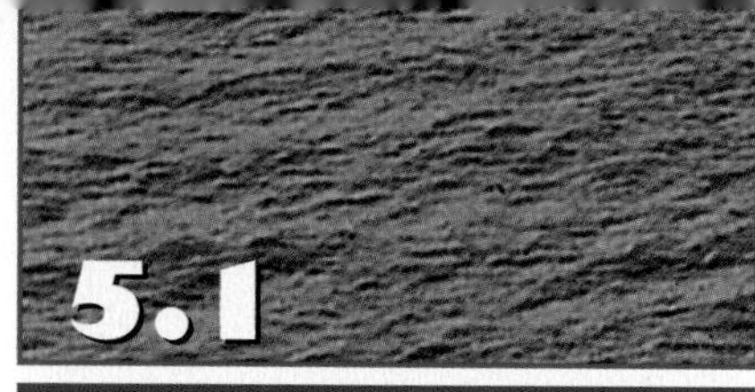

5.1 Poisons In the Water

OBJECTIVES

- ✔ **List** advantages and disadvantages associated with synthetic chemicals.
- ✔ **Compare** and **contrast** the situations at the Superfund sites in Niagara Falls, NY (Love Canal) and in Woburn, MA (Wells G&H).
- ✔ **Relate** the use of toxic chemicals to the health of fish and humans.
- ✔ **Explain** the advantages of biomonitoring over chemical testing.
- ✔ **Identify** potential sources of toxic pollutants and **describe** problems associated with the release of these toxic chemicals.
- ✔ **Develop** a plan to reduce the threat associated with toxic chemicals.

"Sand, gravel, and silt through which water travels do filter out harmful bacteria. But the soil is almost helpless against many man-made organic chemicals."
ANDREW HOGARTH
Michigan Department of Natural Resources

Synthetic chemicals have become essential to our way of life. The manufacture and use of some 70,000 chemicals have made our lives easier and, in some cases, safer. The chemical industry created many new jobs, introduced many new products, improved food production and strengthened the nation's economy. That is the good news.

The bad news is that large amounts of hazardous chemical wastes are produced during the manufacture of products we use, including cars, refrigerators, pesticides, plastics, gasoline, jewelry, and cosmetics. Industries release billions of pounds of toxic chemicals into the air and water each year.

Industries are required to report the release or transfer of more than 650 toxic chemicals to the EPA. According to the EPA, over 2 billion pounds (4.4 billion kg) of the listed toxic chemicals were released into the environment or transferred off-site by industries, in 1997. Hazardous wastes have been stored in lagoons, placed in metal drums and buried in landfills, and injected into deep wells. Until recently, we thought that all of these were acceptable ways to dispose of toxic chemicals.

After many years we have learned that we cannot simply bury or dump unwanted chemicals and forget them. Sometimes the past comes back to haunt us. Many old landfills and lagoons are leaking, and there is concern that the toxic chemicals will contaminate water supplies nearby. In some cases the groundwater is already contaminated.

The EPA has identified more than 37,000 sites that are contaminated with toxic chemicals. Of these sites, more than 1,400 are included on the Superfund's **National Priorities List**. Cleanup of some of these sites can take years. The creation of a **Superfund** for the cleanup of contaminated sites and new regulations for disposal of hazardous waste were the result of events that occurred at a dumpsite known as Love Canal.

Rusting drums leaked toxic chemicals that contaminated the area around the Love Canal dump site.

The Lesson Learned at Love Canal

In the 1890s, Mr. William T. Love dug a canal for a hydroelectric project, but the project was never completed. From 1947 until 1952, the Hooker Chemical Corporation, the City of Niagara Falls, and the U.S. Army dumped toxic chemicals into the abandoned canal in Niagara Falls, NY. Then the canal was filled and sold for a token of $1 to the school board, which built an elementary school and playground directly over the canal. The remaining land was sold to a developer who built single-family houses along the filled canal.

In 1976, heavy rains caused chemicals to leak from the rusting drums, rise to the surface, and seep into basements. Residents were concerned about their health and the health of their children. They reported unexplained miscarriages, birth defects, various forms of cancer and other health problems. In 1978 and 1980, President Carter declared federal emergencies. The school was closed and approximately 950 families were evacuated from a 10 square-block area around the canal. It was the largest environmental evacuation ever.

The school and about 200 homes located nearest to the dump were torn down and buried. The dumpsite has been covered with a clay/synthetic cap, and a special drainage system has been installed. Water draining from the site passes through a special treatment plant. A chain-link fence around the 70-acre site holds a sign that reads: "Danger — hazardous waste area — keep out."

Occidental Chemical Corporation (formerly Hooker Chemical) agreed to reimburse the EPA Superfund more than $129 million. The U.S. Army paid $8 million. The EPA says that the site no longer threatens human health or the environment. Two hundred homes, bought by the government and boarded up, have been rehabilitated and sold. The 60 families that refused to sell and still live in the area now have new neighbors.

Three million dollars of the settlement funds are being used for a comprehensive health study, but the study is complicated by the evacuation of such a large number of people. More than 50 lawsuits for wrongful deaths have been settled, but lawsuits can be filed and settlements made without proof that the chemicals were the cause of the medical problems. We may never know if the people listed in the Love Canal Health Registry would have lived longer or healthier lives if they had not lived near the Love Canal.

Woburn's Wells

Woburn, Massachusetts, is an industrial community located 13 miles northwest of Boston. The community is also the site of a leukemia cluster. A **disease cluster** occurs when a number of people living or working in the same area develop the same disease. Between January 1969 and December 1979 twelve cases of childhood leukemia were diagnosed in Woburn. The number of cases expected was 5.3.

In 1982, eight families, who had lost children to leukemia, filed a highly publicized lawsuit against three companies. They claimed organic chemicals, including trichloroethylene and tetrachloroethylene, dumped by company employees, had contaminated two groundwater wells. The families also claimed that the chemicals were responsible for causing the leukemia.

The jury found W.R. Grace & Co. guilty of causing the pollution of wells identified as G and H. The EPA investigation, concluded in 1988, demonstrated that the chemicals in wells G & H came from five properties. The contaminated wells provided 30% of the city's drinking water. Leukemia had been diagnosed in six children living in houses that

A study by the Environmental Defense Fund (EDF) called "Toxic Ignorance" raised concerns about chemicals manufactured in, or imported into, the U.S. that have not been tested for health and environmental effects. Studies by the Environmental Protection Agency (EPA) and Chemical Manufacturers Association also found that many commercial chemicals have little toxicity information.

High production volume (HPV) chemicals are those chemicals that are manufactured or imported in amounts exceeding 1 million pounds per year. There are about 2,800 HPV chemicals, and the EPA found that complete data on health and environmental effects are publicly available for only about 7% of these chemicals.

The EPA's **Chemical Right-to-Know Program** will obtain test data on these chemicals and collect Toxics Release Inventory (TRI) information. As information becomes available it will be posted on the EPA Chemical Right-to-Know Website, www.epa.gov/opptintr/chemrtk.

TRI information is available at EPA's Envirofacts Websites, www.epa.gov/enviro and www.epa.gov/tri.

For information on the cleanup of the Wells G & H Superfund Site, visit: www.epa.gov/region01/remed/sfsites. The civil lawsuit filed by the families in Woburn was the basis for the book and movie, *A Civil Action*. For the viewpoint of W.R. Grace & Co., visit their Website, www.civil-action.com.

Environmental Challenge: Toxic Releases

Find out what hazardous chemicals are being released from manufacturing facilities in your community at EDF's Website: www.scorecard.org.

- Explore the U.S. map to find out what states are releasing the most toxic chemicals.
- How does your state, county, or city rank in amount of toxics released?
- Search by company name to find out what toxics are being released and how much. Are they being released to the air, water, or land, or injected into deep wells?
- What are the risks associated with these chemicals?

Most of the Great Lakes' shoreline waters are impacted by toxic organic chemicals, mainly PCBs.

received water from these wells between 1964 and 1979, the year they were shut down.

The cause of the leukemia is not known. Twenty-one cases of childhood leukemia had been diagnosed in Woburn's 35,000 residents by the middle of 1986. A study made by the Massachusetts Department of Public Health concluded that the risk of developing childhood leukemia was greater for children whose mothers drank water from wells G and H during pregnancy. The risk increased as the amount of water used in the household increased. The risk declined after the contaminated wells were no longer used.

In 1982, wells G & H were placed on the National Priority List of Superfund Sites. In 1990, the EPA reached a $69.45 million settlement with the parties responsible for the pollution from four of the five properties, and cleanup of the site began. Millions of gallons of contaminated groundwater have been cleaned up and tons of contaminated soil removed.

It is likely that there will be other Woburns and more civil actions. About 51% of the nation's population rely on groundwater as a source of drinking water. The greatest concern is contamination from leaking underground storage tanks. Another concern is the improper disposal of industrial and commercial wastewater in shallow wells or septic systems that are only designed for sanitary wastes.

What the Fish Tell Us

Once in the air, chemicals may travel for several thousand miles before rain or snow cleans the air. Heavy metals, acids, and toxic chemicals are washed from the air by precipitation and deposited in our rivers, lakes, and reservoirs. Air pollution is the major source of mercury in the Great Lakes. Over 90% of some pollutants, including PCBs (polychlorinated biphenyls), in Lake Superior are deposited in the lake from the atmosphere—**atmospheric deposition**.

Industries have spent billions of dollars to prevent pollution. They have eliminated the oxygen-demanding wastes that once made sewers of our rivers and streams. The fish have returned. There are more than 100 species of fish in the New York's Hudson River, but some species have high levels of toxic chemicals stored in their bodies, and there are warnings about eating fish caught in the river.

Nationwide there are more than 2,000 advisories warning that it is not safe to eat certain species of fish caught in some lakes and rivers. According to the EPA, "100% of the Great Lakes' waters and their connecting waters, and a large portion of the nation's coastal waters are under advisory." Anglers fishing in Lake Superior, the cleanest of the Great Lakes, are warned not to eat certain species of fish because they contain unsafe levels of mercury, PCBs, and chlordane. Michigan's state fishing licenses contain this warning:

> *"Certain Great Lakes fish should not be eaten—by children, or women who are pregnant, nursing, or expect to bear children. Limit consumption by all others to no more than one meal per week."*

The National Cancer Institute reports that **carcinogens** affect fish livers in the same way that they affect human livers. In five areas where fish with high numbers of tumors were found, the human cancer rates were significantly above the national average. Scientists have begun to look at fish as an indicator of the health of the environment.

Minnows are an ideal laboratory animal because they are small, easy to keep and inexpensive. At EPA's research laboratory in Gulf Breeze, Florida, scientists use the sheepshead minnow to identify cancer-causing pollutants. In only 14 weeks, scientists can identify developing tumors in minnows exposed to a carcinogen. Scientists look for "safe" or "no effect" concentrations for fish. They also hope that studies with fish may help determine the level of a specific chemical harmful to humans.

Minnows are also good biological monitors in our environment. Since they must constantly take in water, they are continuously exposed to the pollutant. **Biomonitoring**, the use of living organisms to determine water quality, offers two advantages over chemical testing. It allows scientists to study the effect of changing environmental conditions. For example, some chemicals are more toxic in warmer water. Biomonitoring also provides information about the effects of combinations of chemicals. Sometimes these are more deadly than individual chemicals, and very difficult to test.

The National Listing of Fish Consumption Advisories is available at: www.epa.gov/OST/fishadvice. More information on advisories in your state may be available at: www.epa.gov/ow/region.html; scroll to the index below the map to find your state. A brochure from the New Jersey Department of Health's *A Woman's guide to Eating Fish and Seafood*, is online at: www.state.nj.us/health/eoh/foodweb/fishguid.htm.

Water, Water, Everywhere, but ...

Each minute of the day nine million gallons ($3.4 x 10^7$ L) of water flow down the Hudson River past Manhattan. The city grew fast; there were too many people and too much pollution. A 200-mile stretch of the Hudson River, from Hudson Falls to New York Harbor, has been declared a Superfund site because of PCB contamination. But you need not be concerned about toxic chemicals in the Hudson—as long as you don't eat the fish. The city obtains most of its drinking water from reservoirs upstate in the Delaware River watershed.

Unlike New York City, New Orleans doesn't own a protected watershed in the mountains. About 18 million people, including about 60,000 residents of New Orleans, get their drinking water from the Mississippi River. As the river water travels through the municipal water treatment plants in about 70 cities, the water must be cleaned up and levels of pollutants reduced to meet the EPA drinking water standards.

Carcinogens affect fish livers in the same way they affect human livers.

Cleaning Mississippi River water is not an easy task. Between Baton Rouge and New Orleans there are more than 100 major industries along the Mississippi River. The industries have permits that allow them to release toxic chemicals directly into the river. Runoff and contaminated groundwater add nitrates, pesticides, and sediment from agriculture. Storm sewers add more toxic pollutants, and sewage overflows add pathogens during storms.

To view a video or see a slide show on the Hudson River PCB Story, visit: http://clearwater.org/pcb.html.

The EPA found 66 chemical compounds in New Orleans' drinking water. The highest concentration was chloroform. Chloroform is one of a group of chemicals called THMs (trihalomethanes). **Trihalomethanes** are formed when organic chemicals react with chlorine used to disinfect the water. THMs have been identified as probable carcinogens.

Did You Know?

PCBs were dumped by General Electric factories along the Hudson River until the 1960s. The PCBs settled to the bottom of the river and contaminated the mud. The U.S. Fish and Wildlife Service found high levels of PCBs in tree swallows. The muddy bottom is the habitat for the developing larvae and nymphs of insects that the swallows eat. The birds are having problems growing feathers and reproducing. Herons and terns also appear to be affected by PCBs.

Some service stations, like this one, closed because they couldn't afford to upgrade the underground storage tanks. When this property was sold, the new owners removed the tanks.

The federal standard for total THMs in drinking water is 100 ppb. To reduce levels of THMs, New Orleans stopped using chlorine and switched to **chloramines**—a safer but more expensive disinfectant. THMs and other organic chemicals may also be removed by the addition of **activated carbon**, during the treatment process.

The water treatment plant operators in New Orleans are meeting the challenge. EPA reports show that New Orleans' drinking water meets all safety standards. The cost of treating the water is much higher in New Orleans than in New York City. The residents of New Orleans are paying the price of living downstream.

Problems with Underground Storage Tanks

Santa Clara Valley in northern California is better known as the "Silicon Valley." Many companies that make electronic parts, semiconductors, and computers are located in the valley. It is an important center of high-technology industry, which has not been kind to the environment.

There are no smokestacks or buildings that look like factories, but the valley is a major manufacturing area. The major source of air pollution is the automobile. Although the air is cleaner, the valley is not free of pollution. Industries use organic chemicals in the manufacture of computers and other high-tech equipment. The chemicals were stored in underground storage tanks, and some of the tanks leaked.

The region now has 29 Superfund sites, the highest density in the nation. Groundwater is the source of half of the valley's drinking water, and the organic chemicals threaten the water supply. Toxic chemicals from one IBM facility have traveled 3 miles and shut down 17 public wells. Cleaning up the contamination is not an easy task. Each contaminated site must be evaluated and the best solution selected.

During the 1950s and 1960s many gasoline storage tanks were buried. The tanks were made of metal, and contact with the moist soil caused them to rust. As of March 1996, there had been more than 300,000 confirmed releases of chemicals from underground storage tanks. Federal law required owners of underground storage tanks to either upgrade to corrosion-resistant models or close their tanks prior to 1999. The EPA estimates that it will cost billions of dollars to clean up the contamination resulting from leaking underground storage tanks.

Gasoline that floats on the surface of the groundwater can be pumped out and used, but gasoline contains some toxic chemicals that are somewhat soluble in water. One of these is **benzene**, a chemical known to cause cancer in humans. The chemicals can be removed by passing the water through an activated carbon filter, but removal is expensive. [See page 397, Before You Drink the Water.]

Down on the Farm

The quality of the groundwater beneath the Nebraska Sandhills is changing. For years the tall prairie grasses held the sandy soil in place and absorbed most of the rain that fell. Until the invention of the center-pivot irrigation system, there was not enough moisture to grow crops. Large amounts of water and nitrogen fertilizer must be added to grow crops in sandy soils.

Rainwater leaches the nitrogen compounds from the soil and transports it into the aquifer below. The problem is not limited to Nebraska. In a national survey of agricultural and urban areas, the nitrate levels in 15% of shallow wells exceeded the "safe" standard of 10 milligrams nitrate (as nitrogen) per liter of water. The EPA estimates that 4.5 million Americans drink water with nitrate levels exceeding the drinking water standard of 10 mg/L.

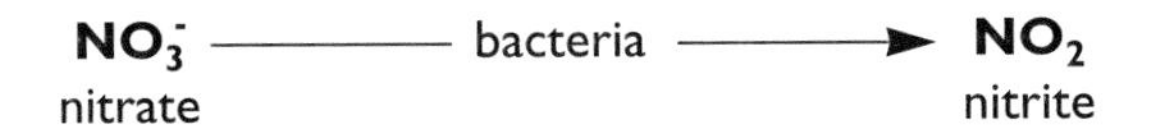

Nitrates are dangerous when they are changed into nitrites. The digestive system of human infants harbors bacteria that change nitrates to nitrites. If water contains more than 10 mg/L of nitrates, it should not be given to infants or children less than one year old or to pregnant women.

Nitrites interfere with **hemoglobin**'s ability to carry oxygen. Babies develop a bluish color, especially around the eyes and mouth—a condition called **methemoglobinemia** or "Blue Baby Syndrome." Instead of the usual red color, the blood is chocolate brown. A blood test must be taken to confirm the diagnosis. Unless the condition is treated, it can cause brain damage or death.

Older children and adults have more hydrochloric acid in their stomachs. The acid kills most of the bacteria that convert nitrates to nitrites. Nitrates are not dangerous to older children and adults. Horses, sheep, cattle, baby pigs and baby chickens also have bacteria in their digestive systems that change nitrates to nitrites. Although no standard is set for livestock, researchers suggest a maximum of 100 mg/L of nitrates in their drinking water.

Until the 1970s, scientists thought that pesticides were attracted to and held by soil particles until they were broken down. Now we know that certain pesticides travel through the soil and into groundwater. In 1988, the EPA reported that normal agricultural use of pesticides had resulted in 46 different pesticides in the groundwater in 26 states. Analysis of water samples collected from 27 wells in Nebraska during the summers of 1996 and 1997 showed pesticides in 15 wells. In two wells the herbicide atrazine was found at levels above the maximum (3 ppb) allowed in drinking water.

Pesticides are more likely to be found in shallow aquifers, which are less than 100 feet deep. New pesticides must be tested, to determine how readily they are **leached** from the soil, before they can be registered for use. Registration of a pesticide may be denied, or its use restricted to specific soil types, in order to prevent groundwater contamination.

Problems at Kesterson

Much of California's farmland was once a part of the sea floor, and the soil has a naturally high concentration of mineral salts. In dry climates where

Think About It

Could this pipeline have an impact on groundwater or surface water? A computer malfunction caused a pressure surge that blew a 2-foot-long break in a pipeline that carried gasoline. About 277,000 gallons of gasoline leaked and flowed downstream in Whatcom Creek where 2 young boys were playing with a cigarette lighter. The explosion killed the youngsters and all aquatic life in the stream. Officials said that if the explosion had occurred a short distance downstream at Bellingham, WA (population 60,000), many more lives would have been lost. Scientists say that it may be two years before the macroinvertebrates will recolonize the stream and support fish populations.

groundwater is used for irrigation, the water leaves behind a deposit of salt as it evaporates. **Salinization**—a buildup of salts and toxic elements in the soil of irrigated cropland—reduces crop yields. The salt deposits eventually make the soil unsuitable for farming.

What effect might pesticides applied by airplane have on ground water?

At first farmers used groundwater for irrigation until a system of dams and canals was constructed to provide surface water. In California's Central Valley, a layer of clay lies beneath the topsoil. Farmers installed drainage systems to prevent the clay from trapping the irrigation water and flooding the plant roots. They couldn't recycle the water because it contained too many mineral salts.

A canal was to carry the wastewater into the San Francisco Bay. When the canal was only half finished, money ran out, and the canal ended at the Kesterson National Wildlife Refuge. Engineers built a series of evaporation ponds that covered 1200 acres (480 hectares). When the canal and ponds were completed, the wastewater was diluted with fresh surface water. When the farmers began diverting the fresh water, the only water entering the evaporation ponds was the wastewater.

Breast tissue of adult coots at Kesterson Wildlife Refuge contained toxic levels of selenium.

In the spring of 1983, biologists found deformities in 42% of newly hatched birds and unhatched embryos. The normal rate of deformed birds is 1%. Scientists had never seen anything like this before. Some birds had no eyes, feet or wings. The bloated bodies of adult birds were found floating in the ponds.

Further investigation found that the problems were caused by **selenium**, a toxic element that had leached from the soil. Birds need a few parts per billion of selenium in their diet, but it is toxic when it is present in a concentration of a few parts per million. Breast tissue of adult coots at Kesterson contained between 3.5 and 9.5 ppm selenium.

In the spring of 1985, the contaminated wastewater draining into the ponds was shut off and later the evaporation ponds were filled with dirt. Studies have identified similar problems caused by a buildup of selenium in irrigation wastewater projects in other western states. New irrigation techniques can reduce the amount of contaminated water draining from the soil. Regulations require construction of **clean mitigation habitat** in a 1:10 ratio with evaporation ponds.

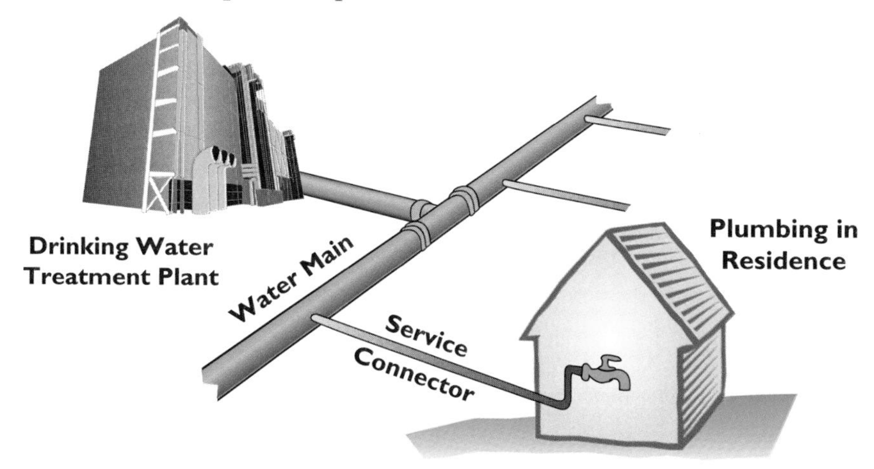

Service connectors in old plumbing systems may have lead pipes. One way to reduce lead levels in water is to remove these pipes.

Lead

Historians believe that the fall of the Roman Empire may have been caused by lead. Water pipes were made of lead. The origin of the words plumber and plumbing is the Latin word for **lead**—plumbum. The Romans used lead acetate, commonly called "sugar of lead," as a sweetener and preservative in wines and cider. The people of Rome may have suffered from lead poisoning.

Lead is especially dangerous to fetuses and young children. It slows their neurological and physical development. Exposure to lead for a short period of time can cause slight deficits in attention span, hearing, and learning abilities. Anemia, a low red blood cell count, may be a sign of high lead levels in a child. Long-term exposure to lead can also cause kidney disease, stroke and cancer.

Lead rarely occurs naturally in drinking water sources, yet the levels of lead in some public water supplies exceed the maximum level allowed by the EPA. The major source of contamination of drinking water is the corrosion of plumbing by acidic water. Lead leaches into the water from old lead pipes and from the solder connecting copper pipes. Congress banned the installation of lead solder, pipes and fittings in 1986.

The EPA has set the **Action Level** for lead at 15 ppb. Water suppliers (water utilities) must collect water samples at points throughout the distribution system, including bathroom and kitchen taps. If lead exceeds the Action Level in 10% of the tap water samples, the supplier must take steps to control corrosion of the pipes. Increasing the pH or hardness of the water will reduce the corrosion and the level of lead in the water.

Manhole covers.

Under the City Streets

It is very expensive to dispose of hazardous wastes properly. In order to avoid the expense, some industries illegally dump their hazardous wastes. In Louisville, Kentucky, a recycling company dumped pesticides in the city's sewers. The sewage treatment plant had to be shut down for several months because the chemicals irritated the eyes, skin and respiratory systems of the workers.

A waste disposal company in Philadelphia rented a warehouse near the Delaware River. Inside the warehouse was an opening to a storm sewer. Haulers brought toxic wastes to the warehouse and poured them into the sewer that carried the waste to the river. A few miles down river from the sewer pipe, the Torresdale water treatment plant draws drinking water for the city of Philadelphia.

To discourage illegal dumping, the city of Los Angles has formed a special Strike Force to catch illegal dumpers. Judges are imposing heavy fines on companies that have carefully planned schemes to illegally dump their hazardous wastes. In some states the white-collar executives, who make the decision to illegally dump the wastes, are being sentenced to several months in jail. The "boss" of the Philadelphia waste disposal company was sent to prison for six months and fined $20,000.

Facing the Issue

Our surface water is significantly cleaner than it was when the Clean Water Act became law in 1972 because we no longer use our rivers as sewers. But toxic chemicals from farms and industries threaten our water supplies. The Clean Water Act prohibited the release of toxic chemicals into U.S. waters after 1985, but we didn't meet the deadline.

While the release of toxic pollutants into the air is declining, industrial releases into water are increasing. In 1997, industries reported the release of 217 million pounds of toxic chemicals into rivers, lakes, and streams from **point sources**—mainly the production of chemicals, metals, paper, petroleum, rubber and plastics. Additional pollution enters the water from **nonpoint sources**—urban and agricultural runoff, and the air.

Until now, nonpoint sources of pollution have been largely ignored. Agricultural runoff is the largest, unregulated source of water pollution, but urban areas are also important sources of pollutants. Water samples collected from streams were analyzed for pesticides. Water samples from urban **watersheds** had higher concentrations of certain insecticides for a greater part of the year than agricultural watersheds. Concentrations of insecticides in urban streams often exceeded guidelines for protection of aquatic life.

Progress is being made in industry. Industries have begun to modify processes to produce less waste and to recycle waste products. While changing processes to reduce pollution often requires huge investments in equipment, the changes can save both money and the environment. Changes made by American Cyanamid in the production of a yellow dye eliminated the use of a toxic solvent. The changes required a $100,000 investment in equipment, but the new process saves the company $200,000 a year in disposal and energy costs.

Reducing or eliminating the use of the toxic chemicals may be the best way to reduce poisons in our air and water. Minnesota has passed a law that limits the amount of cadmium, hexavalent chromium, lead or mercury in packaging. Minnesota incinerates much of its solid waste, and reducing the level of these metals in the waste reduces the metals that find their way into our water supplies.

Cleaning up our water will require greater attention to both point and nonpoint sources of pollution. The goal of the Clean Water Act was zero discharge. Looking back we can see that this was not a realistic goal.

5.1 Questions for Study and Discussion:

1. Define the following terms: **VOCABULARY**

Action level	carcinogens	lead	salinization
activated carbon	clean mitigation habitat	methemoglobinemia	selenium
aquifer	disease cluster	National Priorities List	trihalomethanes
atmospheric deposition	hemoglobin	nonpoint sources	watershed
biomonitoring	leached	point sources	weathering

2. List several ways in which human-made chemicals are helpful.
3. What problem is created by the manufacture of products we use?
4. What natural resource do leaking landfills and lagoons threaten?
5. How did Congress respond to the situation at Love Canal to make our country a safer place to live?

The Lesson Learned at Love Canal

6. Describe the history of Love Canal.
7. What has been done to ensure that chemicals from the site don't contaminate the area's water supply?
8. Do you think that President Carter overreacted when he evacuated families from the Love Canal area? Would you buy a home in the area today? Explain your reasons for each answer.

Woburn's Wells

9. Why were Wells G and H shut down?
10. What was the conclusion of the study conducted by the Massachusetts Department of Public Health?
11. Why is it likely that there will be other situations like the one in Woburn?

What the Fish Tell Us

12. What is the major source of mercury and PCBs in Lake Superior?
13. What is a fish advisory and, if ignored, who might be affected?
14. What are the advantages of biomonitoring over chemical testing?

Water, Water Everywhere, but ...

15. Why does the city of New York transport water from upstate when the city is surrounded by water?
16. What is the source of drinking water for the city of New Orleans?
17. Why is the EPA concerned about the level of THMs in the drinking water?

Problems with Underground Storage Tanks

18. What type of pollution is threatening the Santa Clara "Silicon" Valley?
19. What pollutant is threatening groundwater supplies in other locations?
20. Identify a chemical in gasoline that is known to be a carcinogen and explain the problems associated with removing it from the water.

Down on the Farm

21. What pollutant threatens water supplies in the Nebraska Sandhills and other farming areas? What is the EPA "safe" drinking water standard for this pollutant?
22. In what way does this pollutant affect humans and farm animals?
23. Why doesn't water with high levels of nitrates affect adults?
24. Registration of a pesticide may be denied because of its effects on organisms such as fish, birds, and humans. For what additional reason may a pesticide registration be denied or restricted?

Problems at Kesterson

25. Explain how the irrigation of land sometimes makes the soil unsuitable for farming.
26. How did irrigation of farmland cause problems for birds at Kesterson National Wildlife Refuge?
27. What was done to reduce the threat created by contaminated water?

Lead

28. What are the health effects of high levels of lead in the drinking water?
29. What is the major source of lead that contaminates drinking water supplies?
30. What changes have been made to reduce the level of lead in drinking water in the future?

Under the City Streets

31. What has the city of Los Angeles done to discourage companies from dumping hazardous wastes illegally?
32. What actions have the courts taken against companies for dumping hazardous wastes illegally?

Facing the Issue

33. Identify the major sources of toxins and describe steps that can be taken to reduce their level in our water supply.

5.2 Protecting the Groundwater

OBJECTIVES

- ✔ **Compare** sanitary and secure landfills.
- ✔ **Identify** criteria that should be used to assess potential sites for disposal of toxic waste.
- ✔ **Evaluate** methods used to dispose of toxic chemicals by **identifying** risks and benefits of each method.
- ✔ **Offer** solutions to the problem of toxic waste disposal.

"Part of the price we must pay for the products of modern technology is the price of toxic waste disposal."

There is no question that water is one resource we can't afford to lose. A spokesman for the chemical industry told a senate subcommittee investigating toxic substances: "Groundwater protection should be one of the nation's highest priorities." It is becoming clear that it is less expensive to prevent pollution of our groundwater than it is to clean the water once it has become polluted.

Since the Clean Water Act was passed in 1972, our rivers and lakes have become much cleaner, but some of the actions that were taken to clean up rivers and lakes have increased the threat of polluted groundwater. What is industry to do with pollutants that can't be discharged into rivers and lakes? One answer is to put them underground.

Deep Well Injection—Is it the Answer?

The air in the cottonwood forest at Presque Isle State Park, near the town of Erie, Pennsylvania, smelled like rotten eggs. It was the odor of hydrogen sulfide—a chemical usually associated with industry, but there was no industry nearby. The source of the odor was a puddle of black gunk seeping from the ground in one of the parking areas.

Geologists reported that the discharge was coming from an unplugged natural gas well that had been abandoned in 1920. The well tapped a rock formation known as the Bass Island Formation. A few miles away on the other side of Erie, the Hammermill Paper Company had pumped black sulfur wastewater into the Bass Island Formation.

Did You Know?

In 1995, 279 million tons of hazardous waste were produced in the U.S. Hazardous waste is not only produced by large industries like chemical manufacturers and petroleum refineries, but also by dry cleaners, photo processing centers and hospitals.

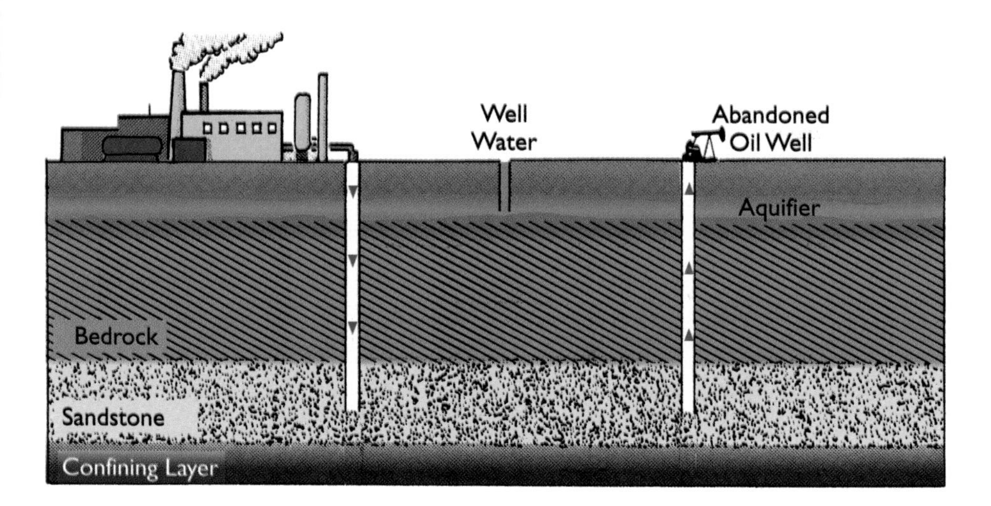

This method of waste disposal is called **deep-well injection**. A double pipe is used to inject chemical wastes into a layer of confined sandstone or other porous rock several thousand feet deep. A pump forces the liquid wastes down the inner pipe and into the layer of sandstone. The outer pipe is filled with cement to prevent the contamination of any aquifers that the pipe passes through.

A clear link was never established between the deep-well injection of wastewater and the black gunk oozing from the abandoned well in Erie. The Pennsylvania Department of Environmental Protection plugged the well with cement down to 900 feet. Although the fluid containing hazardous waste contaminated shallow groundwater, none of the residential wells in the area were contaminated.

Deep-well injection has been used for the disposal of industrial and hazardous wastes since the 1950s. While deep-well injection may seem like a perfect answer to the problem of toxic wastes, it is a potential threat to the groundwater supply. Problems may occur if chemicals in the wastewater corrode pipes, dissolve the rock, or move upward through fractures in the rocks.

Today there are strict rules that regulate the injection of wastes into deep wells. Only certain types of chemicals [volatile organic chemicals (VOCs), fuels, explosives, and pesticides] may be disposed of by this method. Deep-well disposal requires extensive geological studies to ensure that the contaminated water will never penetrate groundwater supplies.

Selecting a Site for a Sanitary Landfill

Suitable Sites	Unsuitable Sites
GEOLOGY	
• clay soils • stable bedrock	• rocks with fractures or folds • sandstone • limestone • faults • earthquakes
WATER	
• several miles from an important aquifer	• near an aquifer that is a source of drinking water • floodplains • wetlands • coastal areas
GEOGRAPHY	
• low population density	• high population density • large population less than 5 years or over 65 years old

The Problem with Landfills

At **sanitary landfills**, garbage is compacted and covered each day with a layer of soil. Sanitary landfills provide several benefits over open dumps—a suitable habitat for rats, flies and wild animals. The problem with sanitary landfills is that chemicals, which are leached from the landfill, may enter the groundwater.

Many industries and cities have buried their liquid and solid wastes in landfills, but it has become evident that this method of burial is not an acceptable method for "safe disposal" of hazardous wastes. According to the EPA, most of the nation's landfills were not operated in an environmentally safe manner. An assessment by California's State Water Control Board found that 77% of landfills are leaking into groundwater.

The EPA issued the first federal rules for solid-waste landfills in 1991. The rules, which went into effect in 1993, prohibit certain liquid and solid wastes in sanitary landfills. Regulations also require special liners, collection of the **leachate**—the liquids that drain from the landfill, and monitoring of the groundwater. Some states have regulations that are tougher than the federal guidelines.

Engineers have designed **secure landfills** for storage of hazardous wastes. A chemical company in Montague, Michigan, spent $15 million to build a pyramid-shaped storage vault, the size of fourteen football fields, to store toxic chemicals. Two permanent granite markers read

Did You Know?

The Fresh Kills Landfill was established on Staten Island in 1948. The site was a tidal swamp and the landfill project was a means of reclaiming the land. Now the unlined landfill is the largest landfill in the world. The size is equal to about 16,000 baseball diamonds. When the landfill is closed in 2001, it will be 505 feet above sea level. Disposable diapers make up only 1.2% of the volume of refuse. A study of 70 diapers recovered from the landfill found no viable disease-causing viruses or protozoans in any of the diapers. That's good news for the groundwater.

Hexachlorocyclopentadiene Toxic Production Waste, while smaller signs inside the chain link fence read *WARNING KEEP OUT*.

The pit is lined and covered with a layer of clay that is more than 3 meters thick. The clay walls were designed so that it would take a molecule of water 100 years to pass through them. The vault is an example of a "secure" landfill, but no one knows for sure how long the liner will keep the toxic wastes contained.

The nation's largest secure landfill is located on a 2,400-acre (960-ha) tract of land near Emelle, Alabama. The landfill consists of a series of trenches up to 175 feet deep located in a massive, thick deposit of relatively impermeable chalk. The trenches have a double liner with leachate collection systems. Wastes must be stored in containers. Wastes placed in the landfill include transformer carcasses (after removal of PCBs) and other solid materials contaminated with heavy metals or organic chemicals. This landfill is not permitted to accept explosives, radioactive wastes or infectious wastes.

In the past, cost was frequently the most important factor in determining where a landfill would be located. Although there is no place that is completely safe, the possibility of danger can be reduced if geology, water and geography are considered when a site is selected for a landfill.

Secure storage areas use large amounts of land, cost large amounts of money, and require constant care. The EPA requires monitoring wells at all new landfill sites, and monitoring the groundwater for at least 30 years after the landfill is closed. Scientists feel that proper selection of a site, good engineering, and long-term monitoring can reduce, but not eliminate, the risks of groundwater contamination.

In spite of the new rules and regulations, residents are often opposed to having a landfill in their community. "Not In My Backyard" (NIMBY) has become a familiar phrase. Many people feel that the potential for groundwater contamination makes "secure" landfills an unacceptable means of hazardous waste disposal.

A synthetic liner and leachate collection system is installed at a sanitary landfill.

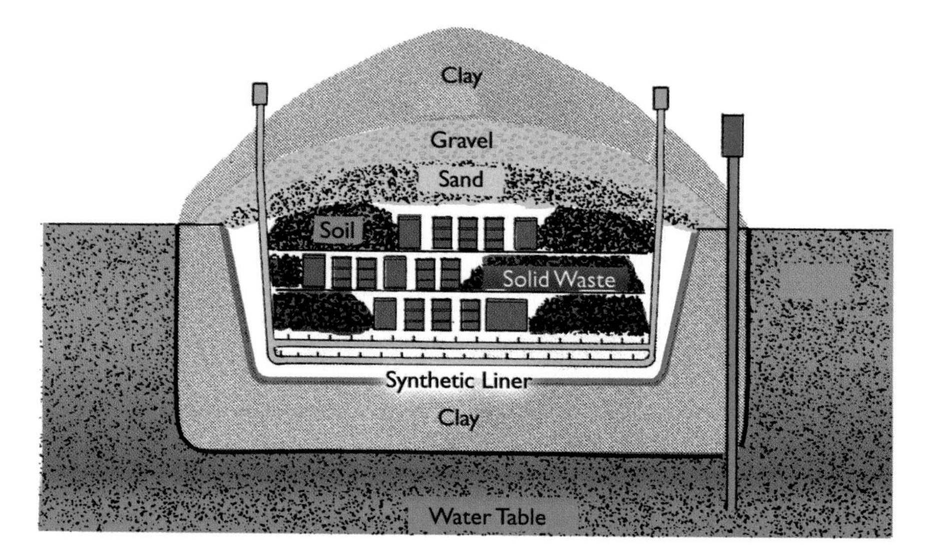

Some states are seeking other solutions. A hazardous waste act passed in Missouri prohibits the landfilling of any hazardous wastes that can be disposed of by treating, recycling, detoxifying or incinerating. California has banned six types of wastes, including PCBs and toxic metals, from landfills. States are beginning to encourage permanent destruction of wastes rather than permanent storage.

Treat, Recycle and Reduce Wastes

As long as companies could place hazardous wastes in landfills or surface waters, they did not investigate alternatives. Today many industries are looking for methods to reduce the volume of hazardous wastes and the cost of disposal. As a part of Michigan's Source Reduction Initiative, Dow Chemical found that they could re-use a solvent several times. At its Cold Lake Oilsands operation in Canada, Esso Resources chose water recycling over deep-well injection. The company now recycles 78% of its wastewater.

Paper companies use large quantities of water and produce large quantities of black sulfur wastewater. Today they are using a recycling process that not only prevents pollution, but also reduces the industry's huge demand for water. The black carbon is removed from the sulfur wastewater, and the sulfur liquid (wastewater) is reused to digest wood chips for making more paper. The carbon is heated with steam to make **activated carbon**. The activated carbon is then used to filter other wastewater.

The EPA is currently studying methods for the treatment and recovery of hazardous wastes. Some of the treatment processes include:

Biological Treatment:

Bacteria can be used to decompose certain hazardous wastes. Environmental Remediation, Inc. developed a biological treatment system to replace deep-well injection of organic waste produced at a Dupont facility. Scientists found that microbes in stream sediment can break down MTBE and TBA, organic chemicals found in gasoline. Microbes are collected from hazardous waste sites to see if they will change toxic chemicals into harmless products.

Physical Treatment:

Specially treated carbon particles (activated carbon) can pick up (adsorb) certain chemicals from wastewater. This process is currently used to remove **trihalomethanes (THMs)** and other organic chemicals, as well as chemicals that cause color and odor, from drinking water supplies. Other physical processes that can remove organic chemicals are evaporation, distillation, and steam stripping.

Chemical Treatment:

Some hazardous chemicals can be chemically changed into substances that are harmless, such as carbon dioxide and water. Toxic metals can be removed from water by chemical reactions which change them into solid compounds. The solids can then be filtered from the wastewater.

Environmental Challenge: Pesticide Problem

Many Third World countries received donations of pesticides during the late 1960's. The donations exceeded the amount of pesticide needed, and the pesticides were stored. After many years in poor storage conditions, the pesticides are now a threat to the environment. North Africa has some 10,000 metric tons of pesticides, including banned **organochlorines** such as DDT and dieldrin. Some pesticides may contain heavy metals such as mercury. At one facility the manufacturers could be identified for only 40% of the pesticides.

- You are responsible for the safe disposal of the pesticides. Describe a plan for disposal and justify the method(s) you chose.

Nickel-Cadmium (Ni-Cd) rechargeable batteries are found in power tools, cordless and cellular phones, camcorders, and laptop computers. To find the retail site where you can recycle your batteries, visit: www.rbrc.org.

Human-Made Rocks

Coliseum in Italy.

Pantheon in Rome.

The idea is not new. The process was used to build the Pantheon in Rome, the Coliseum in Italy, and the oldest well-engineered roadway system in the world—the Appian Way. Volcanic ash and lime were mixed to make cement. The chemical reaction produced a mortar or concrete that is very hard and resistant to erosion.

Today the same process is being used to form waste materials into synthetic rocks. Instead of volcanic ash, fly ash from coal-burning power plants is mixed with certain hazardous wastes. Then lime is added, and the mixture is poured like concrete into a landfill. The synthetic rock may also be used to form the foundation for a new road.

The process may be used to dispose of hazardous chemicals from automotive, electroplating, steel-making and mining industries. It can also be used for the waste from air pollution scrubbers. In fact, 90% of all hazardous waste materials may be permanently stored in synthetic rocks.

A specific recipe must be used for each type of waste material. Quality control is very important. The amount of each type of material must be carefully measured, and the correct amounts of fly ash and lime used. Sometimes other raw materials must be added to change the wastes into a usable form. The process cannot be used for all wastes. Some materials interfere with the chemical reactions or "hardening" of the rock. The process is not suitable for disposal of organic materials.

The EPA has developed chemical and physical tests that are run on samples of the product to ensure that it meets standards. The land-filling process is also regulated by the EPA, and both runoff and groundwater must be tested for possible chemicals that might leach from the synthetic rock.

Incineration at Sea or on Land

Since 1969, European countries have burned **organochlorines** (compounds that contain hydrogen, carbon, and chlorine) in specially built incinerators on ships at sea. Incineration at sea is controlled by national and international regulations. Regulations were adopted at the convention on the Prevention of Marine Pollution by Dumping of Wastes and Other Matter (commonly called the London Dumping Convention). The EPA regulates ocean incineration and dumping in U.S. waters.

Under the correct conditions, incineration changes organochlorines into carbon dioxide, water, and hydrochloric acid. Combustion is nearly complete when the minimum flame temperature is 8,000°F (4,426°C) and plenty of oxygen is available. Nitrogen oxides are also formed.

Combustion of hazardous waste is an important but controversial method of hazardous waste disposal. About 3.5 million tons of hazardous waste are being burned each year in the United States. Incineration is the method preferred by the American Society of Mechanical Engineers for managing hazardous organic chemicals because it permanently destroys the toxic chemicals.

In the ideal incinerator, toxic waste goes in and nothing toxic comes out, but incinerators may produce two types of toxins. Tests have shown

that combustion in many municipal waste incinerators is not complete. Incomplete combustion of organic matter produces compounds called dioxins and furans. These chemicals **bioaccumulate** in the food chain. In animal studies they cause liver damage, disrupt the endocrine system, and weaken the immune system.

Incineration of solid organic materials also produces ash. Ash from municipal waste incinerators often contains toxic metals, including lead, cadmium, arsenic, and mercury. The ash may be classified as a hazardous waste. Ash testing and management is an important part of protecting the groundwater.

5.2 Questions for Study and Discussion:

VOCABULARY

1. Define the following terms:

activated carbon	organochlorines
bioaccumulate	sanitary landfill
deep-well injection	secure landfill
leachate	trihalomethanes

2. On a scale of one to ten with ten the most important, how important is groundwater protection?
3. Explain how the Clean Water Act increased the threat to groundwater.

Deep Well Injection—Is it the Answer?

4. What is the significance of the Bass Island Formation?
5. Explain the process of deep-well injection.
6. How do the EPA regulations reduce the threat to the groundwater from wastes injected into deep wells?

The Problem with Landfills

7. Explain how the design of a sanitary landfill today differs from a sanitary landfill in use prior to 1993.
8. List three factors that must be considered when selecting a site for a secure landfill.
9. Why do people say "Not in my backyard" to a proposal for a secure landfill in their community?

Treat, Recycle and Reduce Wastes

10. What are several alternatives to a secure landfill for hazardous wastes?
11. Why is recycling a win-win situation for industries?
12. Describe two physical processes that can be used to remove pollutants from wastewater.
13. Explain how chemical reactions can be used to remove toxic metals from water.

Human-Made Rocks

14. What two substances were mixed to produce the cement to build the Pantheon, the Coliseum, and the Appian Way?
15. How is this process being used to dispose of hazardous wastes?
16. Why isn't this process suitable for some hazardous waste materials?
17. How can we be assured that the man-made rock is not poisoning the environment?

Incineration At Sea or on Land

18. What type of hazardous material can be destroyed by incineration?
19. What conditions must be met to ensure complete combustion of hazardous waste?
20. Explain why incineration may be the best means of disposal for certain hazardous wastes, and why it may be a poor solution for the disposal of municipal solid waste.

5.3 Before You Drink the Water

OBJECTIVES

- ✔ **Compare** the availability of a safe water supply in developed countries with its availability in developing countries.
- ✔ **Describe** the role of the EPA and the role of the water supplier in relation to safe drinking water.
- ✔ **Identify** organisms that cause waterborne diseases and **describe** treatment methods that kill or remove these organisms.
- ✔ **Explain** why Coliform bacteria are considered indicator organisms.
- ✔ **Evaluate** various treatment methods in relation to their ability to remove contaminants and make the water safe.

"To the list of 'rights' guaranteed by the constitution, we might add the 'right' to a reliable supply of safe drinking water."

In the year 1900, an estimated 27,000 Americans died of **typhoid fever**, an infection caused by bacteria (*Salmonella typhi*) carried in water, contaminated with human waste. Today most cities and towns in developed countries provide their residents with a good supply of safe drinking water. Because of improved sanitation and treatment processes, diseases like typhoid fever and **cholera** have almost vanished from developed countries.

In response to widespread disease outbreaks caused by microorganisms, Pennsylvania passed the Public Water Supply Law in 1905. During the almost 80 years that this law was in effect, Pennsylvania led the nation in waterborne disease outbreaks, with 8 to 10 each year. There was a series of disease outbreaks caused by the parasitic protozoan *Giardia lamblia*. This led to a new law that required filtering of all public water systems that use surface water. Today disease outbreaks in Pennsylvania's public water systems are rare.

The vast majority of people in the U.S. receive water from public water systems that meet state or federal requirements for safety. People in other countries are less fortunate. According to the World Health Organization, approximately 1 billion people do not have access to safe drinking water. Waterborne diseases are very common in India. Each year diarrhea kills 500,000 Indian children.

Many areas in developing countries lack the sanitary conditions needed to guarantee a water supply that is safe to drink. Only about 250 of India's 4,000 cities have sewer systems, and sewage from most systems is not treated. More than two-thirds of Africa's population lacks a means of sanitary disposal of sewage. In 1999, more people in Africa were without safe drinking water than in 1990.

In 1991, more than 300,000 cases of cholera were reported and more than 3,500 people died during an epidemic that began in Peru and spread to several countries. Health officials think that the bacterium *Vibrio cholerae* may have arrived in the country with contaminated water dumped by a Chinese freighter. The bacteria contaminated fish eaten by humans. The bacteria were then spread from humans to the water supply. Only a few cases occurred in the United States.

Outbreaks of cholera have occurred in the United States among people who traveled to parts of Latin America, Asia, or Africa where there are cholera epidemics. Foodborne outbreaks have been caused by food brought back by travelers. Advanced water and sanitation systems required by federal law prevent cholera epidemics in the United States.

The Safe Drinking Water Act

In the United States, the Safe Drinking Water Act (SDWA) was passed in 1974 and revised in 1986 and 1996. The SDWA requires the Environmental Protection Agency to regulate certain substances that may be present in the water supply and may threaten human health. The EPA sets legal limits for substances in public water supplies, determines water testing schedules, and prescribes acceptable treatment methods. States may regulate water systems if their rules are at least as strict as the national standards.

The EPA sets a health goal or **Maximum Contaminant Level Goal (MCLG)** for substances found in drinking water. The MCLG is based on health effects. It is the level that would not produce any health effects in a person who drank 2 liters of water containing the contaminant every day for 70 years. The MCLG for known carcinogens and for lead is zero because the assumption is that any exposure causes some risk.

The EPA also sets a **Maximum Contaminant Level (MCL)** for all substances with a health goal. The MCL is based on the ability of the water supplier to remove the substance using the best available technology. The MCL is the legal limit or highest amount of the pollutant that is allowed in the drinking water. Most MCLs and MCLGs are the same. When this is not possible, the MCL is set as close as possible to the MCLG.

The EPA has set MCLGs and MCLs for more than 80 inorganic and organic chemicals found in drinking water supplies. **Inorganic contaminants** include cadmium, fluoride, lead, mercury, and nitrates. **Organic contaminants** include certain pesticides, industrial chemicals, and **trihalomethanes** (THMs). Long-term exposure to THMs and other organic chemicals may increase the chance of cancer. The water supplier must test the water for these substances and, if levels exceed the legal limit, take corrective measures to ensure that consumers do not receive water that contains harmful levels.

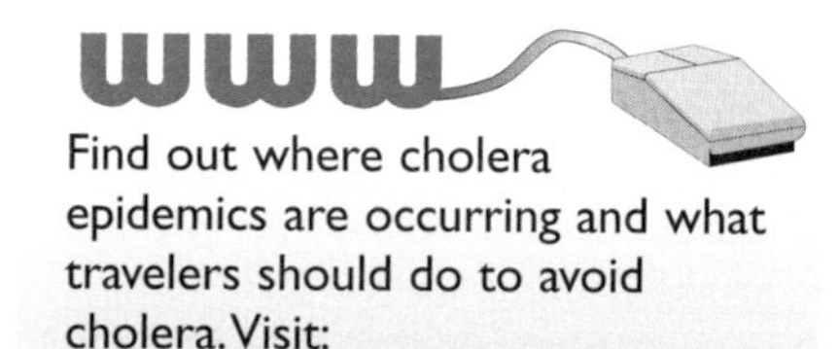

Find out where cholera epidemics are occurring and what travelers should do to avoid cholera. Visit: www.who.int/emc/diseases/cholera.

For a complete list of chemicals with MCLs and information about their potential health effects, search the topic index at EPA's Website: www.epa.gov/safewater.

Organisms in the Water

To prevent waterborne diseases, the Surface Water Treatment Rule sets non-enforceable health goals (MCLGs) at zero for *Legionella pneumophila*, a bacteria that causes a type of pneumonia if inhaled, *Giardia* (a parasitic protozoan), and viruses. These organisms are present in most surface waters. Because they are difficult and expensive to identify, the EPA can establish required Treatment Techniques in place of setting MCLs.

All public water systems must filter and disinfect their water to remove or inactivate 99.9% of *Giardia* and 99.99% of viruses. The EPA thinks methods that remove *Giardia* and viruses will also remove *Legionella*. The effectiveness of filtration is determined by measuring the **turbidity**, the level of small particles suspended in the water. If the source of water is pristine, a system may be granted a waiver for filtration. To ensure that the treated water is protected as it travels through the distribution system, the EPA requires **continuous disinfection**—the addition of a disinfectant that remains in the water and is detectable at the consumer's tap.

If your drinking water comes from a public water system, find out the source of the water and whether your water system is meeting the federal drinking water rules. Visit: www.epa.gov/ow/states, then click on your state on the map or go directly to your state by entering the two-letter abbreviation following "states" as in this example: www.epa.gov/ow/states/IL.

Coliform bacteria are **indicator organisms** because their presence tells us something about water quality. **Coliform bacteria** are normally found in the intestines of humans and many other animals. If they are present in drinking water, the water may be contaminated with human or animal waste. Although coliform bacteria are not usually harmful themselves, they serve as a warning that the water may also contain other harmful organisms.

No water supply is safe to drink unless testing confirms that it is free of coliform bacteria. The EPA has set the MCLG for total Coliforms at zero. The MCL for total coliforms depends upon the number of samples collected. The required number of samples for public water supplies is determined by the size of the system. Less than 5% of samples may be coliform-positive, if 40 or more samples are collected per month. For systems that collect less than 40 samples, no more than one sample may be coliform-positive.

In addition to bacteria, unfiltered water may contain tiny parasitic protozoa. During a period of heavy rainfall and runoff in 1993, the filtration process at a Milwaukee water treatment plant was not effective. A protozoan called *Cryptosporidium parvum* entered the city's water distribution system. Once inside the human intestine, the tiny organism causes **cryptosporidiosis**, a flu-like illness accompanied by diarrhea. More than 400,000 people became ill and more than 50 people died.

Water at dump stations for recreational vehicles is intended for rinsing, not drinking.

The most commonly identified cause of water-related disease in the U.S. today is a one-celled protozoan parasite *Giardia lamblia*. *Giardia* form a football-shaped cyst, or protective capsule, which can survive for two months or longer in water, especially cold mountain streams. The cysts have been found in surface water supplies in all regions of the United States and in other countries.

The parasite lives in the intestines of humans and other mammals — including beaver, deer, cattle, raccoons, dogs and cats. It causes **giardiasis**, sometimes called beaver fever, an illness affecting the stomach and intestines. The symptoms are painful abdominal cramps, nausea, gas and diarrhea. Although some people who have the cyst are not affected by it, others may require hospitalization.

Is Your Water Safe?

Potable water refers to water that is suitable for drinking. All surface water supplies are probably contaminated with organisms and should not be considered safe to drink unless treated. Water from a well or spring may be safe to drink without treatment. This depends upon the soil type, depth and the distance from any source of pollution.

If the source of water is a reliable public water system, the water should be of high quality when it comes from the faucet. Water systems that serve 15 or more connections must provide annual reports, called Consumer Confidence Reports, to notify customers of the quality of their water supply. If you should experience water problems such as an unusual taste, odor, or the presence of sediment, you should call the water supplier.

Even though the water system is supplying water that meets all EPA standards, there is the possibility that water in your home is contaminated with lead or copper. The source of lead is most likely the home's plumbing. Blue-green stains in the bathtub or sink may indicate high copper levels. To see if the levels are high enough to pose a health risk, have the water tested by a state-certified laboratory.

The EPA estimates that more than 40 million U.S. residents use water that may contain up to 15 parts per billion lead. This is the **Action Level** that requires treatment to reduce the corrosiveness of the water. The only way to detect the presence of lead is to have the water tested by a qualified laboratory. The EPA recommends that all homes be tested. One way to reduce lead in your drinking water is to always let the water become cold before using it. Flushing the pipes may not reduce lead levels sufficiently in apartment buildings.

Approximately 23 million people obtain water from a private source, usually wells that tap the groundwater supply. The quality of water in a private well should not be taken for granted. The EPA recommends that well owners have their water tested annually for nitrates and coliform bacteria. Spring is the best time to have the water tested since rain and melting snow leach the excess nitrates from the soil.

Additional testing is also recommended if there are heavy rains. The water should be tested any time there is a change in the water's taste, color or odor. If a problem is suspected, the EPA recommends that well owners have their water tested for other contaminants, such as radon and pesticides. If nitrate levels are high, it is a good idea to test for pesticides that are used in the vicinity of the well.

Wells should be located up the slope from any possible pollution source such as a septic tank or barnyard. The U.S. Public Health Service suggests that a minimum of 100 feet (30.5 m) should separate the well from a septic drain field. The steel casing of the well should extend 6 to 12 inches above the ground level, and cement grout should fill the space between the soil and the casing. The ground level should slope away from the casing. This will prevent the well water from being contaminated by runoff.

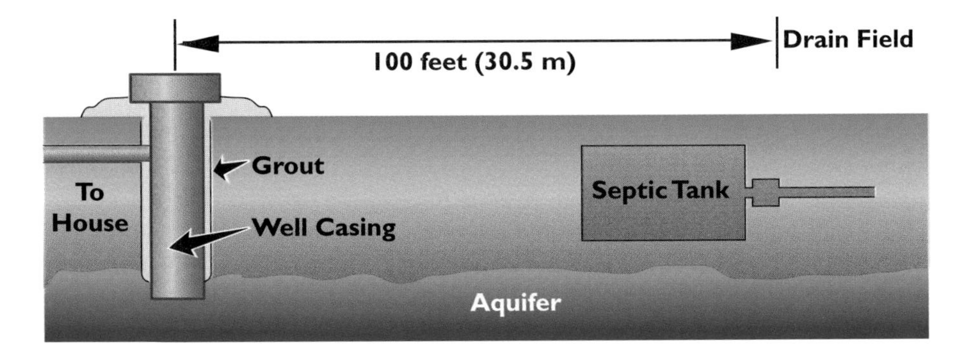

To find out how the age of your home may affect the level of lead in your tap water and additional ways to reduce the lead in your drinking water, search the topic index at the EPA's Website: www.epa.gov/OGWDW.

When choosing a well, consider possible sources of pollution.

Making the Water Safe

Contaminated surface water and well water can be made safe by the following chemical and physical treatment processes. Water quality test results will show which type of treatment, if any, is necessary.

Chlorination:

Chlorine is used to disinfect most public and private surface water supplies. If wells are contaminated with coliform bacteria, chlorinators may be installed. Certain chemicals in the water affect the **chlorine demand**—the amount of chlorine needed to make the water safe. Water containing hydrogen sulfide and/or iron will require higher amounts of chlorine.

The EPA recommends that the water be allowed to stand for 30 minutes after the chlorine has been added. This is called the **contact time**. If the contact time is 30 minutes, there should be 0.4 parts per million of free chlorine in the water, after treatment. The contact time can be reduced to 5 minutes if the amount of chlorine is increased. If the contact time is 5 minutes, there should be between 2 and 5 ppm chlorine remaining in the water after treatment.

Although some people object to the taste of chlorine, it is an inexpensive and effective disinfectant. Another advantage is that the water can easily be tested to ensure that it is safe to use. An inexpensive test kit can be used to measure the **chlorine residual** — the amount of free chlorine remaining in the water.

Giardia and other protozoan parasites can survive the normal amount of chlorine used to disinfect water supplies. The *Giardia* cysts may be killed by higher doses of chlorine — **superchlorination**, or they may be removed by filtration. Cryptosporidium oocysts are highly resistant to chlorine.

Usually the soil acts as an effective filter for well water. **Graded sand filters**, which are used at water treatment plants, will remove protozoans, but the filtering systems must be properly operated and maintained. Outbreaks of giardiasis and cryptosporidiosis occur in areas with water systems that lack filters or have poorly maintained filters. [See page 404, The Waterworks.]

Ultraviolet Light:

Water passes through a sealed chamber with ultraviolet lights. Bacteria exposed to the ultraviolet light are destroyed. The water must be filtered before it enters the light chamber to ensure that bacteria will not be hidden from the light. Although this method of disinfection is fast and does not give the water any taste or odor, it does have some drawbacks.

Ultraviolet light treatment is more expensive than **chlorination**. The lights must be kept clean and should be replaced each year. Another disadvantage is that the water has no residual chemicals that can easily be measured to see if the water is safe. UV treatment may not be effective against spores or cysts.

Heat:

When water quality test results indicate that there are microorganisms in the water, the water supplier must issue a **Boil Water Alert** to protect your health. An alert is also issued when a break or repair of a water main increases the potential for contamination of the water supply. Correct action must be taken and testing must continue until results indicate the water supply is safe.

To kill bacteria or protozoan cysts, water must be heated to a rolling boil for at least one full minute. Only boiled water should be used for: drinking and preparing food, washing fruits and vegetables, making ice, and washing dishes, unless dishes are thoroughly air-dried.

Filtration:

Potable water should be clear and free of color. Well water is usually free of color although chemicals dissolved in it may stain plumbing fixtures and clothing. Algae and tannins from decaying organic matter may give color to surface water. Sediment in the water may make the water cloudy.

Activated carbon filters are designed to remove organic chemicals that cause color, taste, or odor. The organic chemicals stick or adhere to the surface of the carbon particles. The process is called **adsorption**. The EPA requires all water supply systems serving populations over 10,000 people to install carbon filtration systems if their water supplies are contaminated with organic chemicals.

The length of time that the water is in contact with the activated carbon determines how much of the organic chemicals will be removed. If there are high concentrations of organic chemicals in the water, the filter must be changed more often. Home water filters must be changed regularly to be effective and to limit the growth of bacteria.

Small particles suspended in the water make the water cloudy or **turbid**. Although the particles themselves may not be harmful, they provide places for disease-causing organisms to hide from disinfectants. **Turbidity** is a measure of the amount of light scattered or absorbed by particles suspended in water.

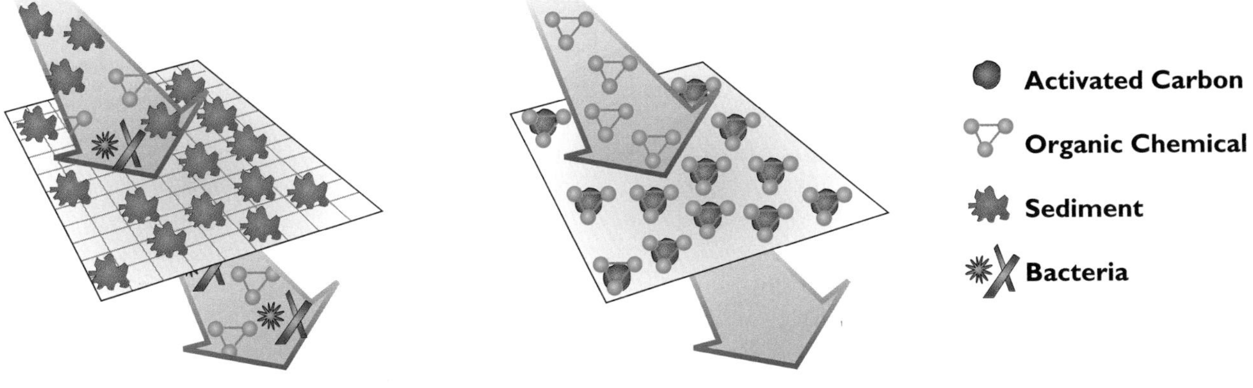

Sediment Filter **Activated Carbon Filter**

Particles may be physically removed by installing cartridge-type **sediment filters** in the water line. These filters work in the same way as a coffee filter or tea bag. They allow the water to pass through and hold back the particles. They do not remove chemicals dissolved in the water. Large water treatment systems use graded sand filters to remove particles. [See page 404, The Waterworks.]

Some chemicals, such as hydrogen sulfide or copper, give water an objectionable odor and/or taste. A high concentration of iron gives water a metallic taste, and it leaves yellow or rust-colored stains. Humans are not the only animals to object to taste or odor. If cattle don't like the way water tastes or smells, they won't drink the water. If there is too much iron in the water at the dairy barn, the cows may not drink enough to maintain maximum milk production.

Iron present in groundwater is dissolved in the water and is colorless. Once well water is exposed to the air, or chlorine is added to the water, the iron changes into iron oxide (rust), which stains laundry and plumbing fixtures. If there is a large amount of iron (more than 10 mg/L) dissolved in the water, it must be chemically changed into iron oxide and then filtered. A sediment filter or a graded sand filter may remove the red particles of iron oxide.

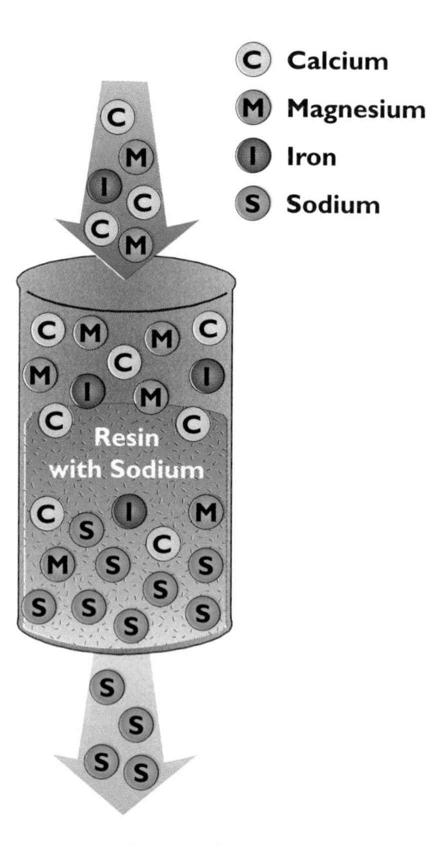

Inside a Water Softener.

Increased public concern about the safety of water supplies has increased the popularity of home filter systems. The first step in the selection of any water treatment is water quality testing. Once the contaminant has been identified, the proper treatment can be selected. Often the contaminants are minerals that are making the water "hard," and a water filter cannot remove them.

Water Conditioners (Softeners)

If the amount of iron dissolved in water is less than 3.0 mg/L, the same type of **ion-exchange system** or "water softener" that is used to remove calcium and magnesium may remove the iron. Calcium and magnesium dissolved in the water do not make it unsuitable for drinking. Instead they are removed because they form mineral deposits called **scale** in water heaters, pipes, bathtubs and on clothing.

An ion-exchange water conditioner is filled with a material called a **resin**. The calcium and magnesium ions in the water are exchanged for sodium ions attached to the resin. People who have high blood pressure, or for other reasons must limit the sodium in their diet, should not drink water that has been treated in an ion-exchange water softener.

Calcium and magnesium are both needed by the body. Some studies indicate that drinking **hard water** is better for you (because of the calcium and magnesium) than drinking soft water. Because of this, homeowners who have hard water often install an ion-exchange water softener in the hot water line. Water passing through the cold water pipes is not treated. It can be safely used for drinking and for watering plants.

Although the technology is available to remove nitrates from the water, the treatment processes are expensive. An **ion-exchange system**, similar to a water softener, can remove nitrates. In a nitrate removal system, nitrate and sulfate ions are exchanged for chloride ions. The same methods used to remove salt from sea water—distillation and reverse osmosis—can also be used to remove nitrates. [See pages 429 and 430, A Closer Look: Making More Fresh Water.]

WWW

NSF International, formerly the National Sanitation Foundation, is an independent organization that tests and certifies water filters for manufacturers to ensure that they meet standards. For example, a filter that claims to remove *Cryptosporidium* must meet Standard 53 for cyst removal. For more information, visit their Website: www.nsf.org.

In an Emergency

If you must drink water and do not know whether it is contaminated with bacteria or protozoan cysts, you should treat it in one of the following ways:

- Bring it to a rolling boil and boil it for at least one minute. This is the best method to use, if practical.
- Add 10 drops of household liquid bleach with 1% chlorine per quart (1.1L) of clear water, and let stand for 30 minutes. Make sure that the only ingredient in the bleach is sodium hypochlorite. Double the amount if the water is cloudy.
- Add 5 drops of 2% tincture of iodine to a quart (1.1L) of water and allow to stand for 30 minutes.
- Add 1 iodine tablet to 1 quart (1.1L) of water.

The tincture of iodine and iodide tablets can be purchased at drug or sporting goods stores. Although iodine is an effective way to kill disease-causing organisms, including *Giardia*, health authorities recommend that it be used only for short periods of time. They think that if it is used for long periods of time, it may have undesirable effects upon unborn children or people with thyroid problems.

5.3 QUESTIONS FOR STUDY AND DISCUSSION:

1. Define the following terms: VOCABULARY

action level
activated carbon filter
adsorption
boil water alert
chlorine demand
chlorine residual
cholera
coliform bacteria
contact time
continuous disinfection
cryptosporidiosis
giardiasis
graded sand filter
indicator organisms
inorganic contaminants
ion exchange system
maximum contaminant level
maximum contaminant level goal
organic contaminants
potable water
resin
scale
sediment filter
superchlorination
trihalomethanes
turbidity
typhoid fever

2. Explain how diseases like typhoid fever and cholera are transmitted.
3. What treatment process made waterborne disease outbreaks very rare in Pennsylvania?
4. Describe the transmission of cholera during the 1991 epidemic and explain why officials were not concerned that an epidemic would occur in the U.S.

The Safe Drinking Water Act

5. What are the requirements of the Safe Drinking Water Act?
6. Explain the difference between the Maximum Contaminant Level Goal and the Maximum Contaminant Level.
7. What does the EPA require of all water suppliers?

Organisms in the Water

8. Why didn't the EPA set a MCL for bacteria that cause typhoid fever?
9. Describe the Treatment Techniques that are required by the Surface Water Treatment Rule.
10. Explain why coliform bacteria are a good indicator organism.
11. Identify two waterborne diseases caused by parasitic protozoa and describe the symptoms.

Is Your Water Safe?

12. Explain why water from some wells is polluted but water from other wells is potable.
13. Do you need to have your water tested if you are drinking water supplied by a public water supplier? Explain.
14. If your water comes from a well or spring, what water quality tests are recommended and how often should the water be tested?
15. What two factors should be considered when locating the well?

Making the Water Safe

16. What method is used to disinfect most surface water supplies?
17. What factors affect the amount of chlorine necessary to disinfect the water?
18. Explain why treatment of surface water supplies requires both filtration and chlorination.
19. Compare the advantages and disadvantages of using chlorine with the use of untraviolet light to disinfect water supplies.
20. Describe the situations that would require a Boil Water Alert.
21. What type of filter is used to remove organic chemicals from water?
Explain how the chemicals are removed.
22. Compare an activated carbon filter, a sediment filter, and a graded sand filter.
23. Give two reasons why filters must be changed regularly.
24. Can a sediment filter be used to remove iron? Explain.

Water Conditioners (Softeners)

25. Why do homeowners want to remove calcium and magnesium from the water?
26. How can people who want "soft" water for washing and bathing install a water softener and yet have "hard" water for drinking?
27. What processes can be used to remove nitrates and why may people choose bottled water over these methods?

In An Emergency

28. How long must water be boiled to kill microorganisms?
29. Why don't water treatment plants that lack filtration equipment use iodine instead of chlorine?

The Waterworks

5.4

"Filtration and watershed protection offer a more prudent and more certain path to what should be a fundamental right in this country—safe, healthy drinking water."

JOHN P. DEVILLARS
EPA Administrator–New England

The ancient Romans built **aqueducts**—canals to carry water from the mountains to the city. Some 260 miles (420 km) of aqueducts carried water to Rome. Some of these canals are still in use today.

Moravians who settled in Bethlehem, Pennsylvania, built the first municipal waterworks in America. At first, men carried water in wooden buckets from a spring near the Lehigh River. When the waterworks were completed, a water-powered pump freed them from this task. The pump moved water up the hill through a system of hollow log pipes.

Industry developed along the river. A tannery and a flour mill were located close to the waterworks. Eventually the spring became polluted, and the city's leaders had to search for a new water source. Today gravity carries water to the city, through 23 miles (37 km) of pipes, from two reservoirs in the Pocono Mountains. Other modern cities, including New York City, Denver and Los Angeles, have gone far beyond the city limits to obtain an adequate water supply.

Have a Drink in New York City

The source of approximately 90% of New York City's water supply is primarily rain and snow that fall in the Catskill/Delaware watershed located 125 miles north and west of the city. Reservoirs in the Hudson watershed, known as the Croton system, supply nearly 10% of the water. The water is stored in reservoirs and flows to the city by gravity through large pipes—some more than 20 feet (6 m) in diameter. State law allows local communities along the pipeline to draw their water supply from the pipes as long as they pay for the costs involved.

The water quality is constantly monitored. Watershed inspectors check the reservoirs, streams and treated wastewater that flow into the reservoirs. In the summer the reservoirs are treated with a chemical, usually copper sulfate, to control the growth of algae. Biologists and chemists collect and analyze more than 1,300 water samples each month from 488 locations.

OBJECTIVES

- ✔ **Describe** the actions taken by some large cities to ensure an adequate and clean water supply for their growing populations.
- ✔ **Describe** the processes that remove pollutants from the water at the waterworks.
- ✔ **Identify** chemicals used in the treatment process and **explain** the function of each.
- ✔ **Compare** methods of disinfecting the water supply.
- ✔ **State** your opinion concerning the need for graded sand filters.

Located 23 miles from the city of Bethlehem, the municipal water authority maintains the reservoirs, monitors the water quality and treats the water before it reaches homes in the city.

For more information about New York City's water supply, search "drinking water" at the Department of Environmental Protection Website: www.ci.nyc.ny.us/html/dep.

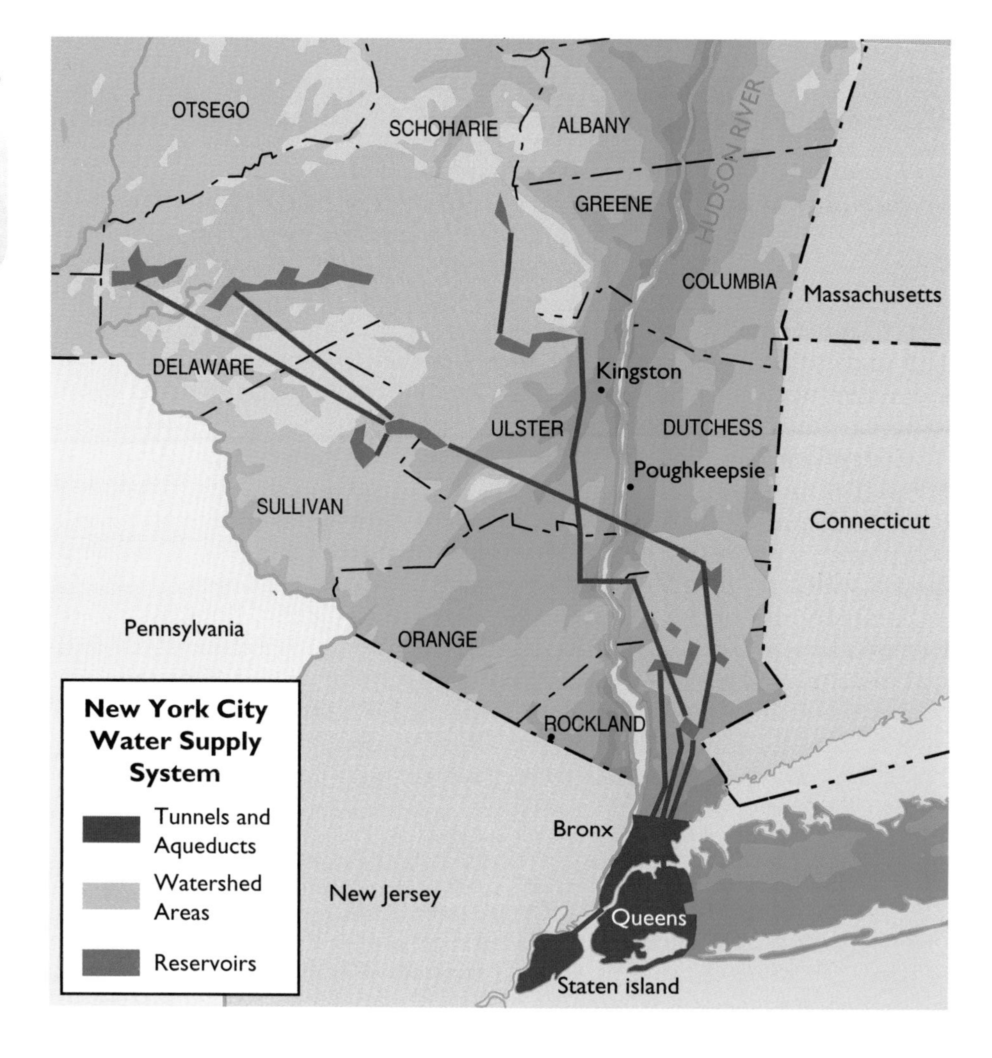

The Aqueduct in Rome.

At the Waterworks

Public water suppliers must ensure that drinking water meets certain criteria that are set by the EPA. When reservoirs or rivers are the source of drinking water, the water must be treated to remove certain substances. At most water treatment plants, the treatment processes occur in the sequence described below:

Intake:

Water enters the treatment plant through an **intake** pipe in the reservoir or river. The pipe is covered with a screen to prevent large objects, such as fish, sticks and plants from entering. Algae and other small organisms that enter the pipe are removed during the treatment process.

Primary Disinfection:

As the water enters the water treatment plant, chlorine is usually added to prevent the growth of algae and bacteria in the water pipes. To reduce the formation of THMs, some cities use a combination of chlorine and ammonia, called **chloramines** rather than chlorine alone.

The Greater Vancouver System in British Columbia has replaced chlorine with ozone for **primary disinfection** even though it is slightly more expensive. Their justification for the expense: (1) ozone is a better disinfectant for all microorganisms including *Giardia* and *Cryptosporidium*; (2) it may reduce the need for future **filtration**; and (3) it significantly reduces the chlorine by-products (THMs) in the drinking water.

When reservoirs are the source of drinking water, the water must be treated to remove certain substances.

Chemical Treatment and Mixing:

Several chemicals are added to the water to help clean the water. The plant operator determines the amount of each chemical that is needed:

- Alum (aluminum potassium sulfate) or iron (II chlorinated calcium oxide) are added to cause the small particles suspended in the water to stick together. These clumps of particles are called **floc**.
- Sodium hydroxide may be added to raise the pH and reduce corrosion.
- Orthophosphate is often added to form a thin coating on the pipes. This reduces corrosion and helps prevent leaching of lead and copper from the pipes.
- **Activated carbon** is sometimes added, especially in the summer months, to remove chemicals that cause taste, odor or color. In some locations it is needed to remove trihalomethanes (THMs) and other organic chemicals that may cause cancer. **Trihalomethanes** are disinfection by-products that form when chlorine combines with organic chemicals in the water.

Flocculation:

After the chemicals are mixed with the water, the water may flow into a large tank that contains a series of dividers or **baffles**. The baffles are arranged so that the water moves over one baffle and under the next baffle. As the water moves slowly through the tank, more and more particles stick together, and the floc grows bigger and bigger until it looks like big dirty snowflakes. In other **flocculation** tanks large paddles slowly stir the water.

Sedimentation:

From the flocculation tank, the water moves into a large storage tank. The floc is heavy, and it sinks to the bottom of the settling tank. The water must remain in the tank for a long period of time to allow the floc to settle.

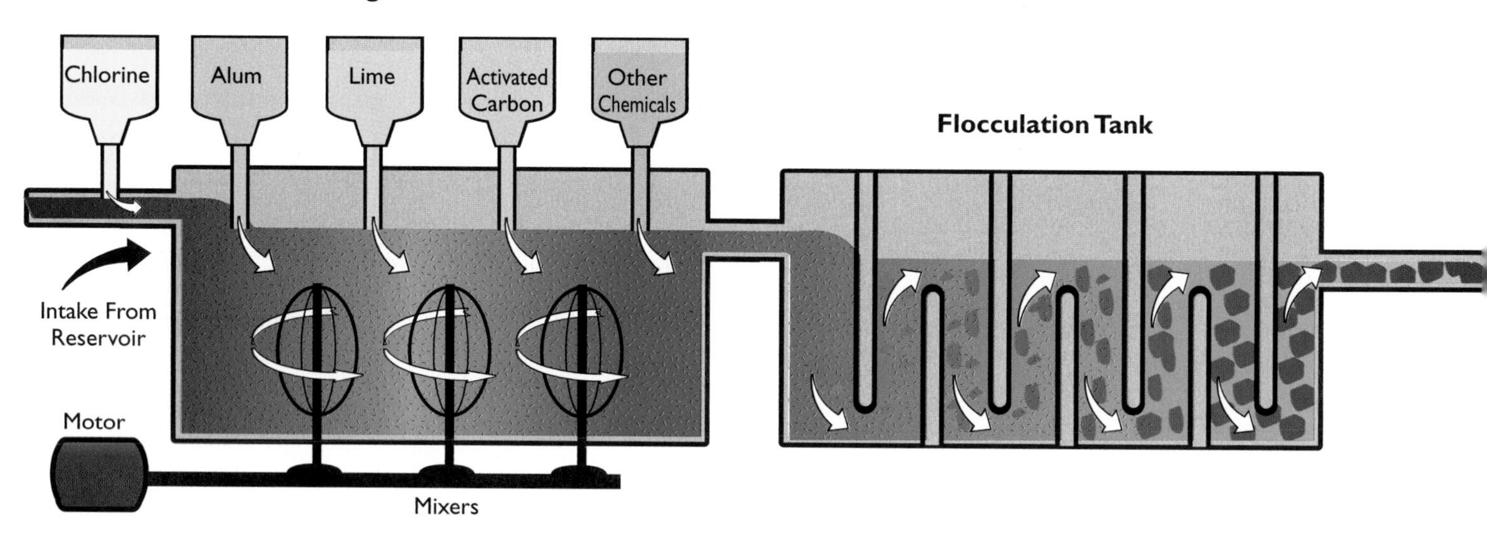

Water Treatment Processes at The Waterworks.

Filtration:

In some treatment plants, the water is pumped from the settling tanks to a **graded sand filter** made of layers of rocks and sand of specific sizes. The sand filters out any remaining particles, including microscopic organisms, which were not removed in the settling tank. As the particles are trapped in the sand, they slow the flow of water. The treatment plant operators monitor the flow and clean the filters when necessary.

The graded sand filter is cleaned by reversing the flow of water and stirring the sand. The process, called a **backwash**, removes the solids that are trapped between the particles of sand. The filters must be backwashed more frequently in the summer months because of the heavier growth of algae.

The water used to wash the filter is pumped to a lagoon to allow the solids to settle. To conserve water, some treatment plants recycle the wash water to the plant where it is treated to meet drinking water standards. At other plants, once the solids settle out, the wash water is returned to the river.

Graded sand filters reduce the risk of illness from chlorine-resistant protozoans such as *Giardia* and *Cryptosporidia*. Water treatment systems without graded sand filters must use much higher levels of chlorine to kill these organisms.

Final Chlorination:

Before the water leaves the treatment plant, a small amount of chlorine or chloramine is added to kill any bacteria that may have survived the treatment processes or that may be in the water system. Ozone is not added during final chlorination because it does not continue to disinfect as it travels through the distribution system.

Additional sodium hydroxide may be added to adjust the pH of the water and reduce the corrosion of the pipes. In some cities, fluoride is added to help prevent tooth decay. [See page 411, Fluoride in Your Water Supply—-How Much is Enough?]

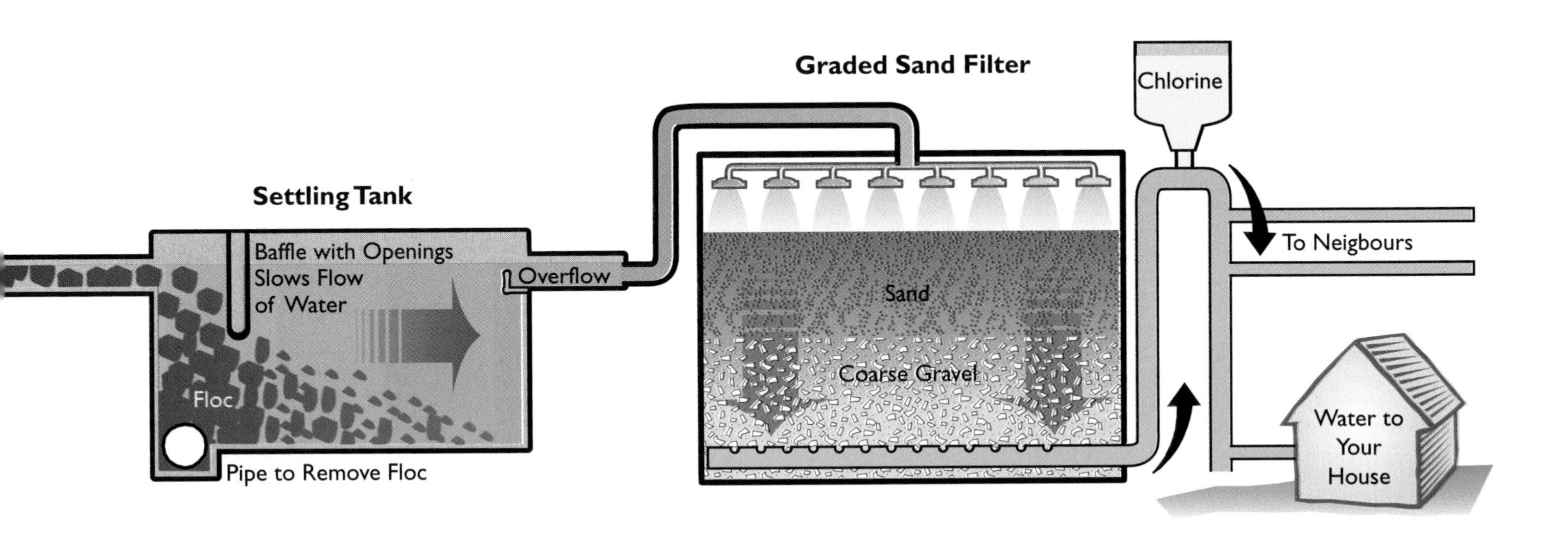

5.4 Questions for Study and Discussion:

1. Define the following terms: **VOCABULARY**

activated carbon	chloramine	graded sand filter	sedimentation
aqueduct	filtration	intake	trihalomethanes
baffles	floc	primary disinfection	
backwash	flocculation		

2. Compare Bethlehem, Pennsylvania's source of drinking water to the source of drinking water in Rome, Italy.

Have a Drink in New York City

3. What is the source of drinking water for New York City? Your City?
4. Why is copper sulfate added to New York City's reservoirs?

At the Waterworks

5. Why is chlorine first added when the water first enters the plant?
6. Explain why good floc formation is important in the treatment process.
7. What time of the year is activated carbon most likely to be used and why?
8. What chemicals are added to protect the plumbing from corrosion?
9. What is the purpose of the baffles in the flocculation tank?
10. What treatment process follows flocculation?
11. Explain how water is filtered at some treatment plants.
12. Describe how filters are cleaned and explain why cleaning is more frequent during the summer months.
13. Identify the chemicals that are added immediately before the water leaves the water treatment plant and give the reason for adding each chemical. Which of these chemicals is required?

Water in a Bottle

OBJECTIVES

- **Compare** the water sold in bottles with water that flows from a faucet.
- **State** and **defend** your position on the safety of bottled water.
- **Give** reasons why people choose bottled water rather than tap water.

Did You Know?

Benjamin Franklin was the first to import bottled water to the United States in 1785.

Many people buy bottled water when they can get water from the tap for practically nothing. On average, tap water costs slightly more than $2.00 per 1,000 gallons (380 L)—the price you might pay for one gallon of bottled water. Compared to tap water, bottled water is very expensive. In spite of the difference in cost, sales of bottled water are booming. Customers are paying nearly $4 billion a year for bottled water.

What is so special about water in a bottle, and where do companies get it? Bottled waters come from protected sources, 75% from wells or from springs that flow from underground aquifers. According to the geological definition, **spring water** flows to the surface naturally from underground aquifers. In Europe all bottled mineral waters come from natural springs.

Water sold as "spring water" in the United States may be collected at a spring or it may be pumped from a bore hole (well) near the spring. The source of water must be the same aquifer that provides water for the spring. The quality of the water (its physical properties and chemical composition) must be the same as the water flowing from the spring. Most spring water is not bottled directly from a spring. Before it is bottled it is filtered and disinfected.

While most bottled waters come from protected underground springs or wells, at least 25% of all bottled waters come from public water systems. Usually the water is further purified before being bottled. Some minerals may be added or removed to improve the taste. The manufacturer is not required to reveal the source of the water, but water that is labeled spring water, artesian water, or mineral water may not come from a municipal water source. The water must come from the source identified on the label.

There are more than 900 brands of bottled water sold in the United States, and many companies sell their water under several different labels. One company may market several different brands of bottled water from the same source. Although the water is the same, prices of the different brands vary.

Bottled water may contain bubbles but it may not contain calories. If water is labelled as naturally **sparkling mineral water**, it must contain the same amount of carbon dioxide that was in the water at the source. If carbon dioxide is lost during the treatment process, it must be replaced. **Seltzer water** is water, probably from a municipal water supply, that has been filtered and carbonated. If minerals are added it is called **club soda**. Club soda, seltzer water and tonic water are not classified as bottled water. They are considered soft drinks and may contain calories.

Water from a Bottle—Is it Safe?

As water travels through the ground, it is filtered, but it also **leaches** or dissolves certain chemicals from the soil and rocks. Some of these chemicals such as pesticides, arsenic, sodium, nitrates and mercury may be present in amounts that are harmful. Bacteria that cause diseases such as infectious hepatitis, cholera, typhoid fever and dysentery may also contaminate the water.

Water and gases bubble from a famous spring in southern France. The spring is the source of Perrier sparkling mineral water. The natural spring water contains benzene in concentrations up to 10 ppm. Benzene—a colorless chemical with a distinctive odor—is a known **carcinogen**. Before the water is bottled and sold, it is purified and filtered.

The filtration process is usually so effective that no benzene can be detected in the water, but traces were discovered in the bottled water in January 1990. Workers who failed to replace filters on schedule caused the problem. Although the contamination was not a health threat, it did create an image problem for a product that was known for its purity. To protect its image, the company voluntarily recalled 160 million bottles, and they put extra controls in place to ensure that the problem would not happen again.

After the Perrier incident, a government investigation focused on the question, "Is bottled water a safe, consumable product?" Representing the Food and Drug Administration (FDA), Dr. Fred Shank testified that "we have no reason to question the safety of bottled water. Bottled water has a low potential for contamination or for causing sickness." The U.S. Centers for Disease Control and Prevention (CDC) has never identified bottled water as the cause of an outbreak of waterborne illness.

The FDA regulates bottled water in much the same way that it regulates food that is transported across state lines for sale in another state. State governments regulate bottled water that is bottled and sold within the state. State regulations may be more demanding than federal regulations. Only water from approved sources can be bottled and sold. Generally bottled water must meet the same U.S. Environmental Protection Agency (EPA) drinking water quality standards as tap water.

Both bottled water companies and public water suppliers are required to test for bacteria at least once a week. This usually ensures that the water does not contain any disease-causing organisms. The FDA also requires bottled water companies to have specific tests performed by an independent laboratory each year. Although the information is not readily available to consumers, the company must maintain records of the test results. Bottled water below the standards for drinking water quality must be labeled as such.

A spring in France is the source of the sparkling mineral water in this bottle.

Environmental Challenge: Glaciers

The source of water for one bottled water company is Eklutna lake at the terminus of Eklutna Glacier near Anchorage, Alaska. The company claims that they are bottling, "nature's purest water."

The treatment process includes removal of fine suspended particles, filtration, ozonation, and UV purification. Even melted water from glaciers is not pure. Would you pay more for water from a glacier than from a spring?

Water from the Tap—Is it Safe?

Tap water is not always fit to drink. Most problems with water contamination are not with large public water supplies, but with private wells and small water companies. Bottled water is safer than tap water that has not been properly treated.

If a farm well contains nitrates or coliform bacteria, drinking bottled water is an alternative to installing expensive filters. Some wells are contaminated with toxic organic chemicals from leaking underground

Did You Know?

Bottled water companies that are members of the International Bottled Water Association (IBWA) must comply with a strict set of standards established by the Association. The company must submit to an annual, unannounced inspection of the plant. The inspection is made by an independent third-party organization. In addition to inspection of the plant operation, records are audited to make sure that the company is complying with state and federal standards. Member companies of IBWA bottle and distribute 85% of the bottled water sold in the United States.

www

NSF International (formerly the National Sanitation Foundation) is an independent, not-for-profit organization that inspects more than 500 bottling plants worldwide, and tests and certifies bottled water brands. To find out more about a specific brand of bottled water, visit their Website: www.nsf.org.

The NSF logo certifies that the claims made on the label are true.

gasoline tanks or landfills. Other wells are contaminated with pesticides. Removal of these chemicals may be prohibitively expensive or impossible. In that case, bottled water may be the only safe supply of water available.

The EPA estimates that some 40 million Americans use drinking water that can contain potentially hazardous levels of lead. If the level of lead in the household water is 15 parts per billion or higher, steps should be taken to reduce the level. If the lead levels cannot be reduced sufficiently, bottled water should be considered. The health benefits will justify the cost, especially if there are young children in the home.

The only way to determine if bottled water is safer to drink than water from the faucet is to compare the results of the laboratory tests. The results of tests for substances regulated by the EPA are available from the municipality or private water company that supplies the tap water. You may be able to obtain test results from the company that packages and distributes bottled water. If the source of tap water is a private well, the owner must have a water sample analyzed by an approved laboratory.

Water from a Bottle—Is it Healthier?

The Fair Packaging and Labeling Act prohibits bottlers from making claims that bottled water is healthier than tap water. The FDA requirements prohibit bottled water labels from listing the minerals the water contains because they believe that the amounts are so small that there is little if any added benefit from drinking bottled water.

Some buyers may feel that the minerals in bottled water make it healthier. According to the American Medical Association (AMA), there may be a slight chance that bottled water is more healthful, but any benefit would be very small when compared to exercising, eating properly or not smoking. Some customers have switched from high-calorie drinks like soda or beer to bottled water. Others drink bottled water because it is a socially acceptable alternative to alcohol.

Unless your tap water is contaminated, bottled water may offer few, if any, health or safety benefits. It may simply be draining money from your wallet. In fact some brands of bottled water may not be as healthy as your own tap water. In some cases, tap water contains a healthier level of fluoride than some brands of bottled water.

Does it Taste Better?

Some brands of bottled water do taste better than water from some taps. Most public and private water suppliers use chlorine as a disinfectant. Most bottling companies purify the water with ozone. Ozone, like chlorine, kills bacteria. It is more expensive to use, but the water has a better flavor. Some people drink water from a bottle because they prefer the taste.

The taste of water usually depends upon the tiny amounts of minerals that have been dissolved from rocks. The only water that is likely to be free of minerals is distilled water. Distilled water is generally not purchased for drinking, but for use in batteries and steam irons where minerals could corrode the metal. **Distilled water** is also used in chemical laboratories where minerals might interfere with chemical reactions.

Although bottled water does not taste better than water from most deep wells, some deep wells are drilled into rock formations with a high sulfur content. The taste of sulfur may make water from these wells unacceptable for drinking. Although filters can remove the sulfur, some people prefer to use the well water for other purposes and buy bottled water for drinking.

According to the Beverage Marketing Corporation, consumption of bottled water in the United States more than doubled between 1986 and 1996. More and more people are buying bottled water for a variety of reasons. For some people it is a safety issue, but for most it is a matter of taste.

Minerals give the water its taste. All minerals are removed when water is purified by distillation.

5.5 Questions for Study and Discussion:

1. Define the following terms: **VOCABULARY**

club soda	sparkling mineral water
distilled water	spring water
seltzer water	

2. List several reasons why some people prefer to drink bottled water instead of tap water.
3. What is the difference between spring water, as a geologist would define it, and "spring water" that you get in a bottle?
4. Some bottled water companies buy water from municipal water suppliers. How does the water they sell differ from the water that comes from the tap?
5. How do seltzer water and club soda differ from naturally sparkling mineral water? Which one is regulated as bottled water?

Water from a Bottle—Is it Safe?

6. Explain why spring water is not pure.
7. Compare the regulation of bottled water and municipal water supplies.

Water from a Tap—Is it Safe?

8. Identify situations where bottled water would be a safer choice than tap water.
9. How can you tell if bottled water is safer than water available at the tap in your home?

Water from a Bottle—Is It Healthier?

10. What is the position of the American Medical Association on the health benefits of bottled water?
11. Can tap water be healthier for you than bottled water? Explain.
12. Identify situations when bottled water would provide a health benefit.

Does it Taste Better?

13. What chemical is frequently used to purify bottled water and why do they use this chemical?
14. What usually determines the taste of untreated water?
15. Although their well water is safe, some people buy bottled water for drinking. What may be present in the well water that would make it unfit for drinking?
16. Under what circumstances would you buy bottled water rather than drinking water from the tap?

Fluoride in Your Water Supply — How Much is Enough?

OBJECTIVES

- **Describe** changes in tooth structure that are caused by fluoride.
- **Describe** the scientific studies that led to the fluoridation of water supplies in many cities.
- **Explain** why the EPA has set a maximum contaminant level for fluoride.
- **State** and **defend** your position on the fluoridation of community water supplies.

"Fifty years ago children dreaded the dentist's drill, but today millions of children greet their parents with 'Look Ma—No Cavities'!"

Some people living in certain parts of Colorado, and some other areas of the United States, have developed tooth enamel that is permanently discolored. In Colorado the condition became known as the **Colorado Brown Stain**. In Texas the discolored teeth were called **Texas Teeth**. In 1901 a young dentist in Colorado Springs, Colorado, noticed that people whose teeth were stained had fewer cavities. A search began for the substance that caused the stains and might be making the teeth more resistant to decay. In 1931 the cause of the stains was found to be fluoride.

Fluorides, compounds that contain the element fluorine, are found in almost all foods and in all water supplies. Most natural water supplies contain 0.1–0.2 parts fluoride per million parts water. Natural water supplies in some areas of the Northeast contain only 0.05 ppm fluorides. In a few areas of the United States natural water supplies contain higher levels of fluoride. In some parts of the Southwest water supplies contain as much as 8 ppm.

Scientific Studies

The proof that Colorado Brown Stain was due to high levels of fluoride came from experiments in which rats were fed fluoride or phosphate rock that contained fluoride. As expected, these rats developed the same tooth structure that is seen in children who live in areas where there are naturally high concentrations of fluoride in the water. These changes in tooth structure were not observed in rats that were in the control groups and were not fed fluoride.

Once scientists knew what caused the changes in tooth structure, they began a 10-year study of humans. The purpose of the study was to examine the effects of water supplies that had different amounts of fluoride. This study and others that have followed have shown that people who drink water that contains between 1.0 and 2.5 ppm fluoride from infancy to the age of 10 or 12 have fewer cavities in their permanent teeth.

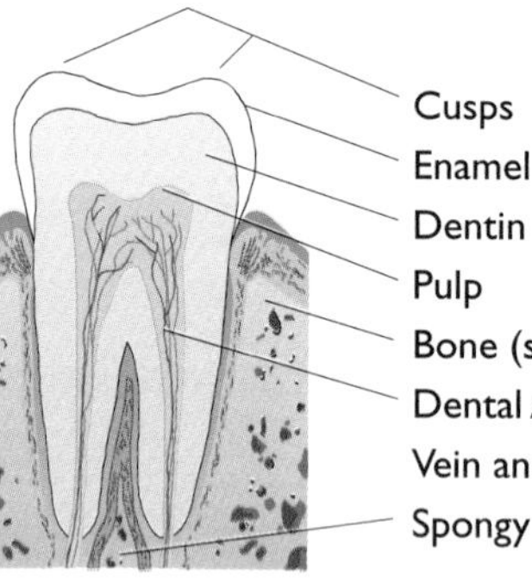

Fluoride—How It Works

Research has shown that fluoride reduces cavities in both children and adults. Recent studies have shown how fluoride works. A substance called **enamel** covers the part of a tooth that is exposed. Although tooth enamel is the hardest substance in the body, acids can dissolve it. Bacteria in the mouth digest sugar in the food we eat, and acids are a waste product of this digestion.

There are millions of tiny spaces between the rods, which form tooth enamel. The acids seep into the tiny spaces between the rods and begin to dissolve the minerals (calcium and phosphorus) in the enamel. At the

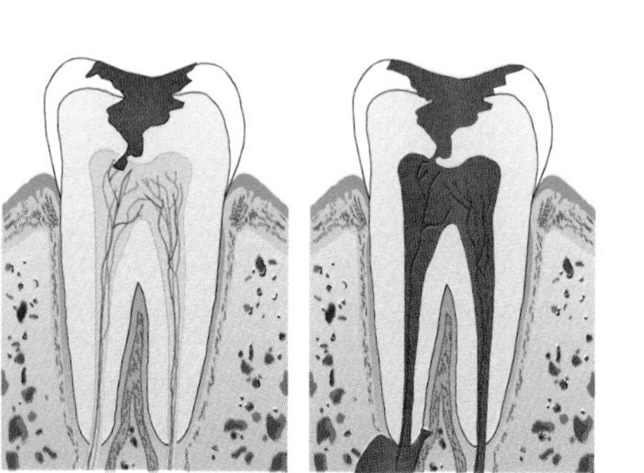
Dental Decay.

same time, more minerals move from the saliva into these spaces and begin to rebuild the enamel. Tooth enamel is constantly being dissolved and rebuilt. If the enamel is dissolved faster than it can be rebuilt, the result is tooth decay or cavities.

Fluoride helps prevent cavities by:

- Interfering with the growth of cavity-causing bacteria.
- Inhibiting enzymes that bacteria need to digest sugar and produce acid.
- Bonding with the enamel making it stronger so it is not as easily dissolved by acids.
- Increasing the repair of enamel in areas where it has been weakened by the action of acids.

Fluoridation of Water Supplies

Studies in several states and in several other countries showed that water with 1 ppm natural fluoride reduced the level of decay by 50–60%. Since natural fluoride reduces tooth decay, scientists thought it might be possible to reduce tooth decay by adding fluoride to water supplies that have less than 1 ppm natural fluoride.

In 1945, scientists began a ten-year study of the effects of fluoride. Three cities that had low levels of fluoride in the water supply were selected as "experimental cities." Fluoride compounds were added to the water supply to increase the fluoride level to 1 ppm. Nearby cities that had low levels of fluoride in the water supply served as "control cities."

Children living in the "experimental" and the "control" cities were provided with extensive dental and medical examinations during the study. The experiment was declared a success after only five years. In all three experimental cities, the number of decayed, missing or filled permanent teeth was reduced by 55–60% in children who were given fluoridated water from birth.

Today more than 145 million people in the United States and 10 million Canadians live in communities with water systems that provide optimal levels of fluoride. This means that the fluoride level of the water is adjusted to about 1 ppm. Water suppliers carefully monitor automated equipment that adjusts the fluoride level to ensure that safe levels are maintained. The Environmental Protection Agency prohibits fluoride levels greater than 4 ppm in community water supplies. If the natural fluoride level is greater than the 4 ppm MCL (maximum contaminant level), fluoride must be removed.

When fluoride is added to a community water supply, the amount is adjusted for the temperature of the region. People living in warmer climates will be exposed to more fluoride because they are likely to drink more fluids. People living in colder climates will receive less fluoride because they are likely to drink less. The recommended levels range from 0.7 ppm fluoride (in warm climates) to 1.2 ppm (in cold climates).

POPULATION LINK

About 23% of the U.S. population live in rural regions without a central water supply. Studies have shown that fluoridation of the school

Flouride Study

Experimental (fluoridated)

Grand Rapids, Michigan
Newburgh, New York
Brantford, Ontario

Control (non-fluoridated)

Muskegon, Michigan
Kingston, New York
Sarnia, Ontario

water supply will improve the dental health of those children living in regions where the natural fluoride level is low. Children who are forming their permanent teeth receive the greatest benefits from drinking fluoridated water, but fluoride also provides adults with protection from tooth decay.

Too Much of a Good Thing—Fluorosis

Emissions from some industrial processes involving rock phosphate, which contains fluorides, have caused widespread damage to plants and animals. A level of only 0.1 parts per billion (ppb) fluoride will cause the death of some plant species. Other plant species, including alfalfa, can change fluoride into a harmless chemical that is stored. Fluoride can cause sickness and even the death of animals when high concentrations enter the food chain.

Cattle and other animals that eat plants containing very high levels of fluorides will develop **fluorosis** or fluoride poisoning. Dairy cattle are the most sensitive to fluoride poisoning. High levels of fluoride reduce the amount of milk produced and cause the animals to become lame. In the 1950s, fluoride emissions from facilities processing rock phosphate led to the death of some 30,000 dairy cattle in Florida.

Fresh waters in the United States have natural levels of fluoride that range from 0.1 to more than 12 parts per million. In those regions where the level of fluoride in the water supply is greater than 1.5 ppm, some people develop **dental fluorosis** or mottled teeth. **Mottling** may occur in children whose mothers ingested high levels of fluoride while they were pregnant. Mottling causes paper white lines or patches on teeth.

Mottling increases as the fluoride level increases. About 10% of children exposed to optimal levels of fluoride (0.7-1.2) will develop the mildest form of fluorosis. The fine white lines may only be detected by their dentist. Moderate to severe cases of fluorosis occur when the level of fluoride in water supplies is greater than 4 ppm. Colorado Brown Stain and pitted teeth may be evidence of moderate to severe dental fluorosis. Scientists disagree about whether moderate to severe dental fluorosis is a health effect or a cosmetic effect. The EPA considers the effect of dental fluorosis to be only cosmetic and not an adverse health effect.

Although long-term exposure to low levels of fluoride benefits dental health, large amounts of fluoride may lead to serious health problems. Too much fluoride in the bones causes **skeletal fluorosis**. In parts of India and Africa where water naturally has more than 10 ppm fluoride, large numbers of people have skeletal fluorosis. The disease has several stages that begin with pain in the bones and joints. Bone spurs and fusion of vertebrae make moving the joints difficult in the advanced or crippling stage.

The risk of skeletal fluorosis is difficult to determine. In addition to fluoride intake, it depends upon other nutritional factors including the amount of vitamin D, protein, calcium and magnesium in the diet. The EPA has estimated that the development of crippling skeletal fluorosis

Environmental Challenge: Nutritional Supplements

Nutritional supplements are added to foods. Vitamins A and D are added to milk. The flour used to make bread and pastas contains additional vitamins in the B group. Iodine is added to most salt. Breakfast cereals are fortified with vitamins and minerals.

Consider the possibility of adding fluoride to foods, and make a recommendation:

- Is it a good idea to add fluoride to food?
- What food would you suggest?
- If you think that this is a bad idea, support your position.

would require a person to consume 20 mg or more of fluoride each day for 20 years. In the United States, no cases have been observed in people who have consumed 8 mg of fluoride per day in drinking water (2 L/day containing 4 ppm fluoride).

To Fluoridate or not to Fluoridate

Since the 1940s the Public Health Service has supported fluoridation of community water supplies. Dr. C. Everett Koop, U.S. Surgeon General (1981–1989) said, "Fluoridation is the single most important commitment a community can make to the oral health of its children and to future generations." More than 75 national health and science organizations, including the American Dental Association, support fluoridation of water supplies.

The Public Health Service set national health goals for fluoridation. The original goal was for 95% of people on public water systems to receive fluoride-adjusted water by 1990. The goal was not met. Only 62% of the population on public water systems received fluoride-adjusted water in 1993. The Surgeon General set a new goal to provide optimal fluoride levels to 75% of people on public water systems, by the year 2000.

The Coalition for Pure Water and other antifluoridation groups have been successful in persuading local governments in many cities to decide against fluoridation of the community water supply. Some communities discontinued fluoridation because of fears about harmful effects. In recent years there has been less public resistance to fluoridation. A law passed in California in 1995 made it one of only ten states and territories in the United States to require fluoridation. Fluoridated water began flowing from the taps in the city of Los Angeles three years later.

Is your community water supplier required to adjust the fluoride level?

Fluoridation is required in these states and territories:

- California
- Connecticut
- District of Columbia
- Georgia
- Illinois
- Kentucky
- Minnesota
- Nebraska
- Ohio
- Puerto Rico
- South Dakota

These states require a public vote before the fluoride level can be adjusted:

- Delaware
- Maine
- Nevada
- New Hampshire
- Utah

Is Fluoridated Water Safe?

There have been reports of illness from drinking fluoridated water, but thousands of carefully conducted scientific studies have found no evidence to support these claims. In 1945, the newspaper in Newburgh, New York, reported cases of nausea and skin rashes that were being caused by fluoride added to the drinking water. These symptoms were reported before fluoride was actually added to the water supply. When fluoride was added to the water supply a few weeks later there were no complaints.

Although fluoride is poisonous in large amounts, there is no evidence that controlled fluoridation of water supplies is harmful. A study reported in 1990 found a small number (4 of 130) male rats receiving large doses of fluoride in their drinking water developed a rare form of bone cancer. Exposure to fluoride was 20–100 times greater than the optimal level in drinking water. None of the female rats and none of the mice in the study developed bone cancer. A more recent study found no evidence of cancer in either male or female rodents.

Animal studies that have linked fluoride to birth defects and infertility have involved far higher doses of fluoride than humans are exposed to in their diet and drinking water. The National Research

Environmental Challenge: The Water Supply

A family has 5 children ages 5–15. When the first child was born, the community where they lived had fluoridated water. When the oldest child was 10, the family moved to a community without fluoridated water and the natural fluoride level was 0.2 ppm.

- What differences would you expect to observe in the children's teeth?

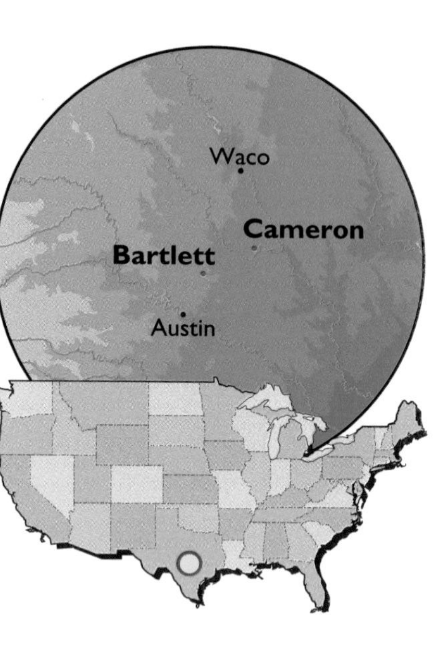

For more information on the issue of fluoridation, visit these Websites: www.cdc.gov, www.ada.org, www.nci.nih.gov, www.cda.org, www.aafp. org, www.epa.gov, and http://fluoride.oralhealth.org.

Council reports that fluoride has caused mutations in animal cells when administered at levels 100 times greater than the level found in most people. Some critics question the value of high-dose cancer tests in animals. A person would have to consume 20,000 gallons of water a day to consume the amount of fluoride in the water given to the mice in the cancer study.

Health studies of people who have lived their entire lives in areas that have high levels of fluoride in the water supply have shown no differences in bone cancer. A recent review of more than 50 human health studies by leading experts for the Public Health Service concluded that the optimal level of fluoride in drinking water "does not pose a detectable risk of cancer to humans." The National Research Council says the levels of fluoride allowed in drinking water do not cause cancer, kidney disease or bone disease.

A ten-year study compared long-time residents of Bartlett, Texas, where water supplies contain 8.0 ppm of fluoride, with those of long-time residents of Cameron, Texas, where the water supply contains only 0.4 ppm of fluoride. The study included a postmortem examination of bones and tissues. The only difference noted between the two groups was a higher occurrence of dental fluorosis in the people who lived in Bartlett.

Yet some people remain opposed to fluoridation. The Coalition for Pure Water is opposed to fluoridation because they feel it is a violation of individual rights to "medicate" the water supply. Some people are concerned that fluoridation of water supplies introduces too much fluoride into the food chain.

Your greatest exposure to fluoride is most likely through the water you drink and the food you consume. Phosphate fertilizers and fluoridated water increase the amount of fluoride in food. Infant foods that are mechanically deboned (chicken and turkey) may contain high levels of fluoride. If fruit juice, infant formula and baby foods are made with fluoridated water, children under the age of two will receive more fluoride than the amount recommended by the American Dental Association (ADA).

Other Ways to get Fluoride

When fluoride is available during the first 10–15 years of life, tooth enamel becomes more resistant to acids. Studies have shown that fluoridation of the community water supply is the most effective and the least expensive way of providing fluoride to everyone. Nationally the average cost of providing residents with fluoridated water is about $0.51 per person per year. The cost for a lifetime of fluoride is about the same as restoring one cavity — $42.00.

According to the ADA, children living in communities with fluoride-adjusted water have 17–40% fewer cavities than children living in communities without fluoridated water. The reduction in tooth decay is not as dramatic as it was in the studies done 50 years ago. Perhaps this is because fluoridation of the water supply is not the only means of increasing the fluoride available to the tooth enamel.

Some toothpastes contain 1000 ppm fluoride. According to the ADA, toothpaste with fluoride is effective in preventing tooth decay. Brands of toothpaste that have been proven effective are given the Seal of Acceptance of the ADA. While a child cannot absorb enough fluoride from toothpaste to cause serious problems, daily swallowing of toothpaste can lead to dental fluorosis. All ADA-accepted toothpastes carry the following warning: "Do not swallow. Use only a pea-sized amount for children under six. To prevent swallowing, children under six years of age should be supervised in the use of toothpaste."

By the time the symptoms of dental fluorosis appear, the changes in the tooth structure are permanent. A study of 916 children found that more than 70% of the fluorosis observed was due to brushing with more than the pea-sized amount of toothpaste recommended. Researchers also found that inappropriate fluoride supplement prescriptions were responsible for 25% of the fluorosis observed. Fluoride is commonly found in baby vitamins.

Swallowing too much fluoride can result in death. The ADA has recommended that manufacturers limit the size of packages containing fluoride. This could prevent the accidental death of a child. Dr. Horowitz, of the National Institute for Dental Research, suggests that children under 5 years old not be given fluoride mouth rinses. Children older than six are not likely to develop dental fluorosis. Many schools have fluoride mouth-rinse programs that have proven to be effective. The dentist or dental hygienist may apply a fluoride solution or gel to the teeth. They may also prescribe fluoride solutions or tablets for use at home.

Family physicians and dentists need to know the fluoride content of local drinking water supplies, and they need to educate parents about fluoride in the diet. The need for fluoride supplements depends upon the age of the child and the amount of fluoride in the drinking water. Current guidelines recommend that children between 6 months and 16 years should receive daily fluoride supplements if they live in an area where fluoride levels are low.

The National Research Council was unable to determine the true exposure of Americans to fluoride because the chemical is present in foods, beverages and a variety of dental products. The committee recommended continued study to determine the effects of lifetime exposure to low levels of fluoride. The American Dental Association also promotes further research to answer questions about optimum levels of fluoride.

Environmental Challenge: Fluoridation in Louisiana

In 1996, approximately 50% of Louisiana's population using public water supplies received fluoridated water. The goal for the year 2000 was 75%. The assessment also found that of 73 water systems adjusting fluoride content in 1986, only 45 were making adjustments in 1996.

The Department of Health and Hospitals conducted a study of Medicaid-eligibility records from July 1995 through June 1996 for children aged 1 to 5 years. Children in communities without fluoridated water were 3 times more likely than children in communities with fluoridated water to received dental treatment in a hospital operating room. At all ages costs were higher in communities without fluoridated water.

Each community must decide the issue of fluoridation if the state does not pass legislation that requires communities to adjust fluoride levels. As an aide to a state senator, you are to present information on fluoride at a briefing to the subcommittee on Human Health Issues.

- Prepare a list of Pros and Cons on the issue of Fluoridation.
- Write a position statement for the Senator on the issue of Fluoridation.

5.6 QUESTIONS FOR STUDY AND DISCUSSION:

1. Define the following terms: **VOCABULARY**

Colorado Brown Stain	fluorosis
dental fluorosis	mottling
enamel	skeletal fluorosis
fluoridation	Texas Teeth
fluorides	

2. Explain why some children who were born and raised in certain parts of Texas or Colorado developed teeth that were stained.
3. Identify the region of the U. S. that has the highest levels of fluoride.

Scientific Studies

4. Describe the difference in treatment between the rats in the experimental group and the rats in the control group.
5. What conclusion was made from the study of human consumption of naturally fluoridated water supplies?

Fluoride—How It Works

6. Describe the structure of tooth enamel and explain how a cavity is formed.
7. List several ways that fluoride helps to prevent cavities.

Fluoridation of Water Supplies

8. What were the results of the fluoridation study that was begun in 1945?
9. What is the maximum level of fluoride that is permitted in a community water supply?
10. What is the recommended level of fluoride in the water supply of Phoenix, Arizona? in Portland, Maine? In your city? Why do the recommended levels differ?

Too Much of a Good Thing—Fluorosis

11. Identify the source of fluoride that caused fluorosis in cattle in Florida. Describe the changes that occur in cattle that develop fluorosis.
12. Describe the changes that may occur in children who live in areas where there is more than 1.5–2.0 ppm fluoride in the water supply.
13. Describe the changes that occur in the teeth of children who drink water with a fluoride level greater than 4 ppm.
14. What other health effects are seen in people who drink water with naturally high levels of fluoride? Why is it difficult to determine the risk of this condition?

To Fluoridate or not to Fluoridate

15. State the position of the following groups concerning the issue of fluoridation of public water supplies:
    - American Dental Association
    - Coalition for Pure Water
    - Public Health Service

Is Fluoridated Water Safe?

16. What are the results of research studying the link between fluoride and cancer?
17. What is the strongest evidence that levels below 4 ppm of fluoride in drinking water are not harmful to humans?
18. How can children under the age of 2 get more than the recommended level of fluoride in their diet even though the level of fluoride in the water supply does not exceed the MCL?

Other Ways to Get Fluoride

19. At what time of life is exposure to fluoride the most beneficial?
20. What method of increasing fluoride exposure is the most effective and least expensive?
21. List several ways that children can get the fluoride they need if the water supply isn't fluoridated.
22. What steps can parents take to ensure that their children are not exposed to too much fluoride.
23. Is your community water supply fluoridated? Do you think that it should be? Explain why you feel this way.

Will There Be Enough?

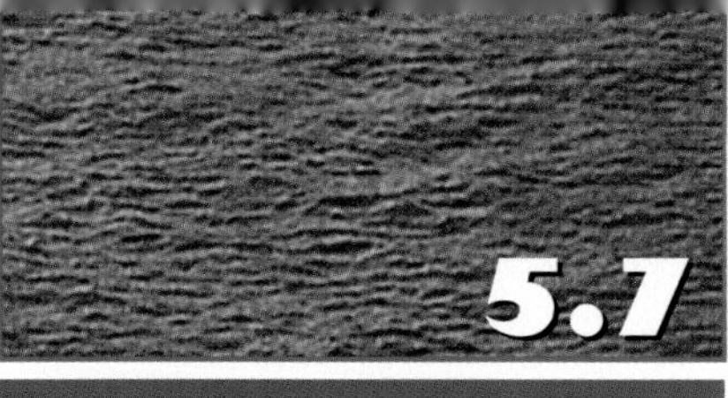

5.7

"When the well's dry, we know the worth of water."
BENJAMIN FRANKLIN

OBJECTIVES

- ✔ **Explain** why so little of the earth's water supply is usable.
- ✔ **Identify** major sources of water locally and **compare** the availability of water to the availability in other areas.
- ✔ **Compare** the water use in the United States with water use in other countries.
- ✔ **Classify** water sources as renewable or nonrenewable.
- ✔ **Relate** population growth to the demand for water and the issue of "water rights."

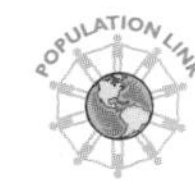

Water is one of the earth's most abundant resources. There are 326 million cubic miles (1.358×10^9 km^3) of water on Earth. Streams carry an average of 1.2 trillion gallons (4.6×10^{12} L) of water to the oceans every day. If water is so abundant and is a renewable resource, it would seem that we couldn't possibly run out of water. Yet streams and wells do go dry.

Most of the earth's water, 97.2%, is in the oceans. Together the oceans, ice caps and glaciers contain 99.4% of the earth's total water supply. The supply of fresh water (groundwater and surface water) that is available to humans is only three-tenths of 1% (0.3%) of the world's total water supply.

If the volume of water in the oceans is represented by a one-inch (2.5 cm) cube, a one-fourth inch (0.6 cm) cube would represent the water stored in the ice caps and glaciers. A one-eighth inch (0.3 cm) cube would represent groundwater, and a one-sixteenth inch (0.15 cm) cube would represent surface water.

To put it another way, the earth's total water supply can be represented as 100 drops of water. Salt water in the ocean is represented by slightly more than 97 of the drops. Slightly more than 2 of the 3 remaining drops represent ice. The ground and surface water supply is only slightly more than one half of the last drop.

The fresh water is not equally distributed or readily available. Eighty-five percent of the fresh water is frozen in polar ice caps and glaciers. Fourteen percent is buried beneath the ground. Half of the groundwater is more than 2,600 feet (800 m) beneath the surface of the earth. Fresh water also occurs as a film of moisture covering particles of soil and as water vapor high in the atmosphere. Less than 1% (0.66%) of the earth's supply of fresh water is found in lakes, rivers and streams.

The Distribution of Water

If all of the water in the atmosphere were to fall evenly as rain, the earth would be entirely covered with one inch (2.5 cm) of water. But when it rains it pours. Rain doesn't fall equally on everyone. Unusual weather patterns sometimes create long periods of drought or disastrous floods. California experienced its worst drought in the last century from 1987 to 1993. The Great Flood of 1993 caused billions of dollars in damage to property in eight midwestern states.

The average annual rainfall in the United States is 30 inches (76 cm), but it is not evenly distributed. Less than 4 inches (10 cm) of rain fall each year on parts of the Southwest while parts of the Pacific Northwest receive 200 inches (508 cm) a year. The wettest place on Earth is Mt. Waialeale on the island of Kauai, Hawaii, where it rains almost every day. The yearly rainfall on Mt. Waialeale averages 451 inches (1,150 cm) a year.

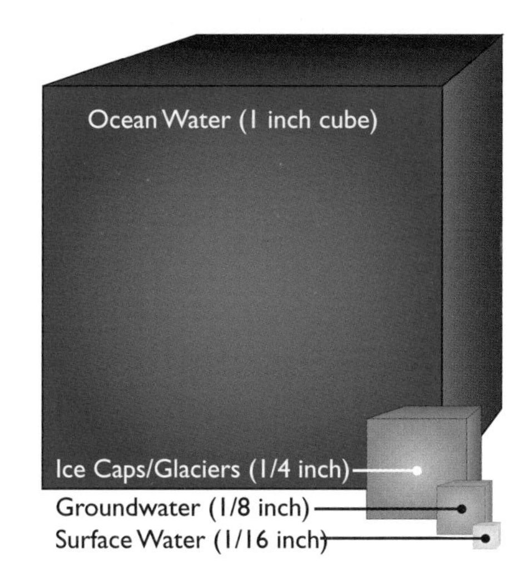

The Earth's Water Supply.

Twenty percent of the world's supply of fresh surface water is found in the Great Lakes.

Most of the rain falling on the United States falls in the East. West of the 100th Meridian—a line extending from North Dakota through Western Texas—there are few major sources of fresh water. Two major rivers draining the Rocky Mountains supply most of the surface water. The Southwest gets much of its water from the Colorado River, and the Northwest taps the Columbia River. The **Ogallala Aquifer**, an underground reservoir about the size of California, provides water for over 7 million acres of irrigated agriculture in the High Plains states.

The survival and success of a community frequently depend upon the water it can provide for agriculture and industry. Water has often become the limiting factor in the growth of communities. Although the eastern part of the United States is usually wet, when droughts do occur, water restrictions are necessary. The high population density along the eastern coast puts great demands upon the region's water supply.

The Demand for Water

In poor tropical countries, where women must walk several miles for water, each person may use less than one gallon (3.8 L) of water per day. It is estimated that each person in the U.S. uses between 80 and 100 gallons (304–380 L) per day. Households in the United States use more water than households do in other developed countries. In some cases, more than 50% of water use may be for watering lawns and gardens.

The rainforest on Mt. Waialeale, on the island of Kauai, Hawaii.

The amount of water used varies with the source of water. A family of four on a public water supply uses about 350 gallons (1330 L) per day while a family that depends upon a private well or cistern uses about 200 gallons (760 L) per day. Families are more likely to use large amounts of water for watering lawns and filling pools when a dependable public water supply is available.

Typical Daily Water Usage for a Family of Four

Water Usage	Usage per Day in Gallons/Liters		Total Daily Usage (%)
Toilet	100	380	39
Bathing & Hygiene	88	334	34
Laundry	35	133	14
Kitchen	27	103	11
Housekeeping	5	9	2
Totals	255	959	100

Our demand for water is great—341 billion gallons a day (12.9×10^{11} L/day) in 1995. The U.S. Geological Survey has collected and analyzed national water-use data every 5 years since 1950. Water use increased steadily from 1950 to 1980. Between 1980 and 1985 water use declined about 7%, mostly due to changes in irrigation technology. Since 1985 water use has held steady even though the population has increased.

The major use of water—134 billion gallons (5.1×10^{11} L) per day—is for agriculture. A large supply of water is necessary to produce the food that we eat. One hundred and twenty gallons (460 L) of water is required to produce an egg for your breakfast. A steak for dinner requires 3,500 gallons (1.3×10^4 L).

Irrigated agriculture is the number one user of water in the western United States. California uses about 22% of the water in the U.S. In California, production of cotton, rice and alfalfa rely heavily on irrigation water. In Kern County, a farmer can make seven cuttings of alfalfa in an irrigated field. Without water for irrigation the fields may produce only one cutting.

The second major use of water in the United States is production of electricity at thermoelectric power plants. Power plants withdraw 132 billion gallons (5.0×10^{11} L) of water per day, but most of this water (97%) is returned to the lake or the river after it has cooled. About 3% of the water will evaporate from the cooling towers.

The charts below show how water was used in the United States in 1995. The charts include only water that is withdrawn from a source. **Nonwithdrawal uses** or in-stream uses, such as recreation, hydroelectric power generation, transportation, or wildlife were not included.

Environmental Challenge: China's Water Shortage

The population of China is expected to increase from 1.2 billion to 1.5 billion by 2030. Research water issues in China and answer the following questions:

- Where will China get the water to meet the needs of this expanding population?
- How will the expansion of China's cities and industries affect the country's ability to produce food?
- How will the diversion of water from agriculture to industry in China affect other countries, including the United States?

Water Use in United States in 1995

Use	Bgal*/day	(10^{10} L)/day	Percentage**
Commercial	2.9	(1.1)	1
Domestic	3.4	(1.3)	1
Industry-Mining	23.3	(8.8)	7
Irrigation	134.0	(50.7)	39
Livestock	5.5	(2.1)	2
Power Generation	132.0	(50.0)	39
Public Supply	40.2	(15.2)	12
Totals	**331.3**	**(129.2)**	**101**

*Billions of gallons. **Percentage exceeds 100 due to rounding.

Some industries use huge amounts of water while others use very little. Paper companies are always located along rivers that provide the large amounts of water required for the production of paper products. Producing one ton of paper for books may require as much as 184,000 gallons (7×10^5 L) of water. Steel mills and oil refineries also require large volumes of water, and many are located along the coast. Some 60,000 gallons (2.3×10^5 L) of water is needed to make the steel for an automobile. More than 450 gallons (1.7×10^3 L) of water is needed to refine a barrel of crude oil. This includes 10 gallons (38 L) of water used to refine each gallon (3.8 L) of gasoline.

Water use in the East differs from its use in the West. The chart shows how the water is used in each region of the country.

East verses West — Water Usage Ranked in Descending Order

The West	The East
Irrigated agriculture	Energy
Domestic and Commercial	Manufacturing
Manufacturing	Domestic and Commercial
Energy	Irrigated agriculture
Minerals	Minerals

The Mining of Water

More than 350 building structures in 10 western Pennsylvania counties have been reported as damaged because the land on which they were built is sinking. Property owners who live above coal mines in Pennsylvania can apply for mine-subsidence insurance. **Subsidence**—the sinking of land—occurs when the resources beneath the land have been removed, and the ground above can no longer support its own weight.

Mining is the removal of a natural substance from an ecosystem at a rate that is faster than the substance is being replaced. Like coal, groundwater is sometimes mined. In Mexico City, the pumping of groundwater that exceeds the **rate of recharge** has removed groundwater that supported the earth above it. The mining of coal did not cause the sagging of Mexico City's famous Metropolitan Cathedral. It is sagging because of the mining of water.

In some regions where water has been mined, the land is sinking. In Baytown, Texas, the pumping of groundwater caused the earth to sink, and the area is now below sea level. Homes along the coast were abandoned when water from Galveston Bay invaded the area. In California's San Joaquin Valley, bridges and roads cracked and 1,200 wells were damaged when the valley floor subsided at least one foot (30 cm).

Think About It

Does the subsidence of land affect the future water-storage capacity of the aquifer?

The annual rainfall in southeastern Arizona is only 12 inches (30 cm) per year. Farmers in the region have been mining water to irrigate their crops. The land is sinking, and where it does not sink evenly, large cracks appear. In Arizona there are hundreds of such cracks. Subsidence is a serious threat in Tucson due to overpumping of the city's groundwater wells.

Roughly a third of today's harvest comes from cropland that is irrigated. Yields from irrigated farmland are 2–3 times those of dryland farms. Groundwater provides about 38% of the water used for irrigation. According to the World Resources Institute, one fifth of the total irrigated farmland in the United States relies on the mining of groundwater, much of it from the Ogallala Aquifer.

A center-pivot irrigation system like this one is only about 50% efficient. Newer, low-pressure, dropline systems can increase the efficiency to 95%.

The **Ogallala Aquifer** lies beneath the High Plains—a region stretching 800 miles (1,280 km) from South Dakota to northern Texas. The aquifer contains groundwater that was absorbed by the earth over the last three million years. Its original supply of water has been cut off by geologic changes. The aquifer receives little water from the surface and is considered a nonrenewable resource.

More than 170,000 wells tap the Ogallala aquifer. About 95% of the water is used to irrigate land that produces 25% of the nation's cotton, 15% of the grain and 40% of the beef cattle. In some areas, the rate of withdrawal has been 10 times the rate of recharge. In the early eighties, the mining of water caused the water table to fall four to six feet (1.2–1.8 m) each year.

The cost of energy to pump the water increases as the **water table**—the level of the water in the aquifer—drops. Today it is no longer economical to pump water from some parts of the Ogallala Aquifer. In other areas, more efficient irrigation techniques have reduced the rate of withdrawal and slowed the rapid decline in the water table.

Rivers and Water Rights

Water is **consumed** if it is not returned to the natural body of water so that it may be used again. Water that is consumed may evaporate, or it may become a part of the finished product. Only about 16% of the water used in industry and mining is consumed. Unlike industry and mining, agriculture consumes more than half of the water withdrawn from wells or rivers.

The Colorado River flows only 7.6 miles (12 km) from where it begins in the Rocky Mountains until the first irrigation ditch diverts part of the water to four ranches. By 1886, arguments over water in the Colorado and Arkansas Rivers were so heated that the state governments were forced to make laws to determine who had the right to withdraw water from the rivers.

An agreement between Colorado and Kansas assigned 60% of the water in the Arkansas River to Colorado. The other 40% must be allowed to flow into Kansas. Demand for the river's water is greater than the supply. When there is little rain and farmers begin to irrigate, the river begins to shrink. At times the Arkansas River flows no more than fifty miles (80 km) past the Colorado border before the water is withdrawn, and the river bed is dry.

The courts used the "first come, first served" rule as the basis to assign water rights. One treaty guaranteed water rights to the Indians. The Supreme Court has ruled that five Indian reservations must be guaranteed enough water from the Colorado River to irrigate their land.

Another treaty signed in 1944, guaranteed Mexico 1.5 million acre-feet (18×10^{11} L) of Colorado River water per year. An **acre-foot** is the volume of water needed to cover one acre (0.4 hectare) of land twelve inches (30 cm) deep. It is about 326,000 gallons (1.2×10^6 L), which is the average amount of water used by a family of five in one year.

Data was collected and the Colorado River's water flow was divided during a wet period. Since that time, the climate has become drier and the Colorado River has not carried as much water. Until recently that did not create a problem. Some of the states along the upper Colorado and some Indian tribes did not demand their share of the river's water supply.

Completion of two projects has made the demand for water greater than the supply. Irrigation of 110,000 acres (4.5×10^4 ha) on the Navajo Reservation, and a 310-mile (496-km) channel that carries water to Phoenix and Tucson, Arizona, has forced Southern California to reduce its withdrawal of Colorado River water from more than 5 million acre-feet (6×10^{12} L) to the 4.4 million acre-feet (5.3×10^{12} L) permitted by law.

Dry regions, like Southern California and Western Kansas, are searching for ways to meet the demand for water. The Army Corps of Engineers proposed a plan to build a canal from the Missouri River to Western Kansas. Construction costs would have been more than $16 billion, and operation costs would have been high since the water must be lifted 2,000 feet (600 m). It is unlikely that such a canal will be built.

It is also unlikely that additional water will be provided by the construction of huge dams. Environmentalists' lawsuits have established

Water from the Ogallala Aquifer irrigates 7 million acres (2.8 million ha) of farmland that was once a prairie ecosytem.

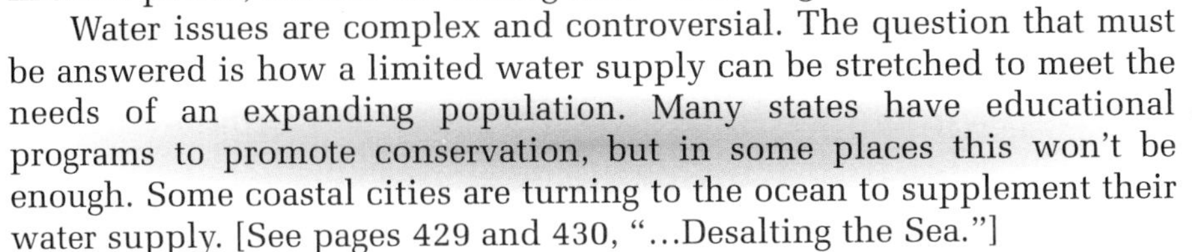

the "rights" of fish and wildlife and other uses of in-stream water. As populations grow and demand increases, societies must choose between water for the densely populated cities and water for irrigated agriculture. In some places, farmers are selling their "water rights" to the cities.

Water issues are complex and controversial. The question that must be answered is how a limited water supply can be stretched to meet the needs of an expanding population. Many states have educational programs to promote conservation, but in some places this won't be enough. Some coastal cities are turning to the ocean to supplement their water supply. [See pages 429 and 430, "...Desalting the Sea."]

5.7 QUESTIONS FOR STUDY AND DISCUSSION:

1. Define the following terms: **VOCABULARY**

acre-foot	Ogallala Aquifer
consumed	rate of recharge
mining	subsidence
nonwithdrawal use	water table

2. Three-fourths of the earth's surface is covered by water, yet the usable supply of fresh water is less than 1%. Explain why.

The Distribution of Water

3. Remembering what you have learned about weather, explain why rainfall is not distributed evenly.
4. Identify the major source of water used to irrigate crops in the Southwest, the Northwest, and the High Plains states?
5. With the exception of the Pacific Northwest, more precipitation falls in the eastern U.S. than in the west; why do parts of the East sometimes experience water shortages?

The Demand for Water

6. Compare the amount of water used by people living in the United States with the amount used by people in other countries, and explain the difference.
7. Rank the top 3 household uses of water beginning with the use that requires the greatest amount of water.
8. Draw a representation of a line graph that shows the trend in water use from 1950 to 1995.
9. Identify the two major uses of water in the United States. Compare the use in the East and the West.
10. Which withdrawal use of water would have the most impact on instream use and use by other communities downstream? Why would this use have the greatest impact?
11. Identify two industries that require large amounts of water.

The Mining of Water

12. Explain how the mining of coal is like the mining of water.
13. What is the relationship between mining of water and subsidence?
14. If irrigation is causing problems, why don't we return to dryland farming?
15. Although water is a renewable resource, the Ogallala Aquifer is considered a nonrenewable resource. Explain why.

Rivers and Water Rights

16. Explain what happens to water that is consumed. Which use consumes more water—agriculture or industry?
17. What is the basis for the water rights given to the Indians?
18. Explain why the Arkansas River goes dry.
19. States in the Colorado River watershed are allowed to withdraw 15 million acre-feet of water annually. Do you think that the United States should be obligated to send more of the Colorado River's flow on to Mexico?
20. How has the flow of the Colorado River changed and what problem did this create?
21. Describe the relationships that exist between population growth, agriculture and water use?
22. What can we do to meet the needs of the expanding population?

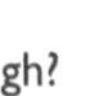

Making More (Water Available) by Using Less

OBJECTIVES

- ✔ **Relate** the use of water to its availability and cost.
- ✔ **Compare** the water supply and demand in Phoenix, AZ, and Tucson, AZ.
- ✔ **Explain** how saving water also saves energy and reduces pollution.
- ✔ **Create** a plan to reduce water use.

"Through water conservation and water recycling, we can meet environmental needs and still have sustainable development and a viable economy."

FELICIA MARCUS
Regional Director, Water Division Region 9 {southwest}

Water is still one of our cheapest natural resources. According to the EPA, the average cost of 1,000 gallons (3,784 L) of treated water delivered to homes by public water systems is slightly more than $2. The cost is slightly less in larger systems. Residents of New York City pay $1.13 for 100 cubic feet (748 gallons; 2,831 L). Because water has been readily available and low in cost, most Americans take water for granted. We have become a nation of water wasters. With increasing population growth we are reaching a point where water conservation must become a way of life.

POPULATION LINK

Meters

Most people who draw water from their own private well must pay for drilling the well and installing a pump, but there is no charge for the water that they use. Some cities with older water systems do not have water meters, and people pay a **flat rate** for each residence regardless of the amount of water used.

All commercial and industrial properties in New York City are required to have water meters, and the city is installing water meters for residential buildings. Water bills for residences without a meter are based on a **frontage rate**. The property width, number of stories and the number of water-using fixtures determine the frontage rate.

People with private wells and people who pay flat or frontage rates for water do not pay an increased cost for taking a longer shower. The only additional cost is for the energy needed to heat the water. Studies show that the use of water declines as water rates increase. Water use dropped 36% after Boulder, Colorado installed water meters. Making people pay more for the water they use encourages them to use the water more efficiently.

Arizona has passed a law that requires users to install water meters on their wells and to report the amount of water that is used. The water is no longer free. Farms larger than two acres (0.8 hectare) must pay a small fee for each acre-foot (325,851 gallons; 1.2×10^6 L) of water used.

The demand for water by residents of Phoenix, Arizona, has been greater than the demand by residents of neighboring Tucson. The cities are only 100 miles apart and have the same climate with less than 12 inches of rain each year. It's a matter of supply and demand. Phoenix had access to more water and one of the lowest water rates in the West.

About 95% of the water used in Phoenix comes from the Salt, Verde and Colorado Rivers; the remainder is groundwater. With a readily

Environmental Challenge: City Water Information

For more information about Tucson's water projects, visit the city's Website at: www.ci.tucson.az.us.

Select a city where you think you might like to live. Try to find information about the quantity and quality of the water supply. Many cities have their own Websites. Example: New York City is www.ci.nyc.ny.us. Search the city services or agencies to find the water department.

www

Fixture	Water Flow
Conventional Toilet	4–6 gal. (15–23 L)/use
Water-Saving Toilet	3.5 gal. (13 L)/use
Low Flow (1994 standard)	1.6 gal. (6 L)/use
Conventional Showerhead	3–15 gal. (10.5–57 L)/min.
Low-Flow Showerhead	2–3 gal. (7.5–11 L)/min.
Low-Flow (1994 standard)	2.5 gal. (9.5 L)/min.
Regular Faucet Aerator	2.5–6 gal. (9.5–23 L)/min.
Flow-Regulating Aerator	0.5–2.5 gal. (2–9.5 L)/min.
Low-Flow (1994 standard)	1.0 gal. (3.5 L)/min.

available supply of water for irrigation, lawns in Phoenix were planted with shade trees, hedges and a carpet of grass—a type of landscape that is normal in much wetter climates. The water demand increases from about 150 million gallons ($5.7x10^8$ L) per day during the winter to more than 400 million gallons ($15.1x10^8$ L) per day during the summer.

The water supply for Tucson comes from 175 groundwater wells, and residents pay significantly more for each gallon of water. One unit (100 cubic feet; 748 gallons; 2,831 L) of water costing $1.09 in Phoenix might cost $3.29 in Tucson. The water rates in Tucson are graduated; customers who use more water pay higher rates for the additional units. As a result, lawns in Tucson are often planted with cactus and other desert plants.

Groundwater in Tucson is pumped at a rate that is 2-1/2 times the rate of natural recharge. The water table has declined 200 feet since the 1940s and continues to drop 3 to 4 feet every year. **Subsidence** is a serious threat. Tucson is artificially recharging the aquifer with water from the Colorado River and reclaimed (treated) wastewater.

Leaky Water Systems

Much water is wasted. Water distribution systems in many big cities are old and need to be replaced. Needed repairs and replacements are so expensive that the faulty systems are still in use. New York City has lost as much as 20% of its water supply through the city's 6,000 miles (9,600 km) of leaky water lines. As part of its ongoing water conservation program, NYC is using sonar to survey all water supply pipes and replacing approximately 40 miles of leaky pipes each year.

In most cities, the city water department is responsible for the major water pipes or water mains, and homeowners are responsible for the house connection—the pipe running from the building to the water main. When New York City's Bureau of Water Supply discovers a leak in a house connection, the owner is given a three-day notice to repair the leak. If the leak is not repaired within three days, the city shuts off the water supply to the building.

While repairs to water pipes and plumbing fixtures may be expensive, they are an effective way to conserve water. Each leaky faucet or toilet wastes water. A faucet with a slow leak can waste 5 gallons (19 L) of water per day, while a leaking toilet can waste 22 gallons (84 L) of water a day. Toilet leaks can easily be detected by adding food coloring to the water in the tank. If the colored water appears in the toilet bowl, the toilet is leaking.

Water-Saving Fixtures

A typical family of four consumes 255 gallons (970 L) of water inside the home each day. By installing water-saving fixtures this amount can be reduced by 90–140 gallons (340–530 L) each day. Depending on water rates, installation of water-saving fixtures may save $100–$300 per year.

By installing a high-quality low-flow showerhead, a family can reduce water use in the shower by more than half and still enjoy a good shower. Not only does this save water, but it also saves more than $150 annually if the water is heated with electricity. Flow control aerators on kitchen and bathroom faucets can save additional water and energy by reducing the flow rate by 60%.

Nearly 40% of all water used in the home is flushed down the toilet. Placing bottles or dams in conventional toilet tanks can reduce water use by 1.5 gallons (5.7 L) of water per flush, without affecting the performance of the toilet. This can save 8,500 gallons ($3.2x10^4$ L) of water each year.

Regulations included in the 1992 energy bill set federal standards for new plumbing fixtures manufactured after January 1, 1994. Showerheads and faucets must limit flow to 2.5 gallons (9.5 L) per minute. Toilets manufactured for domestic use must limit flow to 1.6 gallons (6 L) per flush. These changes are expected to reduce domestic indoor water use by 30%.

Saving water can also reduce problems with some on-lot septic systems and sewage treatment plants. Many sewage treatment plants are too small to handle the amount of wastewater that passes through the plant. Reducing the amount of water used in each home reduces the volume of wastewater that must be treated. The result is more efficient treatment and cleaner **effluent** entering a stream.

A Change in Lifestyle

During drought conditions, restaurants may be required to serve water to customers only if they specifically ask for it. When drought-like conditions occurred in Longview City, Washington, after the eruption of Mt. St. Helens, the district health officer recommended that food services use disposable cups, glasses, and tableware.

Replacing dishes with disposables saves water by eliminating the use of automatic dishwashers. Commercial dishwashers use between 70 and 500 gallons (265–1892 L) per hour. Great amounts of water are not consumed in the manufacture of paper or plastic disposables.

Although making the paper requires large amounts of water, paper mills are located on rivers and streams where water is usually plentiful. The water used in making paper is treated and put back in the streams. Thus, most of the water is not consumed; it is only borrowed and then returned. Water conservation measures at some paper mills have reduced use of water by more than 90%.

The watering of lawns and gardens can double the normal household water used during the summer. A standard garden hose can apply more than 6 gallons (23 L) of water per minute. More than 620 gallons ($2.4x10^3$ L) of water is required to apply 1 inch (2.5 cm) of water to 1,000 square feet (90 m^2) of lawn or garden. Two types of water are now delivered through separate distribution systems to some customers in Tucson, Arizona and Cape Coral, Florida: **potable water** and reclaimed (treated) wastewater.

Even though water rates in Phoenix are low, residents are reminded: "Phoenix is still a desert; conserve our water." They are encouraged to water the grass every three days early in the morning or late in the evening. It's against the law to let water run into streets or alleys. Workshops are conducted on converting grass areas to xeriscapes (zer-i-scapes). **Xeriscape landscaping** uses native, drought-tolerant plants. Xeriscaped lawns use 30–80% less water than conventional lawns.

Environmental Challenge: Low Flush Toilets

On February 8, 1999, Rep. Joe Knollenberg (R-MI) reintroduced his bill to repeal national efficiency standards for plumbing products. Write a position statement on National Water Efficiency Standards as a representative of one of the following groups:

- Plumbing Manufacturers Institute
- Seattle Public Utilities
- Charles River Watershed Association
- Mono Lake Committee

Think About It

There are many ways to reduce the water used in your household without spending money on new plumbing fixtures:

- Use a dishpan or stopper in the sink when washing and rinsing dishes. Wash the dishes only once a day.
- Use the dishwasher only when fully loaded and use a shorter cycle.
- Use the proper water level in the washing machine when washing clothes.
- Avoid letting water run when brushing your teeth or shaving.
- Take a 3-minute shower.

Self seeding annual larkspur are flowering in the back of this xeriscape garden in Dallas, Texas. Perennial iris bulbs are sprouting in front.

Irrigation

As the world population has increased to 6 billion, irrigation has become an important part of food production, but much of the water used for irrigation is wasted. Agriculture uses 70% of water supplies globally. By improving the efficiency of irrigation, farmers can also reduce erosion, prevent loss of fertilizer, and save the cost of energy to pump the excess water.

Farmers using conventional gravity-flow systems can reduce their need for water by 30% by capturing the water that normally runs off the field. Computerized irrigation systems that detect leaks and adjust flow for wind speed and soil moisture make more efficient use of water. The University of California at Davis is building a statewide computer network to provide customized irrigation plans for farmers.

The most efficient method of irrigation is a **subsurface drip irrigation system**, which has buried perforated plastic pipes that feed water directly to the plant roots. While this system can conserve huge amounts of water, few farmers are using this method of irrigation. A subsurface drip system can cost $1,200 per acre ($2,964/ha) to install, and maintenance can be a problem because the holes in the pipes tend to clog. The system is not suitable for grains and other crops requiring cultivation.

Farmers in Texas have cut water losses from evaporation by using **low-energy precision application**, a more efficient center-pivot irrigation system that delivers water closer to the ground. Improved irrigation systems and other water conservation measures in Texas have significantly reduced demand for water. Savings in energy costs and increased crop yields pay for installation of the system.

Did You Know?

A one-inch rainstorm deposits 27,152 gallons of water on an acre of land (approximately the size of a football field).

From Farm to City

With ever-increasing populations, cities need more water and more food. A water district in Southern California is paying farmers to install improved irrigation systems in exchange for the right to use the water saved. This farm-to-city transfer of water will meet the water demands of 800,000 Californians. More efficient use of water can provide water for crops and people too.

In Arizona, cities like Tucson and Phoenix are **water ranching**. In Arizona, the water rights are tied to ownership of the land. Cities are buying farms to obtain rights to their water supply. As cities purchase more irrigated farmland, and divert the water from the farms to the cities, the production of food decreases. Irrigated agriculture is expected to disappear in the area around Tucson by the year 2020.

Subsurface drip irrigation systems in orange groves like this one conserve both energy and water.

Use It Again

The water cycle makes only a certain amount of water available each year. Recycling or reusing water is not new. The water withdrawn from rivers contains the **effluent** from a city upstream. Now water is being recycled within communities. In Irvine, California, recycled water is being used for toilet flushing in high-rise buildings. The additional plumbing adds only 9%

to the cost of a seven-story building. San Diego is planning to send wastewater that has received advanced treatment to a drinking water reservoir.

In 1980, Arizona passed the Groundwater Management Act. The law requires a balance between the amount of groundwater pumped and the amount naturally replaced. Another part of the law requires cities to prove they have enough water to meet their projected needs for the next 100 years. As the human population continues to expand and the demand for water grows, water conservation and water recycling will be essential to ensuring a sustainable water supply.

5.8 QUESTIONS FOR STUDY AND DISCUSSION:

1. Define the following terms: **VOCABULARY**

   flat rate
   frontage rate
   low-energy precision application
   subsidence
   surface drip irrigation system
   water ranching
   xeriscape landscaping

2. Compare the cost of water to the cost of other natural resources.

Meters

3. Explain why people who pay a flat rate or a frontage rate often waste more water than people who have water meters.
4. Which method encourages water conservation?
5. Should people living in the country, who get water from a private well, have to pay for the water they use? Justify your opinion.
6. Give two reasons why the demand for water is greater in Phoenix than in Tucson.
7. What are the sources of water available to Tucson to supplement the groundwater, and how are they planning to use this water?

Leaky Water Systems

8. What technology is New York City using to detect leaks?
9. Describe how toilet leaks can be detected.

Water Saving Fixtures

10. What are the two resources saved by water conservation programs?
11. List several changes that can be made in plumbing to decrease the amount of water used.
12. Explain how water conservation can result in cleaner streams.

A Change in Lifestyle

13. List several changes that can reduce water use and save money without installing water-saving plumbing fixtures.
14. What is xeriscaping, and how could it help the residents of Phoenix reduce their demand for water?

Irrigation

15. Explain how more efficient irrigation systems can also save other natural resources.
16. Explain how a computerized irrigation system can reduce water usage.
17. Describe the most efficient method of irrigation and explain why more farmers don't use this system.
18. How does a low-energy precision application irrigation system (LEPA) reduce water use? Identify two ways that the LEPA system benefits the farmer.

From Farm to City

19. How is the Metropolitan Water District of Southern California getting additional water to meet the needs of its customers?
20. What is "water ranching"? What negative impact might water ranching have in the future?

Use It Again

21. Give examples of water recycling in the past and water recycling today.
22. How will communities in Arizona meet the requirements of the Groundwater Management Act?

Environmental Challenge: The Cooperative Water Project: Water for Las Vegas

The landscape at this golf course near Las Vegas is a stark contrast to the surrounding desert landscape.

Las Vegas is seeking the "water rights" to additional water outside of the city to support its growing population and tourist industry. The population in Clark County, Nevada, grew from 463,087 in 1980 to 741,459 in 1990. The county includes Las Vegas—the fastest growing city in the United States. The city of Las Vegas will outgrow its current water supplies by 2002. A water conservation program could extend water supplies until 2006.

Landscaping often provides the illusion that water is abundant. Industry and city officials say that water provides the fantasy that makes Las Vegas what it is, and more water is necessary for the continued success of the tourist industry. Most of the water is used for fountains, artificial lakes, golf courses and conventional lawns.

Las Vegas Valley Water District charges 91 cents per hundred gallons for the first 1,500 gallons ($5.7x10^3$ L) a day, and $1.01 per hundred gallons thereafter. Most of the water comes from Lake Mead on the Colorado River. The water district filed 139 applications for unappropriated water in 21 watersheds in four counties. The decision, to grant or deny "water right" permits, is made by the State Engineer.

If approved, the Cooperative Water Project includes both groundwater and surface water withdrawals. Up to 180,000 acre-feet ($2.2x10^{11}$ L) of groundwater will be withdrawn from 200 or more wells. The project may require construction of as many as 1,000 miles (1,613 km) of pipelines.

The city also plans to withdraw up to 70,000 acre-feet ($8.4x10^{10}$ L) of water from the Virgin River, a tributary of the Colorado. The water will be withdrawn during high-flow months (November through April). The water exceeds the state drinking water standard of 1,000 mg/L salts and will require **desalination**. Las Vegas is planning to build a desalination plant.

The city hopes that the federal government will pay the cost of desalting the river water because it would decrease the salt-load of the Colorado River and help the government meet the salinity treaty with Mexico. The treaty also grants Mexico a minimum of 1.5 million acre-feet ($1.8x10^{12}$ L) of water per year.

It is anticipated that the water provided by the Cooperative Water Project should meet the needs of Southern Nevada beyond 2030 (with conservation).

- What are the potential impacts on the surrounding counties if the permits are granted?
- What will be the impacts on Las Vegas and the state of Nevada if the permits are not granted?
- Do you think the permits should be granted? What additional information do you need to make a decision?

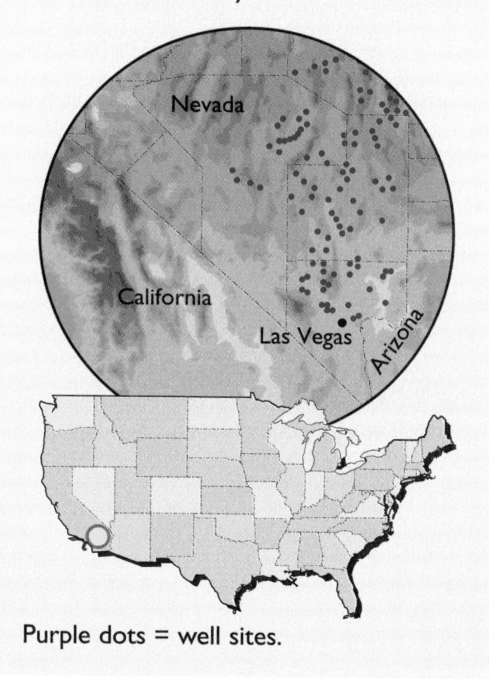

Purple dots = well sites.

Making More Fresh Water — Desalting the Sea

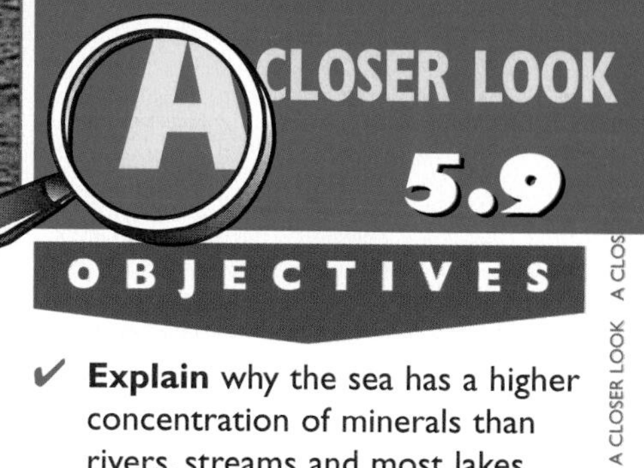

OBJECTIVES

- ✔ **Explain** why the sea has a higher concentration of minerals than rivers, streams and most lakes.
- ✔ **Evaluate** desalination methods on the basis of their ability to remove minerals and their use of energy.
- ✔ **Compare** the environmental and economic impacts of building and operating a desalination plant with the impacts of mandatory water conservation and recycling.

The sea is a very large reservoir. It holds 97% of the Earth's water supply, but seawater is not fit to drink. It contains 3.5% dissolved salts (35,000 ppm). Fresh water contains less than 1,000 ppm dissolved salts. Water is considered slightly **saline** if it has 1,000 to 3,000 ppm dissolved salts. Water with more than 10,000 pmm dissolved salts is highly saline.

How to Desalt the Sea

There are several methods that can be used to remove dissolved ions from saline water. The water can be forced through tiny tubes made of a membrane with openings large enough to allow water molecules to pass through, but too small to allow the ions to pass through. This process is called **reverse osmosis**. This method can be used to desalt seawater or groundwater containing too many dissolved solids, or provide advanced treatment for sewage effluent.

In another process, called **electrodialysis**, saline water flows through a container that is divided into three chambers. One chamber contains an electrode with a positive charge. Another chamber contains an electrode with a negative charge. As water passes through the chambers, ions with a positive charge are attracted to the negative electrode, and ions with a negative charge are attracted to the positive electrode. After it passes through a series of these chambers, water in the center chamber is demineralized, or deionized.

Membranes used for electrodialysis have much larger pores than membranes used for reverse osmosis. Both mineral ions and water molecules can easily pass through the membrane used in electrodialysis. Electrodialysis works best if the water is only slightly salty.

In Webster, South Dakota, the groundwater contains more salt than the government standards allow. A desalting plant in Webster uses electrodialysis to produce 250,000 gallons (9.5×10^5 L) of water a day. If the water were as salty as seawater, this process would be too expensive.

In a **flash distillation** process, water is pumped through a heater that heats it to 250°F (121°C). The super-heated water enters a series of chambers where the reduced pressure causes it to flash into steam. The steam condenses on coils of pipe that are cooled by seawater on its way to the heater. The demineralized water dripping from the pipes is collected and drained into a storage tank.

Solar distillation uses the sun's energy. Water is piped into a large flat container that is covered with a transparent plastic dome. The trapped solar energy (greenhouse effect) causes the water to evaporate. The water vapor condenses on the surface of the dome, and flows down the sides of the dome into collecting troughs. The minerals are left behind.

Removing the dissolved salts from saline water makes the water taste flat. To improve the flavor, the water is mixed with water from local wells before being piped to consumers. Water can also flow over broken coral to replace some of the minerals and give it a more pleasant taste.

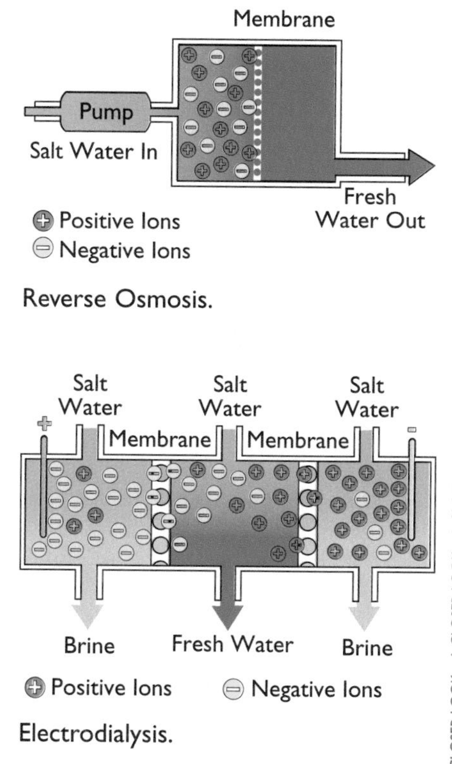

Reverse Osmosis.

Electrodialysis.

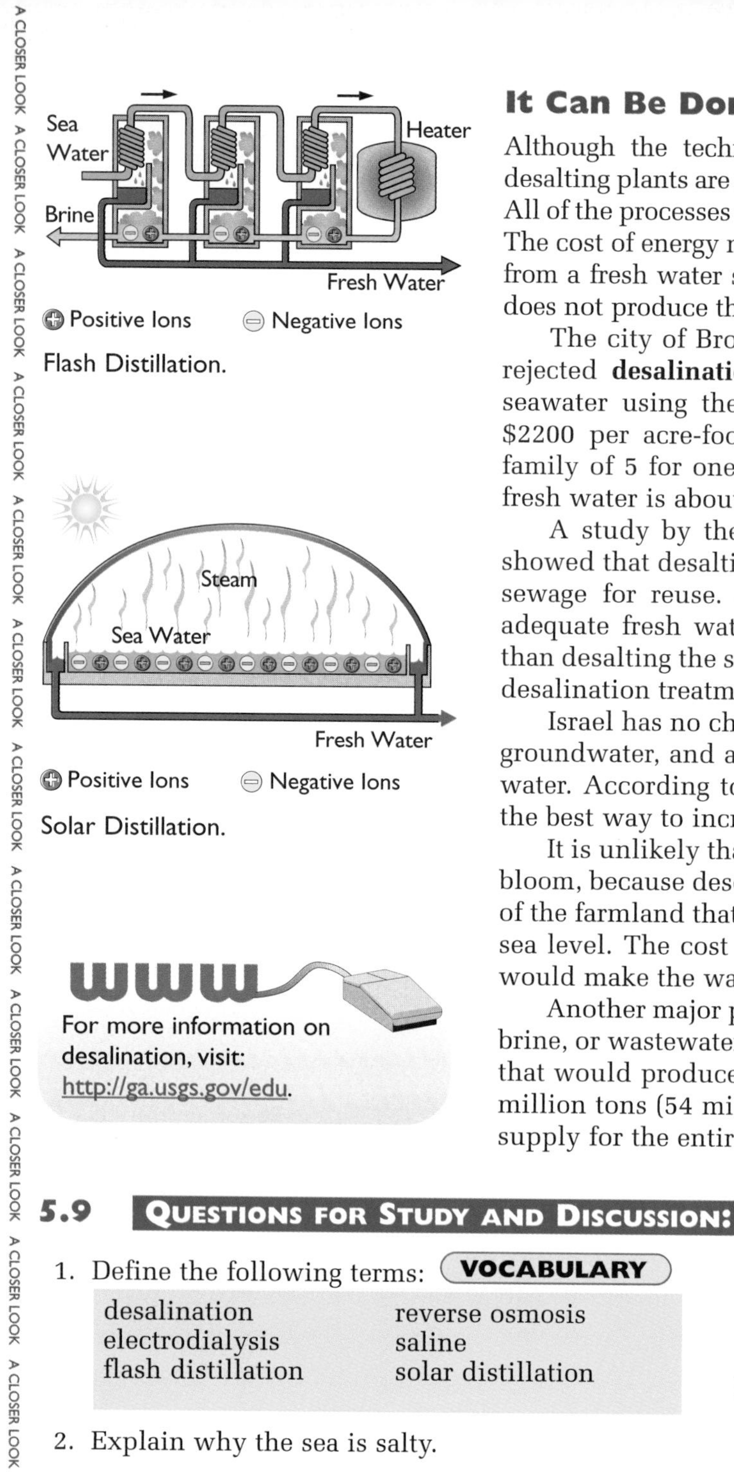

Flash Distillation.

Solar Distillation.

For more information on desalination, visit: http://ga.usgs.gov/edu.

It Can Be Done, but ...

Although the technology exists to desalt the sea, and more than 200 desalting plants are now in operation, there are problems that must be faced. All of the processes except solar distillation require huge amounts of energy. The cost of energy makes desalted water very expensive compared to water from a fresh water supply. Solar distillation is much less expensive, but it does not produce the large amounts of water needed in most areas.

The city of Brownsville, Texas, is close to the Gulf, but the city has rejected **desalination** of seawater because of the cost. Desalination of seawater using the reverse osmosis process costs between $1300 and $2200 per acre-foot (324,850 gallons; 1.2×10^6 L)—enough water for a family of 5 for one year. The cost of treating an acre-foot (1.2×10^6 L) of fresh water is about $200.

A study by the Metropolitan Water District of Southern California showed that desalting seawater would cost five times as much as treating sewage for reuse. Some communities in Southern California without adequate fresh water supplies are choosing to reuse wastewater rather than desalting the sea. Santa Barbara and several other towns are building desalination treatment plants.

Israel has no choice. Israel is using 100% of the available surface and groundwater, and as much as 67% of the water used is recycled sewage water. According to the acting water commissioner, desalting the sea is the best way to increase the water supply.

It is unlikely that desalted water will ever be used to make the deserts bloom, because deserts are not located near the sea. Like the deserts, most of the farmland that requires irrigation is far from the sea and higher than sea level. The cost of desalting and pumping the water to the farmland would make the water too expensive to be used for irrigation.

Another major problem with the desalting processes is disposal of the brine, or wastewater that contains large amounts of salt. A desalting plant that would produce enough water for New York City, would produce 60 million tons (54 million metric tons) of salt each year. This is a two-year supply for the entire United States.

5.9 Questions for Study and Discussion:

1. Define the following terms: **VOCABULARY**

desalination	reverse osmosis
electrodialysis	saline
flash distillation	solar distillation

2. Explain why the sea is salty.

How to Desalt the Sea

3. Identify four processes that can be used to remove the ions from saline water and explain how they remove the ions that make the water salty.
4. Explain why the sea is not likely to become a major source of fresh water for irrigation of farmland.

It Can Be Done, but ...

5. If you lived in a Southern California community that lacked an adequate supply of fresh water, would you be in favor of building a desalination plant to desalt seawater, or a plant to recycle wastewater? Justify your position.

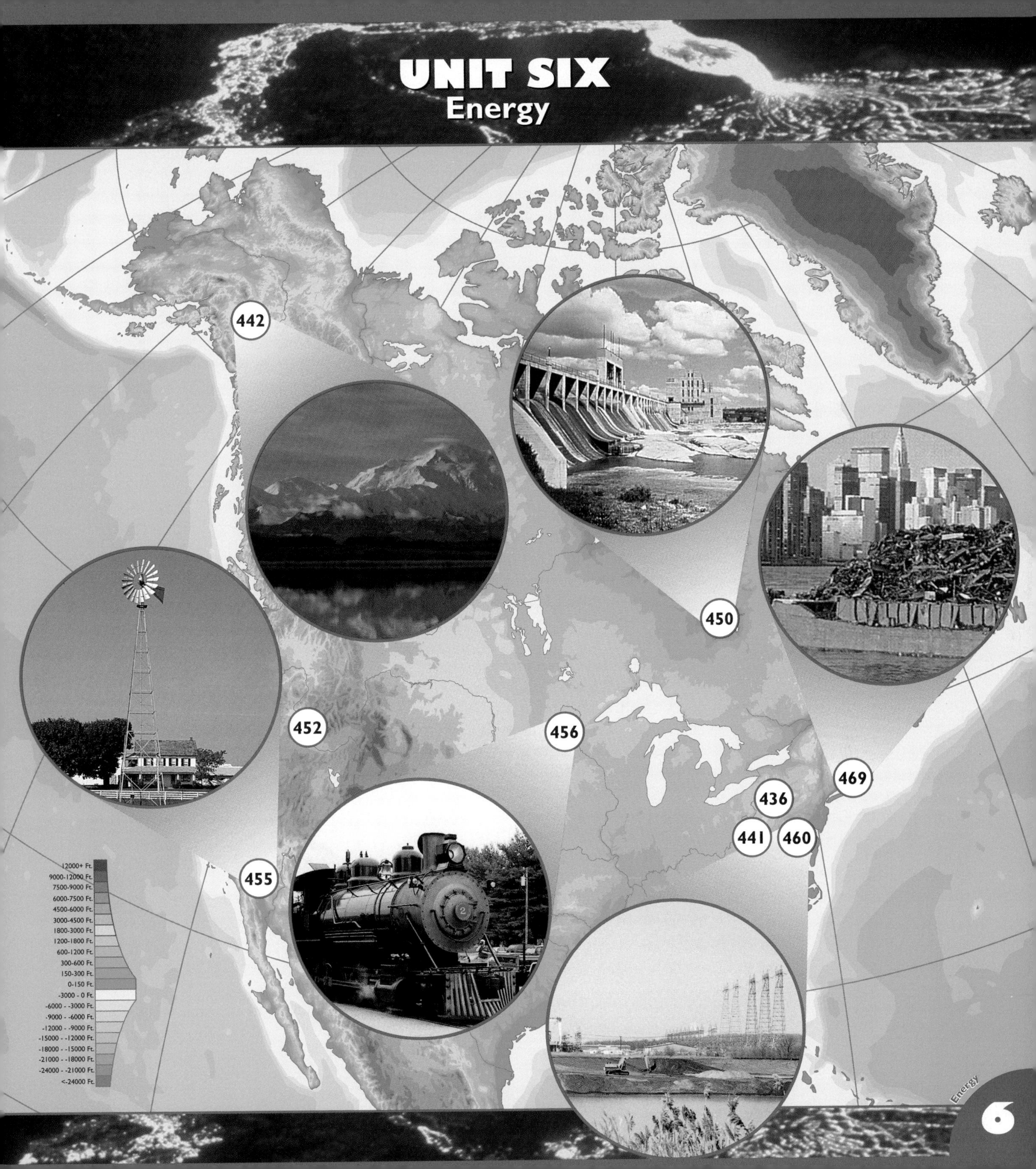
UNIT SIX
Energy
442
450
452
456
455
469
436
441
460
12000+ Ft.
9000-12000 Ft.
7500-9000 Ft.
6000-7500 Ft.
4500-6000 Ft.
3000-4500 Ft.
1800-3000 Ft.
1200-1800 Ft.
600-1200 Ft.
300-600 Ft.
150-300 Ft.
0-150 Ft.
-3000 - 0 Ft.
-6000 - -3000 Ft.
-9000 - -6000 Ft.
-12000 - -9000 Ft.
-15000 - -12000 Ft.
-18000 - -15000 Ft.
-21000 - -18000 Ft.
-24000 - -21000 Ft.
<-24000 Ft.
Energy
6

6.1 Energy — The Rest of the Story

OBJECTIVES

- **Compare** the amount and forms of energy used in modern and primitive societies.
- **State** the two laws that describe what happens to energy and **give** examples that demonstrate each law.
- **Compare** the energy efficiency of modern inventions.
- **Relate** lifestyle and energy use.

Life depends upon a constant flow of energy. In Section 1.6, pages 25–27, we examined energy as it flows through food chains in an ecosystem, but that is only part of the story. Humans, at least in some societies, have become dependent upon tremendous amounts of matter and energy to maintain a "comfortable" lifestyle.

Like other animals, we depend upon the sun's energy to produce our food. In our modern agricultural society, additional energy is needed to plant, grow, harvest, store, transport, prepare, and cook our food. Growing and preparing the food is much easier now than it once was. The grower uses mechanical equipment for planting and harvesting. Once the food reaches the kitchen, the cook stores it in the refrigerator, peels it with an electric peeler, chops it in the food processor, cooks it in the microwave and puts the dishes in the dishwasher. We depend upon many labor-saving devices to make our life easier and to do work for us. All of these devices consume energy.

Think About It

Hunter-gatherers had modest energy needs that were easily met by burning wood. Since the days of the earliest human societies, energy needs have steadily increased. Consider the following chart, indicating the amount of energy, in kilojoules (KJ) used daily, on average, by each person in the world throughout human history:

As developing countries industrialize, what can you predict will happen to the amount of energy used by each person? Think about what worldwide industrialization may mean for societies dependent on fossil fuels.

Society	Energy Used
Hunter-gatherer	21,000 KJ
Early agricultural	50,000 KJ
Pre-industrial agricultural	104,000 KJ
Post-industrial agricultural	290,000 KJ
Modern industrial	766,000 KJ

It's the Law

Energy is the ability to do work, and **work** is the movement of matter. After many observations of energy, scientists made two statements or "laws" that describe what happens to energy. The first law states that: Energy cannot be created nor destroyed, but it can be changed in form. This is sometimes called the **law of conservation of energy**.

Light energy can be changed into chemical energy. The energy in chemical compounds can be changed into heat energy. Heat energy can be changed into mechanical energy, and mechanical energy can be changed into electrical energy. These are just some of the changes that occur. You can think of others.

The **second energy law** states that: When energy is changed from one form to another, some of the usable energy is lost. In other words, some of the energy cannot do any work. This energy is usually in the form of heat that cannot be recovered and which may become a pollutant in our environment. [See page 460, A Closer Look: Brunner Island and Other Solutions To Thermal Pollution.]

The energy efficiency of an invention is a measure of the amount of energy that it can convert to useful work. A model with higher energy efficiency requires less fuel to do the same amount of work. The energy efficiencies of several important inventions are shown in the sidebar on the next page.

A Little History

Animals and slaves provided most of the energy to do the work their masters required in early societies. By the fourth century, the waterwheel had been developed and was mainly used for grinding grains. Later it supplied the power for machines that crushed ore, pumped air, sawed wood and washed clothes (to name only a few uses).

The invention of the water-powered saw, in the thirteenth century, helped supply the wood required by the growing population and the increasing industries in Europe. Soon the forests in Europe were devastated and Europeans turned to coal as a source of energy. Later the water-powered saw was used to cut the logs taken from forests in the American colonies.

The waterwheel and the windmill were the major sources of energy for Europe's Industrial Revolution. The location of the factories and cities was determined by the location of these energy sources. Waterwheels were also an important source of energy for industry in early America.

1776: At the time when the country declared its independence, most people burned wood for heating and cooking. Travel was by horse or on foot. The major use of coal was in the making of cannons. Because of the war against England, coal could no longer be imported from England and Nova Scotia, and there was a push for domestic mining.

Wood became more expensive as trees disappeared, and people turned to coal as the source of energy to heat their homes. Underground water in the coal mines often prevented the digging of deep deposits of coal. In 1698 a patent was granted to Thomas Savery for an engine that could pump water from the mines. Savery's wood-burning steam engine changed heat energy into the mechanical energy needed to move the water.

1786: Fitch's Steamboat had a wood-burning boiler that powered mechanical oars.

1807: Fulton's "Clermont" made a 150-mile (240 km) trip up the Hudson River. The trip took 32 hours, but it won support for the wood-burning steamboat.

1830: In a race between the "Tom Thumb" steam locomotive and a horse-drawn rail car, the horse won.

1868: Steam engines and waterwheels were equally important as power sources for industry.

By the 1860s, 600 years had passed between the invention of the windmill and the invention of the steam engine. Later inventors produced more powerful steam engines, and by the late 1800s steam engines had replaced the waterwheel as the major source of power for industry. The new steam engines burned coal, and coal quickly replaced wood as the major source of energy.

On the farm, steam engines were used to power threshing machines, and windmills were used to pump water. But horses, mules and humans supplied most of the energy for agriculture until after World War I. More than 25 million horses and mules supplied the power for agriculture in 1918. One fourth of the land being cultivated was used to produce feed for the animals. As tractors replaced horses, farmers could grow more food for people. With less human labor needed on the farm, the migration of people from farm to city began.

The discovery of new energy sources and the development of the technology to make use of them were necessary for the development of our

Net Energy Efficiency of Some Common Inventions

Invention	Efficiency
Steam Locomotive	8%
Diesel Locomotive	35%
Internal Combustion Engine	10%
Fuel Cell	60%
Oil Furnace	53%
Wood Stove (high efficiency)	26%
Natural Gas Furnace	70%
Natural Gas Furnace (high efficiency)	84%
Electric Heat from coal-fired plant	25%
Electric Heat from nuclear plant	14%
Incandescent Lamp	5%
Fluorescent Lamp	22%

Wood-burning stoves provided heat for the home and baked bread for the table.

Did You Know?

More than 2,000 years ago, the Chinese knew about the value of natural gas as a fuel. They used bamboo poles to pipe natural gas to places where it was needed. Most often, the natural gas was piped to the seaside and used to provide the energy needed to evaporate sea water to obtain salt.

modern industrial and agricultural society. Modern agriculture requires huge inputs of energy from other (off-farm) sources. This energy is needed to manufacture and transport chemical fertilizers and pesticides, to pump water for irrigation and to power the machines that have replaced the animals.

As the cities grew and industries increased, so did the demand for energy, and the pollution produced by its use. People migrated from the dirty cities to the suburbs. As the miles between home and work increased, so did the energy required for transportation. The economy (industrial growth) of the United States and the "comfortable" lifestyle of its people have been built upon an abundant—seemingly endless—supply of inexpensive energy.

In 1952, President Truman's Materials Policy Commission warned that the United States would be dependent upon oil from the Middle East by the 1970s. Although few people paid any attention, the prediction that had been made by President Truman's administration was correct. By the 1970s, with only 6% of the world's population, the United States consumed more than one third of the energy used worldwide. Much of this energy was imported oil.

By the 1990s, the United States had only 5% of the world's population and consumed 25% of the energy used worldwide. The nation's dependence on foreign oil became quite obvious during the Arab Oil Embargo in the 1970s and the Persian Gulf War.

6.1 Questions for Study and Discussion:

1. Define the following terms: **VOCABULARY**

energy	law of conservation of energy
energy efficiency	work
second energy law	

2. Make a list of the food served the last time your family ate dinner together. Identify the types of energy that were required and describe how they were used to produce and prepare the dinner.

It's the Law

3. Energy cannot be created or destroyed, and it can't be recycled. Explain why.
4. When energy is "lost" (can no longer be used to do work), what form does it usually take?

A Little History

5. Identify the first form of technology that reduced the amount of human labor needed to saw wood and grind grain. Describe other ways in which this technology was later used.
6. Identify the major source of energy used to heat homes in 1776; and identify the source which had replaced it by 1900.
7. Identify the major sources of energy used by factories during Europe's Industrial Revolution. What invention replaced these sources as the major source of energy for industry?
8. Why do you think the inventors of later models of the steam engine designed the engine to burn coal instead of wood?
9. Compare the major sources of energy used on farms prior to World War I with the major sources since World War II.
10. Give examples of ways in which farmers depend upon the oil driller and the coal miner.
11. It has been estimated that people living in the suburbs use 42% more energy than people living in the city. List as many reasons as you can why the demand for energy is greater in the suburbs.
12. What was the prediction made by President Truman's administration and was the prediction correct?

Fossil Fuels — Energy for a Nation

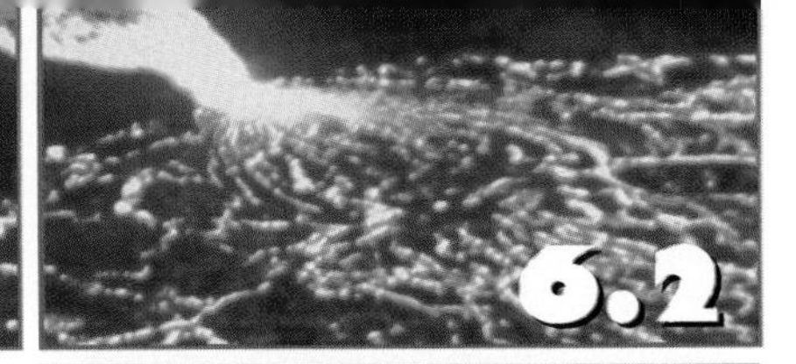

6.2

OBJECTIVES

- ✔ **Relate** changes in the nation's energy policy to the cost and availability of energy sources.
- ✔ **Classify** energy sources as renewable or nonrenewable.
- ✔ **Compare** sources of energy based on their energy content.
- ✔ **List** advantages and disadvantages of coal, oil and natural gas.
- ✔ **Compare** the energy efficiency of different methods of transportation.
- ✔ **Identify** environmental problems associated with the use of fossil fuels.
- ✔ **Evaluate** the role of synthetic fuels as future energy sources.

There was an energy crisis in the 1970s. Shortages of gasoline meant car owners often sat in line at the service station. A natural gas shortage caused schools and industries to shut down. The price of gasoline and fuel oil began a steep climb. In 1980, OPEC set the price of crude oil at $32.00 a barrel. A barrel of crude oil had cost only $3.00 in 1973. People didn't understand what was happening. They thought we were running out of fuel.

There was a flurry of activity in Washington, D.C. An Energy Research and Development Administration was established. Congress passed the Energy Policy and Conservation Act and the Solar Heating and Cooling Demonstration Act. The speed limit on interstate highways was reduced to 55 miles (88 km) per hour.

The federal government promoted energy-efficient technology. Car manufacturers were required to develop cars that would get better gas mileage. Manufacturers of appliances were required to label certain electrical appliances with an **EnergyGuide** that provides the information needed to compare the energy efficiency of different models. Homeowners were allowed tax breaks for making their homes more energy efficient.

Then during the 1980s the lines at service stations disappeared, and the prices of gasoline and fuel oil declined. Congress even voted to allow states to increase the speed limit on interstate highways. Unfortunately this does not mean that our energy problems are over. Another crisis can occur any time there is an interruption in the supply of any energy source, especially crude oil.

The Changing American Scene

A **renewable resource** is one that is produced at least at the same rate it is used. In 1850, almost all energy was derived from renewable sources—wood, wind, and water. But our demand for wood became greater than nature's ability to replace it. In effect, wood became a nonrenewable resource. Today most of the energy we use is derived from nonrenewable fossil fuels—oil, natural gas, and coal. For a long time it seemed that there was an endless supply of inexpensive energy, and the demand steadily increased.

By 1953, we were importing 1 million barrels of petroleum per day, 13% of the petroleum used. By 1973 the United States was importing more than 6 million barrels per day, which was 37% of the petroleum used. Then the Arab oil-producing countries shut off all shipments of oil to the United States—the **Arab Oil Embargo**. Government officials began making policy changes to try to decrease our dependence on foreign oil. As a result, the percentage of petroleum imported in 1983 was 19% less than in 1973.

Consumption of oil in the United States has increased dramatically, but our production has declined. According to the Department of Energy, between 1973 and 1993 petroleum production decreased 22% and imports increased 38%. As a result, the United States remains the world's largest importer of petroleum, importing 8.6 million barrels per day in 1993 and more than 10 million barrels per day in 1998.

Two-thirds of the world's proven oil reserves are located in the region surrounding the Persian Gulf. The political stability of this region is important to the United States, Japan, and other countries that have become dependent upon imported petroleum. On August 2, 1990, Iraq invaded Kuwait. Armed forces were sent to the Persian Gulf, in part to protect the free flow of oil.

Political disputes may once again interfere with the movement of oil tankers and create temporary shortages. But politics and the immediate future should not be our only concern. Petroleum is a fossil fuel and fossil fuels are nonrenewable resources. Transportation and combustion of fossil fuels create pollution. As a nation we must consider the environmental impacts as well as the political issues.

Coal is an important fuel for the production of electricity. The giant machines which remove the coal from deep beneath the soil can quickly destroy the environment. But new laws are forcing coal companies to restore the land.

It Began a Long Time Ago

Coal:

Millions of years ago giant ferns and trees grew in great swamps that covered much of the Earth. As the plants died and fell into the water, they formed layers of partially decayed plant material called **peat**. Movements of the Earth caused the swamps to sink, and they were covered with layers of mud, silt, sand, and water. The weight of the water and sediments created heat and pressure that changed the peat into coal. **Coal** refers to any black or brown rock that contains hydrocarbons formed from decayed plants. The mud, silt, and sand deposits were changed into other rocks such as sandstone or shale.

When coal is first formed from peat, it is very soft and crumbles easily. This soft coal is called **lignite**. The formation of lignite may take more than one million years. Most of the lignite in the United States is in North and South Dakota, Montana, and Texas. Lignite has a 25–35% carbon content and its heat content is lower than that of other coals.

Subbituminous, with a 35–45% carbon content, has a higher heat content than lignite. Large deposits of this coal are found in the western states, especially Montana and Wyoming.

Bituminous coal, sometimes called soft coal, is formed when more heat and pressure are placed on lignite. The formation of bituminous coal may take more than 100 million years. It has a 45–86% carbon content, thus a greater heat content than subbituminous. Most of the coal in the United States is bituminous coal.

More intense heat and pressure change bituminous coal into **anthracite**, or hard coal. Anthracite has the highest percentage of carbon (86–98%). Thus it has the highest heating value. Nearly all of the anthracite in the United States is in Pennsylvania, although some small deposits exist in other states.

Layers of plant material 3–7 feet (0.9–2.1 m) thick produced a one-foot (0.3 m) thick seam of bituminous coal. In some places where coal-forming swamps formed over buried swamps, several seams of coal were formed. Some seams are more than 400 feet (120 m) thick.

Other fossil fuels:

As plants and animals living in the ancient seas died, they drifted down to the bottom. Here they mixed with sand, mud and silt. Layers of sandstone, shale and limestone rich in organic matter (the decayed remains) were formed. As the older layers were buried deeper and deeper, the heat and pressure caused chemical changes. Mixtures of hydrocarbons—natural gas and petroleum—were formed from the organic matter.

The formation of petroleum and natural gas does not always result in deposits that can be found and recovered. The first requirement is a source rock. A **source rock** is a rock that is rich in organic matter. Second, sufficient heat and pressure must be present for a period of time that allows the organic matter to be changed into hydrocarbons.

The oil and gas must then move into a reservoir rock. A **reservoir rock** is a rock that contains many tiny pores with connecting passageways through which the oil and gas can move. A **trap**, or rock without pores, forms a dam or a lid that keeps the oil and gas from escaping. This lid must be tightly sealed in order for oil and gases to collect in the reservoir.

Finding these rock formations is the job of a petroleum scientist. A deposit of oil or gas that can economically be recovered with present technology is called a **reserve**. The process of selecting the site and drilling the well may cost more than $10 million. Depending on the location and the rock structure, well drilling may take a few weeks or several months. Only one out of three wells drilled in areas with known gas deposits will produce gas.

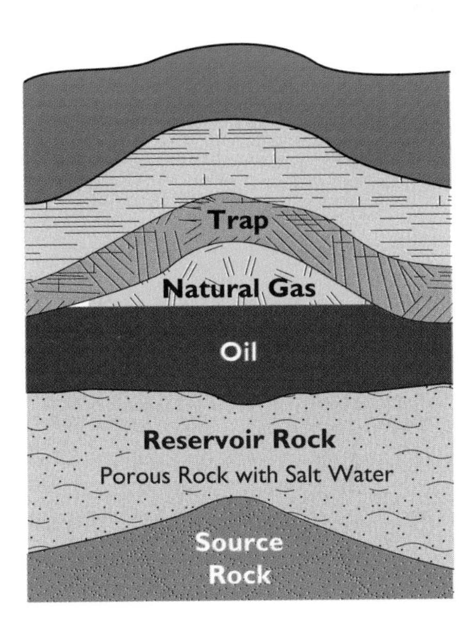

Oil and Gas Deposits.

Natural Gas

Supply and Demand:

Nearly 80% of the natural gas reserves in the world are owned by the countries of the former Soviet Union (59%) and Iran (20%). The United States has 6% of the world's reserves. More than one-half of the natural gas deposits in the U.S. lie beneath five states—Alaska, Oklahoma, Louisiana, Texas and New Mexico.

For years natural gas was considered worthless and burned off at the oil well. Improved drilling technology and federal tax incentives have increased the production of natural gas. There are about 300,000 wells producing gas in the United States with about seven thousand new wells drilled each year. About 10% of the natural gas used in the U.S. is imported, mainly from Canada. Liquefied natural gas (LNG) can be transported from other countries in tankers. Now natural gas supplies about 25% of the nation's energy, and demand for natural gas is increasing, as follows:

- **Industrial:** Industry consumes about 43% of the natural gas used in the United States. Natural gas is used by the food industry to pasteurize milk and bake bread. Textile mills use the heat from natural gas to pre-shrink fabric, and paper companies use it to dry paper. Byproducts of

Pipelines are the most efficient means of transporting natural gas. Do pipelines cause habitat fragmentation?

natural gas are used to make many products including synthetic fibers, ink, photographic film, adhesives, explosives, antifreeze, synthetic rubber and plastics. The manufacture of fertilizers in agriculture consumes vast quantities of natural gas.

- **Residential:** More than 58 million households depend upon natural gas. Homes consume about 27% of natural gas used, mostly for space heating. Other uses include water heating, cooking and clothes drying. It is the most economical source of energy for homes.
- **Electricity:** About 14% of natural gas is used to generate electricity. Power plants are installing new high-technology gas-fired turbines. These convert 60% of the natural gas to electricity. Using natural gas allows power plants to increase production of electricity without installing expensive air pollution controls.
- **Commercial:** About 16% of natural gas is used by businesses. Most is used for heating and cooling office buildings and stores. Some is used for cooking.
- **Transportation:** The United Parcel Service has converted some of its delivery trucks to run on compressed natural gas (CNG). The delivery route of vehicles converted to CNG must be less than 70 miles (112 km). Natural gas is a clean-fuel alternative to gasoline. There are about 60,000 vehicles operating on natural gas, and most of them are in fleets. The use of natural gas in fleets of vehicles can help urban areas meet air quality standards.

Processing:

As it comes from the well, natural gas is mostly methane, but it also contains small amounts of other hydrocarbons, such as propane and butane, water vapor and other elements, including sulfur. Before it is shipped to the customer, the gas is processed to remove these impurities.

Transportation:

By weight, natural gas produces 50% more heat energy than coal, and 30% more than oil. This means that less energy is used to transport each unit of energy. An underground network of pipes delivers natural gas to customers across the nation. Pipelines are the most efficient means of transport because it requires the least amount of energy to move the fuel.

Where pipelines don't exist, natural gas can be changed to a liquid by compressing and cooling it to -161°C (-260°F). This reduces its volume by 615 times. It is then transported in insulated tanker ships or trucks. Some liquefied natural gas (LNG) is imported from Africa. This method is much more hazardous and expensive than pipeline transport.

Environment and Health:

Natural gas is the cleanest burning fossil fuel. It produces much smaller quantities of pollutants than coal or oil. It can be burned without installing expensive air pollution controls. This makes natural gas an ideal fuel for heating homes. The ability to control the flame makes natural gas the perfect fuel for cooking and for other industrial processes where temperature control is important.

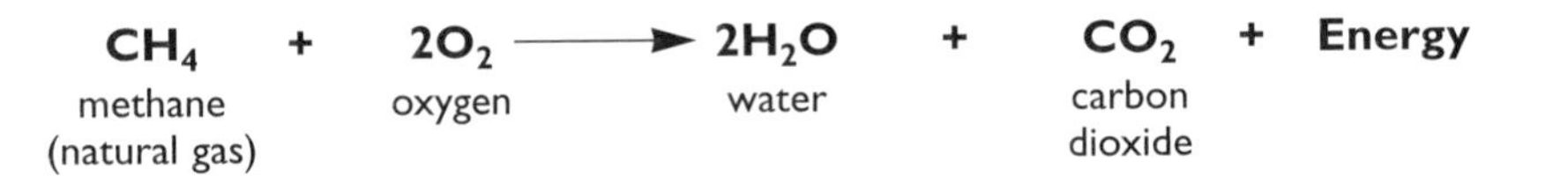

$$CH_4 + 2O_2 \longrightarrow 2H_2O + CO_2 + \text{Energy}$$

methane (natural gas) + oxygen → water + carbon dioxide + Energy

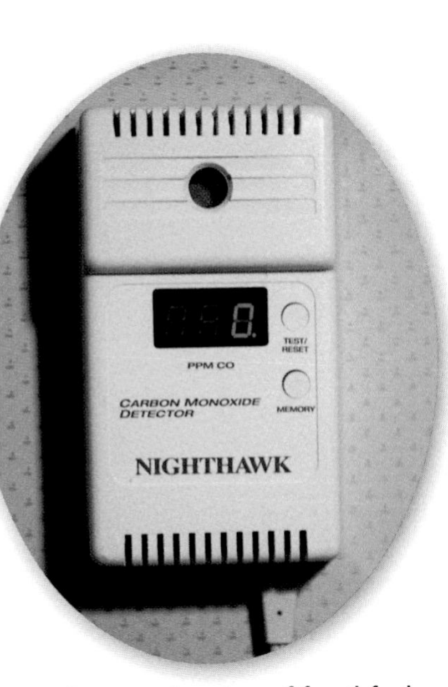

Incomplete combustion of fossil fuels produces carbon monoxide. Detectors like this one will alert a family to the presence of the dangerous gas which has no odor.

Natural gas has no odor or color. As a safety precaution, **mercaptan** (a sulfur-containing chemical) is mixed with the gas to create an odor similar to the smell of rotten eggs. This allows gas leaks to be detected. Although the risk of a gas leak is small, leaking gas is dangerous. A spark may ignite the vapors, and the resulting explosion and fire are destructive and sometimes deadly.

The Future:

According to the American Petroleum Institute's Potential Gas Committee, at current production rates, the United States has about a 55-year supply. This number will change as more reserves are discovered and improved technology increases the ability to recover gas. The search for reserves has intensified. Using new drilling methods, natural gas can now be recovered from some coal deposits.

Petroleum (Crude Oil)

Supply and Demand:

Two-thirds of the world's proven oil reserves are located in the region surrounding the Persian Gulf. Other important reserves are located in Latin America, Africa, North America, Asia, and in countries of the former Soviet Union.

Oil supplies about 40% of the U.S. energy needs and 97% of our transportation fuels. In 1997, the U.S. used 14.7 million barrels a day, but produced only 6.5 million barrels. The additional oil was imported. Although the consumption of oil declined in the 1980s, the demand for oil is again increasing. The amount of oil imported is expected to increase to 60% by 2015.

The railroad is the most economical means of transporting coal over land.

Products made from crude oil, gasoline, and diesel provide the energy for most methods of transportation. Crude oil also provides the raw materials used to make many products, including:

aspirins	detergent	panty hose	shoes
bubble gum	golf balls	perfumes	soft contact lenses
credit cards	house paint	rugs	sun glasses
deodorants	lipstick	shampoo	video cassettes

An offshore oil rig in the Gulf of Mexico. A constant threat to the environment, oil wells and tankers carrying oil are essential to our way of life.

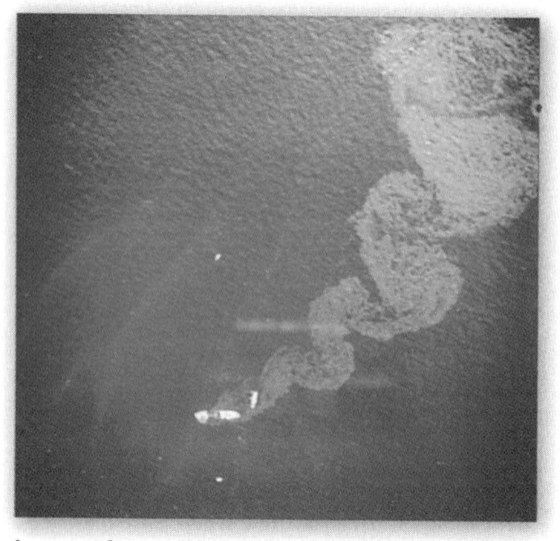

Image from Nimbus weather satellite showing an oil spill at sea.

Production:

When a well is drilled, the petroleum is usually under pressure and it may flow from the well without being pumped. When the petroleum can no longer flow from the well by itself, pumps bring the oil to the surface.

Secondary Recovery Methods

IN
OUT
1st method
Acid
Oil & Water
Petroleum

IN
OUT
3rd method
$CO_2 + H_2O$
Oil, Gases & Water
Petroleum

Technology has been developed to remove more of the oil from the rock. Methods that allow more oil to be removed are called **secondary recovery methods**. In one method (1), acid is injected into the well to dissolve channels in the rock. In another method, fluids are pumped into the well under high pressure to fracture the rock. A third method (3) involves pumping water, carbon dioxide or other gases into the well to force the oil toward the opening. A fourth method uses solvents to dissolve the oil from the rock. Still other methods involve heating the oil so that it flows more freely. Each of these methods is expensive, but they may allow as much as 80% of the oil to be recovered.

Processing:

The processing of crude oil begins with distillation. The crude oil is heated to 650°F (340°C). As the oil is heated, the vapors pass through a series of perforated trays in a fractionating tower. The different hydrocarbons condense at different temperatures. The lighter compounds condense near the top of the tower, and the heaviest compounds condense at the bottom of the tower.

Some of the chemicals separated by distillation require further processing. By rearranging the atoms of molecules, more useful chemicals can be produced. More than 10,000 products are produced from the chemicals removed from crude oil and natural gas. The processes that are used to separate crude oil into its parts and to produce petroleum products are called **refining**.

In the production of gasoline, smaller molecules are combined to make larger ones. This produces the high-octane fuel needed for automobiles. Modern refineries use chemicals called **catalysts** to speed

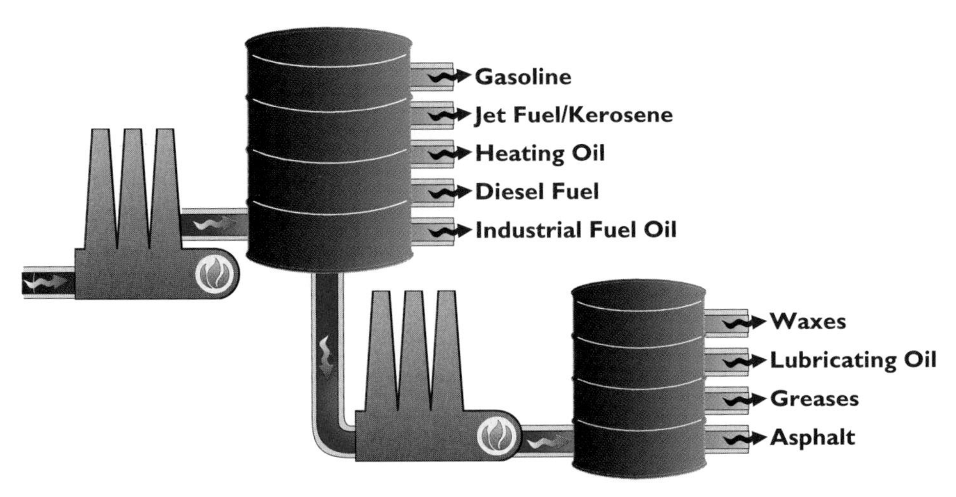

Simplified Diagram of an Oil Refinery.

up these chemical reactions. Catalysts allow refineries to produce gasoline 7,000 times faster than they could by older methods.

Transportation:

Crude oil may be transported to the refinery through pipelines or by tanker. The method of transporting products from the refinery is determined by their destination. Pipelines are the most energy-efficient means of transport, and are used to transport 60% of the crude oil and petroleum products.

Ships and barges transport another one-third of the supply. Transport by ship or barge is more efficient than railroads, but railroads can move the oil faster and transport it to locations that are not near waterways. Tank trucks require more than 4 times the energy used by railroads. They are used for short-distance hauling in areas without access to railroads.

Tankers are an efficient means of transporting crude oil, but there is always the possibility of a spill.

Environment and Health:

A large quantity of oil is spilled into the environment each year from shipping, oil drilling operations and pipeline breaks. Although major oil spills do not occur often, when they do occur, they cause massive kills of marine animals that live near the shore. Birds cannot fly or keep themselves warm when their feathers become matted with oil.

Oil spills may also affect water supplies. It was a bitterly cold January day in 1988 when a storage tank holding 3.85 million gallons ($1.8x10^7$L) of diesel fuel burst at the Ashland Oil Company near Pittsburgh. About 1 million gallons (4.5 million L) of oil flowed over the dike, and through a sewer, into the Monongahela River. Some 23,000 Pittsburgh residents were without water when water companies closed their intake valves. The extremely cold weather hampered cleanup efforts, and the huge oil slick moved down the Ohio River, affecting wildlife and communities along the river.

The burning of oil produces less pollution than the burning of coal, but oil is not a clean fuel. The automobile is the major source of air

Environmental Challenge: Oil Spills

Create and present a lesson on oil spills for an elementary or middle school class using the resources found available at the EPA's Oil Spill Learning Center: www.epa.gov/oilspill/eduhome.htm.

www

pollution produced by the burning of petroleum. As newer models with better pollution controls replace older cars, the pollution levels are being reduced. Cleaner fuels are being tested in urban areas where the combined auto emissions do not meet air quality standards.

Future:

Geologists have extensively studied rock formations. Estimates vary, but oil reserves are between 1 and 2 trillion barrels. These estimates are based on finding new reserves. Most experts agree that the shallow oil and gas reservoirs have already been found, but with new technology, oil rigs can drill wells 3,000 feet deep—ten times deeper than in the 1960s.

Oil companies have drilled for oil in a previously unexplored area near Alaska's Prudehoe Bay oil fields. Sound-wave evidence suggested that there was a large reservoir of oil—maybe as much as 1.5 billion barrels. Rocks were stained with oil. After drilling for 13 months, at a depth of 1.5 miles (2.4 km), drillers found water but no oil. At one time the reservoir contained oil, but there was no trap and the oil had escaped. The dry hole had cost the oil companies $1.7 billion.

Oil companies had drilled 85,800 wells in the United States as of 1982. Nearly 8,000 of these were "wildcat" wells. A **wildcat well** is a well drilled in an unexplored area. More than 6,500 of the wildcat wells were dry. Only 755 of the wells produced enough oil to pump. Now 3-D seismic modeling, CAT scans, and magnetic resonance imaging technologies have improved the success rate for finding oil reserves to nearly 1 in 4 wells.

Clearly no one knows when we will run out of oil. It depends on how much we use and what we're willing to pay. We won't suddenly run out of oil in the same way that you might run out of milk. An oil well is not like a carton of milk that can be emptied all at once. Only about 10% of the oil remaining in the reserve can be recovered each year. Each year the amount of oil pumped declines until it no longer produces enough oil to pay for pumping, and the oil company shuts down the well.

The American Petroleum Institute suggests that the government should permit exploration and development of oil and gas reserves in protected areas such as National Parks and National Wilderness Areas. Nearly 4 million acres ($1.6x10^6$ ha) of a 23-million-acre ($9.3x10^6$-ha) reserve in Alaska, set aside as an emergency source by President Warren Harding, has been opened for leasing to oil and gas companies. Several environmental groups have gone to court to stop exploration in one of the largest remaining untouched wilderness areas.

Even if these protected lands are explored, and reserves are found, it will not change the fact that someday there will be no more oil. The American Petroleum Institute predicts that oil will last for 63–95 years, but they caution that this estimate is based on advances in technology and current consumption rates.

Our need for oil will continue to increase, even with efforts to conserve. It will become necessary to drill deeper and use secondary recovery techniques to recover more oil. This will cause the price of oil to rise. As the price of oil increases, users will begin to look for cheaper alternatives. For some uses, the most abundant and least expensive fossil fuel is coal.

WWW

For more information on natural gas and crude oil, including graphics of oil spills in U.S. Waters, visit: www.api.org.

Coal

Supply and Demand:

Coal is our most abundant fossil fuel. Nearly 75% of all known coal reserves are in three regions—the United States, China, and countries of the former Soviet Union. The U.S. has 12% of the world's coal reserves. The U.S. is the largest exporter of coal, exporting over 70 million tons (63.5 million metric tonnes) of coal each year.

Coal is used mainly for the generation of electricity. Almost 60% of the nation's electricity is produced at steam-turbine plants that burn bituminous coal. Some coal is also used by industries as a source of heat for industrial processes. As the price of natural gas and crude oil increased, more electrical power plants and industries switched to coal.

Because it is the cleanest burning, anthracite is used for heating homes. Since anthracite is more expensive, industrial processes often use bituminous coal. Subbituminous and lignite must be burned in larger amounts because of their lower heat content. They are mainly used for production of electricity. Subbituminous contains less sulfur and is cleaner burning than bituminous. Power plants are built near lignite mines, due to lignite's low heat content and large quantity required.

Steel mills heat bituminous coal to about 2000°F (1100°C) in airtight ovens. Without oxygen, the coal does not burn, but the heat changes some of the solids into gases. The remaining solid mass that is almost pure carbon is called **coke**. The coke is burned with iron ore and limestone to produce the iron needed for making steel. When the coal cools, some of the gases condense to form ammonia (NH^3), used to make fertilizers. Other by-products are used to make dyes, drugs, synthetic fibers and film, adhesives, insecticides, varnish, plastics and other products. The gases that remain are burned to provide heat for the coke-making process.

Heavy equipment must remove the soil and rock that lies above the coal.

Mining:

Most coal is produced from two major types of mining—surface and underground (deep). Surface mining is safer and less expensive, and allows more coal to be recovered than deep mining.

Most surface mining is **strip mining** where the soil and rock, which lie over the coal deposit, are removed by huge earth-moving machines. In the past, strip mining often left pits that were ugly and useless. A law, passed in 1977, requires coal companies to restore all land that is strip mined.

The process of restoring the land to the condition that existed before mining is called **reclamation**. Before mining begins, scientists study the soil, plants, wildlife and water resources. When mining begins, the topsoil is removed and stored in piles that are graded and planted to prevent erosion. After the coal is dug, and the pits are filled with rock, the soil is replaced and prepared for planting. If necessary, the land is

In the past, the coal companies abandoned the land.

The strip pits left behind were hazardous and often too acidic for fish.

irrigated. Reclaimed land can be used for lakes or reservoirs, agriculture or recreation. A special tax, paid on each ton of coal produced, is used to help restore old abandoned coal mines (strip pits).

Some coal, which is buried very deeply, can only be recovered by deep mining. The most common type of underground mining uses the **room and pillar system**. As the miners dig large rooms, they leave pillars of coal to support the roof. Long bolts are also placed in the roof to bind the layers of rock together and keep the roof from falling. Only 50–60% of the coal can be removed when the room and pillar system is used.

The **longwall system** is used in deeper mines. Workers cut coal from a wall 300–700 feet (91–210 m) long which joins the main tunnel. Movable steel supports are used to hold the roof in place over the area being mined. As the coal is mined, the supports are moved, and the roof over the mined area is allowed to fall. Up to 80% of the coal can be recovered in a longwall mine.

Processing:

Most users of coal require the coal to be a specific size. At a processing plant near the mine, coal is crushed, and sorted according to size. It is then washed to remove impurities. Most of the impurities are heavier than the coal, and they settle to the bottom of the washing bin. Some forms of sulfur are removed by washing, but some sulfur is bound to the carbon and is released when the coal is burned. Bituminous coal is often high in sulfur content, and special equipment is necessary to control air pollution when it is burned.

Transportation:

A pipeline carries coal from a mine in Arizona to a power plant in Nevada. The coal is crushed and mixed with water to form a **slurry** that is pumped through the pipeline. Additional pipelines may be built, but in some locations water is not available, and in other cases pumping of the slurry may be less efficient than transport by train or barge.

Frequently coal must be shipped long distances. Barges provide the cheapest way of shipping coal. If shipment must be made over land, railroads offer the most economical means of transport. An increasing number of power plants located east of the Mississippi River are using subbituminous coal from the West, to meet the demand for low sulfur coal.

Environment and Health:

Since 1900, more than 100,000 workers have been killed in coal mine accidents in the U.S. The federal government passed the Coal Mine Health & Safety Act in 1969, and the number of mine deaths has been greatly reduced. Most workers are killed by accidents involving equipment. The federal government now requires each mine to have a training program for miners and a scientific plan for the roof support of each underground mine.

Methane is an explosive gas that occurs naturally in coal seams. Automatic detectors are used to warn workers of a buildup of this gas. Blasting may produce high levels of carbon monoxide if the mine is not properly ventilated. Thousands of miners have developed a condition known as **black lung** as a result of breathing coal dust. Coal dust is also explosive. Now federal law requires that walls in deep mines be sprayed with powdered limestone. Water is sprayed on surfaces being mined to control the dust. The process is called **rock dusting**.

Beneath the surface, a fire burns in the abandoned coal mine.

Water pollution occurs when water pumped from underground mines or water from open pits left during strip mining enters a stream without first being treated. In the past, thousands of fish and aquatic organisms have been killed as slugs of acid water moved down nearby streams. Today mines are required to treat water and remove sediments before it is released into the natural environment.

In 1977 Congress passed a law requiring all U.S. electric power plants built after 1971 to meet federal pollution standards by 1982. To meet the standards, pollution control devices must be used when burning coal that contains more than 1% sulfur. [See pages 184–87, "Clearing the Air—Stationary Sources."] But pollution controls do not remove all pollutants from the air, and there is concern about the respiratory damage that may be caused by air pollution that results from burning coal.

Subsidence, or the sinking of land, occurs when the resources beneath the land have been removed, and the ground above can no longer support its own weight. Fourteen homes in Pittsburgh, Pennsylvania, were abandoned because the land on which they were built was sinking, and the houses were no longer safe. The houses in Pittsburgh were just a few of the thousands built above abandoned coal mines in Pennsylvania, Kentucky, and West Virginia.

After more than twenty years, and $7 million, government officials gave up their attempts to try to stop the fire burning in the abandoned coal mine beneath the streets of Centralia, Pennsylvania. The town's only gas station had been forced to close when temperatures in the basement reached 142°F (61°C). Carbon monoxide and other gases seeped into basements. The heat from the fire would melt snow in the winter. In 1983, most of the citizens sold their houses to the government and left the town. Although Centralia has been the only town threatened by a mine fire, there are more than 500 fires burning in coal deposits and waste heaps remaining at abandoned coal mines in the U.S.

Main Street, Centralia, Pennsylvania, is abandoned.

Future:

As production of crude oil and natural gas declines, coal will become a more important source of energy for America and the world. Each ton of coal used to generate electricity or manufacture goods saves four barrels of oil. Although the supply of coal is limited, at the present rate of use, the estimated reserves are sufficient to last more than two hundred years. The actual amount of coal available may be significantly less due to limitations of technology and environmental limitations placed on mining.

An example of an environmental limitation would be land-use restrictions placed on the area where the coal deposit is located. For example, coal cannot be mined if it lies beneath a national park. In other cases, mining restrictions exist to protect buildings, streams, and wildlife habitats (mainly for surface mining).

WWW
For more information on coal, visit: www.ket.org and http://energy.usgs.gov.

Technological restrictions exist if coalbeds are too thin, too deep or too close together to mine. Other geological factors, such as location of an important aquifer, can also restrict mining.

Synthetic Fuels from Fossil Fuels

History:

Coal may one day be used to replace oil and natural gas. The technology for conversion is not new. Many European and American cities were lit with coal gas or "town gas" during the 1800s and early 1900s. But production of coal gas was dirty and its heat value was low. When long-distance pipelines were built, coal gas could not compete with natural gas that was cheaper, cleaner, and had a higher heating value.

During World War II, synthetic fuel plants changed coal into liquid fuels that supplied many of Germany's fuel needs. After the war, the U.S. government organized a team of more than 100 scientists to study the process. Two coal-liquefaction plants were built, and they succeeded in making a fuel that was used in a diesel locomotive. Then cheap oil from the Middle East became available, and the plants were shut down.

Fuels that are produced by chemically changing fossil fuels or other organic materials are called **synthetic fuels** or **synfuels**. Synthetic fuels are comparable in chemical structure and energy value to petroleum products and natural gas. Fossil fuels, which can be converted to synfuels, are coal, oil shale, and tar sands.

Liquid Coal:

Crushed coal is mixed with a solvent to form a **slurry**. Hydrogen is then added to the slurry as it is heated to a high temperature under pressure. The coal is changed into a liquid that resembles crude oil. This process can be used to produce as much as 3 barrels of synthetic oil from one ton of coal. The synthetic oil contains only 70% of the energy in the coal. South Africa relied almost entirely on coal liquefaction and gasification during the days of apartheid when the imports were not permitted. In the U.S., research continues to try to reduce the cost of producing liquid coal.

Coal Gas:

Coal is heated in a large reactor with oxygen and steam. Impurities are removed, and the gases react with hydrogen to form methane (natural gas). A demonstration plant in California has produced a high-quality gas comparable to natural gas, and emissions have met California's clean air requirements. The gasifiers must be operated continuously, and the gas must be used as it is produced. The gasification plant can be built close to the coal mine. Distributing the electricity rather than shipping the coal saves huge transportation costs.

Rocks that Burn:

Liquid oil lies trapped in rock formations known as **oil shales** and **tar sands**. Large deposits of oil shale reserves are located in Colorado, Utah, and Wyoming. The problem is getting it out. The settlers found Indians making campfires with oil shales. But to provide the oil needed for today's lifestyle, vast amounts of the rocks must be mined, crushed and heated in order to release the oil or tar. Another technology for recovery involves removing some of the rock and using a controlled burn to release the oil from the remaining oil shale in the mine. About one ton of oil shale will produce 25 gallons (112 L) of oil.

Find more information on synfuels at: www.doe.gov.

Problems:

A serious problem with producing synfuels is cost. It is expensive to build the huge plants needed to produce synfuels, and the production process is expensive. Mines to provide the huge amounts of coal needed to heat the rocks and to provide the oil shale for processing would have to be far larger than any mines existing today.

Another problem is the need for water. About two quarts (2.2 L) of water are needed for each pound (2.2 kg) of coal processed. Three barrels of water are needed for each barrel of oil extracted from oil shale. Many of the coal and oil shale deposits are in areas where water is not plentiful. Since the coal will most likely be strip-mined, water will also be necessary for reclaiming the land.

Although synfuels burn clean, the process of production is dirty. Gases produced may cause air pollution. Millions of tons of ash containing traces of cadmium, lead and mercury would have to be disposed of without polluting water supplies.

The production of synfuels from oil shale would require thousands of workers. Exposure of workers to toxic chemicals is a serious concern. Some of the chemicals produced during production of synfuels are carcinogens.

6.2 QUESTIONS FOR STUDY AND DISCUSSION:

1. Define the following terms: **VOCABULARY**

anthracite	lignite	reservoir rock	subbituminous
Arab Oil Embargo	longwall system	rock dusting	subsidence
black lung	oil shale	room and pillar system	synfuels
bituminous coal	peat	secondary recovery method	tar sands
catalysts	reclamation	slurry	trap
coal	refining	source rock	wildcat well
coke	renewable resource	strip mining	
EnergyGuide	reserve		

2. What events caused the energy crisis during the 1970s?
3. How did Congress encourage the conservation of energy?

The Changing American Scene

4. Compare the sources that provided most of the energy used in 1850 with the major sources of energy used today. Which of these were renewable resources?

5. Compare the amounts of oil imported by the U.S. in 1953 and 1973; in 1973 and 1983; and in 1993.
6. Explain why the United States is concerned about the political stability of the Middle East.
7. In addition to reducing our dependence on foreign oil, give two additional reasons for seeking alternatives to fossil fuels.

It Began a Long Time Ago

8. Describe the conditions that are necessary for the formation of coal.
9. Compare the carbon content of the four types of coal. Which type of coal is the most common in the U.S.?
10. Identify the structure that must be present for a recoverable deposit of petroleum or natural gas to form.

Natural Gas

11. Compare our dependence on imported natural gas to our dependence on imported oil.
12. What part of the energy used in the U.S. is supplied by natural gas?
13. Explain why there is an increasing demand for natural gas.
14. Are we running out of natural gas? Explain.

Petroleum (Crude Oil)

15. In addition to the Middle East, what other regions might export oil to the United States?
16. In 1997, what percentage of the energy used was supplied by oil? What percentage of the oil used in 1997 was imported? How will this change in the future?
17. Give two reasons why crude oil is so important to our lifestyle.
18. What is the purpose of using secondary recovery methods? Describe two processes that are used in secondary recovery.
19. Describe how gasoline is produced from crude oil.
20. Rank the methods used to transport oil and other chemicals from most energy-efficient to least energy-efficient.
21. Give two ways in which oil pollutes the environment. How can we reduce this source of pollution without a major change in lifestyle?
22. Do you think that oil companies should be permitted to drill for oil and gas in National Parks and National Wilderness Areas? Give reasons to support your opinion.

Coal

23. Identify the regions with the largest coal reserves. How do the U.S. coal reserves compare to the reserves found in the other countries? What country is the largest exporter of coal?
24. What percent of our electricity is produced at coal-burning power plants?
25. Identify the major use of each type of coal and discuss advantages and disadvantages of using each type.
26. Describe the physical conditions that must be present to make coke from coal. What manufacturing process requires coke?
27. Compare the different methods of mining and give the advantages of each method.
28. How has the reclamation law changed the mining of coal?
29. Compare the methods of shipping coal.
30. Identify changes in the mining of coal that have made mining safer for the miners.
31. Identify the problems associated with abandoned coal mines.
32. Will coal become more or less important in the future? What fossil fuels will still be available for your grandchildren, great-grandchildren?

Synthetic Fuels from Fossil Fuels

33. What was the source of "town gas" and why was it replaced by natural gas?
34. Why weren't the coal liquefaction plants built after World War II successful and why might they be successful in the future?
35. Compare the energy content of liquid coal and crushed coal. In 1997, the U.S. imported 8.2 million barrels of crude oil each day. Assuming that a barrel of liquid coal would produce the same products as a barrel of crude oil, how many tons of coal would have to be mined each day to produce the oil imported in 1997?
36. Describe two methods of getting the oil out of oil shale.
37. Identify two possible environmental problems which may occur during the production of large amounts of synfuels produced from oil shales.

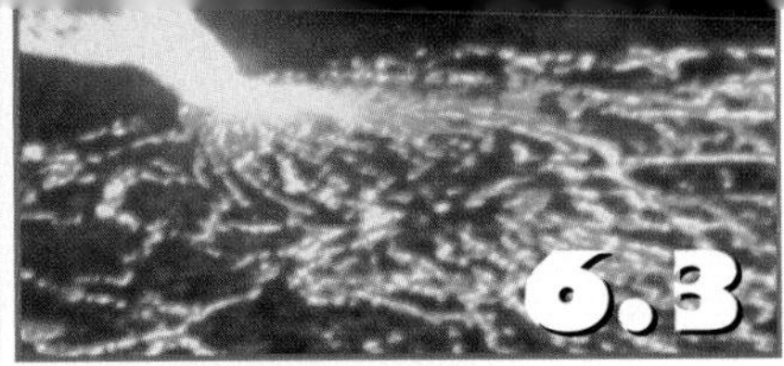

Achieving Energy Independence

6.3

"By the end of the decade we will … meet our own energy needs without depending on any foreign energy sources."

President Nixon spoke those words when he introduced Project Independence at the time of the Arab Oil Embargo. A quarter of a century later (1998), the Department of Energy statistics reveal that nearly 60% of the petroleum used in the United States was imported. Clearly we are still dependent on foreign energy sources.

Hawaii may have felt the effects of the Arab Oil Embargo to a greater extent than any other state. The Hawaiian Islands were formed by volcanic action. They have no oil, no coal, and no natural gas. In the 1970s, more than 90% of the energy used on the islands was imported. Crude oil is the major energy resource that is imported by Hawaii.

To achieve greater independence from foreign oil, the United States must develop alternative sources of energy. Following the energy shortages of the 1970s, Hawaii began to develop the technology needed to produce electricity without using foreign oil. By 1995, the Big Island was producing about 30% of its electricity from renewable energy sources. Using geothermal energy for a 30-megawatt electrical power plant eliminates the need to import 500,000 barrels (7.9×10^7 L) of fuel oil every year.

OBJECTIVES

- ✔ **Explain** why electricity is a secondary energy source.
- ✔ **Identify** the major sources of energy used to produce electricity.
- ✔ **Describe** the advantages of alternative energy sources.
- ✔ **Infer** the potential of alternative energy sources to replace fossil fuels.
- ✔ **Evaluate** environmental impacts of alternative energy sources.

To find out more about the energy resources and technology in Hawaii, visit: www.hawaii.gov/dbedt.

Thank You, Thomas Edison

The production of most electricity depends upon a spinning turbine. A **turbine** is a machine with several curved blades on a large rotating shaft. It looks something like a giant fan or paddle wheel. The spinning turbine is connected to a generator. The **generator** consists of stationary coils of copper wire and an electromagnet. When the electromagnet is rotated, it creates a magnetic field that causes the electrons to flow through the wire. This flow of electrons transmitted along wires is **electricity**.

The first commercial electric generating station, designed by Thomas Edison, burned coal to heat water and produce steam. The steam turned the turbines, and enough electricity was produced to light 1200 street lamps. The first hydroelectric power plant began operation the same year. This was the beginning of a new energy era.

In 1995, 67% of electricity in the United States was produced at power plants that burned fossil fuels, mostly coal. Nuclear power plants produced about 22% of the electricity. **Renewable** energy—wind, geothermal, solar, biomass and flowing water (hydropower)—produced the remaining 10%. We can reduce our dependence on foreign oil and reduce the air pollution caused by the combustion of coal if we use alternative energy sources. As you will see, each energy source has advantages and disadvantages.

Thomas Edison might be amazed at the complexity of a control room at a modern coal-burning power plant.

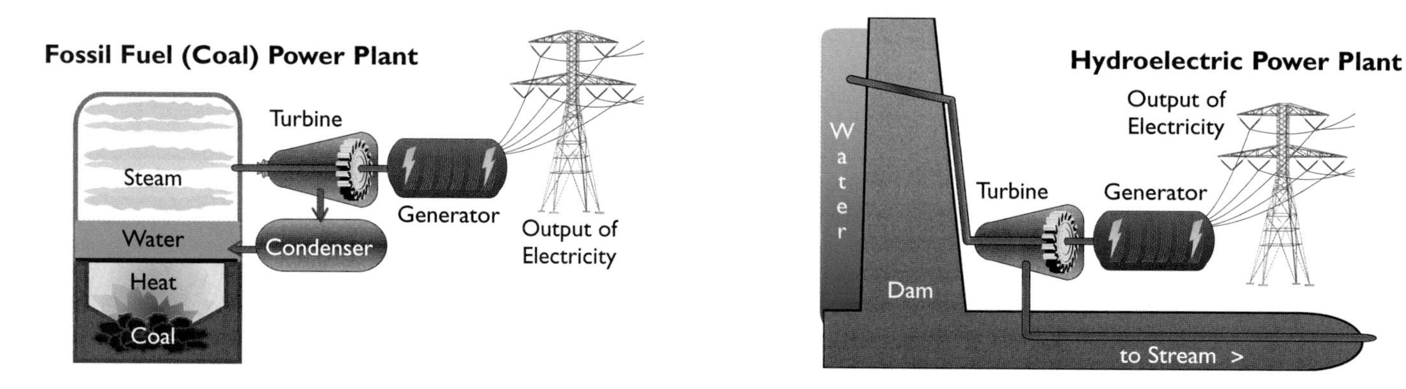

Hydroelectric power plants do not produce any air pollution, but they do cause changes in aquatic ecosystems.

Hydroelectric Power

Hydroelectric power is produced when the energy of falling water turns a water turbine. In the early 1900s, falling water provided the energy for one-half of all electricity generated in the United States. The role of hydroelectric power has declined to 10%. The energy of flowing water at hydroelectric plants replaces 500 million barrels ($7.9x10^{10}$ L) of oil each year.

Usually hydroelectric power is cheaper than electricity from fossil-fuel power plants. Another advantage is that hydroelectric power plants do not produce the air pollution or the heat associated with fossil-fuel power plants. But hydroelectric power plants can have significant impacts on the environment. [See page 340, "Dam the Rivers or Let Them Run Free."]

The amount of hydroelectric power produced in the U.S. is not likely to increase because most sites suitable for large plants have already been developed. Most additional hydroelectric power will be produced by facilities added to existing dams. Canadian hydroelectric power plants sell electricity to utilities in the northern states. Since Canada has the potential to develop much more hydroelectric power, the U.S. may import larger amounts of electricity in the future.

Some homeowners with streams flowing through their property have built small hydro systems to provide their own electricity. Small systems can be economical and efficient. The amount of power produced depends upon the **flow**, the volume of water, and the **head**—the vertical distance the water falls. Some systems can be built with little disturbance to the stream ecosystem. Since streams and rivers are protected by federal and state regulations, anyone planning to build a hydroelectric system must obtain the necessary permits.

www

For more information on the production of electricity, and to identify sources that are considered "green," visit: www.utilityguide.com and www.nrel.gov.

Energy Sources for the Production of Electricity in the United States

Fossil Fuel Plants	%
Coal	55
Gas	10
Oil	2
Other Energy Sources	**%**
Nuclear	22
Hydro	10
Other Renewables	1

Nuclear Power

Instead of the coal, oil, or natural gas used in a fossil-fuel power plant, the fuel used in nuclear power plants is mainly uranium. When the uranium atoms **fission** or split apart, they release huge amounts of energy. This energy heats water and creates steam that drives the turbines.

Nuclear power is considered a relatively clean source of energy because it produces no air pollution. Unlike a coal-burning power plant, a nuclear power plant does not release carbon dioxide and sulfur dioxide into the environment. In fact, the burning of coal releases more radioactive substances into the environment than the normal operation of a nuclear power plant. The mining of both coal and uranium has destroyed ecosystems.

Although it is a **nonrenewable** resource, the supply of uranium is large enough to last for many years. When President Nixon introduced Project Independence, nuclear energy was expected to play a major role in achieving energy independence. There are several reasons why the use of nuclear energy did not replace fossil fuels as the major source of energy for the production of electricity.

One factor was cost. Nuclear power plants are far more expensive to construct than fossil-fuel plants. Although the price of oil reached new highs in the 1970s, the prices began to fall in the 1980s. Nuclear energy could not compete with the low cost of fossil fuels. Electricity from nuclear power plants in the U.S. costs about twice as much as electricity from coal-burning plants.

Plans to build some nuclear power plants were canceled because the growth in demand for electricity had been much lower than expected. The growth rate was 7% each year in the early 1970s, but it has been less than 2% each year since 1980. Programs to increase the energy efficiency of products have led to a slower growth in the demand for electricity.

Safety has been a major concern since the accident at Three Mile Island (TMI) when the core in one of the reactors partially melted in 1979. Although the reactor and the containment building were heavily contaminated, only very small amounts of radiation were released into the environment (less than the annual "background" dose from natural radioactivity). The accident did cause psychological stress that lasted several years for some people, but it caused no immediate injuries or deaths. Long-term studies are still being conducted. [See Section 6.5, "A Closer Look: Three-Mile-Island, from page 464."]

Unfortunately this was not the case at the Chernobyl Nuclear Plant in Ukraine. Within 6 months of the accident, more than 30 people who were near the accident site were dead. Thousands more have an increased risk of cancer. The 1986 accident resulted in the highest levels of radioactive fallout ever recorded in Europe.

In 1998, there were a total of 434 nuclear power plants operating worldwide. In 18 countries, nuclear power plants supply at least 25% of the electricity. South Korea, China, and Japan are continuing to build plants. While some countries continue with plans for increasing use of nuclear energy, other countries are phasing out plans for nuclear power plants. No new plants have been built in the United States since the TMI accident.

Most experts consider it unlikely that nuclear energy will play a major role in the U.S. plan for energy independence. People are still concerned about possible accidents as well as storage of the **spent fuel**—the remaining uranium fuel that is still highly radioactive but can no longer be used to produce energy. The plan is to store these radioactive wastes deep underground. While studies are being conducted to see if a

Nuclear Power Plant

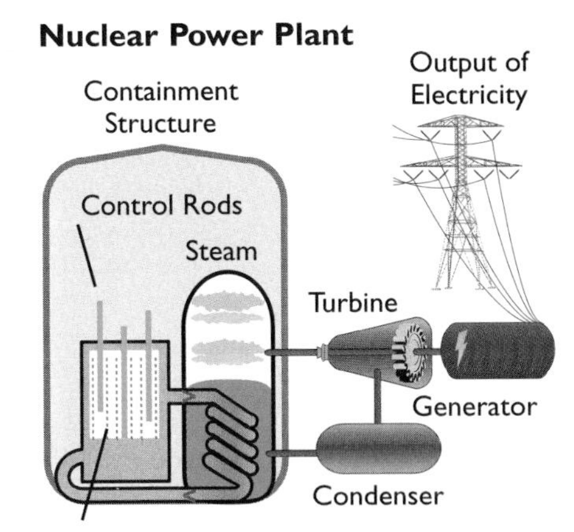

These generators at Hoover Dam convert the power of moving water to electrical power.

Did You Know?

Most electricity is generated by large fossil fuel power plants or huge hydroelectric dams owned by public utilities. The recent deregulation of public utilities that generate electricity is encouraging the development of a technology called distributed generation. In the future, additional electricity demand in large urban areas and electricity generation in remote locations will be produced at smaller, more efficient facilities using fuel cells and other alternative energy sources.

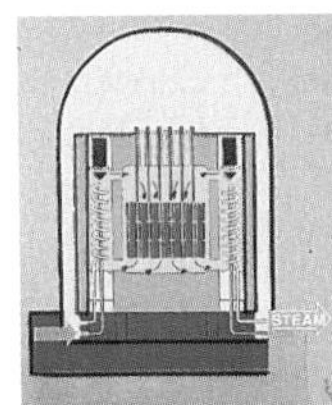

Chernobyl Nuclear:
Although the type of reactor involved in the Chernobyl incident—a water-cooled, graphite-moderated RBMK—is not exported or made by any other country, any type of reactor runs the risk of a similar accident.

The cores of all reactors are cooled in some way, and the nuclear reaction is slowed by a moderator. At Chernobyl, the coolant—in this case, water—was lost, allowing the reactor core to overheat and melt. The graphite, which acted as a moderator, caught fire and sent clouds of radioactive smoke into the atmosphere.

For more information on the Yucca Mountain Site, visit: www.epa.gov.

The geothermal energy beneath Yellowstone National Park is protected from development.

potential site at Yucca Mountain, Nevada, is suitable, radioactive wastes are currently being stored on-site at the nuclear power plants.

Geothermal Energy

Although Hawaii and Iceland have very different climates, they share a common energy source—geothermal energy. **Geothermal energy** is the natural heat or hot water trapped below the earth's surface. Some of the heat was trapped when the earth was formed. Radioactive substances, chemical reactions, and friction created by moving continents produce additional heat energy.

Geothermal energy can be used to heat homes, produce electricity, and power industries. In most places, geothermal energy is too deep to be tapped for electricity, but in Hawaii the heated water lies only 6,000 feet (1,800 m) below the earth's surface. In Boise, Idaho, in 1890, water was piped from hot springs to heat downtown buildings and about 200 homes. Today the system still operates and is one of 17 geothermal "district" heating systems in the United States.

To create electricity, steam or hot water is pumped to the earth's surface and is used to drive turbines. Geothermal power plants usually create minor environmental impacts compared to those that are fired by fossil fuels. Electric power plants must be located at the geothermal field because too much heat and pressure are lost if the energy is transported more than one mile (1.6 km).

Each geothermal site presents a unique set of problems that must be solved. Corrosive minerals dissolved in the steam can damage the pipes and the turbine. At some sites, harmful gases such as radon, hydrogen sulfide and ammonia may be vented into the atmosphere. Geothermal power plants can contaminate aquifers at the site. Sites can be damaged by earthquakes and lava flows from volcanoes. In Hawaii, one geothermal plant has been designed so that it can be easily dismantled in case of a lava flow.

Only a few states in the western U.S. have the high-temperature geothermal fields needed for electrical power plants. The world's largest

Geothermal Power Plant

Turbine
Generator
Output of Electricity
Condenser
Dry Steam
Wet Steam
Hot Water
Hot Rocks

geothermal power plant is The Geysers Power Plant in northern California. It produces about 60% of the world's geothermal electricity, but the output is declining. When water is withdrawn faster than it is recharged, geothermal energy is not a renewable resource. If the water is reinjected into the geothermal field, then the resource can be renewable.

The relatively constant temperature of the earth is warmer than the air above it in the winter, and cooler in the summer. It can be used directly by geothermal heat pumps (GHPs) to transfer heat using an open or closed-loop system. The latter is most common, using pipes buried either horizontally 4–6 feet under, or vertically 150–250 feet under the earth. A GHP exchanger in a building takes heat from the ground in the winter, but transfers heat to the ground in the summer. There are more than 200,000 geothermal heat pumps in U.S. homes, schools, and commercial buildings.

Solar Energy

The sun is the source of most energy on the earth. We have always depended upon solar energy to produce our food. Solar energy powers the water cycle and creates the temperature differences that cause the wind to blow. Before 1850, solar energy was responsible for the creation of the three major sources of energy—wood, wind and water.

Today new houses are designed with windows facing the sun to take advantage of the sun's rays for warming rooms in winter. This form of **passive solar heating** occurs when the light energy passes through glass and is trapped (the greenhouse effect). Roof overhangs shade the windows from the sun's rays in the summer, reducing the amount of passive solar heating and the need for air conditioning.

Objects in direct sunlight absorb solar energy. By adding **thermal mass**—large containers of water or floors and walls made of brick, stone or concrete—the amount of solar energy stored as heat energy can be increased. These materials may be placed in passive collectors attached to a wall facing the sun. As the air in the collector is heated, it rises and flows through a vent at the top of the collector. Cool air enters the collector through a vent near the bottom.

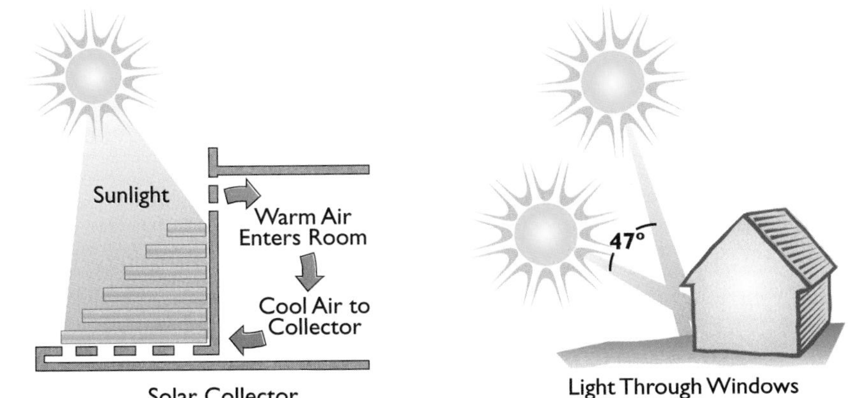

Active Solar Heating Systems

Passive Solar Heating

www

For the history of geothermal energy in the United States, visit: www.eren.doe.gov/geothermal/history.html.

www

For more information on the production of electricity and other renewable energy sources, visit the National Renewable Energy Website at www.nrel.gov. Also search these Websites: www.ornl.gov, www.utilityguide.com and www.edf.org.

Solar Water Heater

A single solar water heater can provide 40–70% of the hot water needs for a typical family of four. With two units in tandem it can provide 70–90% of their hot water needs. These units utilize a heat exchanger coupled with a latent heat storage technique originally developed for the Skylab spacecraft. This system alternately freezes and melts thus absorbs and releases heat through an indefinite number of cycles. The solar panels are also coated with a glazing material developed by Dupont for the Apollo Lunar Module.

Active Solar Heating Systems

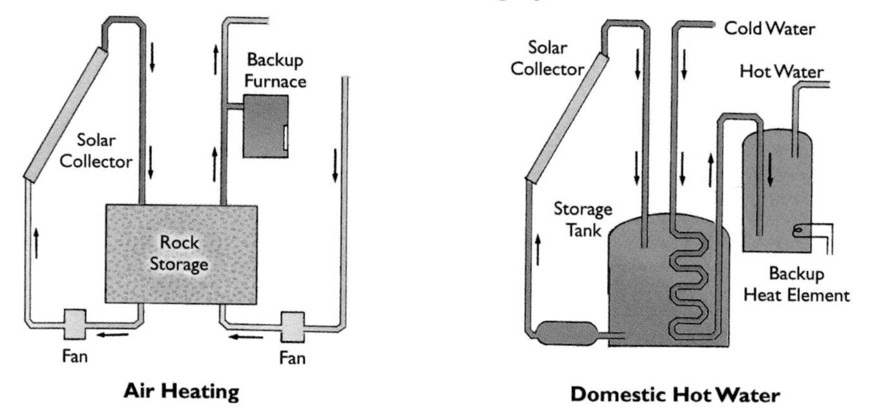

Silicon Solar Cells
Silicon solar-cell arrays are being used in a remote village in Tunisia. This study will determine the effectiveness of a photovoltaic system in remote areas. The primary solar array provides 30 kilowatts of peak power for this residential population of 120, a commercial area of two stores, a barber shop and a café, plus the public area including street lights, a mosque, clinic, meeting house and a school.

To learn more about photovoltaic technology, visit: www.eren.doe.gov and www.utilityguide.com.

Did You Know?
According to NASA, the use of solar power for cooking can reduce the incidence of respiratory disease caused by smoke and fumes from burning wood and kerosene.

Active solar heating systems require electricity for pumps or fans that distribute the heat. Often energy is collected in **flat plate collectors** that are shallow insulated boxes covered with glass and containing a black metal plate. Air or water flowing through the collector is heated and pumped to a storage tank. If the system is designed for space heating, the heat is pumped throughout the building in the same way it is from a conventional furnace. Active solar systems used for domestic water heating are smaller and more cost effective than active space-heating systems.

Photovoltaic cells (solar cells) convert sunlight directly into electricity. When sunlight strikes a thin layer of silicon, electrons are released creating an electric current. Photovoltaic cells have been available since the 1950s and were first used in the space shuttles. Now communications satellites are powered by photovoltaic technology. It is used in remote locations on the earth and to power portable devices such as highway signs and calculators.

There is a large potential for the development of photovoltaic technology. For the 4 billion people who are already connected to electric lines, the cost is 2 to 5 times as much as their current electric rate. But it is often the least expensive method of providing electricity to the two billion people who are not connected to electric power lines. Government support triggered a solar boom in Japan where some 500,000 houses are now generating much of their own power with rooftop solar cells.

Solar thermal technology uses either mirror-lined dishes or panels that rotate with the sun and collect solar energy. Water, heated by the concentrated solar energy, runs an electrical generator. According to the Edison Electric Institute, to supply electricity for a city the size of Pittsburgh would require a solar collector spanning 900 square miles (2,340 km^2).

A 354-megawatt plant in California is the world's largest solar thermal electric power plant. Natural gas-fired boilers are used to supplement solar power during the winter months and at night. The electricity is sold to Southern California Edison for about the same cost as from a coal-fired power plant.

Wind Machines

Wind energy is a source of clean renewable energy. Technology that uses the power of the wind has been used for centuries. Before power plants provided electricity to farms, small ten-kilowatt windmills were used to pump water and generate electricity. In 1941 a giant windmill, able to produce 1,250 kilowatts, was built in Vermont. For three years it provided electricity for the local power plant, but cheap oil and gas were more reliable than the wind.

At many sites, the wind is not reliable enough to generate power. A good site usually has a steady wind with an average wind speed of more than 12 miles per hour. Where it does blow, there may be other problems. The equipment to trap wind energy is expensive and, when damaged by powerful gusts of wind or lightning, it is expensive to repair. While the wind machines take up only 5% of the land where the wind farm is located, they do change the appearance of the landscape and create noise.

California, with more than 16,000 wind machines, produces more than 90% of the wind-generated electrical power in the U.S. The trade winds on the island of Oahu, Hawaii, provide some of the best wind conditions for power generation. Hawaii has several wind farms and encourages wind-generated electricity by offering a 20% tax credit. The nation's greatest potential for developing wind power is the Great Plains.

Advances in technology make today's wind machines more reliable with lower maintenance costs. In many areas, the cost of electricity produced by wind power is less than from a coal-fired power plant. Researchers are trying to find ways to store energy for use when the wind doesn't blow. One storage system would use wind energy to pump water into a reservoir located at a higher level. The falling water can be used to produce electricity if it is needed. Hawaii is also researching wind-diesel hybrid systems.

There are no electric lines leading to Amish farms in Lancaster County, Pennsylvania. Here wind often supplies the power to pump water, and horse power supplies farm labor and transportation.

Most wind-generated electricity is produced at wind farms in California.

Biomass

Biomass refers to any organic substances produced by living organisms and used as a source of energy. Biomass includes wood and wood wastes, agricultural crops and byproducts, municipal solid wastes, and waste from food processing, animals, aquatic plants and algae. The majority of biomass energy is produced from wood and wood wastes. Most of the remainder is produced by incineration of solid waste and gases produced at landfills.

Nearly 4% of all energy consumed in the U.S. and 45% of renewable energy is biomass. Wood and wood products are a major source of energy for the forest products industry. Wood is the primary heating fuel in 3 million homes. More than 100 electrical power plants burn methane generated at landfills.

The major source of biomass in Hawaii is **bagasse**—the fibrous waste produced during the processing of sugar cane. Bagasse is a dry fibrous material similar to the wood shavings produced by sharpening a pencil. When oil was abundant and cheap, the sugar companies disposed of the bagasse by bulldozing it off cliffs or burying it in a landfill. Today they pack it into pellets. The pellets have the same energy value as coal.

Using one system to produce both electricity and heat for an industrial process is called **cogeneration**. The sugar companies burn the pellets to produce steam for electric generators. The used steam still

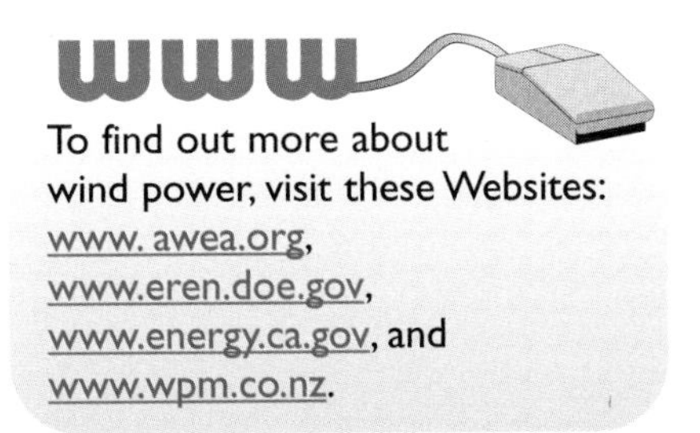

To find out more about wind power, visit these Websites: www. awea.org, www.eren.doe.gov, www.energy.ca.gov, and www.wpm.co.nz.

contains enough energy to process the sugar. At a conventional power plant, the used steam is waste. Due to the large amount of energy remaining in the steam, the energy efficiency of a conventional power plant is about 35%. Cogeneration systems can be 80% efficient.

Biomass can also be used to produce alcohol or methane. During the energy crisis, much attention was given to the use of **gasohol**—a blend of one part grain alcohol and nine parts of gasoline. Most alcohol used in gasohol is distilled from corn. **Biodiesel** is made from soybeans or vegetable oil. Used cooking oil is converted into biodiesel in Hawaii for use in some government vehicles and tour boats.

The Department of Energy (DOE) is sponsoring biomass research to convert fast-growing trees, shrubs, and grasses into biofuels. One biomass crop that can be grown on most cropland is switchgrass, a native American prairie grass. Farmers in Minnesota and Iowa are planting biomass or energy crops on land that is erosion prone and not suitable for corn and other row crops. The results of this research will determine the future role of biofuels in achieving greater energy independence.

The Economics of Alternative Energy Sources

Renewable energy sources are often thought of as free, but more often they are expensive compared to fossil fuels. The cost of generating electricity using some of the alternative energy sources such as wind and photovoltaic cells has fallen since the early '80s, but they are still expensive. To compete with fossil fuels, new energy sources must generate electricity at a cost of about 5 cents per kilowatt-hour (kwh).

In the last decade there have been major improvements in the technologies associated with alternative energy sources. Some alternative technologies require further research and testing or the construction of facilities to make the technology produce commercial quantities of energy. Research and construction can require the investment of billions of dollars. The risks are often bigger than private industry is willing to take.

Government policies can encourage the role of alternative energy sources. The Energy Policy Act of 1992 includes incentives and tax credits for development and production of renewable energy. Electrical power plants must now consider environmental impacts when considering energy sources. This makes alternative energy sources more competitive with conventional energy sources. We did not achieve energy independence by the end of the last century, but we did begin the journey.

Compare the efficiency of this restored steam locomotive to a diesel locomotive.

Are You Willing to Pay for Clean Energy?

Below are comparable generation cost ranges for energy sources in Hawaii. Costs do not include distribution. If you lived in Hawaii and could choose the source of energy that produces your electricity, which would you choose?

Source	Cost
Coal	7–10 cents/kwh
Oil	7–11 cents/kwh
Wind*	8–11 cents/kwh
Geothermal	11–14 cents/kwh
Biomass	19–25 cents/kwh
Solar Thermal	25 cents/kwh
Photovoltaic	40–70 cents/kwh

*not always available

6.3 Questions for Study and Discussion:

1. Define the following terms: **VOCABULARY**

active solar heating system	cathode	flow	photovoltaic cells
anode	cogeneration	gasohol	solar thermal technology
bagasse	cryogenic	generator	spent fuel
biodiesel	electricity	geothermal energy	thermal mass
biomass	fission	head	turbine
	flat plate collector	passive solar heating	

2. Explain why the state of Hawaii is developing alternative sources of energy.

Thank You, Thomas Edison

3. Explain how electricity is produced.
4. Explain how a generator produces electricity.
5. Rank the four major sources of energy used to produce electricity in 1995. Which of these energy sources was renewable?

Hydroelectric Power

6. Explain how electricity is generated at a hydroelectric power plant.
7. Give two advantages of producing electricity at hydroelectric power plants rather than at fossil-fuel power plants.
8. Compare the role of hydroelectric power plants in the future to their role in the past.

Nuclear Power

9. Identify the major fuel used in nuclear power plants and explain how it releases energy.
10. Compare the environmental impacts of a coal-burning power plant with the impacts of a nuclear power plant.
11. What two concerns do people have about the use of nuclear energy?

Geothermal Energy

12. Identify the three ways in which geothermal energy is continually being produced. Is geothermal energy a renewable energy source?
13. Explain why geothermal energy will not become a major source of energy in most states.
14. Identify possible environmental problems associated with geothermal energy.

Solar Energy

15. Identify two renewable energy sources that depend upon solar energy.
16. Give two ways that homeowners can use thermal mass to help heat their homes.
17. What is the major difference between a passive solar heating system and an active solar heating system?
18. Describe two ways solar energy can be changed into electricity and describe the disadvantages of each.

Wind Machines

19. What factors caused the windmill to disappear from the energy picture in the 1940s?
20. What changes have caused a resurgence in wind power and what are the limitations of this energy source?

Biomass

21. Identify several types of biomass that can be used as sources of energy.
22. Explain how cogeneration increases energy efficiency.
23. How may the role of the farm change in the future and what environmental impacts will be associated with this change?

The Economics of Alternative Energy Sources

24. Explain why alternative energy sources have not replaced fossil fuels as a major source of energy for the generation of electricity.
25. Imagine that you are the next President of the United States. What steps would you take to ensure an adequate supply of energy to meet our future needs?

Environmental Challenge: Fuel Cell Technology

Imagine a technology that can power an electric vehicle without requiring an overnight recharge! The same technology can generate electricity for your home or for a hospital. This technology is quiet, produces far less air pollution than combustion of fossil fuels, and reduces our dependence on foreign oil. It is the same technology that provides the Space Shuttle with electric power and drinking water. It is a **fuel cell**.

Sir William Grove first invented the fuel cell in 1839, but a practical working model was not developed until 1950. After further development by NASA, the fuel cell was chosen as the source of power for space missions. Advances in technology have reduced the size and weight of the fuel cell and increased the power output. The challenge now is making fuel cells that are affordable.

Fuel cells are like batteries; they both convert chemical energy to electrical energy. Both fuel cells and batteries produce electricity without combustion, but fuel cells have a distinct advantage over batteries. They can operate continuously as long as they are provided with fuel. The fuel may be hydrogen or natural gas, which is converted to hydrogen before entering the cell. There are several types of fuel cells.

In March of 1999, DaimlerChrysler unveiled NECAR 4. The New Electric Car is powered by a Proton Exchange Membrane (PEM) Fuel Cell. The fuel is liquid hydrogen, which is stored in a **cryogenic** cylinder. A platinum-coated membrane separates hydrogen molecules into protons and electrons. The protons combine with oxygen from the atmosphere to form water vapor, and the electrons flow out of the cell providing the electrical energy to power the vehicle.

Phosphoric-acid fuel cells (PAFC) are about the size of a minivan. This type of fuel cell uses phosphoric acid as an electrolyte. Hydrogen gas is ionized at the **anode**, and the electrons travel through an external circuit to the cathode. At the **cathode**, the oxygen reacts with the hydrogen ions and the electrons to form water. A PAFC at Croton, CT, is fueled by methane gas from a landfill. Each fuel cell provides 20 kw of power, and the heat produced can be used to heat buildings. Using one system to produce both electricity and heat is known as **cogeneration**.

The highest powered fuel cell unit in the U.S. provides power for the municipality of Santa Clara, CA. The two-megawatt, molten-carbonate plant uses methane as the fuel. The methane reacts with steam in a chamber of the fuel cell to produce hydrogen. The hydrogen reacts with carbonate ions forming water and carbon dioxide, and releasing two electrons. Molten carbonate fuel cell plants can achieve a 50% electricity efficiency, while PAFC technology has an electrical efficiency of 41%.

Scientists think that hybrid power plants using fuel cells and advanced gas turbines may be producing electricity with 70% efficiency by the year 2010. These power plants will produce about 30% less carbon dioxide than current gas-burning plants. Replacing the combustion of fossil fuels with the chemical reactions in fuel cells may play an important role in achieving energy independence and protecting the environment.

- What are the advantages of fuel cells?
- When you buy your next car, do you think that you will choose one powered by a fuel cell? What would be the advantages and disadvantages?
- What is the advantage of the molten-carbonate fuel-cell technology over a phosphoric-acid fuel-cell technology?

To see an animation of the process as it occurs in a PEM fuel cell, visit: www.hpower. com.

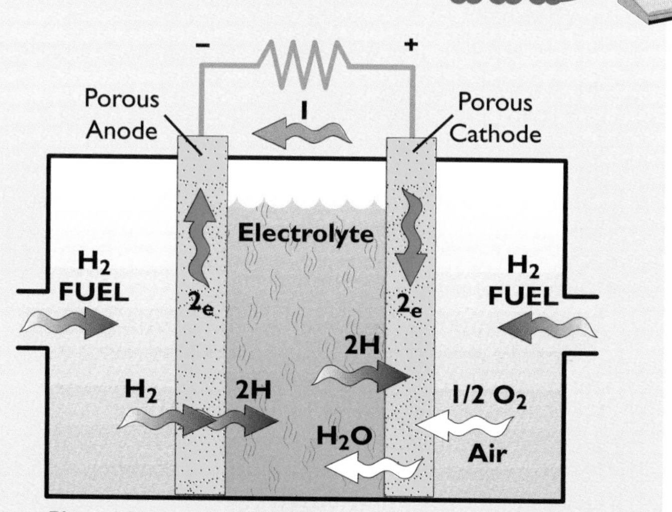

Phosphoric acid fuel cell.

Environmental Challenge: In Search of the Wind

In California's Alamont Pass, there are 7,300 wind turbines. The turbines are near a major corridor for migrating birds. A study revealed that wind turbines are killing birds of prey, including protected golden eagles. During the two-year study, an estimated 500 birds of prey were killed.

U.S. Windpower signed an agreement to build 167 wind turbines in Solano County, California. The turbines would provide electricity for 15,000–17,000 homes in the Sacramento area. According to the California Energy Commission, the impact on birds will be as great in Solano County as in the Alamont Pass. Although the size of the wind farm will be smaller, the area has larger populations of birds. One species that is likely to be affected is the endangered peregrine falcon.

U.S. Windpower is studying the environmental impacts of the wind turbines. The company is testing a more efficient turbine that could produce four times the energy of most turbines. This would reduce the number of turbines needed. The blade of the new turbine is 2.23 times the area of other turbine blades.

Environmental groups such as the Sierra Club and the National Audubon Society could file lawsuits, if the company goes ahead with plans to build the turbines.

- Consider the economic and environmental impacts of wind power.
- Should wind power be banned in areas that serve as migration routes for birds?
- What impact on birds of prey is acceptable?
- What are the alternatives to wind power?
- What are the environmental and economic impacts of the alternative energy sources?

Brunner Island and Other Solutions to Thermal Pollution

OBJECTIVES

- ✔ **Compare** the efficiency of a nuclear power plant with the efficiency of a modern fossil-fueled power plant.
- ✔ **Describe** the environmental impacts of the once-through-cooling method.
- ✔ **List** advantages and disadvantages of cooling towers.
- ✔ **Explain** how waste heat from an electrical power plant can become a resource rather than a pollutant.

Fossil fuel and nuclear power plants produce electricity by heating water to form steam. The force of the steam turns the blades of a large fan-like, or paddle-wheel structure—a **turbine**. The shaft of the turbine is connected to a **generator** that consists of a coil of wire in a magnetic field. Rotation of the coil forces the electrons in the wire to move. This flow of electrons is transmitted along wires as **electricity**.

Nuclear and older fossil-fueled power plants can only convert about one third of the fuel's energy into electricity. Modern fossil-fueled power plants are more efficient, but can convert only 40% of the fuel's energy into electricity. About 10–15% of the energy produced goes up the smokestack as heat along with the products of combustion. The rest (45–50%) of the energy remains as heat energy in the steam that turns the turbine.

Once the steam leaves the turbine, it passes through a **condenser** where it flows over pipes carrying cooler water. The cooler water in the pipes absorbs the heat, and the steam condenses into water and is pumped back to the power plant's boiler or nuclear reactor. The cooling water is supplied to the condenser by one of three methods: once-through-cooling, cooling ponds, or cooling towers.

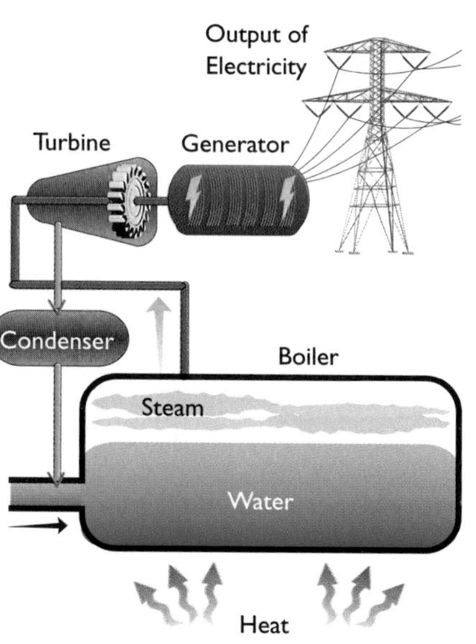

Basic Electric Generating System

Once-Through-Cooling Method

The once-through-cooling method uses water from a river or lake and returns it directly to the source. Because it is the least expensive, once-through-cooling has been the most commonly used method in the past. Although it is cheaper, this method creates problems in some aquatic ecosystems.

- Some species are not able to adapt to the warmer water temperatures. As the temperature of water increases, the ability of water to hold oxygen decreases. At the same time, the warmer temperatures increase the organism's metabolic rate, and the need for oxygen increases.
- Some types of algae and plants cannot grow in the warmer water. The result may be a decrease in certain species that are important producers. Many species of algae that are an important food source may be replaced by species of blue-green bacteria that organisms don't eat.
- **Synergistic effects** may also occur. The increased temperatures make some fish less resistant to disease. Some fish seem to be more sensitive to heavy metals and pesticides in warmer water.
- Those organisms that do survive may not be able to withstand the shock of cooler temperatures when the power plant is shut down for repairs.

Because of these effects, state and EPA water-quality standards limit the increase in water temperature that may occur near a power plant discharge. In Missouri, cooling water from the power plant must not raise the natural temperature of the river water more than 5°F (3°C). The temperature of the water must never be warmer than 90°F (32°C). This means that the cooling water can be returned directly to the river only if the river has a very large rate of flow. The only rivers in Missouri that are large enough to receive cooling water directly from a power plant are the Missouri and Mississippi.

Cooling Towers

Over 80% of the water used by industries is used for cooling. Large steam-electric power plants use as much as 500,000 gallons ($2.3x10^6$ L) of cooling water per minute. Some industries and power plants build **cooling towers** to prevent thermal pollution. There are two types of cooling towers: wet towers and dry towers.

Air enters the base of the cooling tower and rises as the warm water heats it. In **wet towers** the water is sprayed in a fine mist or allowed to fall over a series of wall-like structures called **baffles**. The major problem associated with wet towers is the loss of water through evaporation. Water loss is not a problem in a dry tower.

The heated water flows through a series of pipes in a **dry tower**. A fan at the base of the tower increases the flow of air. The water is cooled in the same way as it is cooled in a car radiator. The major disadvantage of dry towers is that they are more expensive to build and operate.

This heat recovery system recycles waste heat created during manufacturing processes.

Cooling Ponds or Reservoirs

An alternative to a cooling tower is a **cooling pond** or **reservoir**. Two large reservoirs constructed by electric companies in Missouri receive heated water from power plants. The Thomas Hill Power Plant near Macon discharges its water in a 4,500-acre (1800- hectare) cooling lake. The Kansas City Power and Light Company discharges water in the 1,600-acre (640-ha) Montrose Reservoir. Both lakes are leased to the Missouri Department of Conservation, which introduced forage fish that cannot survive in cold water. Bass, crappie and catfish are attracted to the warm water near the power plants, and they provide good fishing through the winter months.

These towers cool the warm water produced at the largest power plant in Ohio.

Waste-Heat Greenhouses

Some companies are finding that waste heat from power plants can be a valuable energy resource. Campbell Soup and Pepperidge Farm, Inc. leased greenhouses near a power plant owned by Pennsylvania Power and Light Company. Producers use the greenhouses to grow tomatoes, flowers, bedding plants and lettuce.

Some of the warm water (90–115°F/32–46°C), that would normally be sent to cooling towers, is sent through insulated pipes to heat-exchange systems in the greenhouses. Back-up heat sources are needed when the power plant is shut down, in extremely cold weather, and during seed germination. Even though the companies must pay for the waste heat and must have a back-up system, their energy costs are reduced by as much as 80%.

The Brunner Island power plant produces electricity and catfish. The low building in the center of the photo is the site of PP&Ls experimental fish farm. The water in the foreground is from the wet scrubber.

Aquaculture with Wastewater

Just a few miles down the Susquehanna River from Three Mile Island is another island that isn't as famous, but there is something important happening on Brunner Island. Brunner Island is the site of a coal-fired power plant that is owned by Pennsylvania Power & Light Company. It is also the site of PP&L's experimental fish farming—**aquaculture** project.

A greenhouse heated by the warm wastewater is being used for hydroponics production of vegetables August through March, and to heat incubators for hatching catfish eggs. Once the small catfish are two inches (5 cm) in length, they are transferred to long concrete pools called raceways. The heat that was absorbed by the water as it passed through the power plant keeps the temperature of the raceways about 80°F (27°C). The optimum temperature for catfish is 84°F (29°C).

Raising catfish offers a solution to thermal pollution as well as an economical source of protein. In 36 weeks on Brunner Island, catfish reach a size that would require two to three years in a natural environment. Since the diet and the conditions for growth can be controlled, the result is a fish that tastes better.

Aerial view of PP&L's Aquaculture Project.

Water from condensers in a nuclear power plant in Pickering, Ontario, Canada, once discharged into Lake Ontario, is now used to raise marketable rainbow trout and perch hatchlings. The water is not radioactive because it does not enter the nuclear reactor. It is used to cool steam from the turbines. Every day 10 million gallons ($4.5x10^7$ L) of water, which is 62°F (17°C) in the winter and 71°F (22°C) in the summer, is piped about a half mile (0.8 km) to Coolwater Farms. The fish farm was a former sewage treatment plant. The 12 former settling tanks at the plant are ideal for the fish.

6.4 Questions for Study and Discussion:

1. Define the following terms: **VOCABULARY**

aquaculture	generator
baffles	reservoir
cooling pond	synergistic effects
cooling tower	turbine
dry tower	wet tower
electricity	

2. Describe how a turbine and generator work together to produce electricity.
3. How much of the energy in coal is converted to electricity in a fossil-fueled power plant? What happens to the remainder of the energy?
4. List the four methods power plants use to cool the "used" steam.

Once-Through-Cooling Method

5. Describe the once-through-cooling method.
6. What are the advantages and disadvantages of the once-through-cooling method?
7. Explain why most industries and power plants cannot use the once-through-cooling method.

Cooling Towers

8. Describe how water is cooled in a wet tower; in a dry tower.
9. Give one disadvantage of each type of cooling tower.

Cooling Ponds or Reservoirs

10. What are the benefits of once-through-cooling at the Kansas City Power and Light Company's plant in Montrose?

Waste-Heat Greenhouses

11. Explain how waste heat from an electric company can be turned into a resource rather than a pollutant.

Aquaculture

12. Give two advantages of combining aquaculture and electrical power production.
13. What type of fish is being raised at Brunner Island in Pennsylvania? At Coolwater Farms in Ontario, Canada?

6.5 Three-Mile-Island

OBJECTIVES

- ✔ **Explain** why health studies of the effects of radiation must be long-term studies.
- ✔ **Explain** why an increase in the total number of cancer cases was expected.
- ✔ **Evaluate** the four health studies that have been conducted and **explain** the differing conclusions.
- ✔ **Predict** the results of future health studies.

"It was a difficult time because the information being released was often contradictory and confusing ... We had to be prepared for the worst. Fortunately the worst-case scenarios ... never happened."

DR. KENNETH L MILLER, Certified Health Physicist
Pennsylvania State University College of Medicine

People in south central Pennsylvania remember what they were doing on March 28, 1979. That is the date of the nation's worst accident at a commercial nuclear power plant. It happened at the Three Mile Island power plant near Middletown, Pennsylvania, when a pressure relief value opened and remained in the open position.

The open valve allowed coolant water to escape from the nuclear reactor and the temperature of the core exceeded 5,000 degrees Fahrenheit. There was a partial meltdown of the reactor core. The reactor's containment vessel was designed to prevent the release of radioactive materials, and it functioned properly. Measurements showed only low levels of radioactive gases were released.

In the years since the accident, many people have been concerned about the possible effects of the radiation that had escaped. More than five years after the accident, the Pennsylvania Department of Health conducted a study to determine if the number of new cancer cases and the number of deaths due to cancer were larger than expected.

Some people wondered why they had waited so long to begin the study. Cancer caused by radiation usually takes a long time to develop. It may take 10–20 years before cancer caused by radiation is diagnosed. Even leukemia, a cancer that has a relatively short period of development, usually isn't detected until five or more years after exposure to radiation.

The best way to analyze the effect of radiation on the health of a population is a before-and-after study. A before-and-after study would compare cancer rates before the TMI accident to cancer rates after the accident. To make a valid comparison, adjustments must be made for the differences in age and gender of the population studied.

The mobility of the human population can affect results of a study. Some people who had lived near Three Mile Island moved away and could not be included in the study. Migrations out of the area cause some cancer cases to be missed that should have been included in the study. Some people who moved into the area may have cancers that had begun to develop prior to their move into the area.

Another type of health study is a comparison of the number of cancers observed after the TMI accident to the number that would have been "expected" in the area. This is known as an observed vs. expected study. The Pennsylvania Department of Health conducted an observed vs. expected study. It was not the first health study after the TMI accident.

A housing development has been built along the Susquehanna River in the shadow of the Three-Mile Island Nuclear power plant.

The results of another study had been made public on June 21, 1984. Newspaper headlines read: "Anti-nuke group's study finds higher cancer rates near TMI." The study, known as the Aamodt Survey, was a health survey conducted by a group of local residents.

A door-to-door survey found 20 cancer deaths in three communities "downwind" from Three Mile Island. According to the survey, this is several times higher than the normal rate of cancer deaths for the area. The accident at TMI was given as the cause of this increase in the cancer death rate. The report gave little information about the methods used to conduct the survey.

The Centers for Disease Control and the U.S. Public Health Service reviewed the Aamodt Survey, at the request of the U.S. Nuclear Regulatory Commission. Analysis of the data presented in the Aamodt survey, along with additional data available from the State Health Department, resulted in the following conclusion: "(The available data) does not support the claim that the TMI accident caused an increase in cancer deaths."

The most important and serious defect in the Aamodt Survey was the "selection bias" in the data collected. There is evidence that the selection was influenced by the pre-existing knowledge of cancer deaths. Only those streets where cancer deaths were known to have occurred were chosen for the survey. Other streets in the same area where there were no known cancer deaths were excluded from the survey.

Other deficiencies in the Aamodt survey were:

- A lack of information about new cancer cases.
- No consideration of age and gender distribution in the local populations.
- No attempt to include former residents and exclude newcomers.
- A difference in time periods for the expected number of cancer deaths (five years) and the observed number of cancer deaths (five years and ten months).
- Of the 20 reported cancer deaths:
  - a) One died before the accident in 1978.
  - b) One who died of a cause other than cancer was apparently confused with a relative who had died of cancer before the accident.
  - c) Six were diagnosed as having cancer before the accident.
  - d) Two were long-term heavy smokers who died of lung cancer.

An increase in the number of cancer cases was expected for the area, even without an accident at TMI. This increase was expected because of:

- An increase in the population of many of the areas included in the study.
- An overall increase in cancer cases throughout Pennsylvania as well as other regions in recent years.
- Improved methods of reporting cancer cases (such as the new cancer registry).

In the top photo steam rises from the cooling towers of the Unit I reactor. The Unit 2 reactor has been shut down and the radiation cleaned up. The baffles have been removed from the bottom of the cooling towers.

On the east bank of the river at the Three-Mile Island nuclear power plant, these radiation monitors continuously monitor the air to determine if radiation levels are above the background level.

- Improvements in diagnosis.
- An increase in life span, since older people are more susceptible to cancer.

Cancer can be caused by many environmental factors including radiation exposure, diet, tobacco, microorganisms, food additives, and occupational-industrial exposure. Genetic factors also determine a person's susceptibility to cancer. Because of these complex relationships, we cannot make quick conclusions about the causes of new cancer cases.

Previous studies indicate that certain forms of cancer are more likely to occur following exposure to high levels of radiation. The remaining ten cancer deaths in the Aamodt survey represented many different types of cancer. These cancers are normally found in any population. This suggests the absence of a single cause.

The population used for the state health study was the 1980 population of the area surrounding TMI. The health department began a review of many records, including the cancer registry files that were set up in 1982. State law requires all new cancer cases diagnosed and/or treated within the state of Pennsylvania to be reported to the State Health Department. Other sources of information included the TMI census data, school records, death certificates and surveys of physicians.

The state health department conducted a census of the 5,296 women of childbearing age who were exposed to the TMI accident radiation and resided within a 10-mile radius of TMI. The expected number of cancers during the 7.5-year period was 35.6. The number of observed cancers was 35. Among women who were pregnant, the number of cancers observed was 15. The expected number was 13.5.

The differences in observed and expected cancers in women of childbearing age were not statistically significant. The results of the study do not provide any evidence that radiation released as a result of the TMI accident influenced cancer risk among these women. If there was an increase in cancer rate, it was too small to be detected or not enough time had elapsed for cancer to develop.

The state health department compared total cancer cases, breast cancer in females, respiratory, digestive system and skin cancers. The analysis showed no systematic pattern in cancer incidence in relation to distance from the TMI power plant. The incidence of cancer was generally higher in the southern quadrant where the radiation exposure was lower. But the difference was not statistically significant.

The results of the state health studies showed no indication of a "rising trend" in leukemia. In other cancer types studied, there was no significant increase. There were two variables that were significant, related to cancer cases—the age and the smoking habits of the person. The scientists responsible for the study could not make conclusions about the effects of the TMI accident at that time because of the long latency period required for most types of cancer to develop.

In 1990, the results of an independent health study were released. Epidemiologists at Columbia University compared the occurrence of cancers from 1975 to 1985 among 160,000 people who lived within 10 miles of the plant. The Columbia researchers analysis was an observed vs. expected study.

The types of cancer that are most likely to develop after exposure to low levels of radiation are childhood cancer and leukemia. The researchers found the incidence of childhood cancer in the areas with the highest radiation was 1.06 times the incidence in low radiation areas. They found only 3 cases of leukemia in people under the age of 24 in the areas with highest radiation and 1 case in the area with the lowest exposure area.

The researchers did find higher rates of certain cancers, mostly lung cancer and non-Hodgkin's lymphoma, among people who lived downwind of the plant. Studies show that non-Hodgkin's lymphoma is not caused by radiation and lung cancer does not develop for at least 10 years after exposure to radiation. Since it had been only 6 years since the accident, lung cancers caused by the release of radiation would not have had time to develop.

Measurements of radiation exposure after the accident ranged from 0.01 rem to 0.025 rem. The low incidence of cancer found in the Columbia University study indicates that the radiation level was low. The analysis also supports the conclusion of Dr. Kenneth L. Miller, a certified health physicist, who said that levels of radiation in samples he collected "were low and posed no threat to anyone."

In 1996, a federal judge dismissed damage claims by more than 2,000 people living near the Three Mile Island plant. The judge cited "paucity (lack) of proof." Psychological studies did show that low levels of stress were common among people living close to the reactor.

In 1997, scientists at the University of North Carolina School of Public Health used the before-and-after method to analyze the same data that was analyzed by the scientists at Columbia University. They concluded that increased cases of cancers were related to the accident. They also believe that the radiation levels were much higher than those reported. The hypothesis of higher radiation doses is based on anecdotal reports of vomiting, diarrhea, hair loss, and dying pets.

The Columbia researchers maintain that the results of the study do not provide "convincing evidence" that the release of radiation influenced cancer risk. A National Cancer Institute study and the state health study reached the same conclusion. Additional studies are needed because of the long period of time it may take for cancers, caused by radiation, to develop. A team of scientists from the University of Pittsburgh is conducting further studies.

There are 79 monitors like this one located within 10 miles of the Three-Mile Island nuclear power plant. The sirens would sound to warn residents in case of an accident that releases radiation.

6.5 QUESTIONS FOR STUDY AND DISCUSSION:

1. What happened at Three Mile Island on March 28, 1979?
2. Why wasn't a study of cancer rates made until 5 years after the accident?
3. What kind of cancer might increase five years after exposure to radiation?
4. How can mobility of the population affect the results of the study?
5. What method did the Pennsylvania Department of Health use in the study?
6. Why was the validity of the Aamodt survey questioned?
7. List several reasons why the number of cancer cases expected would increase in the area of TMI, with or without an accident.
8. Do you think that a person who was a long-term heavy smoker and died of lung cancer should have been included in the study? Why or why not?
9. Compare the Columbia University study and the study conducted by the State Department of Health.
10. What types of cancer are associated with exposure to radiation?
11. Why did the epidemiologists think that the TMI accident was not responsible for increase in lung cancer?
12. Do you think that the body of evidence supports the claim that "only low levels of radiation were released" or the hypothesis that radiation doses were higher than reported?
13. Predict the results of future studies. Will there be an increase in the incidence of cancer and if so, what kind(s)? Support your position.

Reduce, Reuse, Recycle or ...

Burn it or Bury it—That is the Question!

- ✔ **Identify** the method used to dispose of most solid waste and **identify** potential environmental impacts of this method.
- ✔ **List** advantages and disadvantages of incinerators that burn solid waste.
- ✔ **Compare** the impacts of disposal of waste to the impacts of recovery and recycling waste.
- ✔ **Identify** changes in lifestyle that will improve the sustainability of planet Earth.

Solid wastes include household garbage and other discarded materials. For each person (man, woman and child) living in the United States, more than 4 pounds (2 kg) of solid waste is discarded each day. If solid waste from construction sites and sewage treatment plants is included, the waste-per-person rises to 6 pounds per day. In 1998, almost 55% of the solid waste produced in the United States was buried in 2,500 sanitary landfills.

Other countries have refused to accept our garbage. In some cases, after spending months on a barge, the garbage was returned to the United States and buried in a sanitary landfill. So it appears that, unless we can find ways to use our solid waste, we will have to find a place to bury it, here at home—where it will use our valuable land and threaten our water supplies.

EPA regulations for landfills, that took effect in 1993, require installing synthetic and clay liners, collecting and treating the **leachate**—the liquids that drain from the landfill, monitoring ground water and surface water quality, and monitoring for escaping methane gas. Protection of the environment will cause an increase in the cost of solid waste disposal in landfills.

The Fresh Kills Landfill on Staten Island, the largest landfill in the world, must stop accepting garbage in 2001. Although there is plenty of room in other places to bury solid waste, people object to waste being buried in their community. The "Not-In-My-Backyard" (NIMBY) attitude makes it difficult to find a site for a landfill.

If garbage can't be buried, one alternative is to burn it. Most of the waste is paper, but the amount of plastics is increasing each year by about 10%. A plastic soft drink bottle contains slightly more heat content than the same mass of coal. It seems that solid waste might be a good alternative to fossil fuels. In addition to providing energy, burning reduces the volume of waste by as much as 90%.

Although storm sewers caused most of the trash on the beaches in 1988, the barges of trash heading out to sea provided an image that was hard for environmental groups and lawmakers to ignore.

Heat Content of Selected Wastes in BTUs (kwh) per pound			
Mixed food waste	2,370 (0.7)	Rubber Tires	13,800 (4.0)
Mixed paper	6,800 (2.0)	Grass (65% moisture)	2,690 (0.8)
Mixed plastics	14,100 (4.1)	Wood (green)	2,100 (0.6)
Mixed Solid Waste	4,800 (1.4)	Lumber (cured)	7,300 (2.1)
Heat Content of Selected Fuels in BTUs (kwh) per pound			
Coal (Bituminous)	14,000 (4.1)	Fuel Oil	18,000 (5.3)

In the 1960s and 1970s, a large percentage of municipal solid waste was burned. Incineration of waste declined during the 1980s. In 1997, about 17% of solid waste produced in the U.S. was burned in 110 incinerators. Japan and Switzerland burn more than half of their domestic waste. Some of the **waste-to-energy** plants produce electricity while others

Did You Know?

Most countries recycle better than we do.

Environmental Challenge:

Find the answers to these and other questions about solid waste from EPA's Municipal Solid Waste Factbook at: www.epa.gov/epaoswer/non-hw/muncpl/factbook:

- Name 5 states that have bottle bills.
- If you live in Colorado, can you send your yard waste to a landfill?
- How does the recycling rate in your state compare to other states?
- How many steel cans does the average American use per year?
- Where do old tires go when you get new ones?

www

The recycling of aluminum saves energy and reduces pollution. Recycling two aluminum beverage cans saves as much energy as one can filled with gasoline.

produce steam that is used by industries or residential developments.

Not everyone is convinced that solid wastes should be burned. When some plastics and bleached paper are burned, they produce toxic compounds containing chlorine. Some of these chemicals are dioxins that can affect the immune system or fetal development, and are classified as human **carcinogens**. Dioxins are found in the fatty tissues of humans and in the milk of nursing mothers. Municipal solid waste incinerators contribute to the dioxin contamination.

Another concern about burning solid waste is ash disposal. The ash contains heavy metals—cadmium, mercury and lead. Sweden considers it to be hazardous waste. In the U.S. each incinerator operator must determine if the ash is hazardous. If ash contains high levels of heavy metals, it must be disposed of in licensed hazardous-waste landfills. Cost of disposal in these licensed approved landfills may be as much as ten times higher than in other landfills.

Resource Recovery

Resource recovery refers to the salvaging of usable materials from solid waste. Resource recovery and **recycling**—the use of these "waste" materials in the manufacturing process—are increasing. In 1980 only 10% of the solid waste produced in the United States was recycled. By 1997, the recycling rate had increased to 28%.

Until 1975 most soft drinks were sold in glass bottles that were returned to the bottling company and reused. Today most soft drinks are sold in "recyclable" plastic bottles or in aluminum cans. Recycling of containers saves raw materials and energy, and it reduces air and water pollution. Producing an aluminum can from another aluminum can uses only 5% of the energy that is needed to produce aluminum from bauxite, and it also reduces the emissions of aluminum fluoride.

According to ALCOA (Aluminum Company of America), recycling aluminum also creates jobs. In 1991, aluminum recycling employed twice the number of people (30,000) than those working in aluminum manufacturing. Since 1983, the state of New York has required a deposit on beverage containers. A study of the effects showed that the law has saved millions of dollars spent for cleanup and disposal. It has also provided nearly 4,000 jobs. Ten states have passed "bottle bills."

Benefits of Recycling Solid Waste

Benefit	Aluminum	Steel	Paper	Glass
Energy Saved(%)	90-97	47-74	23-74	4-32
Reduce Air Pollution (%)	95	85	74	20
Reduce Water Pollution (%)	97	76	35	—
Reduce Mining Wastes (%)	—	97	—	80
Reduce Water Use (%)	—	40	58	50

Not all materials are suitable for recycling. Materials composed of several different substances may not be easily separated. Some paper products are covered with plastic or foil that cannot be easily separated. Some states have passed laws that ban the sale of certain forms of packaging such as juice boxes. Denmark banned the sale of almost all one-way soft drink containers—including aluminum cans.

Several states have passed mandatory recycling laws. Large communities must collect materials for recycling, and smaller communities must provide drop-off sites for materials to be recycled. Residents are required to recycle certain materials including paper, glass, aluminum or plastic. In some states, leaves and grass clippings are no longer permitted in landfills; instead they are turned into compost. Some communities now have a **"pay-as-you-throw"** policy to encourage recycling and reduce solid waste going to landfills. Residents are charged by the bag or by the pound to dispose of trash.

With decreasing supplies of natural resources, limited space and concerns about the environmental effects of landfills and waste-to-energy plants, recycling is no longer merely a way for boy scouts and other organizations to make money. "Reduce, reuse, and recycle" must be more than a slogan, if we are to provide for our growing population and have a healthy environment. These actions must become an important part of our lifestyle.

POPULATION LINK

Reduce and Reuse

Citizens in the United States and Canada produce more solid waste per person than people in other industrialized countries. People who live in farm communities produce far less solid waste than people who live in cities. Even in farm communities where more women are working away from home, the demand for convenience products is increasing. More energy is often used to package convenience products than is used to produce the product in the package! Disposing of the packaging materials also consumes energy.

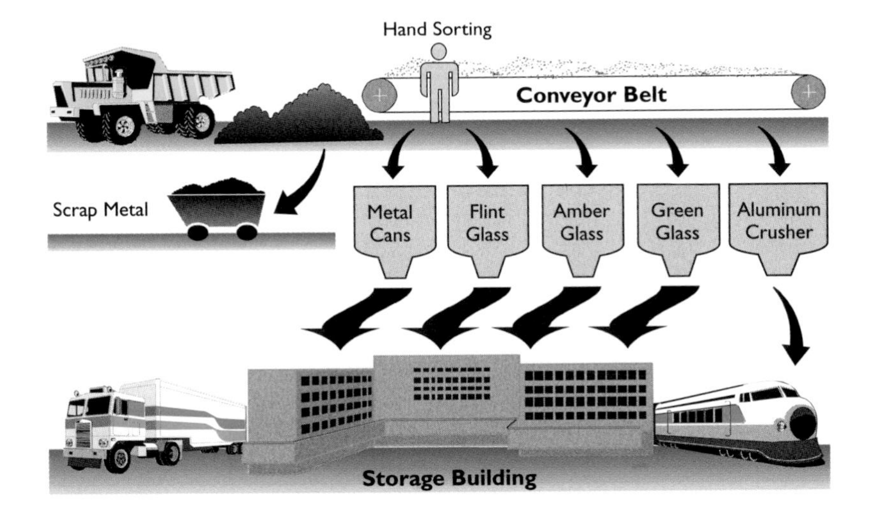

Large containers at convenient locations can be used to separate garbage. This is one way of reducing the amount of solid waste ending up in landfills.

Did You Know?

Paper can be burned to generate electricity, but high-grade paper is more valuable as a resource for making recycled paper than as a fuel. In 1997, 42% of paper and paperboard were recycled.

Recycling saves energy and reduces pollution.

Energy Consumed to Manufacture Certain Packaging Materials (in kwh)	
steel can (16 oz/550 ml)	1.17
polystyrene tray	0.25
aluminum can (12 oz/412 ml)	1.91
molded fiber tray	0.45
plastic bag (2 qt/2.2L)	1.23
aluminum TV tray	1.74

Think About It

Why do we use so much packaging? What are the advantages and disadvantages to packaging? Describe the history of packaging.

In addition to conserving energy, less packaging also conserves other valuable resources. The Worldwatch Institute reports that packaging uses up to 50% of all paper and 25% of all plastics sold. Packaging materials contribute 50% of the volume of domestic waste.

The ultimate answer to the solid waste problem is prevention—**reduce** the amount of solid waste created. McDonald's Corporation reduced its solid waste by 70% simply by changing the way that it packaged hamburgers. The Environmental Protection Agency (EPA) has made **source reduction**—decreasing the amount of waste produced—the top priority in the management of solid waste.

One way to reduce the solid waste is to **reuse**—buy products that can be used again and again. Yvon Chouinard, President of Patagonia Outdoor Clothing, recommends that you, "Buy fewer products, but buy excellent products that you know are going to last." Making products last longer reduces the amount of waste created and the demand for resources.

Recycling is the next best thing, but recycling does have environmental impacts. Although recycling resources saves energy when compared to using virgin resources, recycling does require energy. Recycling also contributes to air and water pollution. But the biggest problem with resource recovery and recycling is the market. Someone needs to buy the products made from recycled waste.

6.6 Questions for Study and Discussion:

1. Define the following terms: **VOCABULARY**

leachate	reuse
pay-as-you-throw	solid waste
recycling	source reduction
reduce	waste-to-energy plant
resource recovery	

Burn it or Bury it—That is the Question!

2. What happens to most of municipal solid waste?
3. Identify problems associated with this method of solid waste disposal.
4. Give two advantages of burning as a method of disposing of solid wastes.
5. What are the concerns about waste-to-energy plants?

Resource Recovery

6. What is the difference between resource recovery and recycling?
7. How have the types of containers used to package soft drinks changed since 1975?
8. List several advantages of recovering and recycling aluminum.
9. Identify types of products that cannot be recycled.
10. What policy changes are helping to increase the rate of recycling?
11. Discuss the importance of resource recovery and recycling to the sustainability of planet Earth.

Reduce and Reuse

12. Compare the solid waste produced per-person in North America with the solid waste produced per-person in other industrialized countries.
13. Compare the solid waste produced by farm societies with the solid waste produced by urban lifestyles.
14. Which packaging material requires the most energy to produce—paper, plastic, aluminum or steel?
15. What is the EPA's top priority in waste management?
16. Compare the environmental impacts of these methods of reducing solid waste: "source reduction" and "recycle and reuse."
17. Evaluate your lifestyle. What changes could you make to help life on planet Earth be more sustainable?

Lab Investigation 1.1

Observations of a Duckweed Population

Objectives:

- **Observe** and **classify** a common type of duckweed.
- **Predict** the growth pattern of a duckweed population.
- **Collect** data and **graph** population growth.

Safety precautions: Follow all safety rules when working in the laboratory.

Materials:

(per class)	(per group)
10-gallon aquarium	petri dish
hood with light	stereoscope (magnifying lens)
air pump	2 dissecting needles
air stone	forceps
plant fertilizer with chelated iron	metric ruler
	duckweed
	Investigation Report

Background Information:

The subject for this experiment appears to be a little green floating leaf. It is one of the smallest flowering plants—a member of the duckweed family. Duckweed plants lack true leaves and stems. The green plant body, described as a **thallus** in some references and a **frond** in others, is commonly called a leaf because it looks like one. One or more rootlets may extend from the lower surface of each leaf.

Duckweed plants seldom produce flowers. The division of the plant body produces new plants. As the tiny new leaf grows, it breaks away from the parent leaf forming a new plant.

It is important that scientists properly identify organisms that are the subject of a scientific study or experiment. The results of an experiment are valid only if they can be reproduced. To confirm the results, the experiment must be repeated using the same type of organism and the exact conditions of the original experiment.

Procedure:

1. Using the stereoscope (magnifying lens), observe a few duckweed plants floating in a small amount of water in a Petri dish.
2. Use a dissecting needle and forceps, observe both sides of several "leaves." Record five observations on your Investigation Report.
3. Classify the duckweed using the identification key on page 474 and record the name of the duckweed in your Investigation report.
4. Fill an aquarium with a dilute fertilizer solution. Continuously aerate the water with an air pump and a single air stone. Replace any water that evaporates with the dilute fertilizer solution.
5. Put the hood in place and turn on the light. The light should be on constantly.
6. It is important to remember that each *Lemna* "leaf" is an individual organism. Place 10 individual *Lemna* plants or "leaves" in the aquarium.
7. Record the date and the number of plants in the data sheet on your Investigation Report.
8. Predict the population changes with time by drawing a "best line" graph in the chart on your Investigation Report.
9. Take a **true census** of the *Lemna* population every 2 or 3 days. A true census is an actual count of all of the individuals of a species in a given area. Although it provides the most accurate data, it is often impossible to take a true census.
10. When it becomes difficult to take a true census, design a procedure to take a **sample census**—an estimate of the population that is made by marking off plots—small areas of the organisms habitat—and counting the individuals in each plot.
11. Take a sample census twice each week for at least one month.

12. On a piece of graph paper, plot the date on the X (horizontal) axis and the population on the Y (vertical) axis. Draw a best line to complete the graph.
13. Complete the analysis questions on your Investigation Report.

Simplified Identification Key for Common Types of Duckweed:

1 A Plant body is 1–2 mm long, lacks rootlets, and resembles a green seed or grain —

Water meal *Wolffia columbiana*

B Plant body is 2–12 mm long; rootlets usually present. **Go to 2.**

2 A Plant body is 6–12 mm long; often stalked; often joined to form a zigzag chain; rootlets may be absent. Plant body is oval or narrow with a tapered tip.

Ivy-leaved Duckweed *Lemna triscula*

B Plant body is not stalked; if connected does not form a chain; one or more rootlets present. **Go to 3.**

3 A Plant body is 5–10 mm long; more than one rootlet present; may be purplish underneath. Plant body is circular —

Greater Duckweed *Spirodela polyrhiza*

B Plant body is 2–12 mm long; only one rootlet present.

Lesser Duckweed *Lemna minor*

Field Investigation 1.2

Assessing Biodiversity in a Microhabitat

Objectives:

- **Collect arthropods** from two different microhabitats.
- **Determine** the species diversity in each habitat.
- **Compare** the biodiversity of the habitats.

Background Information:

A **species** is a group of organisms that are very much alike and that breed to produce fertile offspring. Scientists have identified more than one million species, but the total number of species sharing planet Earth is not known. The number could be 10 million or even 100 million. The survey of the Earth's biodiversity is far from complete.

Biodiversity is the variety of plant and animal species within an ecosystem. We measure biodiversity by the number of species present in an ecosystem. Scientists estimate that there may be 30 million species of insects and other arthropods in the tropical forest canopy. While we cannot travel to the tropical forest to study its biodiversity, we can study the biodiversity of ecosystems near our home or school.

It can be difficult to identify the species to which an organism belongs. Some small insects can be identified only by examining the anatomy of their mouth. Scientists spend many hours collecting and identifying the small organisms in an ecosystem.

In this investigation you will compare the biodiversity of two microhabitats by placing organisms that appear to be alike into a group. Since some of these organisms may actually be different species, we will call these groups of similar organisms **taxons**. It is not necessary to identify each organism, only place it in a group with other organisms that appear to be alike.

The focus of this study will be organisms that are classified as arthropods—animals with segmented bodies and jointed legs. There are large numbers and varieties of arthropods (insects, spiders, mites, centipedes, and millipedes) living in many diverse habitats. The types of organisms that you will observe depend upon the microhabitat selected and the method of collection chosen.

Materials:

(depends upon choice of collection technique)

(per student)

chemical splash goggles
chemical-resistant apron
chemical-resistant gloves

(per group)

berlese funnel	white cloth
lamp with 25-watt bulb	insect killing jar
stereomicroscope	insect aspirator
small bottles with lids	ethyl acetate
petri dish	fine brush
isopropyl alcohol (70%)	forceps
beating stick	pipettes
insect net	field guides (optional)
insect sieve	

Safety precautions: Follow all safety rules when working in the field and in the laboratory.

Procedure:

1. Identify the microhabitats that you will study. Since the goal is to compare the biodiversity of arthropods in two different habitats, you need to select two habitats that are similar but have one characteristic that differs. You may select from the list below or you may think of other habitats to study:
   - Pine cones from two different species of pine trees.
   - Pine cones attached to trees and pine cones lying in the litter on the forest floor.
   - A tree stump or decaying log in a shady forest and a stump or log in full sun.
   - A lawn that is treated with herbicides and a nearby lawn with no herbicides.
   - A grassy area that is regularly mowed and a weedy area with taller plants.
   - A field of alfalfa (a monoculture) and a mowed area with a variety of plants.
   - Litter from the floor near the forest's edge and litter from the interior of the forest.
   - Soil in a garden and soil in an area that is not tilled and planted with crops.
   - Two different species of shrubs or trees.
2. Once you have chosen the microhabitats that will be the focus of your study, you must choose the method you will use to collect the organisms. Choose the method that you think is most appropriate for the microhabitats you have chosen.

   Berlese funnel: A large funnel set in a jar with a low-watt light placed above it. The heat from the light dries out the material placed in the funnel and the organisms migrate to lower levels. Eventually they fall through the neck of the funnel into the collecting jar. Alcohol in the collecting jar preserves the specimens for later identification.

   Insect sieve: Material is placed in the sieve and shaken over a white cloth. Insects and other small organisms fall through the wire mesh and onto the cloth where they can be removed with forceps or an insect aspirator.

   Beating stick: A white cloth is placed under tree branches or shrubbery, which are beaten with a stick. Organisms can be removed from the cloth with forceps or an insect aspirator.

   Insect net: Make a sweeping motion with an insect net, disturbing the plants that are the microhabitat. The number of sweeps must be equal for both habitats.

   Pitfall traps: A small plastic cup is buried at ground level. The cup contains a removable inner cup and a funnel. The small organisms fall into the cup as they crawl along the surface of the ground. This method will require at least two site visits.
3. In your laboratory notebook, design an investigation and submit it to your teacher for approval. Include the following: (a) goal of the investigation, (b) the microhabitats to be studied, (c) a hypothesis, (d) a materials list, and (e) the procedure for collecting the organisms.

   The hypothesis might suggest that one habitat will have a greater biodiversity of arthropods than the second habitat studied.
4. Collect the organisms. The organisms may be observed live and released or they may be preserved. Preserve smaller organisms in isopropyl alcohol (70%). If larger insects are collected, they may be killed using ethyl acetate in an insect killing jar.

Caution: **Follow all precautions on the Materials Safety Data Sheets (MSDS) when using chemicals. Avoid flames, and wear protective goggles, aprons, and gloves when working with ethyl acetate and isopropyl alcohol. Dispose of chemicals as directed by your teacher.**

5. Transfer the organisms to a Petri dish and examine using a stereomicroscope. Remove the organisms as they are identified and place them in groups on a piece of white paper. Identify the groups as Taxon 1, Taxon 2, etc.
6. In your laboratory notebook, create a chart like the one below and record the number of organisms in each group.

Habitat 1:		**Habitat 2:**	
Taxon	Number of Organisms	Taxon	Number of Organisms
1		1	
2		2	

7. Calculate the species diversity using the following formula. See the example below. Include your calculations in your laboratory notebook.

$$\textbf{Diversity} = \frac{N(N-1)}{\Sigma\,[n(n-1)]}$$

N = total number of individuals
n = number of individuals of a species
Σ = summation symbol

Sample Calculations:

Habitat 1	n
Taxon 1	72
Taxon 2	21
Taxon 3	13
N =	106

Habitat 2	n
Taxon 1	15
Taxon 2	2
Taxon 3	24
Taxon 4	10
N =	51

$$\frac{106(106-1)}{72(72-1) + 21(21-1) + 13(13-1)} = \frac{11130}{5688} = 1.96$$

$$\frac{51(51-1)}{15(15-1) + 2(2-1) + 24(24-1) + 10(10-1)} = \frac{2550}{854} = 2.99$$

8. Write a conclusion that summarizes the results of your investigation and states whether the hypothesis was correct or incorrect.

Lab Investigation 1.3

Modeling the Hydrologic Cycle

Objective:

- **Design** and **construct** a model that demonstrates the processes of the hydrologic cycle.

Background Information:

The hydrologic or water cycle describes the movement and storage of water on planet Earth. Scientists and teachers use models as tools to explain how natural systems work. The more we know about the processes involved, the more accurately the models can reflect what actually happens.

You probably began your study of the water cycle in the lower grades and your teachers may have created models to demonstrate the processes, but these models probably showed just a few of the processes that occur in the water cycle. In some models pictures rather than the actual events may have represented the processes.

Refer to [Section 1.7, "Cycles in the Ecosystem"] for a complete description of the hydrologic cycle (pages 33–34) and to review the following processes:

condensation	**precipitation**
evaporation	**runoff**
infiltration	**seepage**
percolation	**transpiration**

Safety precautions: **Follow all safety procedures when working in a laboratory.**

Procedure:

Design a Model

Your team will design a model of the water cycle that demonstrates each of the processes in the list above. The processes should be as much like the events in the natural cycle as possible. Your design should include the following:

(1) A diagram showing the model.

(2) A list of materials needed to construct the model.

(3) Instructions for assembling and using the model.

Cost is an important factor. Expensive models may be great educational tools, but high cost may limit the number of schools that can afford to buy the model.

Your job is to design and create a model that costs less than $20 and is easy to assemble and use. Materials used to make the model should be readily available.

Evaluate the Design

1. Develop a list of criteria that you would use to assess a model of the hydrologic cycle.
2. Evaluate a model designed by another team while another team evaluates your model.
3. Return the design to the team along with your evaluation.
4. Consider the comments on the evaluation of your design and make any changes necessary to improve your design.

Construct a Model

1. Choose one or more of the designs and construct the model(s) of the hydrologic cycle.
2. Observe the model and determine how well the model demonstrates the processes.

Report

1. In your laboratory notebook, draw a diagram of the working model.
2. Write a story that summarizes the path of a molecule of water as it travels through the hydrologic cycle.

Going Further:

Create a design for a model of the carbon-oxygen cycle, the mineral cycle, or the nitrogen cycle. Include as many of the processes as possible, and represent any that won't actually occur. You may design the model for a classroom or a museum.

Field Investigation 2.1

The Effects of Air Pollution on Rubber

Objectives:

- **Identify** the features of a controlled experiment.
- **Conduct** a controlled experiment to determine the air quality at different locations.
- **Evaluate** the design of this investigation.

Background Information:

Look into the sky. Do you detect the presence of any air pollutants? Air pollutants may be present even though you can't see them. Nitrogen oxide and hydrocarbons react in the presence of sunlight to form a brownish haze called **photochemical smog**. Photochemical smog may contain as many as one hundred chemical compounds. One of these chemicals—nitrogen dioxide—causes the brownish color that is characteristic of photochemical smog.

Some pollutants are invisible. Among the invisible pollutants in photochemical smog are compounds called photochemical oxidants. The best known photochemical oxidant is ozone (O3). Ground-level ozone is considered a secondary pollutant because it is usually produced by chemical reactions in the atmosphere.

Electrical motors emit ozone. Nearly all laser printers and photocopiers emit ozone. Because of the health effects of ozone, the U.S. Occupational Safety and Health Administration (OSHA) has set limits for exposure to ozone in the workplace.

The EPA has set National Ambient Air Quality Standards for certain pollutants. One of these pollutants is ozone. The National Ambient Air Quality Standard for ozone—the maximum amount of ozone allowed in the air we breathe—is an 8-hour average of 0.08 ppm. In 1998, the EPA designated 38 nonattainment areas (cities or metropolitan areas in the U.S. where O_3 standards were not met) for ground-level ozone pollution.

Why did the EPA set standards for ozone? Ozone affects the respiratory system of humans and other animals. Ozone causes coughing, chest discomfort, respiratory tract and eye irritation, and decreased pulmonary (lung) function in humans. Unhealthy levels of ozone generally occur during late spring and summer.

Controlled Experiment:

A carefully controlled experiment may prove a cause-and-effect relationship. In a **controlled experiment** there is only one difference between two groups of subjects. The one condition that differs between the two groups is the **variable**. Subjects in the **experimental group** are exposed to the condition being tested.

The subjects that are not exposed to the condition make up the **control group**. The subjects in the experimental group(s) are compared to the subjects in the control group. This comparison is necessary to establish cause and effect.

The effect of ozone on horses was examined in a controlled experiment. Half of the horses were exposed to ozone while exercising on a treadmill. The remaining horses breathed ozone-free air. The lungs of horses in both groups were examined with an endoscope after exercise. The examination revealed swelling and bleeding in the lungs of horses exposed to ozone during exercise.

Controlled experiments have shown that certain air pollutants have damaging effects upon materials. Sulfur dioxide damages stone, metals, paper and leather. Ozone causes rubber products to deteriorate. See the following chart for more details:

The Harmful Effects of Air Pollutants on Selected Materials

Material	Principal Air Pollutants	Effects
Stone Concrete	sulfur dioxide nitric acid particulates	surface erosion discoloration soiling
Metals	sulfur dioxide sulfuric acid nitric acid hydrogen sulfide	corrosion corrosion tarnishing loss of strength
Paper	sulfur dioxide	embrittlement discoloration
Rubber	ozone	cracking loss of strength
Leather	sulfur dioxide	surface deterioration loss of strength

Designing a Controlled Experiment:

Scientific investigations often begin with an observation. The observation leads the scientist to ask questions.

- **Observation**: The leaves of a plant are stunted and curled.
- **Question**: What is causing the abnormal appearance of the leaves?

The scientist may find the answer to the question by reviewing information available on the subject. A visit to the library may be required to find out what studies have already been done. If the question has not been answered by previous studies, the scientist may design a controlled experiment to determine the cause of the abnormal condition.

When designing the experiment, the scientist must consider the following:

- **Grouping of subjects**: There must be a minimum of two different groups of subjects—an experimental group and a control group. In some experiments there will be more than one experimental group.
- **Number of subjects**: The validity of the results is improved with a larger number of subjects (samples or organisms). Ten subjects are better than one. One hundred subjects are better than ten.
- **Controlling conditions**: Ideally there should be only one variable or condition that differs between the two groups. This is difficult in experiments where the subjects are humans.
- **Cost**: The design of the experiment may be limited by the funds available for the research. The observations that can be made may be limited by the cost of the equipment necessary.
- **Space**: The size and number of the samples or organisms may be limited by the space that is available to house the experiment.
- **Accuracy**: Is descriptive data sufficient or must precise measurements be taken?

Investigating Pollution in the Parking Lot

Observation: As you walk across the school parking lot, your eyes might begin to water and burn. Your friends haven't complained of any symptoms. The symptoms occur only in the afternoon as you leave school. They appear on some days, but not on others. The symptoms always disappear shortly after leaving the parking lot.

First Question: Could it be that air pollution in the parking lot is causing the symptoms?

Searching for Information: A search of information on air pollution reveals that ozone might be causing the symptoms. According to the table, ozone also damages rubber. The tires on your car are made of rubber. This leads you to a second question.

Second Question: Could the level of air pollution in the parking lot be high enough to damage rubber?

The Experiment: The level of pollutants in the air (ppm) can be measured using specially designed equipment. Equipment that is designed to measure levels of air pollutants is expensive. Although the equipment will provide quick and accurate information, it is not necessary to answer the questions above.

The effects of pollutants can be demonstrated by a controlled experiment. In this experiment, rubber is used as a detector of air pollution. By examining the effects of the air on rubber samples, we can compare the quality of air at different locations.

Materials:

(per class)
louvered shelter (see picture on next page)
string or wire

(per group)
2 clothes pins
2-2x2 slide mounts
rubber balloons
masking tape
ink pen
plastic wrap
stereoscope (magnifying lens)
scissors
modeling clay
2 tin cans
Investigation Report

Safety precautions: Follow all safety rules when working in the laboratory or field.

Procedure:

1. Use scissors to cut the "neck" off of a round 9-inch party balloon. Then insert the tip of the scissors and cut the balloon in half following the fold.
2. Stretch one half of the balloon across a 2x2 slide mount.
3. Secure the balloon with masking tape being sure to cover only the edges. Make sure the corners are secured with tape. The portion of the balloon stretched across the opening in the slide mount must be exposed on both sides.

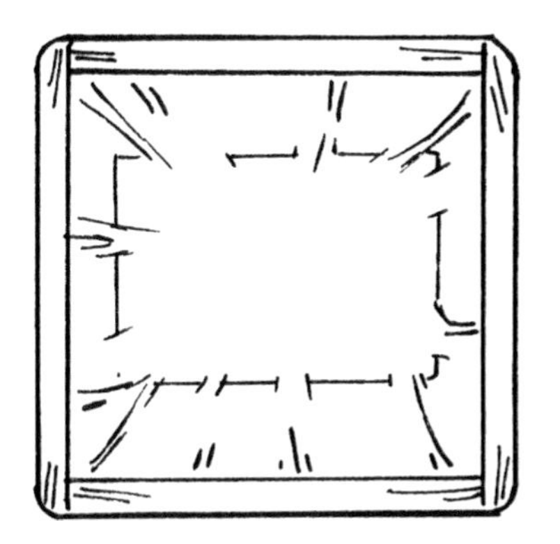

4. Use an ink pen to write labels on the masking tape. If using a marker, make sure it is a permanent marker. Label one rubber sample "experimental" and one slide "control." Also include names and class information on this label.
5. Use a stereoscope or magnifying glass to observe both rubber samples and record any marks, holes, or other imperfections in the balloons. The record may include drawings and/or descriptions.
6. Wrap the slide marked "control" in one layer of plastic wrap and secure with tape along the edge of the slide. Make sure the tape does not cover the center of the rubber sample. As an alternative, you may place the sample in a clear plastic bag.
7. Place these "pollution detectors" in various locations at school and/or at home. Mark each detector with the location and the date. Both an experimental and a control sample must be placed at each location.

Consider the following when determining where to place the detectors:

A. Locate each detector so that the sun or light does not shine directly on the material and so that the material is exposed to the air. Place detectors in a louvered shelter or use modeling clay to secure a 2x2 slide in a tin can or juice can that has both ends removed.

B. Locate one set of detectors so that they receive exhaust fumes from nearby traffic.

C. Locate one set of detectors near an electric motor or copy machine.

D. Locate one set of detectors in a room in your house.

8. Collect and observe the detectors once each week for two months or until obvious changes occur in the experimental sample. Use a magnifying glass or stereoscope to examine the rubber for cracks. Gently press your finger against the balloon to assess the strength of the rubber. Compare the experimental samples to the control samples.
9. Record observations in the chart on your Investigation Report.

Louvered shelter for air pollution detectors.

Field Investigation 2.2

Monitoring the Intensity of Ultraviolet Radiation

Objectives:

- **Compare** the intensity of ultraviolet radiation in different environments.
- **Evaluate** various forms of protection from exposure to UV radiation.

Background Information:

We have learned that the ozone shield in the stratosphere prevents most but not all of the sun's harmful ultraviolet rays from reaching the Earth. We know that chlorine from CFCs and other related chemicals destroys the ozone, and that the thinning of the ozone shield is a global environmental problem. Scientists tell us that exposure to ultraviolet light increases our risk of developing skin cancer and cataracts.

Some people enjoy sun bathing. In the 1960s and 70s people covered themselves with baby oil or suntan lotion and basked in the warmth of the sun's rays. Today, according to researchers at the University of Florida, the use of sunscreen is an everyday necessity in all seasons anywhere the sun is shining, not just in warm sunny climates.

UV exposure varies with the time of day, season of the year, latitude and altitude. Clouds partially screen UV rays. Water, sand and snow reflect UV rays and increase exposure. UV exposure is strongest between the peak hours of 10 a.m. and 4 p.m.

To protect yourself from the sun, you might sit in the shade or at least under a beach umbrella. The American Academy of Dermatology and the Skin Cancer Foundation recommend that you wear clothing that covers your body and shades your face and neck. They also recommend that you apply sunscreen with SPF-15 or higher to all exposed areas of the body, even on cloudy days.

In this investigation you will examine the difference in the intensity of ultraviolet radiation in different environments. You will also examine the amount of protection provided by different types of clothing, sunglasses, and sunscreens.

Materials:

(per class)

acrylic sheet
sunscreens
lotions without sunscreen
wax pencil
black plastic bag

(per group)

UV intensity meter & lens tester
sunprint® paper envelope
three-dimensional objects
cardboard or clipboard
watch or timer
paper towels
container with water
scraps of material or clothing
sunglasses
hats or caps
Investigation Report

Safety precautions: Follow all safety rules when working in the field or laboratory.

Procedure:

Measuring Ultraviolet Radiation using a UV Intensity Meter and Lens Tester

1. The National Weather Service monitors the ultraviolet radiation in 58 cities throughout the United States. Some newspapers report UV Index levels along with air quality and weather predictions. Ultraviolet Index forecasts are also reported on the Internet at http://iwin.nws.noaa.gov/iwin/us/ultraviolet.html. Find the UV Index forecast for the city nearest your location on the day of this investigation.
2. The UV Index forecast by the National Weather Service is based on predicted cloud cover and atmospheric conditions for a particular city. Changing weather conditions may alter the UV Index. As you travel away from the city, changes in cloud cover, elevation, and reflective surfaces (sand, snow, etc.) may also alter the UV Index.

   Use the UV Monitor and Lens Tester to determine the range (high, moderate, or low) of UV radiation at the location where there is direct sunlight. Be sure to read the instructions carefully and do not overexpose the UV Monitor to the sunlight. This will reduce the accuracy and life span of the monitor.
3. Return the UV Intensity Meter to the envelope and avoid laying the envelope in the direct sunlight. Assign one person in your group to be the caretaker of the meter.
4. Record the date and the UV Intensity Meter Reading in the first row of the table on your Investigation Report.

Procedures for using Sunprint® paper:

1. Select a three-dimensional object. A small paperback book or box works well.
2. Place the flat surface (cardboard, clipboard) in direct sunlight. If using a box or tray, turn it upside down to avoid reflections or shadows.
3. Pour 5 cm of water in a flat container.
4. Remove a sheet of Sunprint® paper from the protective envelope and place it on the flat surface with the blue side facing the sun.
5. Immediately place the three-dimensional object on the paper and note the time. Expose the paper until the exposed area turns almost white (1 to 5 minutes). Do not overexpose.
6. When the paper is almost white, note the time that has elapsed and immediately rinse the paper in the water for about 1 minute.
7. Place the paper between two paper towels to absorb the excess moisture and lay the Sunprint® on a flat surface to dry.
8. In the chart on your Investigation Report, record the intensity of the blue color using one + for light blue and increasing the number of +'s to indicate darker color.

Compare the Intensity of Ultraviolet Radiation in Different Environments:

1. Select several other locations to monitor the intensity of the ultraviolet radiation.
2. Use both the UV Intensity Meter and the Sunprint® paper. Be sure to follow the same procedures, and use the same exposure time as the direct sunlight exposure.
3. Record the results in the data chart.
4. On a cloudy day, monitor the UV intensity at the location where the direct sunlight was moitored.
5. Compare the results and answer the questions on your Investigation Report.

How Well can we Protect Ourselves from Ultraviolet Radiation?

1. Test the effectiveness of clothing in protecting your skin from UV radiation using one or more of the following methods.

   A. Place small pieces of different types of cloth on

a piece of paper and label each. Quickly transfer the pieces of cloth to corresponding positions on a sheet of Sunprint® paper. Expose the paper to direct sunlight using the same exposure time as in prior tests. After rinsing, compare the intensity of the color in the areas covered by each type of cloth. When the paper has dried, write the name of the material on the space that it covered.

B. Place a small piece of Sunprint® paper beneath clothing you wear for outdoor activities. Leave part of the paper exposed to the sunlight for comparison. Use the same exposure time as in prior tests. Rinse, dry in a flat position and label.

C. Repeat the procedure placing a piece of Sunprint® paper in the shade created by a hat or cap. Allow the paper to extend below the shadow created by the hat.

D. Repeat the procedure placing a piece of Sunprint® paper behind sunglasses allowing the paper to extend beyond the rims of the glasses.

E. Place the lens tester located on the upper right-hand corner of the UV Intensity Meter behind the lens of the sunglasses and hold them in direct sunlight for 20 seconds. Note any change in color.

2. Record the results in the data chart on the Investigation Report.

3. Compare the effectiveness of sunscreens using the following procedures. Consider testing baby oil and a lotion that does not contain sunscreen.

A. Cover a small area of the acrylic sheet with a thin layer of the substance to be tested.

B. Using the wax pencil, write the name of the substance and SPF number of the sunscreen on the acrylic sheet below the area covered.

C. Repeat steps A and B for each substance to be tested. Be sure to leave one area untreated (no sunscreen) as a control.

D. Place a sheet of Sunprint® paper on a flat surface and place the acrylic sheet with the lotions on top of the paper. Expose the paper for the same exposure time as in prior tests. Rinse, dry in a flat position and label.

E. Record the results in the data chart on your investigation report and answer the questions.

Lab Investigation 2.3

Weather Conditions and the Germination of Seeds

Objective:

- **Design** and **conduct** an investigation that will answer questions about the effects of weather conditions on the germination of seeds.

Background Information:

Each spring farmers spend thousands of dollars to plant crops. The cost includes the fuel for tractors to pull the various pieces of equipment that prepare the soil and sow the seeds. More money is spent for hybrid seeds, fertilizer to provide the nutrients to make seeds grow, herbicides to reduce competition with weeds, and insecticides to protect seeds from being eaten by uninvited guests.

Farmers make a huge investment of time and money without any guarantee of producing a crop. They can improve their chances of a successful crop if they know the conditions necessary for the germination of the seed. Choosing the correct time to plant a crop may improve the germination rate of the seeds.

To find out if the soil and weather conditions are favorable for germination, farmers rely upon the weather forecast. What would happen if:

- The farmer plants the seeds and it doesn't rain for 2 weeks?
- It rains and the low-lying field is flooded for a few hours or a few days?
- There is a hard driving rainstorm that packs the soil?
- It is an unusually cold and wet spring?

Your assignment:

Your team will plan and conduct an investigation that is designed to answer specific questions about the effects of weather conditions on the germination of seeds. In this investigation you will determine the question to be answered and design the procedure to find the answer.

Discuss each step in the planning process with your teacher. This will ensure that you don't waste time planning an experiment that cannot be conducted due to the lack of necessary equipment or time. Your teacher will also need to confirm that you are following proper safety procedures.

Your first job is to decide what question you want to ask. Questions are often stated in the form of a hypothesis. Your investigation will prove whether your hypothesis is correct or incorrect. Refer to the background information on pages 478–479 of "The Effects of Air Pollution on Rubber," to review the design of a controlled experiment.

To design your experiment, refer to the following checklist:

Using the Scientific Method to Design and Conduct an Investigation

- ☐ Ask the question and formulate a testable hypothesis.
- ☐ Plan an investigation to test the hypothesis. Decide what observations and measurements will be made.
- ☐ Select suitable equipment (consider cost and space available).
- ☐ Conduct the investigation.
- ☐ Collect and record data.
- ☐ Analyze data and make inferences or predictions.
- ☐ Report the conclusions drawn from the results of the investigation.

Lab Investigation 3.1

Testing and Fertilizing the Soil

Objectives:

- **Determine** the pH and the level of nutrients in a soil sample using a soil test kit.
- **Select** synthetic and organic fertilizers that supply the proper balance of nutrients.
- **Select** an additive, if needed, to adjust the pH.

Background Information:

Whether planting a garden, trying to establish a new lawn, or planting a field of corn, it is important to know the level of nutrients in the soil. If the soil has not been tested, it is best to send soil samples to a professional laboratory for analysis. The results of the soil tests will also tell you which kind and how much fertilizer to apply.

A quick way to check for the three primary nutrients and the pH level is to use a soil test kit. These kits are available at lawn and garden supply centers. Information provided with the kits explains how to interpret the test results and how to choose the correct fertilizer.

Materials:

(per student)
chemical splash goggles
chemical-resistant aprons
chemical-resistant gloves
Investigation Report
(per group)
soil test kit with instructions
Material Safety Data Sheet (MSDS)
soil sample

Safety precautions: Safety goggles and chemical-resistant gloves must be worn when testing the soil samples and cleaning up. Follow all safety rules when working in the field or laboratory. Dispose of test samples as directed by your teacher.

Procedure:

1. Determine the source of the soil to be tested. Collect a sample using clean equipment. Do not touch the sample with your hands.

2. Follow the directions in the soil test kit and appropriate safety procedures. Test the soil for nitrogen, phosphorus, and potassium levels and determine the pH.
3. Record the test results for nitrogen, phosphorus, and potassium as high, medium, or low in the data chart. This describes the amount of nutrient in the soil. Also, record the pH number.

Analysis of Data:

1. In the "amount needed" row of the chart of your Investigation Report, use the following statements to write the word that describes the amount of each nutrient needed to improve the soil:
   - If the amount of the nutrient present is low, the amount needed is high.
   - If the amount of the nutrient present is medium, the amount needed is medium.
   - If the amount of the nutrient present is high, the amount needed is low or none.
2. Most plants grow well if the pH of the soil is between 6.0 and 7.0. If the pH number is less than 6.0, write "raise" in the space provided in the chart. If the pH number is greater than 7.0, write "lower." If the pH is between 6.0 and 7.0, write "o.k." in the space provided.
3. Synthetic fertilizers usually contain a mixture of the three major nutrients—nitrogen, phosphorus and potassium. The amount of each of the nutrients in the mixed fertilizer is listed on the label as a series of three numbers such as 5–10–5. Other combinations are available including 12-12-12, 8-24-8, 10-20-20, and 8-32-16.
   - The first number always represents the percentage of nitrogen.
   - The second number is the percentage of phosphate as (P_2O_5).
   - The third number is the percentage of potash as (K_2O).

   One hundred pounds of fertilizer labeled 12-12-12 contains: 12 pounds of nitrogen, 12 pounds of phosphate and 12 pounds of potash. Thirty-six of the 100 pounds are nutrients. Synthetic fertilizers may also contain secondary nutrients and micronutrients. The law requires that all nutrients and their concentrations be listed on the label. Most of the weight of a bag of fertilizer is the filler substance that allows the dry fertilizer to be more evenly spread.
4. Based on the results of your soil test, which of the synthetic fertilizers listed in Step 3 would you select for your soil? Record your choice in the data chart on your Investigation Report.
5. Listed below are some "organic" fertilizers that are available. The numbers are approximate values and depend upon the source of fertilizer.

Bone Meal	4-24-0
Composted Cow Manure	1-1-1
Dried Blood	12-0-0
Fish Emulsion	5-1-1
Peat	2-0.5-1
Rock Phosphate	0-5-0
Soybean Meal	7-1-2
Wood Ashes	0-1.5-5

   Based on the results of your soil test, which of the organic fertilizers listed above would you select for your soil? Record your choice in the data chart on your Investigation Report.

6. Listed below are some examples of plants and the pH range that they prefer.

   pH 4.0–5.0: rhododendrons, camellias, azaleas, blueberries, fern, spruce

   pH 5.0–6.0: pines, firs, holly, spruce, oaks, birch, willow, rhododendron

   pH 6.0–7.0: maple, mountain ash, pansy, peaches, carrots, lettuce, pines, firs

   pH 7.0–8.0: beech, mock orange, asparagus, sagebrush

   Based on the results of your soil test, which of these plants would grow well in your soil without any adjustment of the pH?
7. Complete the analysis questions on your Investigation Report.

The Human Population–Too Many People?

Objectives:

- **Analyze** population data.
- **Predict** future population trends.
- **Evaluate** the impacts of population growth and lifestyle on natural resources.

Background Information:

Experts tell us that we are living in the midst of an explosion—an explosion of the human population. The world population has increased from an estimated 6 million in 10,000 BC to more than 6 billion in 2000 AD. The world's population continues to grow by about 78 million people each year.

The rate of population growth is dependent upon two factors—birth rate and death rate. The **birth rate** is the number of infants born in a given year per 1000 people in the population. The **death rate** is the number of people who die in a given year per 1000 individuals in the population.

Zero population growth means that the population is in equilibrium—the number of births and deaths are equal. If the birth rate is less than the death rate, the population declines or there is **negative population growth**. If this trend continues the species will eventually become extinct.

If the birth rate exceeds the death rate, the population increases. Without limiting factors that control the birth rate, there is a population explosion. The **growth rate** describes how fast a population is increasing or decreasing. The world population growth rate in 1999 was 1.4%.

The natural growth rate or **natural increase** is calculated by subtracting the deaths from the births per 1000 population and then dividing by 10. The total population growth of a country is also affected by the net migration (immigrants – emigrants) of people.

The Earth may be considered as one huge ecosystem. What is the Earth's carrying capacity? How many people can the Earth support? No one knows the answer to this question, but we do know that the number and the lifestyle of the people using the resources affect the carrying capacity. While most of the population growth—as much as 97%—is occurring in developing countries, each person born in an industrialized nation places a greater demand upon the Earth's resources.

As the world population continues to increase, will we be able to sustain our current lifestyle? Currently food shortages are often due to political actions or poverty rather than the ability of the planet to produce and provide. Will the world population eventually exceed the Earth's ability to provide food and other natural resources? Study the data and see what you think about the issue of overpopulation.

Table A:
World Population Data 1-2000

Year	Poplulation (in Millions)	Year	Poplulation (in Millions)
1	170	1600	545
200	190	1700	610
400	190	1750	760
600	200	1800	900
800	220	1850	1210
1000	265	1900	1625
1100	320	1950	2515
1200	360	2000	6020
1300	360	2050	?
1400	350	2100	?
1500	425	2150	?

SOURCE: Zero Population Growth and Population Reference Bureau

Table B:
World Population Data 1950-2000

Year	Population (in Billions)
1950	2.6
1955	2.8
1960	3.0
1965	3.3
1970	3.7
1975	4.1
1980	4.5
1985	4.9
1990	5.3
1995	5.7
2000	6.0*

SOURCE: World Watch Institute Vital Signs 1993, Population Reference Bureau.
*Year 2000 is estimate based on U.S. Census Bureau Projection

Food Production 1950-1997

Year	Grain Production (kg per person)	Soybean Production (kg per person)	Fish Catch (kg per person)
1950	247	6.5	7.5
1955	273	7.0	9.5
1960	271	8.2	12.0
1965	270	9.5	14.7
1970	291	11.9	15.7
1975	303	16.1	15.3
1980	321	18.2	15.0
1985	339	20.0	16.2
1990	335	19.7	16.2
1995	301	22.0	15.9
1997	322	26.0	16.0

SOURCE: World Watch Institute Vital Signs 1998.

Materials:
Graph paper
Environmental Issues Worksheet

Procedure:
1. Using data in table A, plot the world population data from the year 1500 to the year 2000. Place the independent variable (time) on the horizontal or x axis and the dependent variable (population) on the vertical or y axis.
2. Determine a scale that will allow use of the full page (at least three-fourths) of the graph paper. Label the graph "World Population Growth 1500–2000."
3. Draw a best line to fit the plotted points. This graph shows the growth in the human population since the discovery of America.
4. Following the procedure outlined above, create a separate graph using the data in Table B. Use 5-year time intervals. Label the graph "World Population Growth 1950–2000. This graph shows the population growth during the life of a middle-aged person—perhaps your parents or teachers.
5. Analyze the data in the charts and graphs by answering the questions and completing the charts in the Investigation Report.
6. Create a concept map connecting the Environmental Factors from question 13 to the word HUMAN POPULATION and write a few words on the connecting line to show the impact of an increasing population. Also draw lines to show connections between changing Environmental Factors.

POPULATION LINK

Going Further:
California's Central Valley lost 140,000 acres of farmland between 1974 and 1986 to development. Some of the best farmland (nutrient-rich soil) in the United States is in California's Central Valley. Based on current development demands, the valley will lose an additional 300,000 acres of farmland by 2010.

Your job is to create a plan for development that will provide the housing needs of the expanding population and at the same time maintain open space and reduce the pressure on the development of farmland. Your plan should also address other environmental problems such as water use and air quality.

Environmental Issue 3.3

Examining the Causes of Human Population Growth

Objectives:
- **Relate** family size to exponential growth of a population.
- **Calculate** exponential growth of a population.

Background Information:
The UN officially recognized October 12, 1999, as the day the Earth's population reached six billion, only 12 years after it reached five billion. Two countries, India and China, are officially population "billionaires." According to the UN Population Division, India's population reached 1 billion in August 1999.

Although India had the first family planning program of any developing country, in many areas of the country the government's efforts to control population growth have not been successful. According to the director of the UN Population Division, it took 454 years for the world population to increase from 345 million to one billion, and it took only 52 years for India's population to grow from 345 million to one billion.

World population growth has slowed slightly, but growth is expected to continue. India is not the only country concerned about population growth. Government statements discouraging high birth rates, appear in the national policies of 85 developing countries. As many as 65 of these countries are expected to double their populations in the next 30 years or less.

Net migration also affects the population of countries and cities. Pennsylvania has one of the slowest growing populations in the U.S. because the natural increase is offset by the migration of people to other states. Since World War II, Florida's population has grown mostly due to migration from other states and from Latin America. In this Environmental Issue, we will examine the effects of the birth rate and migration on the population of various countries and states.

Materials:

Graph paper
Large sheets of paper
Colored pencils
Calculators
Environmental Issues (Worksheet)

Procedure:

Family Size and Population Growth

1. Although it is relatively rare, more people are living to the age of 100. Three women—one in China, one in the United States, and one in India—live to celebrate their 100th birthday. Create diagrams (family trees or pedigrees) that show the difference in the number of direct descendants attending the celebrations if:
   A. The Chinese woman's family is a "one-child family."
   B. The American woman's family is a "two-child family."
   C. The Indian woman's family is a "three-child family."

   For this problem, use the following assumptions:
   - Although the number of children represent more recent birth rates for women in these countries, these families have maintained the birth rate for 6 generations.
   - The first child in each generation was born when the mother was about 20.
   - All children produce the same number of offspring.
   - All of the direct descendants are surviving and able to attend the celebration.
   - Although spouses would be present, they will not be included in the family tree.
2. On the left side of the diagram mark the generation. On the right side of the diagram mark the number in each generation and the total number of people surviving following the births in each generation.
3. Graph the population growth in the three families. Use a full sheet of graph paper and plot the generations on the x axis and the total number of people on the y axis. Use different colors or symbols for each family.
4. Answer the analysis questions on the Worksheet.

Calculating Exponential Growth

Earth City has the fastest annual growth rate (10%) of any city on the planet. At the entrance to the city, construction workers have posted a new sign that says: "Earth City — Population: 1 Million."

1. Your job is to determine the population growth of the city during the next decade. Assume that the growth rate remains constant. To find the size of the population, multiply the current population by 10% (0.1) and add the answer to the current population. Repeat this for each of the 10 years.
2. Record your answers in the chart on the Worksheet and answer the analysis questions.

SOURCE: World Watch Institute Vital Signs 1998

Lab Investigation 4.1

The Effect of Temperature on Dissolved Oxygen

Objectives:

- **Determine** the effect of temperature on DO.
- **Calculate** the percentage saturation.
- **Describe** the effect of an increase in temperature on the aquatic ecosystem.

Background Information:

Dissolved oxygen (DO) is essential to most aquatic life. Some species of fish require higher amounts of DO than other species. While trout and salmon need between 6 and 15 mg/L of DO, carp and catfish can survive in water with only 4 to 8 mg/L of DO.

Much of the oxygen dissolved in the water comes from the atmosphere. Algae and plants also produce oxygen through photosynthesis. The amount of oxygen that can dissolve in water depends upon the water temperature. Sometimes during heat waves when the temperature of the water increases, some species of fish are not able to survive.

In this investigation, you will determine the DO levels and the percentage oxygen saturation in two model lakes. The lakes are similar, and usually the DO levels in both lakes are nearly identical. One of the lakes has experienced a heat wave. Compare the DO levels in the two lakes and determine which lake has been affected by the heat wave.

Materials:

(per class)	(per group)	(per student)
2 large containers (10-12 quart)	DO test kit instructions	chemical splash goggles
hot plate	Material Safety Data Sheet (MSDS)	chemical-resistant apron
tap water	thermometer	chemical-resistant gloves

Safety precautions: Safety goggles and chemical-resistant gloves must be worn at all times when collecting and testing samples and cleaning up. Follow all safety rules. Dispose of chemicals as directed by your teacher.

Procedure:

1. In your laboratory notebook, create a chart to record the names of the lakes, the temperatures (°C), the DO test results (mg/L) and the percentage saturation.

Name of Lake	Water Temperature	Dissolved Oxygen (mg/L)	Percent Oxygen Saturation

2. Determine the temperature of the model lakes. Record the temperatures in the chart in your laboratory notebook.
3. Obtain a DO test kit and read the instructions. Identify each piece of equipment in the kit. Read the labels on the containers of chemicals (reagents) and note any safety precautions (each item in a Lamotte test kit has a number). By matching the number in the instructions with the number on each item, you can be sure that you are following the correct procedure.
4. Collect a sample of water from one lake as described in the kit instructions. It is very important that no air bubbles are present in the sample.
5. Test the sample for DO according to the instructions. Record the results in the chart.
6. Test a sample from in the second lake according to the instructions. Record the results in the chart.
7. Use the table on page 489 to calculate the percentage oxygen saturation. Use the formula below and record the results in your chart.

$$\frac{\text{Actual (measured) DO (mg/L)}}{\text{Maximum Potential DO (mg/L)}} \times 100 = \%\ \text{Saturation}$$

In the Field:

Determine the DO level and percentage oxygen saturation of aquatic ecosystems near your home or school. Find out what type of fish live in the ecosystem. Infer what might happen during a prolonged heat wave.

Analysis:

Write the answers to the following questions in your laboratory notebook:

1. Which of the lakes tested was most likely affected by a prolonged heat wave?
2. What other conditions might account for the difference in the DO levels?
3. Based on the DO level, what type of fish would you expect to find in each lake? What effect would the heat wave have on the fish?
4. The percentage oxygen saturation of aquatic ecosystem is one factor that determines whether it is a healthy ecosystem. According to the *Field Manual for Water Quality Monitoring*, an aquatic ecosystem is considered excellent if it is 91–110% saturated, good if it is 71–90% saturated, and fair if it is 51–70% saturated. Below 50% oxygen saturation the health of an aquatic ecosystem is poor. Based on your results, is either lake a healthy ecosystem? If so, which one(s)?

   Note: Even though the percentage oxygen saturation may be good, if there is not enough dissolved oxygen to meet the needs of the fish, the fish cannot survive.

Maximum Potential Dissolved Oxygen Table

Temp. °C	DO (mg/L)	Temp. °C	DO (mg/L)
0	14.60	23	8.56
1	14.19	24	8.40
2	13.81	25	8.24
3	13.44	26	8.09
4	13.09	27	7.95
5	12.75	28	7.81
6	12.43	29	7.67
7	12.12	30	7.54
8	11.83	31	7.41
9	11.55	32	7.28
10	11.27	33	7.16
11	11.01	33	7.16
12	10.76	34	7.05
13	10.52	35	6.93
14	10.29	36	6.82
15	10.07	37	6.71
16	9.85	38	6.61
17	9.65	39	6.51
18	9.45	40	6.41
19	9.26	41	6.31
20	9.07	42	6.22
21	8.90	43	6.13
22	8.72	44	6.04

Lab Investigation 4.2

Thermal Pollution

Objectives:

- **Explain** the effect of temperature on the density of water.
- **Observe** the effect of heat on the metabolism of fish.
- **Describe** the effects of thermal pollution on an aquatic ecosystem.

Background Information:

Industries and electric power plants discharge warm water into rivers. This can create a condition called thermal pollution. In this investigation you will examine the effect of the warm wastewater on an aquatic ecosystem and how the warmer temperatures affect the metabolism of fish.

Part I: When Hot Water meets Cold Water

Materials:

1 large beaker or jar
1 foam-insulated drinking cup
red food coloring
blue food coloring
dissecting needle
stirring rod
hot and cold water
ice cubes

Safety precautions: Follow all safety rules when working in the laboratory.

Procedure:

1. Fill the beaker or jar 3/4 full of cold water. This represents a lake or river.
2. Nearly fill a foam-insulated drinking cup with hot water, add one or two drops of red food coloring and stir. This represents the hot water produced by an industry or power plant.
3. Hold the cup of hot water so that the bottom of the cup is submerged approximately 2 cm below the surface of the cold water in the beaker or jar.

4. Submerge the dissecting needle and make a hole in the side of the cup below the level of the water. Make sure the hole is large enough for water to flow from the cup. This represents the industry or power plant outfall pipe through which the hot wastewater is released into the lake.
5. In your laboratory notebook draw a diagram or describe what happens to the hot water.
6. Fill the beaker or jar 3/4 full with warm water. You may use hot water from the tap. **Caution**: Do not use water that is hot enough to burn you. This represents warm water in a lake or river.
7. Nearly fill a foam-insulated drinking cup with cold water and add one or two drops of blue food coloring. Add one ice cube to the water and stir.
8. Hold the cup of cold water so that the bottom of the cup is submerged approximately 2 cm below the surface of the warm water in the beaker or jar. This represents the water from the melting snowpack.
9. Submerge the dissecting needle and make a hole in the side of the cup below the level of the water. Make sure the hole is large enough for water to flow from the cup. This represents the spring snowmelt flowing from a mountain stream into a lake with warmer water.

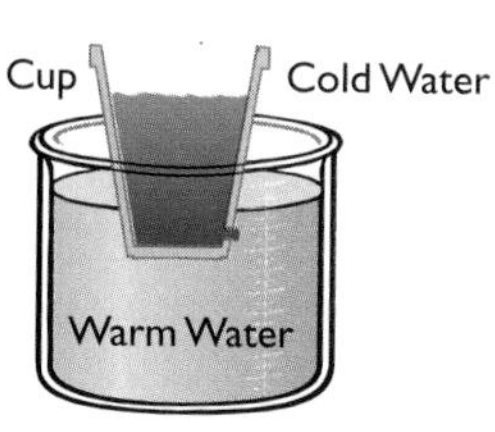

10. In your laboratory notebook draw a diagram or describe what happens when the cold water and hot water meet.

Analysis:

Write the answers to the following questions in your laboratory notebook.

1. Describe what happens when the wastewater discharged by an industry is warmer than the temperature of the water in the river. How does this affect the level of DO in the river?
2. In many bodies of water, fish move into deeper water in the summer and shallower water in the winter. Explain why some species of fish, such as trout, do this?

Part II: The Effect of Temperature Change on Fish Metabolism

Safety precaution: In this activity the safety of the fish is our greatest concern. If at any time during the investigation the breathing rate of the fish slows down (for example: 36, 24, 12 per minute) or the fish appears distressed, return it to your teacher and obtain another fish.

Creating a quiet environment with a minimum amount of movement by students at your laboratory table is important during this investigation. The breathing rate of the fish will be altered if quick movements startle it.

Materials:

(per class)
- 3 aquaria or large containers
- aquarium air pump(s)
- 1 aquarium heater
- clock with second hand

(per group)
- thermometer
- baby food jar
- 600 mL beaker
- 2 goldfish
- hydrogen peroxide (3%)
- pipette
- fish net

Procedure:

1. Copy the following table to your laboratory notebook.

Temperature	Breaths Counted/ 15 sec.	/minute	Average breaths/min.
	Trial 1. ____ x 4 = Trial 2. ____ x 4 = Trial 3. ____ x 4 =	____ ____ ____	
	Trial 1. ____ x 4 = Trial 2. ____ x 4 = Trial 3. ____ x 4 =	____ ____ ____	

2. Nearly fill a baby food jar with water from the aquarium that does not have a heater. The temperature of this aquarium should be about 68°F (21°C).
3. Add 4 drops of hydrogen peroxide to the water. This will provide an additional oxygen supply for the fish.
4. Place one gold fish in the jar and put the cap on the jar.

5. Set the jar in the 600 mL beaker. Add enough water from the aquarium to cover the jar.
6. Carry the beaker to your lab table and allow the fish a few minutes to adjust to the new environment.
7. Patiently observe the fish and count the number of "breaths" it takes in 15 seconds. One "breath" is an opening and closing of the mouth. You may need to start the count again if the fish moves. Be quiet and patient. Repeat the count for two more trials and record the data in the first row of the table.
8. Record the temperature of the water in the beaker in the first row of the table.
9. Return the fish to your teacher.
10. Nearly fill the baby food jar with water from the aquarium that has a heater. The temperature of this aquarium should be near 80°F (26°C).
11. Add 4 drops of hydrogen peroxide to the water. This will provide an additional oxygen supply for the fish.
12. Add one gold fish to the jar and place the cap on the jar.
13. Set the jar in the 600 mL beaker. Add water that has been heated to a maximum temperature of 100°F (38°C). Add enough water to cover the jar.
14. Repeat step 6 through 8 recording the data in the second row of the table.
15. Return the fish to your teacher.
16. Calculate the average number of breaths per minute. Share and discuss class data.

Analysis:

Write the answers to the following questions in your laboratory notebook:

1. How does the breathing rate of a fish change as the temperature of the environment changes? What does this indicate about the metabolism rate?
2. Give two ways in which the dumping of hot water by industries contributes to the death of fish in the lake or river.
3. How can industries avoid harming the fish in a river or lake?

Environmental Issue 4.3

Blue Crabs from the Bay–Managing a Natural Resource

Objectives:

- **Develop** a strategy for managing a natural resource that will provide a sustainable harvest.

Background Information:

There are many other bays, but no other bay is as complex or as productive as the Chesapeake. Estuaries, like the Chesapeake Bay, are important protein factories. The Chesapeake Bay supports more fish and wildlife than any other estuary. Most of the seafood for the Atlantic Coast comes from the Bay.

Adult blue crabs live in the upper and middle parts of the Bay. Men and women whose occupation is harvesting crabs and oysters from the bay are commonly called watermen. Each year watermen take large numbers of adult crabs from the Bay.

In this simulation we will examine the potential effect of the watermen on the population of blue crabs in the Chesapeake Bay. Based on the definition of **sustainability**—the ability to keep in existence or maintain, how can we ensure that there is a sustainable population of blue crabs in the bay?

Materials:

(per class) 2 pounds of peanuts or other nuts
(per group) 1 plate

Safety precaution: Do not eat the peanuts used for this laboratory investigation.

Procedure:

1. Form groups of 3–5 students and give each group a plate or bowl with 20 peanuts. In this simulation each student represents a waterman who is trying to support his/her family by harvesting blue crabs from the Chesapeake Bay. Each peanut represents a quantity (number of pounds) of blue crabs. The family may eat the crabs or they may be sold to provide for the family's needs.
2. For this simulation, the crab season is only 4 days long. A day will be represented by a period of 30 seconds.

3. At the end of each day (30-second harvest) one peanut will be added for each peanut that remains in the bay (plate) but the total number of peanuts can never exceed 20.
4. You are allowed to harvest as many crabs as possible each day. During the first season, there is no discussion allowed among the watermen. Each of the watermen must decide for themselves how many crabs they will harvest.
5. At the end of the first season, make a chart that lists the name of each waterman in your group and record the number of peanuts harvested beside each name.
6. Convene a meeting of the Chesapeake Bay Watermen's Association (your group) and discuss the strategy for the harvest of blue crabs during the upcoming season. The meeting shall last no more than 5 minutes.
7. During the second season of harvest, follow the strategy outlined during the meeting. Repeat the 4-day (30 second) harvests. Record the results.
8. If you have not developed a strategy for a sustainable harvest of blue crabs, convene another meeting of the watermen's association and review the strategy for the harvest of blue crabs during the next season. The meeting shall last no more than 5 minutes.
9. During the third season of harvest, follow the strategy outlined during the meeting. Repeat the 4-day (30 second) harvests. Record the results.
10. Share your results with the class and answer the following analysis questions in your laboratory notebook.

Analysis:

1. Who harvested the most crabs during the first season? The second? The third?
2. Why were no peanuts added if there were none remaining on the plate?
3. Why was the number of peanuts added to the plate never allowed to exceed 20?
4. During your meetings, were you successful in developing a strategy for a sustainable harvest of blue crabs? If, so describe your strategy.
5. In real life, what steps have been taken to ensure a sustainable harvest of blue crabs from the Chesapeake Bay?
6. How did the size of the group affect the harvest of blue crabs? What does a larger group simulate in real life?
7. What additional factors affect the sustainability of the blue crab population in the Chesapeake Bay?

Lab Investigation 5.1*

The Sandbank Township Groundwater Problem

Objectives:

- **Make** a prediction that explains the water quality test results.
- **Analyze** water samples to **determine** the amount of a specific pollutant present.
- **Identify** the origin of the pollutant and the potentially responsible party (PRP).
- **Determine** the area of the aquifer that is contaminated by the pollutant.

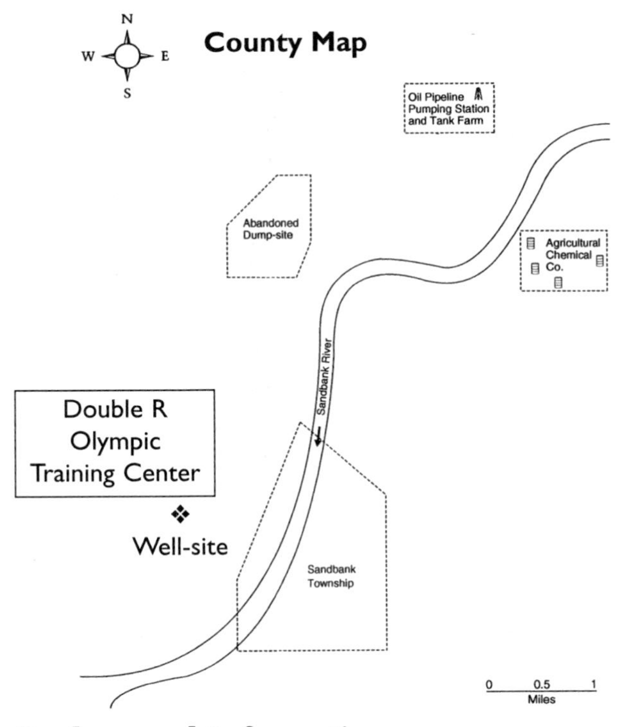

Background Information:

The Sandbank River runs through the prime agricultural region of the state. For years the economy of communities along the river has been dependent upon farming, but the economy is changing as cities expand and new landowners develop farmland. A large farm along the Sandbank River was recently sold. The new owners plan to build a facility for athletes who are in training for the Olympics.

When completed, the new facility will be called the Double R Olympic Training Center. A new well was needed to provide water for hot tubs, showers, and swimming pools, as well as for cooking meals and for drinking. Test results of water from the new Double R well revealed that the water contained 25 ppb of a toxic chemical. The maximum contaminant level (MCL) for the chemical is 10 ppb.

The population of Sandbank Township is growing rapidly as people move from the city. The source of water for the entire township is groundwater. The people in Sandbank Township are concerned about the water supply. The township officials voted funds for drilling monitoring wells and for water quality tests to determine the source of the pollutant and the area of the aquifer that is contaminated. Since this investigation was not a part of the annual budget, only limited funds were available. Officials approved funds for only 6 monitoring wells.

A water quality specialist consulted by township officials explained that the chemical may have entered the groundwater from activities at the farm or it may have come from another source and moved through the aquifer to the well site. Once chemicals reach the aquifer, they tend to spread out and form a plume of contamination much like smoke spreads out as it exits the smokestack. If the pollutant is coming from a **point source**, the highest levels of contamination will be found nearest the source and as distance from the source increases, the concentration of chemicals will be lower.

Your company has been hired to select the sites for the monitoring wells and conduct the water quality tests. Due to the presence of a toxic chemical, safety precautions must be taken.

Materials:

(per group)
6-well reaction plate
test solution (TS)
thin stem pipette for test solution
map of proposed well sites
thin stem pipette with indicator solution
white paper
colored pencils

(per class)
containers with well water samples
graduated pipettes

(per student)
chemical splash goggles
chemical-resistant gloves
chemical-resistant apron

*Lab adapted with permission from Flinn Scientific, Inc. Groundwater Contamination Investigation Kit (FB1002)

Safety precautions: Safety goggles and chemical-resistant gloves must be worn at all times when collecting and testing samples and cleaning up. Follow all safety rules when working in the laboratory.

Procedure:

1. After reading background information, make a prediction that explains the water quality test results and write it on a separate piece of paper.
2. Refer to the potential well sites on the map and select three sites to drill monitoring wells. Put on your goggles and gloves before going to the site to collect the water samples. Follow the procedure described below to collect the samples.
3. Locate the first well (lowest number) you want to sample. Use the correct pipette to collect the sample. Use the graduated pipette marked with the well number to extract exactly 1 mL of well water from the sample container and put it in the first (left-hand) depression or "well" on the reaction plate.
4. Locate the second well (second highest number) you want to sample. Use the correct pipette to collect the sample. Use the graduated pipette marked with the well number to extract exactly 1 mL of well water from the sample container and put it in the second (center) depression or "well" on the reaction plate.
5. Locate the third well (highest number) you want to sample. Use the correct pipette to collect the sample. Use the graduated pipette marked with the well number to extract exactly 1 mL of well water from the sample container and put it in the third (right-hand) depression or "well" on the reaction plate.
6. Add 2 drops of indicator solution from the thin stem pipette to each of the three wells containing water samples.
7. Fill the second thin stem pipette with the "test solution" from the container marked "TS."
8. Add one drop of the test solution to the first "well." Swirl the plate to mix the solution with the sample. Add a second drop and swirl. Continue to add drops until there is a color change. Be sure to count the drops and swirl the plate on a flat surface after each drop is added.
9. Continue adding and counting the drops until the color changes (yellow to purple) irreversibly. Then record the count on the map beside the well number.
10. Repeat steps 5–8 with the second and third samples.
11. Consider the results of these tests and select 3 additional wells to test. Repeat procedure steps 1–8 for each sample.
12. Clean up the work area and return materials to the proper location. Chemicals may be disposed of by rinsing down the drain with a large quantity of water.

Data and Analysis:

1. Based on the information below, record the concentration of pollutant in parts per billion at each site on the map.

Conversion Chart			
1 – 3 drops	=	<10 ppb (Water is safe to drink.)
4 – 6 drops	=	25 ppb
7 – 10 drops	=	50 ppb
>10 drops	=	200 ppb

2. If your test results did not confirm your hypothesis, you may need to revise your hypothesis. If you need to conduct more tests to identify the source of pollution, present your results to the township officials (teacher) and ask for funds to drill additional monitoring wells and conduct more water quality tests. Your revised hypothesis must justify the additional sites selected.
3. On the map shade the area of the aquifer that is contaminated.
4. Report your findings to the Sandbank Township Officials and recommend actions the township could take to solve the problem. If additional information is needed in order to make decisions, include this in your report.

*Lab adapted with permission from Flinn Scientific, Inc. Groundwater Contamination Investigation Kit (FB1002)

Lab Investigation 5.2

Testing the Tap Water: Part 1

Objectives:

- **Demonstrate** proper procedures for bacteriological and chemical water-quality testing of tap water.
- **Evaluate** the quality of the tap water based on the test results.

Background Information:

Most cities and towns in developed countries provide their residents with a good supply of safe drinking water. The vast majority of people in the U.S. receive water from public water systems that meet state or federal requirements for safety. Since 1998 the EPA has required drinking water systems to provide annual reports to their customers.

Information about drinking water systems is also available on the Internet at http://www.epa.gov/safewater. At this website you may be able to find out if the water system that serves your school, church, workplace or home has violated the drinking water standards. If the water supply for your home comes from a private source, usually a well, you must have the water tested.

In this investigation we will learn more about the quality of the water flowing from the tap in your school and/or home by conducting some of the same water quality tests used by water suppliers and by EPA-certified laboratories.

Copy the chart below into your laboratory notebook leaving space to describe the meaning of the test results. As you complete each test, record the results and assess the water quality based on the test results.

Date:	Water Source:	
Water Quality Test	Results	What do the results mean?
Turbidity		
Chlorine		
Coliform		
Nitrates		
Fluoride		

Safety precautions: Follow all safety rules when working in the laboratory. Follow all safety precautions and procedures on the Material Safety Data Sheet (MSDS) and instructions provided with the kit. Dispose of treated samples as directed by your teacher.

Test 1: Turbidity

Small particles in the water make the water cloudy or turbid. Although the particles themselves may not be harmful, they provide places for disease-causing organisms to hide from disinfectants. **Turbidity** is a measure of the amount of light scattered or absorbed by particles suspended in the water.

Materials:

2-250 mL beakers
tape
turbidimeter or colorimeter (optional)
distilled water
tap water

Procedure:

1. Label one beaker "tap" and one "distilled."
2. Pour 200 mL of tap water into the beaker labeled "tap".
3. Pour 200 mL of distilled water into the beaker marked "distilled."
4. Wait at least 30 seconds. As the DO is released from the cold tap water, it forms small bubbles that make the water appear cloudy.
5. Cover the labels on the beakers and change the positions of the beakers so that you do not know which sample came from the tap. Compare the water in the two beakers. Hold the beakers in front of a page with printed words. Can you see any difference in the turbidity of the two samples? Remove the labels and record the result and explain what it means in the chart in your laboratory notebook.
6. If a turbidity meter or colorimeter is available, follow the specific instructions with the meter and determine the turbidity of the tap water. The EPA standard for the turbidity of drinking water is less than 0.5 NTU (nephelometric turbidity unit). Does the tap water meet this standard? Record and explain your results.

Test 2: Chlorine Residual

Chlorine is not present in natural waters. It is used to disinfect most surface water supplies. Before the water leaves the water treatment plant, a small amount of chlorine or chloramine is added to kill any bacteria that may have survived the treatment processes or that may be in the water system.

Although some people object to the taste of chlorine, it is an inexpensive and effective disinfectant. Another advantage is that the water can easily be tested to ensure that it is safe to use. The **chlorine residual** — the amount of free chlorine remaining in the water — is usually between 0.1 and 0.4 parts per million. In some situations, a higher chlorine residual may be required to ensure the safety of the water supply.

Materials:

chlorine test kit
instruction sheet
chemical splash goggles
chemical-resistant gloves and apron
MSDS
water sample

Procedure:

1. Test the water sample for chlorine following the instructions provided with the test kit.
2. Record the test result and explain what it means in the chart in your laboratory notebook.
3. Dispose of the treated sample as directed.

Test 3: Total Coliforms

The news media reports a "Boil Water Advisory" when a water supply does not meet the standard of zero Total Coliforms. An advisory may also be issued when the water supply might be contaminated because of a water main break. The advisory is lifted after the water is tested and the test results show that the water is safe.

Most coliform bacteria are harmless, but they are often found in the presence of other organisms that cause disease. A positive test for coliforms is an indication that disease-causing organisms may be present. If more than 5% of samples tested each month contain coliform bacteria, the water system operators must report the violation of the "Total Coliform Rule" to the state.

Materials:

coliform test equipment and supplies
water sample
sterile sample containers
instruction sheet
MSDS

Procedure:

1. Test the water sample for total coliforms according to the instructions provided.
2. Incubate the sample for 24 hours and count the coliform colonies.
3. Record the test results and describe what they mean.
4. Dispose of contaminated test tubes or plates as directed.

Test 4: Nitrates

In a national survey of agricultural and urban areas, the nitrate levels in 15% of shallow wells exceeded the "safe" standard of 10 milligrams nitrate as nitrogen (NO_3–N) per liter of water. The EPA estimates that 4.5 million Americans drink water with nitrate levels exceeding the drinking water standard of 10 mg/L (NO_3–N). Nitrate levels can be reduced by reverse-osmosis or by ion-exchange systems but the processes are slow and expensive.

$$\text{Nitrate } (NO_3^-) \xrightarrow{\text{bacteria}} \text{nitrite } (NO_2)$$

If water contains more than 10 mg/L of nitrates (as nitrogen) it should not be given to infants or children less than one year old or to pregnant women. The digestive system of infants harbors bacteria that change nitrates to nitrites. Nitrites interfere with hemoglobin's ability to carry oxygen. Babies develop a bluish color, especially around the eyes and mouth — a condition, called **methemoglobinemia** (met-hee-me-glo-be-nee-mee-e) or "Blue Baby Syndrome," which can be fatal. Nitrates are not dangerous to older children and adults.

Materials:

nitrate or nitrate-nitrogen test kit
instruction sheet
chemical splash goggles
chemical-resistant gloves and apron
MSDS
water sample

Procedure:

1. Test the water sample for nitrates following the instructions provided with the kit.
2. If the test results are for nitrates (NO_3^-) rather than nitrate-nitrogen (NO_3–N), divide the result by 4.4.
3. Record the test results and describe what they mean.
4. Dispose of the treated sample as directed.

Test 5: Fluoride

Fluoride occurs naturally in some groundwater and is added to some public drinking water supplies. Very high levels of fluoride are toxic to humans, but there are few places where the water contains such high concentrations of fluoride. Most authorities agree that drinking water containing about 1 mg/L (1 ppm) of fluoride will reduce the dental decay, especially in children.

The recommended level of fluoride in drinking water is 0.7–1.2 mg/L (0.7–1.2 ppm) with the highest level recommended for cooler climates. The Environmental Protection Agency prohibits fluoride levels greater than 4 ppm in community water supplies. In regions where the natural fluoride level is greater than the 4 ppm MCL (maximum contaminant level), the amount of fluoride in the water must be reduced.

Materials:

fluoride test kit
instruction sheet
chemical splash goggles
chemical-resistant gloves and apron
MSDS
water sample

Procedure:

1. Test the water sample for fluoride following the instructions provided with the kit.
2. Record the test results and describe what the results mean.
3. Dispose of the treated sample as directed.

Analysis:

Write the answers to the following questions in your laboratory notebook.

1. Assume that you are the laboratory technician and you must mail a report on the water quality of the sample tested to the customer who brought the sample to the laboratory. Write a summary describing any problems identified and make recommendations for addressing the problems.
2. If the water supply is a public water supply, would you recommend adding fluoride to the water treatment process? Justify your position.

Lab Investigation 5.3

Behind the Scene at the Waterworks

Objectives:

- **Observe** sedimentation and flocculation of water samples.
- **Compare** two methods of flocculation.
- **Model** the treatment process to purify a water sample.

Background Information:

The first municipal waterworks was a place where a water-powered pump moved water up a hill through a system of pipes made of hollow logs. Today municipal waterworks are more frequently called water treatment plants or water filtration plants because the water from reservoirs and rivers must be chemically treated to make it safe to drink. The water may also be filtered before it is distributed to consumers.

When water enters the waterworks from the reservoir or river, it has small particles floating in it. Bacteria that will cause water-borne illnesses may be hiding among these particles, so one of the first tasks is to remove the particles. Aluminum potassium sulfate (alum) or a mixture of iron II chloride (ferrous chloride) and calcium oxide (lime) are added to the water to cause the small particles suspended in the water to stick together. These clumps of particles are called **floc**.

The process of floc formation is called **flocculation**. From the flocculation tank, the water moves into a large storage tank. The floc is heavy, and it sinks to the bottom of the settling tank. The water must remain in the tank for a long period of time to allow the floc to settle. This process is called **sedimentation**. Any particles that do not settle out of the water are removed by **filtration** as the treated water passes through a **graded sand filter** made of layers of rocks and sand.

Another chemical that may be added during the treatment process is activated carbon. Activated carbon is charcoal, which has been heated with steam in the absence of air. When heated, the charcoal becomes very porous with a vast internal surface area. This property makes activated carbon very effective in removing certain types of chemicals from the water. These chemicals that cause color, odor and taste adhere to the surface of the activated carbon.

It is the job of the plant operator to determine the types and amount of chemicals that are needed to treat the water. The operators monitor the processes and perform water quality tests in a laboratory at the plant. Samples are also taken for testing by independent laboratories to ensure that the water meets EPA standards. In this investigation you will observe some of the processes that are used to purify the water at a water treatment plant.

Part I: Removing the Particles

Materials:
(per group)

chemical splash goggles
chemical-resistant aprons
chemical-resistant gloves
3 liters untreated surface water
3 1-liter bottles
labels or markers
balance
turbidimeter (optional)
5 grams alum crystals (aluminum potassium sulfate)
2.5 grams iron II chloride
2.5 grams calcium oxide (lime)
weighing paper
spatula
3 stirring rods

Safety precaution: Wear safety goggles, apron and gloves while working with chemicals during this laboratory. Follow all laboratory safety procedures when working in the laboratory. Dispose of chemicals as instructed.

Procedure:

1. Obtain three 1-liter containers and label one container "alum," one "iron mixture," and one "none."
2. Fill each of the containers with untreated surface water that has suspended particles. If water appears clear add 5 mL of soil to each liter of water and shake to mix.
3. Weigh 5 grams of aluminum potassium sulfate and place it beside the container labeled "alum."
4. Weigh 2.5 grams of iron (II) chloride and 2.5 grams of calcium oxide and mix the two chemicals; place the mixture beside the container labeled "iron mixture."
5. Add the chemicals to the containers with the appropriate labels.
6. Using a stirring rod, slowly stir the water in each of the 3 containers for 5 minutes.
7. Set the containers on the table and observe for the next 30 minutes. Do not disturb the containers.
8. Place a white sheet of paper with printed words behind the containers and view the words. Hold the lettering just below the top of the water. Compare the turbidity (cloudiness) of the water in each container using the chart below:

CLEAR	**print can easily be read**
SLIGHTLY CLOUDY	**print can be read but looks fuzzy**
CLOUDY	**print can be seen, but looks fuzzy**
VERY CLOUDY	**print can barely be seen**
OPAQUE	**print cannot be seen**

9. If a turbidimeter is available, follow the instructions to calibrate the meter, and then remove a sample of the water from each container and measure the turbidity.
10. Create a chart like the one below in your laboratory notebook and record the results:

Treatment	Turbidity after 30 minutes	Turbidity after 24 hours
Alum		
Iron mixture		
None		

11. Allow the samples from at least one group to remain overnight and compare the samples the following day. Dispose of the water samples as directed by your teacher.
12. Answer the analysis questions in your laboratory notebook.

Analysis:

1. Why were no chemicals added to the water in one of the containers?
2. What process removed suspended particles from the water in the container without added chemicals?

3. What processes removed suspended particles from the water in the containers with chemical treatments?
4. Which chemical treatment was the most effective in reducing the turbidity of the water?
5. The iron II chloride and calcium oxide mixture is more than 3 times as expensive as the aluminum potassium sulfate (alum). Which treatment would you recommend? Explain.

Part II: Removing Dissolved Chemicals

Flocculation and sedimentation remove suspended particles from the water, but the water may still contain dissolved substances that are undesirable because they affect the appearance, taste, or odor of the water. Some organic chemicals, such as trihalomethanes, may cause cancer if the concentration exceeds the Maximum Contaminant Level. These substances must be removed from the water.

Your group has applied for the contract to operate the local water treatment plant. You are given a water sample that contains a dissolved substance, which gives the water a blue color. You will be hired to operate the plant if you can remove the chemical causing the blue color. The goal is to produce a colorless water sample. The group that produces the water sample with the least amount of color and turbidity will be hired to operate the water treatment plant.

Materials:

(per group)

- 50 mL colored water sample
- funnel
- small test tube
- stirring rod
- 2 small beakers or jars (baby food jar)
- test tube rack
- large plastic pipette
- washed sand
- washed gravel
- alum (aluminum potassium sulfate)
- activated carbon (granular charcoal)
- spatulas
- chemical splash goggles
- chemical-resistant gloves and apron

Safety precautions: Follow all laboratory safety procedures when working in the laboratory. Dust from activated carbon is potentially toxic if inhaled. Be careful to create as little dust as possible when working with activated carbon. Use an operating fume hood or a well-ventilated area when dispensing or grinding activated carbon. Dispose of chemicals as instructed by your teacher.

Procedure:

1. A graded sand filter may be made by following these instructions:
   A. Use scissors to remove the top one-third of the bulb from the large pipette.
   B. Using the funnel, pour a small amount of the washed gravel into the stem of the pipette. The gravel should fill only one to two inches of the stem.
   C. Using the funnel, pour washed sand into the stem of the pipette until it nearly reaches the base of the bulb.
2. On a piece of paper, outline a procedure that you will follow to treat the water sample. Once the procedure is final, record it in your laboratory notebook.
3. Treat the water sample following the procedure in your notebook. If any changes are made in the procedure, be sure to record these changes in your notebook.
4. Pour the treated sample in the small test tube and give to your teacher.

Analysis:

1. Compare the treated sample from your group with the samples from the other groups. Record the results in your laboratory notebook.
2. Describe any changes you would make in your treatment process that might improve your results if you were to treat another sample.
3. How did your treatment process compare to the treatment process at a water treatment plant?

Field Investigation 6.1

Alternative Energy Sources–Wind Machines

Objective:

- **Evaluate** a location near your home or school to determine if conditions are suitable for locating a wind machine to make electricity.

Background Information:

Wind energy is a source of clean renewable energy. For centuries, technology has used the power of the wind. Advances in technology make today's wind machines more reliable with lower maintenance costs. In many areas the cost of electricity produced by wind power is less than from a coal-fired power plant.

In this investigation you will evaluate the conditions at a site near your school or home to determine the potential for harnessing wind energy to produce electricity. Find out more about wind power by visiting these Websites: www.awea.org, www.eren.doe.gov, www.energy.ca.gov, and www.wpm.co.nz.

Materials:

wind speed and direction indicator (optional)

Procedure:

1. Measure the wind speed at a selected site for a period of two weeks at different times during the day. Use the Beaufort Wind Scale or a wind speed and direction indicator.
2. Make a chart in your laboratory notebook to record the wind speeds and the time of day the wind speed was recorded. Wind speeds should be monitored 4 times each day, preferably in the morning, midday, the afternoon, and evening.
3. Answer the analysis questions in your laboratory notebook.

Analysis:

1. What time of day are the winds fastest?
2. What time of day are the winds the calmest?
3. Any wind over 8 miles an hour can be used to generate electricity. Based on your observations, estimate the number of hours a day that a wind generator could make electricity at this site.
4. Where the wind does blow, there may be other problems. The equipment to trap wind energy is expensive and can be damaged by powerful gusts of wind. Is the wind at the site you monitored best described as steady or gusty?
5. Investors will not realize a return on the money spent to construct a wind machine unless a location has a steady wind which averages more than 12 miles per hour. Would you recommend your test location to someone who wants to invest in alternative energy sources?
6. Should federal or state governments encourage the construction of wind machines by providing tax incentives? Support your position.

Beaufort Number	Description	Observation
0	Calm (0-1 mph)	Smoke rises vertically.
1	Light air (2-3 mph)	Smoke drifts slowly
2	Slight breeze (4-7 mph)	Leaves rustle; windvane moves
3	Gentle breeze (8-12 mph)	Twigs moves; flags extend
4	Moderate breeze (13-18 mph)	Branches move; dust and paper rise
5	Fresh breeze (19-24 mph)	Small trees sway
6	Strong breeze (25-31 mph)	Large branches sway; wires whistle
7	Moderate gale (32-38 mph)	Trees in motion; walking difficult
8	Fresh gale (39-46 mph)	Twigs break off trees
9	Strong gale (47-54 mph)	Branches break; roofs damaged
10	Whole gale (55-63 mph)	Trees snap; damage evident
11	Storm (64-72 mph)	Widespread damage
12	Hurricane (73-82 mph)	Extreme damage

Lab Investigation 6.2

Absorption and Storage of Solar Energy

Objective:

- **Evaluate** materials to determine their ability to absorb and store solar energy.

Background Information:

The sun is the source of most energy on the Earth. Today new houses are designed with windows facing the sun to take advantage of the sun's rays for warming rooms in winter. This form of **passive solar heating** occurs when the light energy passes through glass and is trapped (the greenhouse effect). Roof overhangs shade the windows from the sun's rays in the summer reducing the amount of passive solar heating and the need for air conditioning.

Objects in direct sunlight absorb solar energy. By adding **thermal mass**—large containers of water or floors and walls made of brick, stone or concrete—the amount of solar energy stored as heat energy can be increased. These materials may be placed in passive collectors attached to a wall facing the sun. As the air in the collector is heated, it rises and flows through a vent at the top of the collector. Cool air enters the collector through a vent near the bottom.

In this investigation we will compare the ability of different types of materials to absorb and store solar energy.

Materials:

(per group)

5 insulated foam cups
5 thermometers
1 clip-on lamp (150 watt bulb)
support stand with ring
meterstick
string
scissors
activated carbon
gravel (light color)
gravel (dark color)
sand
water
graph paper
colored pencils (optional)

Safety precautions: Follow all safety rules when working in the laboratory. Be careful when working with the scissors and the hot light bulb. Dust from activated carbon is potentially toxic if inhaled. Be careful to create as little dust as possible when working with activated carbon. Use an operating fume hood or a well-ventilated area when dispensing activated carbon.

Procedure:

1. Measure and mark the insulated cups at a height 3 cm from the bottom. Cut the cups on the mark.
2. Fill each cup with a different material (thermal mass): light-colored gravel, dark-colored gravel, activated carbon, sand, and water.
3. Attach the ring to the support stand, and set one of the cups below the ring. Attach a thermometer to the ring with string. Adjust the height of the ring so that the thermometer bulb is below the surface of the material.
4. Set the other cups on the support stand and insert thermometers as described in step 3.
5. Clip the lamp to the support stand at a height of 30 cm.
6. Copy the chart below into your laboratory notebook.

Time (minutes)	1	2	3	4	5	6	7	8	9	10
Material (thermal mass)										
Gravel (light color)										
Gravel (dark color)										
Activated carbon										
Sand										
Water										

7. Make a prediction about the results of this investigation and record it in your laboratory notebook.
8. Turn on the lamp and record the temperature of the material in each cup at the end of each minute for 5 minutes.
9. Turn off the lamp and record the temperature of the material in each cup at the end of each minute for the next 5 minutes (columns 6 through 10).

10. Construct a graph plotting the time on the horizontal (x) axis and the temperature on the vertical (y) axis. Use a different color or symbol for each material.
11. Answer the analysis questions in your laboratory notebook.

Analysis:

1. Which material showed the largest increase in temperature?
2. When the light was turned off, which material showed the largest decrease in temperature after 1 minute? After 5 minutes?
3. Which material showed the smallest decrease in temperature after 1 minute? After 5 minutes?
4. Which material showed the most gradual decrease in temperature? Which material would be the best selection for the release of thermal energy over a period of time?
5. Write a paragraph that describes your conclusions from the results of this investigation. Be sure to include data that support your conclusions.
6. A client has asked you to design a thermal collector to attach to an existing wall of a sunroom. Describe the collector that you would design. Be sure to identify the material that you would use as the thermal mass.

Environmental Issue 6.3

The Consumer's Choices

Objectives:

- **Relate** standard-of-living and lifestyle to energy use.
- **Identify** the natural resources used to make common consumer products.
- **Compare** the environmental impacts of making consumer products from wood, mineral ores, and crude oil.
- **Identify** choices that a consumer might make to reduce the environmental impacts on planet Earth.

Background Information:

The United States uses more energy per person than any other country. Our high standard of living is directly related to our ability to produce products, and our ability to produce products depends upon available energy supplies.

Oil and natural gas are important sources of energy. These fossil fuels are also the sources of many synthetic industrial chemicals—**petrochemicals**. These petrochemicals are used to make some 3,000 different products. Some petrochemicals are used to manufacture soaps, pesticides and medicines. Others are important raw materials for making synthetic fiber, rubber, and plastic.

Disposable diapers are a life-style indicator. We live in a "buy it—use it—throw it away" society. We have changed from a society that once used "returnables," such as glass milk jugs, to a society that prefers "disposables"—plastic jugs and paper cartons. Diapers and shirts are no longer "natural" products made of 100% cotton. Today these products are often made of synthetic materials or a blend of natural and synthetic materials. Although cotton is a natural fiber, it is grown with synthetic fertilizers and pesticides.

Every day people make decisions regarding the use of products. Personal preference plays an important role in their decisions. Convenience is the most important consideration for some people. Others would prefer to use the product that has the smallest environmental impact, but they often lack the information necessary for this decision. In this

Environmental Issue, we will examine some of the environmental impacts associated with a variety of consumer products made from petrochemicals. What are the alternatives? Which has the greatest environmental impact?

Procedure:

It's Saturday morning and you must go shopping. Consider the following choices. In each situation, select the material you prefer and write your selection on your shopping list on the worksheet. Explain the reason for your choice.

A. You have decided it's time to take that canoe trip you've been talking about. You must either rent a canoe or buy one. You decide to look at canoes. You stop by a sporting goods store and find that canoes are made of ABS plastic or aluminum.

B. You've been invited to a wedding and your son needs a new shirt. You stop by your favorite clothing store and find that you have a choice of a shirt made of 100% cotton or a shirt made of a cotton/polyester blend.

C. You stop by the drug store to pick up a prescription and remember that you have run out of 3-ounce cups in the bathroom. You have a choice of cups made of paper and cups made of high-impact polystyrene (HIPS) plastic.

D. Finally your last stop is the grocery store. You need eggs. Some of the eggs are packed in polystyrene foam cartons. Others are packed in pressed paperboard cartons. The only difference is the carton.

E. In the dairy department you must choose between a high-density polyethylene (HDPE) jug or milk in 1/2 gallon polyethylene-coated paperboard containers. You need one gallon of milk.

F. You make your way to the aisle with all the carbonated beverages. Your son wants root beer and he's the only one in the family who likes it. You decide to buy a 6-pack and you find that you have several choices: returnable glass bottles, nonreturnable glass bottles, plastic bottles, or aluminum cans.

G. When you get to the check-out, you are asked if you want your groceries packed in paper bags or plastic bags. Which bags do you choose, or do your reject both because you brought your own canvas bags?

Consider This Information — Buying a Canoe:
When you went shopping you made choices, and those choices were most likely based on personal preference. Each choice had environmental impacts. How does the total environmental impact of making a canoe of ABS plastic compare to the total environmental impact of making a canoe of aluminum?

The environmental impact of the drilling and transportation of oil and natural gas must be weighed against the impacts of mining and transporting the bauxite ore. The air and water pollution caused by the refining of crude oil and the manufacture of the plastic resin must be compared with the pollution caused by smelting the ore. The energy required for the production and transportation of the aluminum canoe must be weighed against that needed to produce and transport the canoe made of ABS plastic.

This information is not readily available for most products. One study by the Midwest Research Institute provides some useful information. This study compared the environmental impacts of various materials used to make containers. The data given in the chart below represents the impact of making one million of each type of container. This data allows us to compare the environmental impact of certain metals and plastics.

Consider the information in the chart on page 507. Which material has the least environmental impact — ABS plastic or aluminum? If you chose aluminum, put 30 beneath the letter A in your shopping list. If you chose ABS plastic, put 10.

Choosing a Shirt—Is a shirt made of natural fibers a better choice?
Cotton and wool are both natural fibers—renewable resources. Synthetic fibers, like polyester, are made from crude oil. Which requires more energy—a shirt made of 100% cotton or one made of a blend that is 35% cotton/65% polyester? A group of scientists examined this question. They calculated the energy used producing the material, making the shirt and maintaining it (washing and ironing) in kilowatt-hours of fossil fuel equivalents. A watt is a unit of electrical

Container	Material	Raw Material (kg)	Energy (kwh)	Water (kL)	Solid Wastes (m^3)	Atmos. emmisions (kg)	Wastes in water (kg)	Post use wastes (m^3)
8-ounce	ABS plastic	740	0.56	1,860	2.1	3,126	515	20.0
dairy tub	Aluminum	14,598	1.70	3,909	57.4	11,233	8,208	6.8
Gallon	HDPE	11,760	4.72	6,909	26.0	27,414	3,617	168.7
oblong	Steel	517,458	5.96	80,023	1,135.4	36,554	89,324	44.5
9-ounce cup	HIPS	262	0.16	814	0.4	766	190	6.4
	Paper	3,772	0.09	1,152	1.1	687	336	6.4
Gallon of	HDPE	3,952	2.20	2,750	8.7	12,422	1,851	90.0
Milk	Paper	86,354	2.11	25,587	26.0	15,447	7,497	134.9
Meat Tray	PS Foam	137	0.26	447	1.0	1,674	148	7.5
	Pulp	16,129	0.25	1,284	3.7	1,592	798	22.8
Gallon bag	LDPE	174	0.16	167	0.6	899	112	5.5
	Paper	10,225	0.18	2,015	2.3	1,590	622	15.2

power. A kilowatt-hour (kwh) is one thousand watts of power used for one hour. To produce one kwh of electrical energy requires ten ounces (30 mL) of oil or thirteen ounces (370 g) of coal.

Energy (in kwh) Needed to:	100% Cotton	65–35% Blend
Produce the fiber	5.0	9.6
Manufacture the cloth	18.5	20.2
Sew the shirt	2.8	2.8
Total manufacturing (kwh)	26.3	32.6
Wash the shirt (automatic)	32.2	15.8
Dry the shirt (automatic)	40.8	18.7
Iron the shirt	16.2	5.3
Total maintenance (kwh)	89.2	39.8
Total kwh per 50 washings	4460.0	1990.0

The growing of cotton is dependent upon fossil fuels. Large amounts of coal are used to make the steel needed for farm machinery. Oil supplies the energy to run the machines used for preparing the ground, planting and harvesting. Natural gas is used to synthesize the nitrogen fertilizer needed to grow the cotton. Herbicides and pesticides that are made from petrochemicals are also used to grow most cotton.

The chart gives the energy in kilowatt-hours of fossil fuel equivalents. In many areas, coal-fired power plants produce the electricity required to maintain the shirt. In other areas the source of energy for electricity is hydropower or nuclear. Check with your utility company to determine if oil or natural gas is used for the production of electricity in your area. If you chose the material with the least environmental impact, put a 4 beneath the letter B. If you chose the material with the greatest environmental impact, put an 8 beneath the letter B.

To Market, To Market — What Should You Buy?

At the drug store you chose "bathroom cups." If the outside of the plastic cup is colored and the rim and inside are white, the resin may be high-impact polystyrene (HIPS). Using the information in the chart above, try to determine which cup will have the least environmental impact.

The figures in the chart reveal that there is not a significant difference between the HIPS cup and the paper cup. Dr. Jan Beyea, author of the Audubon Energy Plan, suggests choosing the plastic cup only if it weighs the same or less than the paper cup. Since a pound of most plastic is produced with less pollution than a pound of paper, the production of a plastic cup that weighs less than a paper cup will have the least environmental impact. If you chose the material with the least environmental impact, put a 2 beneath the letter C. If you chose the material with the greatest environmental impact, put a 3 beneath the letter C.

The Midwest Research Institute did not compare egg cartons, but they did compare meat trays made of the same materials as egg cartons. If you chose egg cartons made of the material with the least environmental impact, put a 2 beneath letter D. If you chose the material with the greatest environmental impact, put a 3 beneath letter D.

Another decision! Should you buy a gallon of milk in a plastic jug or two one-half gallon paper containers of milk? Check the data in the chart below and select the type of container that has the least environmental impact. If you chose the material with the least environmental impact, put a 2 beneath the letter E. If you chose the material with the greatest environmental impact, put a 3 beneath the letter E.

Even though it is the most energy efficient, the use of glass is declining. Some stores no longer carry carbonated beverages in refillable glass bottles. You may have to choose between plastic bottles made of the polymer polyethylene terephthalate (PET) or 12 ounce aluminum cans. Compare the information in the following chart. If you chose the material with the least environmental impact, put a 1 beneath the letter E. Put numbers 2 to 4 for increasing environmental impacts.

The Economic and Environmental Impact of Carbonated Beverages

Container	Consumer's Cost	Energy*	Solid Waste**
Returnable glass	$0.21	1.4	1.4
Non-returnable glass	$0.35	6.3	5.8
Plastic bottle	$0.40	3.1	7.0
Aluminun can	$0.48	8.5	4.0

*oz. of gas equivalent used to make, transport, etc. (1 oz. = 2.88 mL)
**cubic inches of crushed solid wastes (1 cubic inch = 16.77 cm^3)
Source: Wisconsin Dept. of Natural Resources.

The chart below provides an estimate of the energy-savings that result from using recycled glass, plastic, and aluminum containers. If you will recycle the beverage containers put an ® beneath the letter F.

Potential Energy-Savings from Recycling

	Energy required for materials (kwh/kg)	Energy saved by use of recycled containers (percentage)
Aluminum	80.57	95.0
Glass	5.02	5.0
Plastic	31.5	88.0

Finally, at the checkout counter the person bagging the groceries asks—paper or plastic? If you chose the material with the greatest environmental impact, put a 2 beneath the letter G. If you chose the material with the lesser environmental impact, put a 1 beneath the letter G. If you pull out your own "personal carrier," put a 0 beneath the letter G.

Everything we do, every choice we make, has certain environmental impacts. We can step more lightly on planet Earth by considering these choices before we act. Consider this important question. How do our choices affect the sustainability of planet Earth? Complete the analysis questions on your Environmental Issues Worksheet.

When you recycle plastic, certain recyclers request only certain types of plastic resin. One might only recycle the type of plastic that has the numbers 1 or 2 inside the "recycle triangle." The following chart shows what type of plastic resin each number represents:

1	**PETE**	Polyethylene teraphthalate Soft -drink bottles
2	**HDPE**	High-density polyethylene Laundry detergent bottles, grocery bags
3	**PVC**	Polyvinyl chloride Shampoo bottles
4	**LPDE**	Low-density polyethylene bread bags
5	**PP**	Polypropylene Margarine tubs, ketchup bottles
6	**PS**	Polystyrene Meat trays, egg cartons
7	**OTHER**	Polycarbonate, acrylic, ABS, others

Environmental Issue 6.4

Natural Resources and You

Objective:

- **Identify** materials used to make consumer products that we value.
- **Determine** the natural resources required to make the materials.
- **Classify** the natural resources as renewable or nonrenewable.
- **Describe** methods to conserve or alternatives for nonrenewable resources.

Background Information:

We live in a society that places great value on possessions. Advertisements on radio, television, and the Internet try to convince us that we need more possessions. Sometimes they are successful and we add more things to the belongings we already have. Our economy depends upon consumers buying and using products.

The society in which we live is not a closed ecosystem. Many of the natural resources we depend upon are not found locally. For this reason, our lifestyle may impact other ecosystems that are located a great distance from our home.

In this Environmental Issue, we will examine some of the objects we use in our daily lives and consider the environmental impacts of their manufacture, use and disposal. We will also investigate alternatives to nonrenewable resources.

Materials:

references
Environmental Issues Worksheet

Procedure:

1. In your laboratory notebook make a list of 10 consumer products that are important to you. The products should be made of at least 3 different materials.
2. Copy the headings from the following chart into your laboratory notebook. Following the example given under Product, "pencil," complete the chart for each of the consumer products on your list. This may require some research to find out how the products on your list are manufactured. If in your research you find the location of a natural resource, include this as a footnote to the chart.
3. Analyze the information in your chart and answer the following questions in your laboratory notebook.

Analysis:

1. What was the most common natural resource used in the products analyzed? Is it a renewable or nonrenewable resource?
2. The most widely used source of wood for pencils is old-growth trees. Can we avoid depleting this natural resource without giving up our use of pencils? Make suggestions for alternatives to pencils. What are the advantages and disadvantages of the alternatives?
3. Identify materials that are nonrenewable and suggest alternatives for these materials where possible.
4. Some products that we use, like pencils, cannot be recycled. Identify products on your list made of materials that can be recycled, even though these materials may not currently be recycled in your community.
5. Identify one item from your list that you think could be produced with less impact on the environment than the impact from current production methods.
6. What impact will the depletion of a natural resource have on the economy?

Product	Materials	Natural Resources	Renewable or Nonrenewable	Disposal
Pencil	wood	trees[1]	nonrenewable	landfill or incinerator
	"lead"	Graphite[2] and clay	nonrenewable	
	paint (nonpoisonous lacquer)	trees (cashew family)	renewable	
	glue	animals (skins, bone, hooves)	renewable	
	eraser (rubber)	trees	renewable	
	metal band	ore	nonrenewable	

1. The most widely used wood for pencils comes from incense cedar trees in the Sierra Nevada Mountains, northern California. The best wood is from trees between 150 and 200 years old.

2. Some of the best graphite for pencils comes from Sonora, Mexico.

Safety Rules for Science Classrooms

1. Do not eat or drink in the science laboratory, and always wash your hands after performing experiments.
2. Control hair and loose clothing and wear approved eye protection (chemical-splash goggles) during all chemical experiments. Wear chemical-resistant laboratory aprons and gloves as directed by your teacher.
3. Know the location of the eye wash, safety shower, fire extinguisher, and fire blanket, and know how to use them.
4. Do only those experiments authorized by the teacher.
5. Do not open bottles of chemicals unless directed to do so.
6. Do not taste chemicals; test for odor by fanning the hand over the open container and carefully sniffing.
7. If chemicals are spilled on the skin or eyes, immediately flush with water for at least 15 minutes. Immediately notify the teacher.
8. If chemicals are spilled on clothing, cabinets, or floor, notify the teacher immediately.
9. Report any burn, injury or accident to the teacher.
10. Never use mouth suction on a pipette; always use a bulb or pump supplied for that purpose.
11. Work in a well-ventilated area and use the fume hood when directed to do so.
12. Check the label twice before using a chemical. Read instructions twice and follow them exactly. Ask questions if you are unsure of the procedure.
13. Never point the open end of a test tube containing chemicals or a test tube being heated at another individual.
14. Keep all flammable liquids away from sources of heat.
15. Discard chemicals as directed by the teacher. Do not return any chemical to the original container. Do not discard matches, filter paper or solids in the sink.
16. Make sure electrical cords are plugged securely into the outlets. Do no allow the electrical cords to hang below the laboratory table.
17. If you feel faint, sit down and lower your head or lie down. Do not lean out of a window. Ask someone to notify the teacher.

Metric Tables

Conversion of Metric to U.S. Units

Length		
Unit	*Number of Meters*	*Approximate U.S. Equivalent*
kilometer (km)	1,000 m	0.62 mile
meter (m)	1 m	39.37 inches
centimeter (cm)	0.01 m	0.39 inches
millimeter (mm)	0.001 m	0.039 inches

Mass		
Unit	*Number of Grams*	*Approximate U.S. Equivalent*
metric tonne (t)	1,000,000 g	2,204.6 pounds 1.102 short tons
kilogram (k)	1,000 g	2.2 pounds
gram (g)	1 g	0.035 ounce

Area		
hectare (ha)	10,000 m^2	2.47 acres 0.00386 sq. mi.

Capacity		
Unit	*Number of Liters*	*Approximate U.S. Equivalent*
liter (L)	1 L	1.057 quarts 0.264 gallons
milliliter (mL)	0.001 L	0.061 cu. in.

Other Useful Conversions

Temperature:

$C = \frac{5}{9}(F - 32)$ $F = \frac{5}{9}C + 32$

ppb (parts per billion) =
1 part per 1,000,000,000 (1 billion)

ppm (parts per million) =
1 part per 1,000,000

Wildlife biologists plan and carry out wildlife management programs. They identify conditions that affect wildlife, restore and manage wildlife habitat, conduct research to determine the best management methods, regulate hunting and fishing, and conduct programs to educate the public. A bachelor's degree with a major in wildlife studies or a closely related field is the minimum education required for employment.

Naturalists prepare exhibits, give talks, and conduct trail hikes at nature centers and national parks. Their job is to interpret the environment for the public. They must enjoy working outdoors and have a good ability to communicate both orally and in writing. A bachelor degree in environmental science is usually required.

Loggers are workers who fell trees, trim the branches and tops from the trees, cut them to the desired length, and load them for transport. Logging operations are becoming more dependent upon hydraulically operated equipment. Work is physically demanding. Loggers must be alert and able to follow instructions. Most employers hire applicants who have graduated from high school. During high school, students should take courses in mathematics, mechanics, and shop. Beginners start as helpers and learn the job by working with experienced workers.

Foresters are trained in the management of forest land and the use of its resources. The management plan that they develop will have both environmental and economic impacts. Their duties may include planting seedlings, inspecting trees for signs of disease and insect damage, and marking trees for cutting; prevention and control of forest fires, soil and water conservation, and wildlife management. A bachelor's degree in forestry, wildlife management, conservation, or a related field is required.

Forest technicians work under the direction of professional foresters. They may be responsible for marking trees for harvest, harvesting or planting trees, detecting and controlling fires, and protecting wildlife. They must be willing to assume responsibility work without direct supervision. Most employers require a two-year degree in forest technology. While they are in high school, students should take courses in mathematics and science.

Mechanics are responsible for repairing vehicles and inspecting them to ensure that they meet emissions standards. They may learn their skills by on-the-job training, but they often complete courses at vocational-technical schools or community colleges.

Farm managers are responsible for planning schedules for planting and harvesting. They must be aware of signs that indicate potential problems caused by pests or diseases and take corrective steps to minimized the damage. They are also responsible for decisions concerning buying and selling of farm products, employing workers, and keeping financial records. Graduation from high school and vocational courses in agriculture or horticulture is desirable.

Soil conservationists study soil and water conservation problems and develop programs for the proper use of these resources. Most are employed by the NRCS and the EPA. They work with private landowners, public utilities, government agencies, and other groups concerned with conserving soil and water resources. They conduct surveys and prepare maps of soils. They recommend methods of farming to help conserve soil. They also develop plans for soil conservation during the building of highways and developments. Soil conservationists must have a degree in science.

An **agronomist** designs and conducts experiments to develop better ways of growing crops. Agronomists study the effects of planting, cultivating, and harvesting crops. They investigate methods of controlling weeds, pests, and diseases. They also investigate the effects of weather and pollution on crops. They may be employed byagricultural corporations, governments, or universities. A bachelor's degree in agronomy or agricultural science is required.

Do you have a question concerning the use of a pesticide? Call your **agricultural extension agent**. The agent will be able to answer your question, or he/she will be able to find the answer for you. This is just one of the ways that an extension agent can help you. Although the agents work mostly with farmers, they provide information for anyone with a problem related to agriculture. Each spring the agents get many calls from gardeners and homeowners concerning soil testing, planting and cultivating techniques, and pest control. The extension agent may inform interested readers through a column in the local newspaper. Agents must have a bachelor's degree in agriculture or agricultural education.

A **wetland refuge manager** is responsible for protection of the ecosystem. He/she supervises and monitors activities on the refuge. In some cases the manager may be responsible for buying additional land and restoring or improving the habitat for certain species. They also supervise employees, direct population studies, and develop education programs. Decisions concerning hunting at some refuges may be the responsibility of the manager. Managers must have a bachelor's degree in wildlife management or some related field. On-the-job training is also necessary.

Water treatment plant operators control processes and equipment to remove solids, chemicals, and organisms from the water. They must maintain equipment, read and interpret meters and gauges, and make sure processes are working properly. They take samples of water, perform chemical and biological analyses, and make adjustments in treatment. Operators learn their skills on the job under the direction of an experienced operator. Larger plants may have more formal training programs. Some states require a high school diploma. Operators, in most states, must pass an examination to certify that they are capable of overseeing operations.

Hazardous waste technicians may travel to sites where possible hazardous materials are located. They take samples and transport them to laboratories where they can be identified. They determine the best method of safe disposal and submit a plan to the appropriate environmental agency. They must follow safety procedures to avoid risk of exposure and limit damage to the environment. They supervise the disposal operation and file the required reports. A degree in science or engineering is recommended.

An **urban planner** usually works for a smaller city; large cities may have a team of planners. Their responsibilities include planning for future industrial and residential development, transportation needs, and developing programs to provide adequate health and welfare services. They must consider the conservation of natural resources, adequate water supply, flood control, and regulations concerning water and air quality. Plans must include approved methods of disposal of hazardous and solid waste. Planners must have leadership qualities, be able to organize and analyze data, and communicate ideas effectively. Graduates with a bachelor's degree will be placed with experienced planners as part of a training program.

Electric power plant operators monitor the equipment, record readings, and detect any malfunctions. Operators must have an understanding of mechanics and electricity. High school courses should include mathematics, industrial arts, and science. Power plants provide on-the-job training. Some cities and states require operators to be licensed.

Glossary

abiotic [29] the nonliving components of the ecosystem which include chemical matter and physical factors including sunlight, temperature, and precipitation.
acid deposition [170] any substance in the atmosphere that produces a pH lower than natural rainfall (usually 5.0–5.6), often called acid rain. See pH.
acid rain [170] both wet and dry substances in the atmosphere that produce a pH lower than natural rainfall, more accurately called acid deposition.
acid shock [173] a condition which occurs in fish when there is a sudden increase in the amount of acid in the water. It often kills the entire population of fish.
acid tolerant [174] species which can survive and reproduce in water with a very low pH.
ACM [137] asbestos-containing material.
acre-foot [421] the amount of water that is needed to cover one acre of land 12 inches deep.
Action level [383] the legal limit of a chemical (lead) in drinking water that requires water suppliers to take corrective action to reduce the corrosiveness of the water and to ensure consumers receive water that does not contain harmful levels of that chemical.
activated carbon [380] carbon (granular charcoal) that has been heated with steam and is used to filter water.
activated carbon filter [398] a type of water filter that is designed to remove organic chemicals that cause color, taste, or odors.
activated sludge process [365] type of secondary sewage treatment in which oxygen is added to wastewater.
active solar heating system [454] a heating system which uses pumps or fans to distribute heat collected and trapped by the greenhouse effect.
adsorption [398] the process in which pollutants stick or adhere to the surface of activated carbon particles.
aeration [216] the ability of air to move through the soil.
aerosols [118] small droplets of liquid.
agriculture [198] the process of growing crops for food.
air quality standard [181] maximum amount of a pollutant allowed.
algal bloom [299] excessive growth of algae that can be observed by the color of the water.
alkalinity [309] a measure of the buffering capacity of water. See buffer.
allowance [183] a permit that allows a power plant to release 1 ton of sulfur dioxide.
alloy [151] a substance created by fusing two or more metals, or sometimes a metal and nonmetal.
alpha radiation [140] radioactive particles that lack the ability to penetrate the outer dead layer of human skin.
ambient air [121] the outdoor air.
anode [458] the positive terminal of an electrolytic cell; the electrode of a fuel cell at which oxidation occurs (hydrogen ions are created).
anthracite [436] a bright and shiny hard coal which is formed under intense heat and pressure. It has the highest percentage of carbon and the highest potential heat content.
aquaculture [462] a method of growing fish or other aquatic organisms.
aqueduct [401] a canal (channel) built to carry water.
aquifer [34] layer of permeable or porous rock where water is stored.
Arab Oil Embargo [435] during the Arab-Israeli War in 1973, Arab oil-producing nations cut off oil supplies to the United States and the Netherlands because they supported Israel.
archaeologist [198] scientist who studies things which were made or used by early humans.
artifact [198] object modified by early humans.
asbestos [136] a group of natural minerals which are heat-resistant and very durable.
asbestosis [136] a disease of the lungs caused by the presence of asbestos in the lungs.
atmosphere [90] a mixture of gases that surrounds planet Earth.
atmospheric deposition [334] the process in which air pollutants are deposited in the water with precipitation or by diffusion.
atom [140] a unit of matter that has a nucleus and is surrounded by particles called electrons.
attrition [118] the wearing or grinding of a substance by friction.
avicide [250] pesticides that kill birds. See pesticide.
Bacillus thuringiensis* *(B.t.) [277] a very small rod-shaped bacterium, one of the safest pesticides used today.
background level [140] the level of naturally occurring radiation.
backwash [300] the process in which the direction of the water flow through a filter is reversed in order to clean the filter.
baffles [403] a series of wall-like structures that slow the flow of water.
bagasse [455] fibrous waste produced during the processing of sugar cane.
ballast [63] items of weight added to a hold of a ship to replace unloaded cargo, in order to keep the ship upright and stable.
bark rights [44] an agreement made between the buyer and seller of land, that the seller could retain the right to log the land and sell the bark of the trees.
bedrock [216] solid rock beneath the subsoil.
beech-maple forest [38] a final stage in succession or a climax community.
benthic [288] refers to bottom-dwelling organisms of an aquatic ecosystem.
benthic macroinvertebrates [288] aquatic insects or other small organisms that have no backbone and are large enough to be seen without a microscope.
benzene [380] a hydrocarbon found in gasoline.
Best Management Practices (BMPs) [336] agricultural practices that reduce water pollution and reduce the cost of producing a crop.
beta radiation [140] radioactive particles that can penetrate the skin.
binder twine [207] a type of string used to tie bundles of grain.
bioaccumulation [254] the concentration of chemicals as they are stored in the bodies of organisms and passed up the food chain.
biochemical oxygen demand (BOD) [308] The amount of oxygen consumed (demanded) by microorganisms and combined with chemicals in the water.
biodegradable [253] chemicals that can be broken down by organisms in the environment.
biodiesel [456] a fuel made from soybeans or vegetable oil.
biodiversity [45] the variety of plant and animal species within an ecosystem. The term also refers to the variety of ecosystems on planet Earth.
biogeochemical cycles [29] the movement of chemicals between the environment and organisms in it.
bioinvasion [61] the introduction of species, by direct or indirect human actions, to areas where they did not previously exist.
biomass [25] the total mass of all organisms in an ecosystem.
biome [3] a large geographic region determined by the climate and soil type and a distinctive type of plant life.
biomonitoring [379] the use of living organisms to determine water quality.
biosolids [245] the solids that settle out during the process of treating sewage; sometimes called sludge.
biosphere [2] the region of the earth, including air, water, and land, that supports life.
biotic [29] the living components of the ecosystem which include plants, animals, and microorganisms.
birth rate [485] number of infants born in a given year per 1000 individuals in a population.
bituminous coal [436] a type of soft coal with a relatively high heat content. It is the most common type of coal found in the U.S.
black blizzards [219] dark skies created when strong winds pick up and carry large amounts of topsoil.
black lung [455] a lung condition resulting from the breathing of coat dust. Symptoms of the disease include excess mucus, shortness of breath, and a chronic cough.
bog [40] stage of succession that replaces the marsh and swamp stages in a lake or pond without a good flow of water.
boil water alert [397] a notification made by a water supplier to customers when tests indicate that there are microorganisms in the water or when a break or repair of a water main increases the potential for contamination.
Bordeaux mixture [250] a fungicide made of calcium hydroxide and copper sulfate.
boreal bog [41] a northern bog found in Canada and the northern U.S.
bottom [286] the area of the aquatic environment that is covered with rocks, sand or mud and is the habitat for a variety of small organisms.
bottomland hardwood forests [325] swamps that support hardwood trees such as maples and are periodically flooded but may be dry for half of the year.
boulders [285] rocks with a diameter greater than 10 inches (25 cm).
bounty [17] the money paid for a dead predator to increase certain game species.
brass [151] an alloy made by fusing metallic zinc with copper.
broadcast seeder [206] a piece of equipment that uses a small fan to scatter seeds.
broad-spectrum pesticide [256] chemical which kills many different kinds of organisms.
bronchial asthma [130] an allergic reaction that causes swelling of the membranes and spasms of the muscles in the bronchial tubes.
brucellosis [77] a contagious disease that affects cattle, caused by the bacteria *Brucella abortus.*
buffer [174] a substance that, when placed in water, prevents large changes in the pH.
calcite [212] calcium carbonate found in limestone and marble.
canopy [45] the leafy roof that is created by the tops of the trees in the forest.
Captex [172] short for Cross-Appalachian Tracer Experiment, the name of an experiment in which a tracer substance was released and air samples were collected to plot the path of air pollutants.
carbamate pesticides [164] made from methyl isocyanate, a gaseous class of insecticides toxic to humans; examples are SEVIN and Temik.
carbon dioxide [111] gaseous compound/molecule consisting of one carbon atom and two oxygen atoms.
carbon monoxide [131] poisonous, gaseous compound/molecule consisting of one carbon atom and one oxygen atom.
carbonic acid [170] chemical which is formed when carbon dioxide dissolves in water; it dissolves metals, marble, roofing slate and mortar in buildings.
carcinogen, carcinogenic [130] a substance that causes cancer.
carnivore [13] animals that eat other animals (meat).
carrion [22] dead animal carcasses.
carrying capacity [21] the maximum size of the population that an ecosystem can support.
catalysts [440] chemicals that speed up chemical reactions.
catalytic converters [191] stainless steel containers that contain a platinum catalyst and are installed on exhaust systems to reduce hydrocarbon and carbon monoxide emissions.

cathode [458] the negative terminal of an electrolytic cell; the electrode of a fuel cell at which reduction occurs (hydrogen ions are reduced).

cavity nesters [6] animals that live in natural cavities or cavities that they excavate within trees.

center-pivot irrigation [238] a self-propelled sprinkler system that is used to spray water over field crops.

CERCLA [159] Comprehensive Environmental Response, Compensation, and Liability Act of 1980, commonly known as Superfund, enacted to provide a nationwide program to address the most serious threats from hazardous waste, and to make the polluters pay for cleaning up the sites that they contaminated.

chaff [207] protective sheaths that cover individual kernels of grain.

channel [284] a natural bed of a river or a stream in which the water usually flows.

chemosynthesis [13] a food-making process whereby bacteria in a deep-ocean ecosystem make food from hydrogen sulfide dissolved in hot spring-fed waters.

Chesapeake Bay Agreement [336] a cooperative effort, by states in the Chesapeake Bay watershed, to improve and protect the water quality and living resources of the Bay.

chisel plow [222] A method of conservation tillage using chisels to loosen the soil without turning under the sod or other plant material.

chloramine [380] a combination of chlorine and ammonia used to disinfect the water.

chlorinated hydrocarbon [251] a chemical compound made by removing hydrogen atoms from a hydrocarbon and adding chlorine atoms.

chlorination [368] disinfection of water by using chlorine.

chlorine demand [396] the amount of chlorine needed to make the water safe.

chlorine residual [396] the amount of free chlorine remaining in the water.

chlorofluorocarbons (CFCs) [92] nontoxic, nonflammable compounds that contain carbon, fluorine and chlorine.

chlorosis [133] the loss of chlorophyll in leaves.

cholera [392] a disease caused by the bacteria, *vibrio cholerae,* found in water contaminated by human waste.

chronic bronchitis [129] a respiratory disease in which cilia are damaged and cells lining the bronchial tubes produce excessive amounts of thick mucus. Symptoms include a chronic cough and shortness of breath.

cinder bank [159] solid waste that was produced during the smelting of zinc, contaminated with zinc, copper, lead and cadmium.

Clean Air Act [121] a law passed by Congress in 1970 to control air pollution.

Clean Air Act Amendments [179] signed into law in 1990 by President Bush, these amendments officially recognized acid rain as a serious environmental problem and set up an ambitious program to control air pollutants that cause it.

clean coal technology [184] refers to methods to control sulfur dioxide emissions from the burning of coal.

clean fuels [194] fuels like natural gas, methanol, ethanol, and electricity, that produce 90% less pollution than conventional gasoline.

clean mitigation habitat [382] an environment created to lessen or minimize the effect of polluting the original habitat.

clean-water organisms [288] organisms that are sensitive to pollution.

clear-cut logging [51] removing all of the trees regardless of size or condition; also called clear-cutting.

climate [3] the average weather pattern of a region over a long period of time.

climax community [38] the final stage in succession that remains until it is disturbed by some event such as fire or human activity.

closed cylinder [189] where the fuel burns or explodes inside the internal combustion engine.

cloud [103] airborne masses of microscopic water particles.

club soda [406] a soft drink made when minerals are added to seltzer water.

coal [436] a black or brown rock which contains hydrocarbons formed from decayed plants.

cobbles [285] rocks with a diameter greater than 2 inches (5 cm) but less than 10 inches (25 cm).

cogeneration [455] the use of one system to produce both electricity and heat for industrial processes.

coke [443] a solid mass of nearly pure carbon which is formed by burning coal at high temperatures without oxygen. It is used in the manufacture of steel.

coliform bacteria [394] bacteria that are normally found in the intestines of humans and many other animals.

collectors [288] organisms that feed on decomposing organic matter.

Colorado Brown Stain [410] a condition of permanently discolored tooth enamel caused by fluorides in our water and food.

combine harvester [207] a modern self-propelled machine that reaps and threshes grain of all types.

combined sewers [368] pipes that carry both sewage and storm water.

combustion [30] the chemical combination of certain substances with oxygen which results in the release of energy; the oxidation (burning) of compounds containing carbon.

compost [246] a mixture of soil and decomposed organic materials (humus).

condensation [34] process in which water changes from water vapor into a liquid.

condensation nuclei [34] small particles in the atmosphere that provide surfaces on which water vapor collects and condenses.

condenser [460] equipment in a power plant that uses cool water pipes to convert steam from a turbine back to water to be reused.

confluence [284] the place where two streams meet.

coniferous forest [4] a biome in the northern reaches of the planet which gets and stays extremely cold for most of the year.

conservation district [220] a geographic area, usually a county, where a group of local people help plan and implement conservation projects.

Conservation Reserve Program [227] a USDA program that provides incentives to farmers and ranchers who take highly erodible and environmentally sensitive cropland out of production in order to reduce damage caused by erosion.

conservation tillage [222] planting crops without using a moldboard plow.

consumed [421] water that is withdrawn and not returned to its source so that it may be used again.

consumers [13] organisms that cannot make their own food.

contact time [396] the amount of time that is needed for chlorine to react with the water in order to disinfect it.

continuous disinfection [393] the addition of a disinfectant that remains in the water and is detectable at the consumer's tap.

contour planting [221] plowing and planting across a slope rather than up and down the slope.

control group [(128), 165] the group that does not receive the experimental treatment being tested in a controlled experiment.

controlled experiment [128] an experiment in which there is only one difference between two groups of subjects, the control group and the experimental group.

cooling pond [461] a large reservoir built to receive heated water from power plants or industries.

cooling tower [461] huge structures built by power plants or industries to cool water before it is returned to the source in order to prevent thermal pollution.

corn peg [207] a hand-held instrument used to husk corn.

corn picker [207] a mechanical harvester that replaced the binder.

corn sheller [208] a machine that removes corn kernels from the cob.

cosmic radiation [140] ionizing radiation that enters the Earth's atmosphere from outer space.

coulter [205] a circular steel blade that is attached in front of the plow and cuts through sod or debris.

cover [6] a place where animals can hide from predators and be protected from the weather.

cover crops [223] grasses or legumes that are planted to hold the soil in place.

cradle [206] a wooden attachment for a scythe that catches the stalks of grain.

crop rotation [221] planting a series of crops such as corn-beans-wheat-clover-corn.

crumb (structure) [215] a soil structure where individual particles are glued together to form irregular clumps with a diameter of less than 1.5 cm.

cryogenic [458] pertaining to very low temperatures; liquid hydrogen is stored in cryogenic cylinders (to keep it liquefied at a very low temperature).

cryptosporidiosis [394] a flu-like illness accompanied by diarrhea that is caused by the protozoan *Cryptosporidium.*

cull trees [59] trees that will not yield high-quality lumber.

curie [146] the amount of radiation from one gram of radium.

cutting coulter [222] The part of a no-till planter that cuts a slit in the soil.

cyclone [186] a vertical tube in which a whirlwind action removes larger particles from flue gases.

days-to-harvest [264] number of days between the last application of the pesticide and the day the crop can be legally harvested.

DDT [76] dichloro-diphenyl-trichloroethane, the first chlorinated hydrocarbon used as an insecticide.

death rate [485] number of people who die in a given year per 1000 individuals in a population.

deciduous forest [4] a temperate biome with distinct seasons, a 5-month growing season, evenly spaced rainfall, and soil rich in humus with a medium nutrient level.

decomposers [13] organisms that feed on the waste products or bodies of dead organisms.

deep forest species [52] species that live in the interior of the forest.

deep-well injection [386-7] a method of waste disposal in which chemical wastes are injected into a layer of confined sandstone or other porous rock several thousand feet deep.

delta [350] a mass of land that forms at the mouth of a river as the river drops its load of silt and clay particles.

dental fluorosis [412] a condition in which paper white patches or lines develop on teeth due to exposure to fluoride in the water supply.

desalination [430] the process of removing salt from water.

desert [5] a region that receives very little rainfall and can only support plants that are drought-tolerant.

development right [237] the right of a landowner to develop land can be sold for a restricted deed to prevent development.

die casting [151] the process of pouring heated metal into a die to create parts used to make appliances and equipment.

diesel engine [192] a type of internal combustion engine where only air enters the chamber during the intake stroke. An exact quantity of fuel is injected into the cylinder during the compression stroke. Compression is greater in the diesel engine, causing molecules to collide more often, creating the heat that ignites the fuel.

diffusion [305] the process by which molecules move from an area of greater concentration to an area of lesser concentration.

digesters [366] large tanks.

digging stick [204] a tool used for planting roots and bulbs and later planting seeds; it may have been the first farm tool.

dike [200] ridge formed by hard rock that remains when softer material is eroded away; massive walls of concrete or earth built along a river or stream to protect the land from flooding.

Dingell-Johnson Act [82] a law passed by Congress that requires taxes collected on fishing and boating equipment and boat fuel be used for fishing habitat, also called the Federal Aid in Sport Fish Restoration Act.

discs [206] iron or steel part of a plow used to cut through clods of dirt before a harrow is used to smooth out the seedbed.
disease cluster [377] a number of people living or working in the same area who develop the same disease.
dissolved oxygen [289] oxygen gas that is dissolved in the water.
distilled water [409] water that has gone through a process of evaporation and condensation.
diversion terraces [221] ridges of soil across a slope which slow the speed of water moving down the slope.
dose [142] the quantity of radiation given at one time.
dose rate [142] the amount of radiation given per unit of time.
double-disc opener [223] Part of a no-till planter that pushes the slit (that the cutting coulter has made) open before the planter drops the seeds.
drainage basin [284] the land area that is drained when drops of rain join others to flow to a particular stream, river, lake, or wetland; a watershed.
drip irrigation [426] a method of watering plants through a series of subsurface pipes.
drought-resistant [219] crops that can tolerate long periods without water.
dry steam [452] steam created by geothermal energy and trapped at shallow depths in some locations.
dry tower [461] a type of cooling tower in which warm water flows through a system of pipes and a fan increases the flow of air to speed cooling of the water.
duff [54] the blanket of twigs and needles that remains after logging.
Dust Bowl [219] the southern part of the Great Plains including parts of Kansas, Oklahoma, Texas, New Mexico, and Colorado.
Earth [2] a complex environmental system with constant interactions between the atmosphere, the oceans and the land.
ecological succession [36] the series of changes that occur in an ecosystem with the passing of time.
ecologist [2] a scientist who studies organisms as they interact with other organisms within an ecosystem.
ecology [2] the study of living things in relation to their physical environment and to each other.
ecosystem [3] a group of plants, animals, and other organisms which live together and interact with each other and with the surrounding physical environment.
edge [9] place where one ecosystem meets another ecosystem.
edge effect [52] a large number of species and a larger population of each species is present at the place where two ecosystems meet (edge) because of the increase in the amount of food and cover.
effluent [365] treated wastewater.
El Nient [365] treated wastewater.
species and a larger populatelectricity [449] the flow of electrons transmitted along wires.
electrodialysis [429] a method of removing salt from sea water by passing the water through a chamber that contains electrodes with positive and negative charges.
electromagnetic radiation [2] a form of energy that is given off in a definite pattern by both living and nonliving objects forming a sort of fingerprint for different types of matter.
electrostatic precipitator [185] electrically charged metal plates that attract particles from flue gases.
elevated sand mound [370] where a layer of sand is placed on the soil to increase the depth of the absorption area. See subsurface absorption field.
embryonic [100] initial stage of a tornado, detected by Doppler radar which detects wind currents inside storm clouds.
emerging plant stage [37] stage of succession with plants that float or extend above the surface of the water.
emerging plants [300] plants that grow in shallow water with most of the stems, leaves, and flowers growing above the water level.
emigrate [9] movement of an organism away from the area where it has been living to take up permanent residence in a new area.
emission standard [181] the maximum amount of a pollutant that is allowed to enter the atmosphere from exhaust or smokestack.
emissions [181] gases and particles entering the air from smokestacks, chimneys and exhaust pipes.
emissions cap [183] the maximum amount of sulfur dioxide that can be released in the atmosphere from all electrical power plants.
emphysema [129] a respiratory disease in which the air sacs lose their elasticity and are not able to push the air out of the lungs.
enamel [410] a substance that covers the part of a tooth that is exposed.
endangered species [72] animals whose chances of survival and reproduction are in immediate jeopardy.
Endangered Species Act [72] a law that requires the Dept. of the Interior to identify and protect species that are in danger of extinction.
endocrine [264] a system in your body that uses hormones to synchronize bodily functions.
endocrine disrupters [265] chemicals, like pesticides, that interfere with hormonal messages within the body's endocrine system.
energy [432] the ability to do work.
energy efficiency [432] a measure of the amount of energy which an appliance or other invention can convert to useful work.
EnergyGuide [435] labels which contain the information needed to compare the energy efficiency of different models of appliances.
environmental impact statement [16] conclusions about how an event influences the environment.
EPA [181] Environmental Protection Agency, the branch of the federal government which makes and enforces standards for pollution control.
erosion [33] the removal of mineral particles from an ecosystem by the action of wind or water; the movement of soil from one location to another by wind or water.
estuary [331] an area where fresh water from a river mixes with salt water from the ocean.
ethylene [133] a gaseous pollutant in car exhaust that damages plants.
evaporation [25] process in which water is converted from a liquid into a vapor state.
evaporative emission system [193] a closed system that collects vapors from the gas tank, preventing hydrocarbons from entering the atmosphere.
even-aged stands [54] all trees are of the same age and are ready for harvest at the same time.
excavator [57] a species of animal that makes cavities (hollow places) in dead or dying trees.
exoskeleton [37] external skeletal skin of certain nymphs in certain species of insects.
exotic species [61] species that have been introduced to an area beyond their natural range.
experimental group [(128), 165] group of organisms that received the chemical being tested.
extinct species [72] animals which are no longer surviving on earth.
eye of the bog [40] an area of open water that is the last remnant of a lake.
fabric filter [185-6] the process in which fabric bags are used to remove particles from emissions.
Farm Service Agency [219] the government agency, formerly the ASCS, established to provide money to help pay for the cost of conservation work.
feces [21] nitrogen-bearing animal wastes.
felling [51] the cutting of a tree.
fertile soils [242] soils which have chemicals which plants need for growth.
fertility rate [232] the average number of children per woman.
fertilizer [31] any substance which is added to the soil to provide nutrients for plant growth; nitrate or ammonium ions that plants can use to get nitrogen.
FIFR Act of 1947 [261] the law that required manufacturers to test a pesticide for short-term or acute effects, later amended to require testing for long-term or chronic effects.
filamentous algae [299] colonies of algae with cells attached to form long strands or filaments.
filtering collectors [288] organisms that use structures to trap and strain small particles out of the water; also called filter feeders.
filtration [403] the process of removing pollutants including microscopic organisms, from the water.
first-order consumer [14] primary consumer.
first-order stream [284] the stream at the headwaters.
fish kill [299] when fish die as a result of too much or too little oxygen dissolved in the water.
fish ladders [315] pools of water arranged as a series of steps for fish to bypass low dams.
fission [450] the splitting apart of atoms.
fix [31] referring to how special bacteria in soil and water change nitrogen gas into nitrogen fertilizers or ammonium ions that plants can use.
flail [207] a long stick with a heavy beater stick fastened to the end for threshing grain.
flash distillation [429] a method of removing salt from sea water by superheating the water in chambers where reduced pressure causes it to change into steam which condenses on coils of pipe cooled by sea water.
flash flood [352] floods which occur within a few minutes or hours of an excessive rainfall or a sudden release of water such as a dam or levee failure or breakup of an ice jam.
flat plate collector [454] shallow insulated box covered with glass and containing a black metal plate to absorb heat.
flat rate [423] a system of payment that requires the same payment regardless of the amount of the resource used.
floating plants [300] plants that grow with only their leaves and flowers on or only slightly above the surface of the water.
floc [403] clumps of particles that collect together and adhere to each other.
flocculation [403] the process in which particles stick together to form large, heavy particles called floc.
floodplain [285] the low flat land along a stream or river that is periodically flooded.
floods [350] the result of water overflowing its banks.
flow [450] the volume of water moving in a river or stream.
fluidized bed combustion—See pressurized fluidized bed combustion.
fluoridation [411] process of reducing tooth decay by adding fluoride to water supplies that have less than 1 ppm natural fluoride.
fluorides [410] compounds that contain the element fluorine.
fluorosis [412] fluoride poisoning.
fly ash [124] small pieces of minerals that are released during combustion; small particles carried up a smoke stack with exhaust.
food chain [14] a diagram that shows the flow of energy from green plants or algae to consumers.
food web [14] a diagram that shows many of the possible food chains in an ecosystem.
forage [52] plants that are eaten by grazing or browsing animals.
forest decline [176] forest where many trees show signs of stress, a thinning of foliage, premature yellowing or loss of foliage, and an increase in number of dying trees.
fossil fuels [184] coal, oil, natural gas.
FQPA Act of 1996 [265] an amendment to the FIFR and FFDCA Acts that requires the EPA to regulate all pesticides used on foods in a way that provides a "reasonable certainty of no harm."
fragmentation [9] the division of an ecosystem into small isolated tracts. See also habitat fragmentation.
friable [136] the condition of substances which can be easily crumbled with the hand.
frond [473] a thallus shoot resembling a leaf.
frontage rate [423] system of payment based on the property width, number of stories and the number of water-using fixtures.
fuel cells [458] like batteries, both convert chemical energy to electrical energy without combustion, but fuel cells can operate continuously as long as they have fuel.

Fujita Tornado Intensity Scale [101] categories of tornadoes, describing wind speed, types of damage expected, etc.
fungicide [250] pesticide that kill fungi.
fusion [102] joining of two atoms to form one atom of a different element; the process of heating two substances to form a metal alloy.
galvanizing [151] The coating of iron or steel with zinc to prevent rusting.
Game—See game species.
game management [85] the science that uses the knowledge of population density and carrying capacity to determine the limits on the harvest of game species.
game species [17] animals that humans can legally hunt.
gamma radiation [140] energy waves (rays) that travel at the speed of light.
gang plow [205] a piece of farm equipment with several coulters and moldboard plows.
gas bubble disease [307] condition in which gases come out of solution forming bubbles in the blood vessels or the body tissues of aquatic organisms.
gasohol [456] a blend of one part grain alcohol and nine parts gasoline.
gathering collectors [288] organisms that feed on the bottom of an aquatic ecosystem where organic matter accumulates.
generator [449] stationary coils of copper wire with electromagnets which can be rotated to create a flow of electrons.
genetics, genetic engineering [200] a branch of biology dealing with heredity in organisms; directed alteration of genetic material.
geothermal energy [452] the natural heat or hot water trapped below the earth's surface.
giardiasis [394] an illness affecting the stomach and intestine that is caused by the protozoan *Giardia lamblia.*
glacier [39] large masses of ice that glide very slowly along the ground.
global warming [110] an increase in the Earth's average temperature.
GOES [100] Geostationary Operational Environmental Satellites that orbit the earth at a speed matching the earth's rotation to collect information used to create short-range forecasts.
graded sand filter [396] a filter made of layers of rocks and sand of specific sizes.
grain drill [206] a planter that has a long box with planting tubes that deliver seed into a shallow ditch made by two discs.
granular [215] a soil type which is dry and sandy.
green manure crops [246] crops which are grown for the purpose of adding organic matter to the soil.
Green Revolution [235] the development of new varieties of wheat and rice that produced higher yields during the 1960s.
greenhouse effect [103] the warming of air caused by the sun's radiation (light) passing into the atmosphere and being changed to heat energy which is absorbed (trapped) by gases in the atmosphere.
greenhouse gases [110] gases which trap heat and have a warming effect on a planet.
groundwater [34] water beneath the earth's surface that supplies wells and springs.
growing degree days [280] a calculation of the daily accumulation of heat that determines when the insect will be in a particular stage of its life cycle.
growth rate [485] how fast a population is increasing or decreasing.
gully erosion [220] the formation of large ditches by water as it moves down a steep slope.
habitat [6] the place that provides all of the needs of an organism.
Habitat Conservation Plan (HCP) [80] a series of steps taken to mitigate or lessen the impacts of human activities such as development or logging.
habitat fragmentation [8] the breaking of habitats into smaller isolated pieces.
half-life [198] the amount of time it takes for one-half of a radioactive element to break down.
halons [95] stable chemicals that contain bromine, fluorine and carbon.
hard coal [184] anthracite, containing very little sulfur compared to other coals.
hard water [175] water which contains many dissolved minerals.
harrow [205] a mechanical device used after plowing a field to break clods of dirt and level the soil; a series of spikes attached to a frame and used to smooth the seedbed before planting.
head [450] the vertical distance water falls at a dam.
header [207] a part of a combine or corn picker that guides the stalks into the machine.
headwaters [284] the beginning of a stream.
hemoglobin [381] the part of blood that carries oxygen.
herbicides [55] chemicals that are used to kill plants that are considered "weed" species.
herbivore [13] organisms that eat plants.
histoplasmosis [61] a respiratory disease in humans caused by a fungus from the droppings of starlings, an introduced species.
host [14] an organism which a parasite lives in or on and which provides the parasite with food.
human-made channels [287] straight box-like ditches dug to move water more efficiently.
humus [37] partly decayed organic matter; decayed remains of dead organisms.
hunters and gatherers [198] people who depend upon wild plants and animals for food.
hydric soils [325] soils that are identified by their color and texture as wetland soils which contain little or no oxygen and support wetland plants.
hydrocarbon [118] compounds that contain only hydrogen and carbon.
hydroponics [211] method of growing plants with roots suspended in a solution of nutrients (fertilizers).
hypovirulent [65] a non-lethal form of a fungus that enables chestnut trees to recover from chestnut blight.
immune [66] to be unable to become infected with a disease.
incidental take or taking [80] the loss of some members of a species as a part of a recovery plan that ensures the survival of the species.
index species [288] organisms whose presence in large numbers tells us where the water is clean or polluted.
indicator organisms [394] organisms whose presence in the water tells us something about the quality of the water.
indicator species [45] a species whose presence signals a healthy ecosystem.
infertile soils [242] soils that are unable to support good plant growth; worn out soils.
infiltration [34] the process of water soaking into the soil.
inorganic contaminants [393] inorganic chemicals found in drinking water supplies, including cadmium, fluoride, lead, mercury, and nitrates.
insecticide [250] a pesticide that kills insects.
intake [402] the place where the water enters the water treatment plant.
Integrated Pest Management [275] the use of several different methods of control to reduce the population of a particular pest, minimizing the use of pesticides.
intensively managed forests [55] forests that are planted with high-quality seedlings, weeds are controlled with herbicides, pests are controlled, and fertilizers are used to increase the growth rate.
internal combustion engine [189] an engine in which fuel burns or explodes in a closed chamber.
introduced species [61-71] a species that is living in an area beyond its historic natural range.
invasive species [61] species that are aggressive and spread over large areas, disrupting natural ecosystems and interfering with human activities.
inversion [107] a layer of cold air trapped by a layer of warm air above it.
ion exchange system [398] a type of water treatment that is used to remove certain ions such as calcium, magnesium and iron; a water softener.
ionizing radiation [140] high-energy radiation that can knock electrons from atoms; includes alpha, beta and gamma radiation.
jab planter [206] a mechanical device used for making a hole and planting corn seeds.
jet stream [101] a 200-mile-an-hour river of air that flows 20,000 to 30,000 feet above the Earth's surface.
kettle lake [39] a lake that has no entrance or exit.
keystone species [79] a species that is essential to the balance of the ecosystem.
kilowatt-hour [456] one thousand watts of power used for one hour.
Kyoto Protocol on Climate Change [116] a set of rules for reducing greenhouse gases established by UNFCCC delegates from a conference in Kyoto, Japan. These rules include a set of binding emissions targets for all greenhouse gases: carbon dioxide, methane, nitrous oxide and synthetic substitutes for ozone-depleting CFCs.
lactic acid [39] a waste product produced when your muscle cells work without enough oxygen.
lagoon [369] shallow ponds where sewage is held.
lake [284] a lentic body of water that is usually larger than a pond and has areas that are too deep for rooted plants to grow.
landslide [205] a straight piece of metal that guides the moldboard plow.
larva [292] an immature form of an organism.
latent period [142] the period of time that is necessary before damage can be observed.
law of conservation of energy [432] the first law of thermodynamics, which states that energy cannot be created nor destroyed, but it can be changed in form.
leachate [387] the liquids that drain from a landfill.
leaching [32] the process in which water dissolves and removes minerals from rock or soil and carries them away by the movement of the water.
lead [131] an element that leaches from plumbing and interferes with the normal activity of the nervous system and the kidneys.
legumes [31] a family of plants that have nitrogen-fixing bacteria in small nodules located on the roots.
lentic [284] a slow-moving body of water where the water seems to stand still; lakes, ponds, and wetlands.
lignite [436] a very soft coal formed from peat. It has a lower percentage of carbon and a lower heat content than other forms of coal.
limiting factor [21] anything that prevents the population size from increasing.
load [350] the clay and silt particles that are carried by water in a stream or river.
loam [213] soils which contain less than 20% clay and nearly equal parts of sand and silt.
lock [345] the area between two massive steel gates in which the water level is raised or lowered to the water level on the opposite side of the dam.
longwall system [444] a method of mining coal in deep mines. The coal is removed along a wall several hundred feet long and the roof is allowed to collapse behind the miners.
lotic [284] freshwater ecosystems with relatively fast-moving water.
low-energy precision application (LEPA) [426] a more efficient center-pivot irrigation system that delivers water closer to the ground.
lower reaches [286] the sections of a river system with a gentle, steady flow.
lung cancer [130] abnormal cells in the lung grow and divide at an unusually fast rate, filling the air sacs and bronchial tubes. They may break away and travel to other sites in the body.
machete [204] a big knife used for clearing brush.
market hunting [86] killing and selling game without any restrictions.
marsh [37] an area of rooted plants whose roots are often covered with shallow water.
mass erosion (slumping) [221] a mass of soil, which is saturated with water, moving down a slope.
mast [52] acorns and other nuts or fruit that lie on the forest floor and become food for wildlife.

matter [29] anything that occupies space and has mass.
maximum contaminant level [265] the legal limit or highest amount of a pollutant that is allowed in the drinking water.
maximum contaminant level goal [393] a level for substances found in drinking water set by the EPA and based on health effects.
meanders [285] curves in a stream.
mechanical preparation [54] the removal of slash, duff and other wastes from tree-cutting, in order to allow new trees to germinate and grow.
mercaptan [439] a chemical additive that allows natural gas to smell like rotten eggs to help find a leak.
mesothelomia [136] a form of cancer in the lining of the chest and abdomen.
metals [150] minerals that conduct electricity and can be shaped or molded to a specific form.
metastasis [130] the spread of cancer in an organism.
meteorology [98] the study of the physics and chemistry of the atmosphere.
methane [112] natural gas, a waste product produced during the treatment of sewage.
methemoglobinemia [311] a "blue baby" condition in which nitrites in the blood prevent hemoglobin from combining with oxygen.
micronutrients [242] elements which are needed by plants in very small amounts.
middle reaches [285] sections of a river system of moderate slope with third- or fourth-order streams.
Migratory Bird Hunting Stamp [82] also called "the duck stamp," its purchase is a federal requirement for those hunting migratory birds, in order to raise the necessary funds that established the National Wildlife Refuge System (more than 90 million acres set aside for wildlife).
millirem [140] one one-thousandth of a rem.
minerals [150] naturally occurring solids with specific chemical and physical structures.
mining [33] the removal of a substance from an ecosystem at a rate which is faster than it is replaced.
Mississippi Flyway [17] a migratory route for certain species of birds.
mitigation [326] the process of creating wetlands in order to reduce the impact of destroying wetlands.
moldboard [204] a piece of curved metal that is attached to a plow share and turns the soil.
moldboard plow [204] a plow with a curved metal blade that is designed to work in all soils.
monoculture [52] the planting of a single species.
Montreal Protocol [95] a legal agreement signed on September 16, 1987, by 35 countries to reverse or prevent the thinning of the ozone shield. Its full name is the Montreal Protocol on Substances that Deplete the Ozone Layer.
mortar [199] a bowl-shaped container in which foods are pounded into a powder.
mottling [412] paper white patches that develop on teeth due to exposure to fluoride.
mouth of river [284] the place where the river enters a lake or ocean.
muck soil [214] soils which contain more than 20% humus.
multiple use [47] refers to the management of National Forests and other federal lands for more than one purpose. Uses include timbering, mining, watershed protection, grazing and recreation.
muskgrass algae [299] a name given to stonewort algae because of its appearance and odor.
nanometer [93] one-billionth of a meter—how wavelengths of light are measured.
National Ambient Air Quality Standards (NAAQS) [121] maximum amount of specific air pollutants allowed in the outdoor air.
National Forest Management Act, The [48] a 1976 law requiring that management plans be made for all national forests, to provide sufficient habitat for all native vertebrate species.
National Priorities List [376] a list of hazardous waste sites (contaminated with toxic chemicals) that are the most important to clean up via the EPA's Superfund.
National Wildlife Refuge System [82] land that is set aside and managed for wildlife and other public uses.
natural increase [232, 485] increase in a country's population due to a greater number of births than deaths, calculated by subtracting the deaths from the births per 1000 population, then dividing by 10.
natural regeneration [54] germination of seeds from trees that remain after logging.
Natural Resources Conservation Service (NRCS) [220] replacing the SCS, a government agency to help individuals, organizations, cities, counties and states to protect their land and water resources.
Natural Valley Storage Plan [356] an agreement to buy and preserve wetlands in the Charles River watershed to prevent flooding downstream.
Nature Conservancy, The [44] an organization whose goal is to preserve best examples of a wide variety of unique ecosystems.
negative population growth [485] a decline in population when the birth rate is less than the death rate.
nematicide [250] a pesticide that kills nematodes (round worms).
nematode [266] round worm that blights certain species of plants.
net migration [485] number of emigrants subtracted from the number of immigrants.
NEXRAD [100] Next Generation Radar, a Doppler radar system that can detect tornadoes.
niche [13] an organism's role or job in the ecosystem which is usually described by its position in the food chain.
nicotine sulfate [250] a natural chemical pesticide produced by the tobacco plant.
nitrate poisoning [243] an event that occurs if e.g., cattle eat plants that have accumulated high levels of nitrogen (nitrates).
nitrates [301] a form of nitrogen found in most fertilizers (NO_3^-).
nitrites [311] a form of nitrogen (NO_2^-), produced by certain bacteria, that interferes with the ability of hemoglobin to carry oxygen.
nitrogen [242] a gaseous element found in the atmosphere necessary for survival of life.
nitrogen fixers [31] organisms that change nitrogen into a form of fertilizer that plants can use.
nitrogen oxide [123] a chemical compound formed at hot temperatures (like when lightning strikes) from nitrogen and oxygen.
nitrous oxide [112] a potent greenhouse gas, a pollutant in the atmosphere, mostly created by burning fossil fuels.
nodules [31] small growths (houses) on the roots of legumes that contain nitrogen-fixing bacteria.
nonattainment area [121] areas where air pollution levels persistently exceed the NAAQS.
nongame [83] species that are protected from being killed.
non-native species [61] an introduced species, one living beyond its natural historic range.
nonpoint sources [301] pollutants (sometimes called nutrients) that flow directly into the water with runoff from the land.
nonrenewable [451] a natural resource which is **not** replaced by ecological cycles at the same rate as it is being used up.
nonwithdrawal uses [419] activities that use water without removing it from the stream, river or lake.
no-till planter [206] a planter that prepares the soil and plants the seed in one operation.
N-P-K [242] the elements nitrogen, phosphorus, and potassium found in fertilizers in varying ratios.
nurse log [45] fallen log that becomes a nursery for new trees.
nutrients [242] chemicals which plants need for growth; can be water pollutants.
nymph [295] an immature form of some invertebrates.
obsidian [199] a type of stone used to make arrows.
Ogallala Aquifer [238] a region of ground water which extends from South Dakota to Texas; a vast underground reservoir beneath the High Plains states.
oil shales [446] type of porous rock that contain oil.
oil slick [335] a layer of oil on the surface of the water.
Old River Control Complex [360] a set of levees and water control gates built by the COE 70 miles north of Baton Rouge, LA, to keep 70% of the water in the Mississippi River channel during normal flow and to send more water into the Atchafalaya River during floods.
old-growth forest [45] virgin stands of timber whose ancient trees have never been logged.
omnivore [13] consumers that eat both plants and animals.
once-through-cooling [460] a method of producing electricity that uses water from a river or lake and returns it directly to the source.
open water [287] the area of an aquatic ecosystem where the rooted plants do not reach the surface of the water.
ore [150] a rock that is mined to extract a useful mineral.
organic compounds [30] chemicals that contain carbon.
organic contaminants [393] organic chemicals found in drinking water supplies, including certain pesticides, industrial chemicals, and trihalomethanes (THMs).
organic fertilizers [244] natural products which provide plant nutrients.
organic pesticides [251] Naturally occurring insecticides, including nicotine sulfate, pyrethrum, and rotenone.
organism [2] a living thing.
organochlorines [389-90] compounds that contain carbon, hydrogen, and chlorine.
organophosphate [251] a class of inexpensive pesticides (e.g., AZM, diazinon, malathion, parathion, and methyl-parathion) that are highly effective against a broad range of insects, but are extremely toxic to agricultural workers.
OSHA [167] Occupational Safety and Health Administration, the federal agency that regulates toxic chemicals in the workplace.
outfall pipe [368] a pipe through which treated wastewater is discharged to a body of water.
oxygenated fuels [194] a fuel with additives that reduce the amount of carbon monoxide produced during combustion.
ozone [(91)] a form of oxygen that contains three atoms instead of the usual two. In the stratosphere, it blocks the sun's harmful UV rays, but in the troposphere, it is a harmful pollutant.
ozone shield [91] a protective shield or filter in the stratosphere where 90% of the earth's ozone protects us from most ultraviolet radiation.
papoose [40] a Native American's infant, often carried behind a mother's back.
parasite [14] organism which feeds on another organism while it is still living.
parching, parched [201] the process used to dry grain.
parent material [216] fractured bedrock which lies beneath the subsoil and which is the source of minerals in the soil.
particulate matter [124] a mixture of solid particles and liquid droplets that are small enough to remain in the air for long periods of time.
particulates [118] tiny particles that remain suspended in the air.
passive solar heating [453] the use of building design and collectors to increase the amount of heating caused by light energy which is trapped by glass.
pathogens [94] diseases; Webster says, "a specific causative agent (e.g., bacterium or virus) of disease."
pay-as-you-throw [471] a policy in some communities where residents are charged by the bag or by the pound to dispose of leaves and grass clippings, in order to encourage recycling and composting, and reduce solid waste going to landfills.
peat [40] mat of sphagnum moss that is partly decayed.
pedestals [230] odd mushroom shapes in the Badlands, formed when rocks that are more resistant to erosion protect a column of softer material below them.
percent oxygen saturation [307] a measure of the relative amount of oxygen contained in water.
percolating or percolation [34] water moving down through the soil or rocks toward the aquifer.
percolation rate [370] rate at which water moves through the soil.

permafrost [4-5] layer of permanently frozen soil.
persistent pesticides [253] pesticides which are not easily broken down by organisms in the environment, and which may remain in the environment for many years.
pest [249] any troublesome, destructive, or annoying organism.
pesticides [250] chemicals that kill insects, fungi, nematodes, and weeds.
petrochemicals [502] chemicals made from oil and natural gas.
pH [243] a measure of a solution's acidity or alkalinity.
pH scale [170] a scale developed to measure a solution's acidity or alkalinity.
pheromones [278] chemicals that are produced by a female insect to attract a male.
phosphates [301] a form of phosphorus (PO_4^{-3}) that is a plant nutrient and stimulates the growth of algae and aquatic plants.
phosphorus [243] a mineral in fertilizers, necessary for good root growth as well as flower and seed formation.
photochemical smog [123] a brown-colored haze produced when sunlight causes the formation of nitrogen dioxide; it occurs only when there is enough sunlight and heat to provide energy for certain chemical reactions.
photosynthesis [13] process in which green plants use the sun's energy to combine water and carbon dioxide to form oxygen.
photovoltaic cell [454] a device which converts sunlight directly into electricity.
picocurie [146] the radiation given off by a trillionth of a gram of radium.
pioneer stage [36] a stage of ecological succession of a pond when it is first formed; it has a sandy or muddy ("bare") bottom.
piston [189] a movable plunger.
Pittman-Robertson Act [82] a law passed by Congress that requires taxes collected on hunting licenses, firearms, ammunition and archery equipment be used for wildlife conservation.
plankton algae [287] microscopic plants and animals that float in the open water.
plant manager [167] person who is responsible for the safety precautions taken at the workplace.
planter [223] an instrument or tool used in farming to deposit the seed into the ground.
plantlings [55] young trees that have been produced by tissue culture from a few selected parent plants.
platy [215] a soil structure where particles are glued into thin horizontal plates.
plow [204] large digging sticks that were pulled by oxen and used to turn the soil.
plow share [205] a blade that cuts through the soil.
pneumonia [130] a common infectious disease that is more likely to occur when the bacteria-destroying cells are killed by pollutants. Excessive production of mucus limits the flow of air across the membranes in the air sacs.
poaching [86] the taking of a species by any illegal means.
pod corn [202] type of corn which has each kernel wrapped separately.
POES [100] polar-orbiting environmental satellites that collect data from remote ocean areas needed for long-range weather forecasting.
point source [301] a specific place from which pollutants (sometimes nutrients) flow into the water, usually through pipes or ditches.
pollutant [118] a substance that is present in an amount that is undesirable or harmful.
pollution [305] the presence of substances in amounts that are undesirable or harmful.
pollution-tolerant [288] when an organism can survive certain type of pollutants.
polychloride byphenyls (PCBs) [159] toxic, organic chemical pollutants of air and water.
pond [284] lentic body of water so shallow that rooted plants grow across the entire bottom.
pond scum [299] a floating mat of filamentous algae.
pools [285] areas of a stream with slower moving water.
population [6] the total number of a species living in a defined region.
population density [10] number of species per unit area of living space.
population explosion [19] an above-normal increase of a certain species.
population growth rate [232] the percentage change in population over time.
potable water [394] water that is suitable for drinking.
potassium [243] a mineral necessary for proper growth and resistance to disease, used in fertilizers.
potato digger [208] a modified moldboard plow that digs and picks up potatoes.
prairie [4] a grassland that is maintained when fire prevents the growth of trees; a stage of ecological succession after marsh, when a climate will not support the growth of trees.
prairie potholes [325] shallow basins found in the Great Plains states.
precipitation [34] any form of moisture falling from the atmosphere.
predator [14] an organism that feeds on other animals that it must first hunt and kill.
press wheel [223] part of a no-till planter that closes the soil over the seeds.
pressurized fluidized bed combustion [185] a technology for burning coal and other low-grade fuels, including high-sulfur coal using injected air and crushed limestone.
pretreatment [367-8] process that removes heavy metals from industrial wastewater before it is dumped into sewers.
prey [14] an organism that is killed and eaten by a predator.
primary consumer [14] a herbivore or first consumer in a food chain, sometimes called the first-order consumer.
primary disinfection [403] the disinfection of water as it enters the water treatment plant.
primary nutrients [242] chemicals needed by plants in large amounts.
primary treatment [365] the first stage in the treatment of sewage that involves the physical separation of solids and liquids.
producer [13] an organism that can use the sun's energy to make its own food.
productivity [27] the biomass of plants that can be produced by an ecosystem.
***Protista* kingdom** [299] a classification segment in biology; e.g., algae are members of the *Protista* kingdom (referred to as protists).
PRP [159] Potentially responsible parties who contributed to the release (or potential release) of hazardous substances, and are liable and may be sued by the EPA for costs of the cleanup of the hazardous waste site.
pupa [292] an inactive stage of metamorphosis of some invertebrates.
pyramid of biomass [26] a diagram that shows the decrease in biomass as organisms move through a food chain.
pyramid of numbers [27] a diagram of the number of organisms at each step in a food chain.
pyrethrum [250] a pesticide made from the dried flowers of chrysanthemums.
radiation [102] the transfer of heat or light waves of energy.
radioactive decay [140] the process of nuclei of atoms disintegrating without any outside force.
radiocarbon dating [198] process used to determine the age of objects which contain carbon.
radon [145] a naturally occurring radioactive gas which is produced by the decay of uranium and radium in the earth.
radon daughters [146] solid particles which are produced when radon decays.
rain forest [4]—See tropical rain forest.
rapids [285] shallow areas in a stream where the water appears white because its surface is broken as it flows over rocks.
rate of recharge [420]—See recharge rate.
Reading Prong [145] a granite rock formation which extends from Reading, PA into New York and New Jersey.
reaper [206] a horse-pulled machine that cut and tied bundles of grain.
recharge rate [235] the rate at which water being used from an aquifer can be replaced to maintain a constant level (equilibrium); the rate at which water is returned to the aquifer by the processes of infiltration and percolation.
reclamation [309] the process of restoring land to the condition which existed before mining operations took place.
recycling [470] use of recovered "waste" materials in the manufacturing process.
reduce [471-2] preventing the creation of solid waste.
refining [440] the process used to separate crude oil into its parts.
reformulated gasoline [194] a cleaner burning fuel with fewer highly volatile organic compounds.
rem [140] a measure of the result of energy deposited in tissue.
renewable resource [435] a natural resource which is replaced by ecological cycles at least at the same rate it is used.
reserve [437] a deposit of oil or gas which can economically be recovered with present technology.
reservoir [342] lakes that store a supply of water for future use.
reservoir rock [437] a porous rock through which oil and gas can move.
resin [398] the material in an ion-exchange water conditioner that contains ions which are exchanged for ions in the water being treated.
resistant [252] organisms which have become immune to a chemical.
resistant varieties [275-6] plants that produce chemicals that discourage pests from attacking.
resource recovery [470] salvaging of usable materials from solid waste.
respiration [30] process in which organisms break down compounds containing carbon and release energy.
restricted-use [262] a classification of pesticides that are only available to farmers and commercial applicators who have been certified by the state's department of agriculture.
reuse [471-2] to use the same product again and again.
reverse osmosis [429] a method of removing salt from sea water or toxins from tap water by forcing it through a membrane that has openings large enough to allow water to pass through but too small to allow the ions to pass through.
riffles [285] shallow areas of swiftly flowing water.
Right-to-Know Act, Emergency Planning and Community [167] requires reporting of toxic releases and specific actions by companies and communities in order to be prepared for a possible accident.
rill erosion [220] the formation of small ditches by water as it moves down gentle slopes.
riparian [54] referring to streamside habitat.
riparian zone [284] the ecosystem along a stream or river that is strongly affected by water.
river [284] a body of flowing water that is much larger and deeper than a stream; fed by smaller streams and sometimes rivers called tributaries.
rock [150] a collection of minerals.
rock dusting [445] a process in which coal mine walls are sprayed with powdered limestone to control coal dust.
room and pillar system [444] a method of coal mining in which columns of coal are left to support the mine roof.
rotenone [250] an organic pesticide—a natural chemical produced by legumes that grow in the East Indies.
runoff [34] water that flows freely across the surface of the soil and into streams or lakes.
saline [429] water that contains dissolved salts.
salinization [238] a buildup of salts and toxic elements in the soil or irrigated cropland, reducing crop yields.
salt front [343] the line where fresh water from the river meets the ocean water.
sample census [473] an estimate of the population, made by marking off areas of the organisms' habitat, and counting the individuals in each area.

sanitary landfill [387] a method of waste disposal in which garbage is compacted and covered each day with a layer of soil.
saturated [307] when a liquid holds all of the gas that can be dissolved at a given temperature.
savanna [4] a tropical biome with cool and hot dry seasons separated by warm and rainy seasons, with fertile soil and grass.
sawlogs [54] mature, high-quality trees that are removed for sale.
scale [398] mineral deposits that collect inside water heaters, pipes, bathtubs and on clothing.
scat [21] animal feces.
scavengers [14] carnivores which feed on organisms that died naturally or were killed by another organism.
scrapers [289] organisms that graze on algae that is attached to surfaces of submerged rocks and other objects.
scrubber sludge [185] the wastewater produced by wet scrubbers at an electrical power plant.
scythe [206] a curved blade on a long handle used for harvesting grain.
second energy law [432] the second law of thermodynamics, which states, "When energy is changed from one form to another, some of the usable energy is lost (cannot do any work)."
secondary consumer [14] a carnivore or second consumer in a food chain, sometimes called the second-order consumer.
secondary nutrients [242] elements needed by plants in smaller amounts than the primary nutrients.
secondary pollutants [123] pollutants produced by chemical reactions in the atmosphere.
secondary recovery method [440] technology developed to remove more of the oil from the rock than can be removed by pumping.
secondary treatment [365] a biological process that usually increases the oxygen in the wastewater and allows time for organisms to remove organic matter.
secondhand smoke [130] environmental tobacco smoke or passive smoke that is inhaled by nonsmokers. The EPA has determined that secondhand smoke is a human carcinogen.
second-order consumer [14]— See secondary consumer.
second-order stream [284] a stream formed at the confluence of two first-order streams.
Section 404 [325] a section of the Clean Water Act that requires a permit for anyone planning to place dredged or fill materials in the "waters of the United States."
secure landfill [387] a method of waste disposal for hazardous wastes.
sediment filter [398] a filter designed to remove particles.
sedimentation [403] the process in which water is held in a large tank to allow the floc to sink to the bottom.
seed tree logging [54] a variation of clear-cutting in which selected mature trees are left to provide seed for regeneration of the cut area.
seepage [34] groundwater flowing naturally from the ground at a spring.
selection logging (selective cutting) [54] individual trees or small groups of selected trees are removed.
selective pesticide [255] chemicals which kill only one type of organism.
selenium [382] an element found in soil that is toxic when present in a concentration of a few parts per million.
seltzer water [406] a soft drink consisting of water that has been filtered and carbonated.
sensors [2] sensitive equipment that gather information for scientists, e.g., aboard spacecraft for weather-related events, space exploration, maps, etc.
septage [371] mixture of liquids and solids pumped from the septic tank.
septic tank [370] a large tank buried in the ground to treat sewage from an individual home or business.
shale [229] soft black rock formed by the pressure of layers of mud and organic matter over a period of many years.
shatter-resistant (rice) [200] a variety of rice where the outer covering is able to withstand outside forces.
sheaves [206] a bundle of stalks of grain that are cut and tied together.
sheet erosion [220] a thin layer of soil removed from very gentle slopes.
shelling board [208] an instrument first made of wood, that was used to remove kernels of corn from the cob.
shelterwood logging [54] mature trees are harvested in a series of cuts over several years.
shin [205] a metal plate attached to the front edge of the moldboard plow that cuts through the soil.
shocks [206] groups of bundles (sheaves) of grain that were collected into a group in a way that they supported one another and stood upright to dry.
shredders [289] organisms that break large pieces of dead plant material into smaller pieces.
sick building syndrome [125] a condition where certain air pollutants are higher indoors than outdoors due to energy conservation measures.
sickle [206] a curved blade on a short handle used for reaping.
skeletal fluorosis [412] a condition in which exposure to large amounts of fluoride causes bone spurs and fusion of the vertebrae and may cause crippling effects and make movement difficult.
slash [55] limbs, tree tops and other waste.
slash burning [55] a method of clearing planting sites by burning the brush and duff.
sludge [160] the solids that are removed from wastewater at sewage treatment plants; also called biosolids.
slumping [221] mass erosion seen as a landslide on a steep slope or the cave-in of a bank that overhangs a stream.
slurry [444] a mixture of water and crushed coal which is pumped through a pipeline.
smelting [150] process in which ores are heated to high temperatures to separate impurities from metals.
smog [127] a mixture of smoke and fog.
snag [45] a dead tree that is still standing.
soft coal [184] bituminous, containing more sulfur than hard coal.
soft water [175] water which contains few minerals.
soil [211] that thin layer on the surface of the earth that is made by the interaction of rocks, sunlight, water, air and living organisms.
soil absorption field [370] a system of pipes that carry effluent from septic tanks and allow it to percolate through the soil.
Soil Conservation Service [219] a federal agency created to help people understand and protect the soil; superseded by the Natural Resources Conservation Service.
soil survey maps [220] maps which show the location of soil types in a specific region.
solar distillation [429] a method of removing salt from sea water that uses the sun's energy for evaporation and a dome-shaped surface for condensation of the water vapor.
solar thermal technology [454] a type of technology that uses either mirror-lined dishes or panels that rotate with the sun to collect solar energy to generate heat and electricity.
solid waste [124, 469] garbage and other discarded materials.
solubility [306] the ability of a substance to dissolve in a liquid.
soot [124] small carbon particles.
source reduction [472] the decrease in the amount of waste produced—the EPA's top priority in the management of solid waste.
source rock [437] a rock which is rich in organic matter which is changed into hydrocarbons if conditions provide sufficient heat and pressure.
sparkling mineral water [406] water that must contain the same amount of carbon dioxide that was in the water at the source.
species [6] a group of organisms that are very much alike and that breed in their natural environment to produce fertile offspring.
spent fuel [451] the remains of uranium fuel which is still radioactive but can no longer be used to produce energy at a power plant.
spring [34] place where groundwater flows naturally from the ground.
spring water [406] water that flows to the surface naturally from underground aquifers.
stage II recovery system [194] system that collects vapor during refueling of vehicles and sends it back to an underground storage tank.
stalactite [213] an icicle-like form (made of minerals deposited as dripping water evaporates) that hangs from the ceiling of a cavern.
stalagmite [213] a blunt icicle-like form (made of minerals deposited as dripping water evaporates) that projects from the floor of a cavern.
stalk-puller [224] a new conservation tillage tool which plucks cotton stalks from the ground.
stomata [33] microscopic openings in a leaf through which water vapor is lost and carbon dioxide enters.
stonewort algae [299] algae found in lakes with limestone soil and identified by whorls of branches that may grow to one meter in length.
storm sewers [351] large pipes beneath the ground where runoff flows from developed land to the nearest river.
stratified internal combustion engine [192] an engine with two combustion chambers that allows the fuel to burn at a lower temperature in the main chamber.
stratosphere [91] an upper layer of the atmosphere, mostly ozone, that forms a protective shield around planet Earth; sometimes called the ozone shield.
strip mining [443] the most common type of surface-mining coal where the soil and rock covering the coal deposits are removed by huge earthmoving machines.
strip-cropping [221] planting of alternating bands of close-growing crops with row crops.
structure [215] physical characteristic of the soil which is formed when particles are glued together to form larger particles.
subbituminous [436] a type of soft coal with 40–60% carbon. It has a heat content higher than lignite, but lower than bituminous.
Submerged Aquatic Vegetation (SAV) [332] underwater grasses.
submerged plant stage [37] stage of succession with plants that do not reach the surface of the water.
submerged plants [300] plants that grow entirely below the surface of the water except for the flower and are usually rooted to the muddy bottom.
subsidence [420] the sinking of land which occurs when the resources beneath the land have been removed.
subsoil [216] the layer of soil beneath the topsoil which does not contain humus.
subsurface absorption field [370] a special field that exists below (or, in some cases, above) the surface of the natural soil, to help the absorption of effluent from a septic tank that is moving through the soil.
subsurface drip irrigation system [426] a system of buried perforated plastic pipes that feed water directly to the plant roots.
subsurface system [370] any system of absorption fields that exists below the surface of the soil.
succession [151] natural process that eventually produces a new forest ecosystem after a fire.
sulfate aerosols [109] tiny particles containing sulfur.
sulfur dioxide [130] a colorless gaseous pollutant that has a strong and irritating odor.
sulfur oxides [133] these include sulfur dioxide and sulfur trioxide, which react with moisture to form sulfuric acid.
sulfuric acid [125] a liquid formed from sulfur dioxide, oxygen, and water that creates a haze that scatters sunlight and reduces visibility, makes paper brittle, and dissolves certain building materials.
superchlorination [396] higher than normal amount of chlorine used to disinfect the water and necessary to kill *Giardia* cysts.
Superfund [159] See CERCLA; can refer to the $8.5 billion Superfund Trust Fund, used when no responsible party can be identified to pay the cost of the cleanup of a hazardous waste site.
superphosphate [244] a synthetic fertilizer formed when rock phosphate is treated with a chemical (sulfuric acid) to make the phosphate more readily available to plants.

supersaturation, supersaturated [307] condition in which more gas is dissolved in water than normally would be at a given temperature.
surface film [286] the place where the water meets the air.
sustainability [48] the ability to keep in existence or maintain (an ecosystem).
sustainable development [80] development that meets the needs of the present without compromising the ability of future generations to meet their own needs.
swamp [38] an area of trees which is often wet and may flood in spring and fall.
Swamp Lands Act [325] a law that gave control of millions of acres of federal wetlands to the states for the purpose of "reclaiming."
synergistic effect [129] the total damage caused by a combination of pollutants is greater than the sum total damage caused by each pollutant acting separately.
synfuels [446] fuels which are produced by chemically changing fossil fuels or other organic materials.
synthetic fertilizer [244] man-made nutrients which provide plant nutrients.
tannic acid [39] waste produced by bacteria when they break down plant material.
tannin [200] a bitter chemical found in acorns.
tar sands [446] oil-bearing soil type.
taxon [474] group of organisms that appear to be alike (even if of differing species).
technology [199] knowledge which is used to make products or develop objects which make life easier.
tertiary consumer [14] a carnivore that is the third consumer in a food chain, sometimes called the third-order consumer.
Texas Teeth [410] a condition of permanently discolored tooth enamel caused by fluorides in our water and food.
texture [213] the size of particles in the soil.
thallus [473] the body of a plant lacking distinct stems, leaves, or roots.
thermal mass [453] materials which absorb sunlight and store it as heat energy, such as brick, stone, concrete, or water.
third-order stream [284] a stream formed at the confluence of two second-order streams.
threatened species [72] a species that is likely to become endangered.
threshing floor [207] the floor of the barn where grain was beat with flails to separate the straw from the chaff.
threshing machine [207] a machine that separated the grain from the straw and the chaff.
tidal marshes [325] wetlands that are regularly flooded by ocean tides.
tissue culture [166] cells grown in laboratory dishes for the purpose of studying the effects of poisonous substances.
tolerance level [265] the maximum amount of pesticide residue, set by the EPA, that is allowed in or on food, or in drinking water.
tolerance value [221] the rate at which topsoil can be replaced.
TOMS [2] total ozone mapping spectrometer aboard orbiting satellites, used by scientists to monitor ozone levels in the upper atmosphere and predict possible effects of the changing levels.
topography [352] the surface features of the land.
topsoil [216] the upper layer of soil which contains humus.
total ozone mapping spectrometer—See TOMS.
toxic [165] poisonous.
toxic substances [335] chemicals that can harm living organisms.
toxicology [165] the study of the effects of poisonous compounds.
toxics release inventory [168] a report by the EPA of more than 600 hazardous chemicals by larger companies that make or use certain chemicals released to the environment.
tracer [172] a chemical which is usually absent or present in the atmosphere in very small amounts, and which is used to trace the movement of chemicals in the atmosphere.
transpiration [25] loss of water vapor from the leaves of plants.
trap [437] a rock without pores which forms a cap or lid that keeps the oil and gas from escaping from the reservoir rock.
tributaries [284] smaller feeder streams or rivers that empty into a larger stream or river.
trickling filter [366] a tank filled with a rock-like or grid system that is coated with slime, which contains algae, bacteria, and other pollution-tolerant organisms that remove organic compounds from wastewater.
trihalomethanes (THMs) [368] carcinogenic compounds that are formed when chlorine reacts with organic chemicals.
tropical rain forest [5] a biome with abundant rainfall and consistently warm temperatures that create a continuous growing season.
troposphere [112] the lower layer of the atmosphere nearest to the Earth's surface and extending to the upper limit of most clouds.
true census [473] an actual count of all individuals of a species in a given area.
true cost [178] the cost of making a product including the cost of pollution prevention.
truffle [46] a kind of fungus that produces a massive network of filaments that grow through the soil and penetrate the outer cells of tree roots.
tufa towers [321] irregular columns of calcium carbonate that form at the mouth of fresh water springs due to a chemical reaction between fresh water and lake water high in carbonates.
tundra [4] an Arctic biome which has a layer of permanently frozen (permafrost) soil.
turbidity [286] a measure of the amount of light scattered or absorbed by particles suspended in the water.
turbine [449] a fan-like or paddle wheel structure which may be turned by steam or moving water; a machine with a series of curved blades on a large rotating shaft.
typhoid fever [392] a disease caused by the bacteria *Salmonella typhi* transmitted in water contaminated with human waste.
U.S. Army Corps of Engineers (COE) [325] the agency of the government that has been given the responsibility of maintaining the nation's navigable waterways and protecting its wetlands.
ultraviolet radiation [480] several types of light from the sun come through the stratosphere and do varying degrees of harm to organisms exposed to such light.
uneven-aged stands[54] stands of trees that are of varying ages and are not all ready for harvest at the same time; loggers use selection logging or selective cutting to harvest the maturer trees.
UNFCCC [116] The United Nations Framework Convention on Climate Change, an international treaty signed by more than 150 nations to (1) develop a greenhouse gas inventory, (2) develop programs to slow climate change, and (3) share technology and cooperate to reduce greenhouse gas emissions.
upper reaches [284] the regions of the stream with the greatest slope.
uranium decay series [141] the radioactive decay of uranium, resulting in the formation of radon gas, a toxic carcinogen.
urban heat island effect [106] the warming of an area due to its altered landscape.
urea [245] a nitrogen-containing compound filtered out of the blood by the kidneys, and excreted by the body.
vaporization [118] the process in which a substance is changed from a liquid into a gas.
variable [128] the difference that exists between the treatment of the subjects in the control group and the experimental group during a controlled experiment.
vetches [31] plants, classified as legumes, which have bacteria on their roots that can fix nitrogen gas into nitrate (fertilizer).
viable [49] (an ecosystem) able to survive with all the functional parts.
virgin forest [44] a forest ecosystem which has not been disturbed by man.
visibility [134] the greatest distance that one can see without the aid of technology.
vog [119] smog that is created by the eruption of a volcano.
volatile organic compounds [122] organic chemicals that readily vaporize and react in the atmosphere to form ozone.
waste-to-energy plants [469] systems which burn solid waste to produce electricity or steam which is used by industries or residential developments.
water ranching [426] the buying of land to obtain water rights.
water table [314] upper surface of the water in the aquifer (underground reservoir).
water vapor [33] water in a gaseous state; the most important atmospheric greenhouse gas, contributing to the natural greenhouse effect.
water-borne diseases [362] disease caused by organisms in the water.
water's edge [286] the place where the water meets the land.
waters of the United States [325] navigable waterways, streams and lakes that flow into navigable waterways, and wetlands that lie beside these bodies of water.
watershed [39] an area of land surrounding a body of water that receives the runoff; the land area that is drained when drops of rain join others to flow to a particular stream, river, lake or wetland.
watershed boundary [284] the line along the highest elevation that divides two watersheds.
waterway [221] a wide ditch planted with a permanent grass cover to prevent gully erosion.
watt [114, 503] a unit of electrical power.
weather [98] the atmospheric conditions which result when temperature, moisture, winds, and clouds interact.
weathering [32] action of wind, water, and changing temperatures on substances such as rocks.
weathering agent [212] chemical and physical forces which break apart rocks and/or remove minerals from them.
weed [63] a plant that is growing where it is not wanted.
wet meadows [325] grassy areas that are seldom flooded, but have soil that is usually saturated with water.
wet scrubber [184] a device in which water is mixed with gases to remove sulfuric acid.
wet tower [461] a type of cooling tower in which the warm water is sprayed in a fine mist or allowed to fall over a series of baffles to cool.
wetlands [325] areas that normally have plants adapted for life in soil that is saturated or inundated with water for part of the growing season.
whorls [299] a system of branches of stonewort algae, coming from a central stem.
wildcat well [442] oil or natural gas wells drilled in unexplored areas.
windbreak [222] strips of trees, shrubs, or tall grasses which are planted perpendicular to the direction of the prevailing wind.
winnowing [201] the process in which the hulls are separated from the kernels of grain.
work [432] the movement of matter.
World Plan of Action on the Ozone Layer [94] an environmental impact statement by the UN Environmental Programme, which led the US, Canada, and several European countries to ban the use of CFCs in aerosols.
xeriscape landscaping [425] the use of native, drought-tolerant plants that require less water than conventional lawns.
yield [234] the amount produced per unit area of land.
zero population growth [485] a population is in equilibrium, whereby the number of births and deaths per 1000 individuals are equal.

General Index

Internet Connections

Visit us on-line at **www.lebel.com**

Photo and Illustration Index